Applied Statistics (Continued)

Books of Related Interest

Sample Survey
Methods and
Theory

A WILEY PUBLICATION
IN MATHEMATICAL STATISTICS

Sample Survey Methods and Theory

VOLUME I   METHODS AND APPLICATIONS

MORRIS H. HANSEN

Assistant Director for Statistical Standards
Bureau of the Census

WILLIAM N. HURWITZ

Chief Statistician
Bureau of the Census

WILLIAM G. MADOW

Chairman, Statistical Research Laboratory
University of Illinois

New York · John Wiley & Sons, Inc.
London · Chapman & Hall, Limited

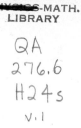
To

MILDRED, HANNAH, and LILLIAN

Foreword

BY

HOWARD C. GRIEVES

Assistant Director
Bureau of the Census

BUSINESS, THE GOVERNMENT, AND THE PROFESSIONS, IN A FREE
and progressive society, all seek the broadest possible factual basis for
decision making, policy formulation, and the development of social and
economic theory. It is the joining of these diverse interests in the common search for economic and social facts which accounts in large part
for the very great importance of statistics in the United States. Hundreds of millions of dollars have been expended for statistics in this
country by public and private groups during the past twenty-five years
alone. The development of sampling during the same period made
possible much of this activity. Sampling theory and methods therefore
are the proper concern of practical businessmen, public officials, and
social scientists because they all do now, and will increasingly hence-
forth, depend upon the results of sampling for much of their factual
information.

The rapid development of the theory and practice of sampling has,
of course, made it possible to measure directly attributes which could
previously only be "estimated" more or less intuitively by experts or
otherwise indirectly approximated. As a matter of fact, progress has
been so rapid that constant re-examination of existing series has become
necessary to assure that they meet the new standards of reliability and
efficiency which probability theory is making attainable. In this connection recent history suggests a new "law," namely, that "good samples tend to drive bad samples out of existence."

A probability sample properly handled provides a quantitative measure of its sampling error. With such knowledge comes the ability to
control its extent. This confronts the statistician and the user of his
results with the question of how much any given reduction in the sampling error is worth. In turn, this compels a careful evaluation of the
purposes which the statistics are to serve. Thus, a wholesome and

often much-needed review of ultimate objectives results in order to determine specifically how much a given degree of accuracy is worth. This is as it should be, since the science of statistical measurement should be expected to utilize quantitative standards wherever it is possible to do so.

Modern sampling theory has also profoundly affected statistical work in another way. It has been the means of introducing rigorous scientific thinking into many statistical programs. Nothing is taken for granted in the scientific habit of thought, and once brought into a statistical operation through the application of probability theory its influence is soon felt throughout the entire undertaking. Sampling error in almost all surveys is not the only source of error and often not the primary source. Hence, if greater accuracy is needed, it may be possible to reduce the total error, e.g., by correcting some other weakness in the total project. But such an alternative, if it exists, cannot be correctly evaluated unless an effort is made to measure quantitatively the non-sampling errors. This brings under review such things as response error; deficiencies of enumerators; coding or classification errors; processing errors; definitional weaknesses; and other aspects of the operation which through faulty functioning, incomplete communication, or other defects can contribute error to the final statistical product. These factors may be the cause of large errors, and until they are measured and brought under control it becomes logically impossible to determine how much of the total survey resources should be devoted to reducing sampling error and how much should be devoted to the control of other sources of error. This should be a major concern of all who are responsible for the management of surveys or their financing.

Because of the wide variety of its programs and the scale of its operations the experience of the Census Bureau illustrates many of the ways in which modern sampling can affect the workings of statistical programs. In the program of complete censuses there are numerous opportunities to obtain economies, increase timeliness, and control quality of results through the application of sampling methods. In addition, the application of sampling has made possible many monthly, quarterly, annual, and special reports on many topics including the topics covered by the complete censuses. In these facts is to be found an explanation of the very great emphasis which the Bureau has given to the development and application of sampling theory and methods during the past decade or more. Even if it wished, it could not escape the fact that comparisons of its sample results with its complete enumerations could and would be made. Thus, the Bureau was faced with the absolute

necessity of employing sampling procedures which would yield valid results and at the same time be feasible within the practical limitations
which every survey administrator must face.

In developing its sampling program, the Bureau ultimately accepted
the principle that it should provide a quantitative measure of sampling
error in its published reports. This policy imposed the condition that
probability sampling be employed. This, in turn, brought into play the
rigorous logic of mathematics and probability theory in the design of
its surveys. The sampling staff of the Census Bureau, under the direction of the authors of the present volume, in company with other able
statisticians in all parts of the world faced with similar problems, developed the required theory and practice at a rapid rate. A sufficient
incentive was the ever-present demand for more efficient sampling designs to reduce the unit costs of the data compiled and to maintain required standards of reliability within the limits of the resources which
could be made available.

That they have been largely successful is evidenced by the fact that
as of this writing, the beginning of the year 1953, it has been possible
to place virtually all the sample surveys of the Census Bureau on a
probability basis and to furnish quantitative measures of sampling
variation along with its published reports. In addition, new series have
been provided which would have been impossible without the development of suitable sampling theory. Likewise, much has been learned
about other sources of error through carefully designed studies of the
over-all quality of survey results. Many steps have been taken to bring
into better balance the total resources devoted to sampling and to other
kinds of error.

Sample Survey Methods and Theory presents in a comprehensive
form both the theory of sampling as it exists today and its application
to practical problems. In fact, most of the theory and practice it describes has been tried and tested in actual operation. It should, therefore, be of real assistance to those charged with the tasks of applying
modern sampling methods to survey problems in a wide variety of subject fields. It should be of equal assistance also to users of sample
studies in appraising the methods employed in surveys and evaluating
the results obtained.

April, 1953

Preface

THIS VOLUME IS DESIGNED AS A TEXTBOOK AND REFERENCE manual for the student and for the investigator engaged in the design of sample surveys. It is also intended for the user of the results of surveys who wishes to know the circumstances under which he may place confidence in information based on samples.

Volumes I and II combined represent an attempt to give a comprehensive presentation of both sampling theory and practice. Volume I gives the principles and methods of sampling and their applications to various types of problems. Formulas appropriate to the methods presented are given without proof. Volume II contains the fundamental theory on which sampling methods are based, together with derivations of the formulas and proofs of statements made in Volume I.

A nonmathematical survey of the basic principles of sample design is given in the first three chapters of Volume I, where illustrations rather than formulas are used to clarify the discussion and to aid the intuition. Those who are interested in interpreting sample survey results, but not in designing samples themselves, may find these three chapters a sufficient guide to the basic principles. We have tried in the succeeding chapters, also, to provide an intuitive basis for most of the theory, primarily through the use of illustrations, and the only requisite assumed is an elementary course in statistics. The primary requirements for understanding the concepts in these chapters are an interest in the subject and persistence. Although many of the illustrations presented are based on applications in the United States Bureau of the Census, the methods and principles are directly applicable to sample survey design in any subject field.

Throughout Volume I an attempt has been made to present some simple rules for approximating the optimum sample design for a number of types of problems commonly encountered in practice. When a quick decision must be made on sample design, even at some sacrifice in efficiency, these rules will not lead one too far astray. Nevertheless, the main emphasis is on basic principles. To depend too heavily on a few simple rules might indeed stifle progress in a field which depends primarily on the ability of the investigator to adapt basic principles to a variety of situations. Such adaptations are illustrated in the case studies presented in the last chapter of Volume I.

For those with mathematical training through college algebra who not only desire to obtain an intuitive notion of the meaning of the formulas and the conditions under which they can be applied, but also wish to be able to derive them and extend them to other designs, Volume II should be consulted along with Volume I. Some calculus is required for a few of the proofs in Volume II. For the most part, the theory presented in Volume II has been limited to the minimum required for Volume I.

These volumes are not intended to cover all phases of survey work. The design of the questionnaire, administration of the survey, and methods of processing and tabulating are omitted, and the treatment of response errors is considered but briefly. Similarly, the emphasis is entirely on estimating characteristics of a finite population, without any consideration of the question of more general inferences so well discussed in Deming's *Some Theory of Sampling*.

For textbook purposes, the following suggestions may serve as guides in the organization of different types of courses. A one-year course without proofs may well begin with Chapter 1 of Volume I, then proceed through Chapters 4–6 and 8, parts A and B of Chapter 9 taken together with Case Study A or B of Chapter 12, sections 2 and 3 of Chapter 11, and Chapter 2. The remaining material may be covered as time is available, or serve as supplementary reading. A one-year course with proofs may begin with Chapter 1 of Volume I, followed by the development of the more important theorems of Chapters 2 and 3 of Volume II, and then followed by Chapters 4–12 of Volume II and the corresponding chapters of Volume I. Chapters 1 through 6 of Volume I with selected sections from the remaining chapters will provide sufficient material for a one-semester course without proofs, and the corresponding material from Volume II can be introduced for a one-semester course with proofs. For courses with proofs either volume can serve as the textbook, the choice depending on the emphasis desired, and the other can serve as a reference book and provide supplemental material for the teacher.

For reference purposes, a comprehensive index has been provided in each volume. In addition, cross references between the volumes relate the material in one volume to the corresponding material in the other. Finally, Chapter 3 of Volume I provides a short description of some commonly occurring problems and references to appropriate methods and theory in other chapters.

Acknowledgments

We shall make no attempt to trace or give credit to the original sources of sampling theory from which we have drawn. Most of the theory of sample survey design is an immediate consequence of the statistical theory that has been developed and modified by many people over a long period of years. Many of the extensions in the theory of sampling are traceable to research workers in subject matter who, unaided by theory, have introduced innovations in survey procedure that have provided inspiration for theoretical studies.

This work is, in a sense, a report on the sampling work in the United States Bureau of the Census. During the past two decades the Bureau of the Census has broken from its traditional emphasis on complete coverage and has applied sampling methods increasingly, so that today there are few activities in the Bureau of the Census in which sampling does not have an important role. A great deal of credit for giving sampling its early impetus in the Bureau of the Census is due to Frederick F. Stephan, who not only contributed to the solution of technical problems involved in the application of sampling methods in censuses and surveys but was also effective, with Calvert L. Dedrick and Philip M. Hauser, in obtaining initial acceptance of sampling in the Bureau of the Census. Equally, credit is due Calvert L. Dedrick for initiating research on sampling in the Census and for stimulating the authors' interest in this field; and to Philip M. Hauser for extending the applications of sampling, and later, as Deputy Director and Acting Director of the Bureau, for enthusiastically encouraging research on sampling and other methods.

The specific experience from which the material in this book is selected represents primarily the joint work of the statistical methods staff of the Bureau. Members of this staff in charge of various activities include Joseph F. Daly (Assistant Chief of the Statistical Methods staff), Ralph S. Woodruff (Business Division), Floyd W. Berger (Agriculture Division), Leon Gilford (Operations Research Section), Eli S. Marks (Response Research Section), Harold Nisselson (Field Division), Jack L. Ogus (Industry Division), Joseph Steinberg (Population and Housing Division), and Max A. Bershad and Benjamin J. Tepping (Sampling Research Section).

For reviewing the book, and for making numerous suggestions, we are indebted to Blanche Skalak, Margaret Gurney, Robert H. Hanson, Alice S. Kaitz, Richard J. Rice, Herman Hess, and Thomas Jabine. Miss Skalak, in addition to reviewing and making revisions in Volume I, was primarily responsible for identifying the places where proofs were required, writing up the proofs for Volume II, and developing a number of proofs. Miss Gurney was responsible for reviewing and making revisions in Volume I, developing numerous exercises and illustrations, and preparing the index. Mary Healy and Jane Wilson were responsible for the typing and proofreading through a number of drafts.

Outside of the Census sampling staff, we are strongly indebted to William G. Cochran and W. Edwards Deming, who read the manuscript, and to Philip M. Hauser and Frederick F. Stephan, who read the earlier chapters and gave many suggestions for improvement. Dr. Deming has given unstintingly of his time in reviewing and revising the manuscript.

We want to acknowledge, particularly, our indebtedness to A. Ross Eckler, Deputy Director of the Bureau, not only for his encouragement in preparing this book but also for his strong support for research in sampling and the measurement and control of response errors; to Howard C. Grieves, whose statistical insight, enthusiasm, and stimulation have extended the use of modern statistical methods in both survey design and administration; to J. C. Capt, Director of the Census from 1941 to 1949, and to Roy V. Peel, the Director from March 1950 to January 1953, who have continuously supported and encouraged this work and authorized publication of the Census materials that have been used.

Finally, we are indebted to Mildred Hansen, Hannah Hurwitz, and Lillian Madow for their assistance and encouragement through the long period this book has been in preparation.

MORRIS H. HANSEN
WILLIAM N. HURWITZ
WILLIAM G. MADOW

April, 1953

Contents

xv

CONTENTS

Introduction

1. The decision to consider a survey. Whenever the problem of obtaining information concerning a large aggregate of people, farms, firms, records, or other units occurs, a sample survey or sample study is likely to provide results of the desired precision at relatively low cost. Often the exact point at which a decision is made to consider taking a survey will be obscure. We must be prepared in the early stages of planning to encounter a certain vagueness concerning why the information is needed, what information is needed, how important the information is, how the information will be used, and why a survey is needed to obtain the information. Often, as the discussions develop, the need for the survey will become clear. Sometimes, however, it will become obvious that a proposed survey will not serve a useful purpose, as, for example, if the desired information can be obtained at lower cost and with sufficient accuracy by other means than making a survey.

In order to reach the decision to take a survey we must usually have some idea of the relationship between the cost and the accuracy of information that might be obtained. Naturally, we should like to have the survey conducted as efficiently as possible, and hence we shall seek methods of making surveys that yield maximum information per unit of cost.

Early in the consideration of a survey at least preliminary answers to the following questions should be prepared:

(1) What information is believed to be necessary?
(2) Why is the information needed? How important are the various reasons?
(3) How will decisions be affected by alternative possible survey results?

As a preliminary to deciding on the accuracy required for the survey it is often helpful to obtain illustrative uses to be made of the information desired. This involves an effort to determine the levels of inaccuracy in the desired information at which wrong decisions might be made and an effort to evaluate the cost of such wrong decisions.

2. Bases for planning a survey. Ordinarily, if one decides to go ahead with the preliminary planning of the survey, there will be known at least roughly, and more exactly at a later stage of planning:

1

a. The population for which information is desired. Information may be needed concerning the people living in a specified city, the families in the United States, the grocery stores in a given state, the electric light bulbs in a given shipment, the farms producing wheat, and so on. These are populations (or universes) of elementary units, such as people, families, grocery stores, electric light bulbs, or farms.

b. The information wanted concerning this population. The information wanted will usually consist of certain numbers which we call true values of the population. These might be the "average income per family," the "proportion male," the "proportion of electric light bulbs that will burn out with 1000 hours of use," and so on. The true value of the population is ordinarily an aggregate or average of the true values for the individual members of the population.

The measure of income to be used, or the conditions under which the light bulb is to be tested, must be defined. The characteristics to be measured will finally be defined by the questionnaire and instructions for filling it out or by other methods of measurement. The definitions may necessarily allow for some judgment to be applied even if no errors are made; and in opinion surveys the element of judgment may dominate. The approximation to the true value yielded by the survey may differ from that wanted because of a difference between the concept embodied in the questionnaire and the concept desired, because of the indefiniteness of the questionnaire, and because of errors in the survey itself. Thus, it should be clear that we may distinguish between the approximation to the "true value" associated with the survey and the "true value" indicated by the objectives of the survey.

Clearly, if the responses to the questionnaire or other measurements made do not have a reasonably close relationship to the desired true values, there is not much point in making a survey. Moreover, if errors of measurement are a problem, the survey design must take account of such errors as well as of sampling errors. We shall find it convenient to consider sampling and other sources of error separately; and, except where otherwise specifically indicated, we shall assume that the non-sampling errors are inconsequential in the measurements obtained for the units included in the sample. Theory and methods to take account of errors of measurement or response will be indicated in the form of an extension of the theory and methods developed for sampling. Chapters 2 and 12 of this volume, and Chapter 12 of Vol. II, indicate some additional considerations involved in evaluating errors of measurement or response and in the joint consideration of sampling and other sources of error.

c. The required precision of results. The estimates from a sample will ordinarily be different from the values being estimated. The important question to answer is whether the differences between the estimates made from a sample and the values being estimated are small enough to achieve the purposes of the study.   We shall see later that, if the sample is selected and the estimate is obtained by methods that permit the use of the theory of probability, we can evaluate the precision of the sample estimate.   It is a remarkable fact that the measure of precision can be estimated from the sample itself, without knowing the true value being estimated.

When the sample estimate differs from the true value, the administrator may suffer some loss when he takes action on the basis of the estimate, and the seriousness of the loss may depend on the magnitude of the error in the estimate.   If the expected loss for different levels of error can be approximated, we can arrive at the precision to be required of the sample survey.   Ordinarily direct measurement of expected losses is not feasible. The required precision is then arrived at by joint consideration of the expected costs of achieving differing levels of precision, which can be measured, and the expected losses associated with different levels of precision, which will be a judgment.*

3. The design of surveys.   An effort is made in the following chapters to provide a guide for the efficient design of sample surveys.   In applications of sampling to various problems the same fundamental principles of sampling theory appear again and again, and an attempt is made in what follows to introduce illustrative problems in which these common principles are applied.   At the same time, some principles have a great deal more importance than others in certain sampling problems, and the differences in the importance of various principles are emphasized.

---

* For a case where losses can be measured directly, see R. H. Blythe, "The Economics of Sample Size Applied to the Scaling of Sawlogs," *Biom. Bull.*, **1** (1945), 67–70, and W. G. Cochran, *Sampling Techniques*, John Wiley & Sons, New York, 1953, p. 64.

CHAPTER 1

An Elementary Survey of Sampling Principles

A. SOME FUNDAMENTAL NOTIONS OF SAMPLING

1. Scope of this chapter. This chapter gives a summary view of fundamental sampling principles, which will be discussed in greater detail in subsequent chapters. We shall indicate how it is possible, with a relatively small sample, to secure results that approximate very closely some of the characteristics of a large population, and we shall introduce in simplified illustrations some of the fundamental principles of sample design. The solution of the problem of sample design in much more complicated situations consists in large part of the repeated application of the simple principles presented here. The complexity of the designs actually used, however, does not change the underlying principles involved. It is particularly important that the reader understand the meaning of the measure of precision developed in this chapter, and its relationship to the confidence that can be placed in the results of a sample survey.

The precision of the results obtained from a sample survey depends not only on the size of the sample but also on the other parts of the sample design, i.e., on the way in which the sample is selected and the way in which the estimates are prepared from the sample survey returns. To have an efficient sample design one must make effective use of available resources. These resources will include not only such items as staff, equipment, and physical facilities, but also statistical information and other knowledge of the population to be sampled, together with available sampling theory and methods.

Ordinarily, there are many alternative sample designs that may be applied to a particular problem, and an understanding of alternative designs and a comparison of their efficiency are necessary if a rational choice is to be made. Sampling theory provides powerful tools with which to choose methods that are relatively efficient.

2. Criteria for choice of good sample designs. Before one can make an intelligent choice between alternative designs, he must determine how to tell a more efficient design from a less efficient one. This in turn implies the existence of a set of criteria that will serve to distinguish between good and bad designs.

Limitations of some criteria in current use. If one wishes an estimate of total wheat acreage in the United States or in a particular state, many methods of estimation are available. One method would be to ask some expert who has contact with farmers and with local officials in various communities, and who is acquainted with what is going on in farming areas, to give his judgment of the number of acres of wheat. This judgment would be based upon the expert's knowledge of what has happened in the past and his speculations regarding the approximate present situation. This sort of approach might, in fact, give the results wanted with extremely high precision. It frequently happens, however, that two experts, both considered well informed, give widely different answers. For example, with respect to unemployment in the 1930's, there were estimates for 1935 ranging from* 6,000,000 to 14,000,000. The estimates were generally based on projections of time series, with adjustments made from current but fragmentary data. The range of the estimates indicates the differences in interpretation put on the same data by different persons. When estimates are based on such a method, we have no guide in selecting the best estimate except our judgment as to who is the best-qualified expert.

The use of an expert's opinion is generally a relatively inexpensive method of obtaining information. Moreover, there are numerous situations where objective measurement methods are not available, and complete dependence must be placed on expert judgment. However, if methods for objective measurement are available, and if an important decision depends upon the accuracy of the estimates (e.g., timing the sale of a large government-held wheat surplus), an error may prove more costly in the long run than the most expensive type of survey that could reasonably be considered.

Instead of using the judgment of one or a few individuals, we might, for a question of an agricultural nature, send out questionnaires to a number of farmers, analyze the responses, and build up evidence based on a variety of sources. From prior experience and other information available, we might be able to speculate about the reliability of the results of our questionnaires. On the basis of this added information, we might arrive at a sounder judgment. Here there is a difference in degree, but not in kind, from the situation where an expert is forced to arrive at a

---

* Social Security Board, Bureau of Research and Statistics, *Selected Current Statistics*, Vol. I, No. 6, pp. 43–45 (1937).

judgment without these further aids.   The method is fundamentally based
on relationships observed in past experience, and the precision of the
estimate cannot be measured objectively.

We do not mean to imply that expert judgment is usually not good, or
that an expert will not welcome or make full use of objective data.   But,
often, expert judgment does not provide a substitute for objective measurement.   There are many situations in which it is important to know how
far off an estimate may be from the result of a carefully conducted complete count.   In such instances it becomes exceedingly desirable that
survey methods be used which can produce results giving an assurance of
reliability within known bounds of error.   Reliance upon relationships
observed in past experience may be particularly dangerous in times of
important economic or social change, yet it is in such times that the need
for reliable results is most vital.

In the evaluation of estimates which rely heavily upon the opinions of
experts, the criterion used is faith in the validity of these opinions.
Limitations are the inability to evaluate this faith, and the lack of an
objective basis for choosing between the opinions of two or more experts.

There are numerous other ways of obtaining information that go far
beyond the simple expedients described above and that ostensibly depend
on objective sample surveys for their results, but that still do not provide
guarantees that the personal judgments used cannot bias the estimates.
A casual reading of a description of some surveys might lead the reader to
believe that the sampling was carried out in a wholly objective manner.
Use may be made of a number of the factors that play an important role in
sample design, such as the size of sample, stratification (setting up more
or less homogeneous groups for purposes of sampling), elaborate methods
of estimation, and other devices, together, sometimes, with formulas that
presumably measure the reliability of the results.   Still the design may be
such that the sample estimate is essentially dependent on judgment.

For example, one sometimes finds investigators using mail questionnaire
surveys with inadequate rates of response, justifying their findings with
statements that, for example, the questionnaires were widely distributed
and the sample estimates are based on returns from tens of thousands (or
perhaps millions) of cases.   The law of averages may even be mentioned,
and unwarranted confidence placed in the sample results because the
sample was large.   A little investigation may unearth the fact that the
addresses were drawn from inadequate (incomplete or seriously out-of-
date) mailing lists or that a relatively high proportion of those receiving
the mailed questionnaires did not respond.

The method [of mail canvass] was carried farthest by the *Literary Digest*,
which polled millions of citizens during the 1920's and early 1930's with its

postcard ballots. . . . The record of the *Digest* was surprisingly good on some points. In 1932, for example, it erred in predicting the vote for Roosevelt by less than 1 percentage point. In 1936, as is well known, it made a very large error of 19 percentage points in predicting Roosevelt's vote. Roughly 20 per cent of the ballots mailed out were returned to the *Literary Digest*. From a mailing of ten million or more it received some two million ballots, yet this huge mail vote was so far wrong that the poll was abandoned.

There is general agreement that this mail-ballot method was subject to a serious distortion because the better educated and more literate part of the population, as well as those who were higher on the economic scale, tended to return their ballots in greater proportion than those who were lower in educational and economic status. In addition, the *Digest* obtained the names of persons to whom they mailed the ballots from automobile registration lists, telephone directories, and similar sources. These sources were biased upward in education and economic status.*

The first limitation of such sampling is the mailing list itself. It is quite obvious that a sample, no matter how carefully drawn from a list, can be no more representative than the list. The second limitation arises when the proportion of nonresponse is high. It cannot be assumed, at least without continual testing, that nonrespondents will have characteristics similar to those of respondents. Nonrespondents may be of various kinds—not at home, unwilling to answer, or otherwise different from respondents. When the nonrespondents are an appreciable portion of the total, one cannot place much confidence in the results unless by some means he obtains information about the nonrespondents.

Remark. This does not mean that the mail survey cannot be used effectively. A proper use of mail surveys, combined with follow-up of nonrespondents, is a very important technique (see Ch. 11, Sec. 3).

The inadequacy of the mailing lists and the high rate of nonresponse in some types of mail surveys have given impetus to the so-called "field survey" method. Here interviewers are sent to selected areas spread throughout the country. The descriptions of the method often indicate that a great deal of time and effort is spent in setting up "controls" to insure obtaining a sample that is a "good" cross section of the population. Very elaborate methods of estimation may be developed. With all this care we often find sampling procedures in which the interviewer is permitted considerable latitude in the selection of the sample. The interviewer may be told, for example, to pick 10 persons whose ages are between 18 and 25, who have completed high school, and who live in the

---

* F. F. Stephan, Ch. II, p. 10, in Mosteller, Hyman, McCarthy, Marks, Truman, and others, *The Pre-election Polls of 1948*, Social Science Research Council, New York, 1949.

northeast section of the city, but he is given latitude within these limitations to exercise his discretion in deciding whom to choose. As will be indicated more fully below, the exercise of judgment in the final selection of the individuals, even with great care imposed up to the very point of selecting the sample, makes it impossible to evaluate objectively the reliability of the sample results.

Another survey method which may also involve serious biases, and whose reliability we are likewise unable to measure, is the selection of typical persons, cities, or areas to represent the whole population. Even if the persons or areas were "average" or "typical" in the past, there is no assurance that they will remain "typical." The fact that such a purposive selection can be "validated" by comparing its results with those of other surveys with respect to certain characteristics of the persons involved does not insure that it will be adequate for these or some other characteristics at a different date.

The types of surveys indicated above have two important limitations. One is the difficulty of ascribing the proper emphasis to the various factors affecting sample design. Some may overemphasize size of sample (as in the mail questionnaire illustration); others may emphasize unduly the use of effective "controls"; others may rely almost entirely on elaborate estimating procedures. What is lacking is a theory that will indicate a desirable allocation of resources to such factors of sample design. Some guidance is required for evaluating the various factors entering into the design and contributing to the sampling error, and for selecting the "best" one of a number of alternative designs. Without such guidance the resources available for the survey may be dissipated in taking care of some aspects of the sample design, whereas other factors equally or more important may be disregarded.

The second limitation is the inability to measure the precision of the sample results. For the methods described above, no objective basis is known for measuring the amount of confidence which can be placed in the sample estimates. True, we sometimes find certain sampling formulas applied, ostensibly measuring precision.* The use of these formulas is often misleading because they involve assumptions that may be difficult to defend on two fundamental grounds:

(1) Formulas that measure sampling errors depend on knowledge of the probability with which an individual is included in a sample.
(2) The formulas for sampling errors depend on the particular sample design used.

---

* A common error is the indiscriminate use of pq/n as the variance of a proportion, without regard to the manner in which the sample was selected.

The sampling methods described above have one common characteristic: the probability that an individual is included in the sample is unknown. The probability will be unknown in any method in which a probability method is not used in the ultimate selection of the sample. Randomness is not insured, as we shall see later, unless specific steps are taken to control the probabilities of selection of the sample. When the determination of the individuals to be included in a sample involves personal judgment, one cannot have an objective measure of the reliability of the sample results, because the various individuals may have differing and unknown chances of being drawn. We shall refer to such methods as *nonmeasurable* or *judgment* designs. Conversely, we shall refer to samples in which the probabilities of selection are known as *random* samples or as *probability* samples.

In the absence of known facts against which to check his sample estimates, one may be prone to go along blithely without fear of contradiction. Facts sometimes become available subsequently, however, against which a sample estimate may be verified. We often find administrators who do not know what to expect from a sample expressing amazement as to how close the sample estimates were to the "true" figures that have become available. However, if one uses a design where the error can be estimated from the sample results, he should be surprised only when the results of the sample do *not* agree, within the expected sampling error, with the results of a complete count taken with the same care as the sample survey. In the absence of a census, the only real insurance that we have of the adequacy of the sample is the careful use of probability sampling methods and the measures of precision derived from the sample results themselves.

Criteria used in this book. This book will consider primarily methods of sample design for which the sampling error can be measured objectively, i.e., probability samples. With probability designs it will be possible to:

(1) Compare the precision of different designs and of different modifications of the same design.
(2) Evaluate objectively the precision of the sample results.

With probability samples it is possible to state an objective basis for choosing from among the alternative methods of sampling and methods of estimation. The criterion that we propose to use is to design the sample so that it will yield the required precision at a minimum cost or, conversely, so that at a fixed cost it will yield estimates of the characteristics desired with the maximum precision possible. This implies that we:

(1) Use sampling methods for which one can get from the sample itself an objective measure of the precision of the sample estimates.

(2) Use only simple, straightforward procedures, such that it is feasible to carry them through in practice and such that the execution of these procedures will meet the necessary time schedules and other administrative restrictions.

(3) Use, from among the alternative methods that meet the first two criteria, a method that in addition yields results of maximum reliability per unit of cost.

(4) By means of adequate supervision and control, actually carry out the survey in accordance with the specifications that have been prescribed. When this is accomplished, close conformance will be assured between theory and practice.

·Although there is not now theory to guide one uniquely to the best design among all the possible ones, the available theory is an exceedingly useful guide in the choice of an effective method.

3. Precision of sample results. In referring to *sampling error*, or to the *precision* of a sample result, we are referring to how closely we can reproduce from a sample the results which would be obtained if we should take a complete count or a census, using the same methods of measurement, questionnaire, interview procedures, type of enumerators, supervision, etc. The nonsampling errors that arise from the method of measurement or interviewing, the design of the questionnaire, and other sources of errors in surveys that are present in a complete census as well as in a sample are considered in Chapter 2. These nonsampling errors may be equally as important as sampling errors, or perhaps more so, depending upon the circumstances. Here, however, we are considering only the question of predicting from a sample what would have been shown by a complete count, using essentially the same definitions and procedures. The difference between a sample result and the result from a complete count taken under the same conditions is measured by what we will refer to as the *precision* or the *reliability* of the sample result. The difference between the sample result and the true value, we call the *accuracy* of the sample survey. It is the *accuracy* of a survey in which we are chiefly interested; it is the *precision* which we are able to measure in most instances. We strive to design the survey so that the combined effect of the two will be minimized.

With probability sampling methods one can get away completely from dependence upon judgment for determining precision. Under these circumstances, and with reasonably large samples, the precision of the results from the sample can be measured from the sample itself. Outer bounds on the possible sampling errors can be set, such that the probability of exceeding these bounds is very small. Generally, the sample will yield results with much smaller errors than these outer bounds indicate.

We have already indicated, but wish to emphasize, that a sample design yields a probability sample when the probability of inclusion in the sample is known and is not zero for every one of the individuals or elementary units in the population. As will become clear later, there are many ways in which personal judgment, when it is good, can be utilized effectively in improving sample design, provided this personal judgment is not exercised in the final selection of the individuals or elements that are to be included in the sample. If it is, the investigator will be subject to the possible criticism that he has introduced more or less serious biases* into the results, biases that may reflect his own predilections rather than the real facts in the population being sampled.

B. BASIC PRINCIPLES ILLUSTRATED WITH SIMPLE RANDOM SAMPLING

4. Meaning of "simple random sampling." Before beginning a discussion of the principles to be followed in actual practical design, we shall illustrate the fundamental character of random sampling through a discussion of what we shall call *simple random sampling*. We shall first, define simple random sampling; then we shall try to explain how it works and how it can produce results whose precision can be measured. It will be noted, in the treatment of more complicated sampling problems which are taken up after this exposition of the fundamentals of simple random sampling, and throughout this book, that all the principles of sampling that are introduced, over and above those included in the description of simple random sampling, are introduced in order to increase efficiency, and that such further principles involve various ways of making more effective use of available knowledge and resources, so as to get the maximum return for the money expended.

To simplify the discussion it is desirable to introduce some terminology. Sample surveys cover a variety of fields. The purpose of a survey might be to estimate the proportion of persons that use a product, or to estimate the average number of acres per farm or the total acres or crop land, say for the state of Iowa, or to estimate the proportion of punch cards that are in error. The individuals whose characteristics are to be measured in the analyses are called *elementary units*; and the aggregate of the units, i.e., the entire group whose characteristics are to be estimated, is termed either the *universe* or the *population*. Thus, if a sample of farms is drawn

---

* See Sec. 9 of this chapter for the meaning of the word *bias*, as used in mathematical statistics.

to estimate the average acres of crop land per farm in the United States, the totality of all farms of the United States is the population, and each farm is an elementary unit of this population. As another illustration, if a sample of punch cards is drawn from all the cards punched on a particular project during the course of a month, the totality of all cards punched during that month is the population, and each punch card is an element of the population.

By the term *simple random sample of n elements* we shall refer to a sample selected from a population in such a manner that each *combination* of *n* elements has the same chance or probability of being selected as every other combination. Whenever the method of selecting the sample is such that each combination of *n* elements does not have the same chance of being selected, the method of selection is not simple random sampling. Thus, the term *simple random sampling* is not applied to such methods of sampling as stratified sampling or such methods as taking every *k*th individual from a list (systematic sampling) or selecting a set of blocks in each city and including in the sample a subsample of the individuals in the selected blocks (cluster sampling), etc. Such methods of sampling (which are sometimes referred to as restricted sampling methods) will be discussed later.

Simple random sampling is not used frequently in practice, but because of its importance in sampling theory, its simplicity, and its close approximation to some types of sample design that are widely utilized in practice, it is discussed in this chapter and developed more fully in Chapter 4 to illustrate some of the fundamental principles of sampling.

For the discussion of simple random sampling let us set up a hypothetical population consisting of only 12 individuals (Table 1), and assume that we wish to estimate their average (mean) income from a sample. We are using a very small population here because the principles involved can be observed more readily for a small population. They apply equally well to samples from populations of any size, as will be seen.

After considering how to draw a simple random sample from this population, we shall show how to prepare an estimate from the sample and how we may increase the precision of the sample estimate by increasing the size of sample. Then we shall show how these estimates can vary and how we can obtain a measure of the precision of a sample estimate.

5. Selection of a simple random sample. To draw a simple random sample from this population we might proceed in a number of ways. For example, we might get 12 equal-sized smooth chips each having 1 of the 12 letters, *A, B, C, · · ·, L* designated on it, no 2 chips having the same letter.   Each person in the population above would be represented by the 1 chip having the same letter designation.

Now suppose that the chips were placed in a bowl and mixed thoroughly and 2 were drawn in such a way that the predilections of the person

Table 1.   Incomes of a hypothetical population of 12 individuals

Individual	Income (dollars)
A	1,300
B	6,300
C	3,100
D	2,000
E	3,600
F	2,200
G	1,800
H	2,700
I	1,500
J	900
K	4,800
L	1,900
Total income	32,100
Average income	2,675

making the drawings did not affect the selections.   Suppose that the chips C and K happened to be drawn.   It would follow that the sample consisting of individuals C and K had been obtained by simple random sampling. There are 66 possible combinations of 2 chips which could be drawn.* If the process is repeated a large number of times, and if counts are made of the number of times each of the 66 possible combinations occurs, the proportion of times that AB occurred would be, for all practical purposes, the same as that for BC, or any other of the 66 combinations.   Table 2 gives a listing of all the possible simple random samples of 2 elements from the population of Table 1.   All these possible samples have the same chance of being drawn with simple random sampling.   Whichever of the 66 possible samples is actually selected to be the sample we call a simple random sample of size 2.

There are difficulties in the use of the method above of drawing a simple random sample: the mixing must be much more persistent than

---

* An alternative way of getting a simple random sample of 2 individuals would be to place 66 chips in the bowl, 1 for each of the 66 possible combinations of 2 persons, and draw 1 of the 66 chips.

most people imagine; the chips may not be the same size or weight; a number of other kinds of inequalities may affect the drawing, with the result that every combination does not have the same chance of being drawn. Moreover, if the population is of any considerable size, the job

Table 2.   All possible samples of 2 drawn from the population of individuals given in Table 1

Individuals in sample	Average income (dollars)	Individuals in sample	Average income (dollars)	Individuals in sample	Average income (dollars)
AB	3800	CD	2550	FG	2000
AC	2200	CE	3350	FH	2450
AD	1650	CF	2650	FI	1850
AE	2450	CG	2450	FJ	1550
AF	1750	CH	2900	FK	3500
AG	1550	CI	2300	FL	2050
AH	2000	CJ	2000		
AI	1400	CK	3950	GH	2250
AJ	1100	CL	2500	GI	1650
AK	3050			GJ	1350
AL	1600	DE	2800	GK	3300
		DF	2100	GL	1850
BC	4700	DG	1900		
BD	4150	DH	2350	HI	2100
BE	4950	DI	1750	HJ	1800
BF	4250	DJ	1450	HK	3750
BG	4050	DK	3400	HL	2300
BH	4500	DL	1950		
BI	3900			IJ	1200
BJ	3600	EF	2900	IK	3150
BK	5550	EG	2700	IL	1700
BL	4100	EH	3150		
		EI	2550	JK	2850
		EJ	2250	JL	1400
		EK	4200		
		EL	2750	KL	3350

of getting a simple random sample in the manner described above may be very difficult. A simpler and more satisfactory method is to use a table of random numbers.*

If one wished to get a simple random sample of 2 persons by using such a table, he could first assign the numbers from 1 to 12 to the 12 persons in the population (arranging the population in any convenient order).

---

* For more complete details on how random numbers are defined and the description and use of a table of random numbers, see Ch. 4, Sec. 5.

He could, for example, number the individuals in the order in which they are listed in Table 1. Then he could obtain 2 random numbers between 1 and 12 from a table of random numbers. Suppose that these numbers turned out to be 03 and 11. These would indicate that individuals C and K are to be included in the sample. This procedure insures that every possible combination has equal probability of being selected. The random numbers accomplish the equivalent of thorough mixing.

6. Probability of selection is known. If we follow the rules indicated above, we know the probability that each individual has of being selected in samples of any size, i.e., the proportion of samples in which he will be included. In a sample of 1 element drawn from the population according to these rules, each of the 12 elements would have the same chance of getting into the sample. Hence, the probability of any individual being selected is $\frac{1}{12}$. Suppose now that we wish to know the probability that A will be included in a sample of 2. To determine this probability, note from Table 2 that there are exactly 66 combinations of 2 individuals and that each of these has the same chance of being drawn. Moreover, we note that A occurs in 11 of the possible combinations. Hence the probability of drawing A is $\frac{11}{66}$ or $\frac{1}{6}$. In a similar way, one may show that the probability is the same for each of the remaining persons in the population.

For samples of 3, a count of the number (55) of samples in which A or any other specified individual occurs, divided by the total number (220) of possible samples, yields $\frac{55}{220}$ or $\frac{1}{4}$ as the probability of any specified person being selected.

The probability that an individual will be drawn in a simple random sample of any size turns out to be simply n/N, where N is the number of individuals in the population and n is the number drawn in the sample.

Thus, simple random sampling is a probability design. The process of selection is such that the probability of any individual being drawn is known. This method of selection differs markedly from one in which an interviewer stands on a street corner and picks the first n individuals who pass. In simple random sampling, one must take positive steps such as those indicated above to insure that each individual has the same probability.

7. The estimate from the sample. The average income of the persons in the sample is an estimate of the average income of the population. If, in drawing a sample of 2, we happened to have chosen the sample consisting of C and K, our estimate of the average income would be $3950. In practice, we wish to know whether such a sample estimate can be used with confidence; i.e., we want to know how accurate an estimate it is of the result that would have been obtained from a complete census covering every individual in the population.

In order to determine the precision of an estimate based on one particular sample, it will be helpful to examine all the possible samples of specified size that can be drawn from the population under consideration. Table 2 (p. 14), in addition to listing the possible samples, gives the estimate of average income made from each.

By examining all possible samples of a given size we can see what kinds of results are obtained, on the average, from a given sampling procedure. From this examination, we may infer what error may be expected, on the average, for an estimate based on a single sample, and what is a reasonable maximum for the error of a single sample. From such knowledge, we know how much confidence to place in an estimate from a single sample that is a random selection from among all the possible samples.

8. The expected value of a sample estimate. The average of the 66 results listed in Table 2 is $2675, which is exactly equal to the average income of the population. Thus, we see that, on the average, the sample estimate is exactly equal to the population average that is being estimated. This will be true for a sample mean based on simple random sampling no matter what size of sample is used and no matter from what population we are sampling.

The average of the estimates over all possible samples plays an important role in sampling and is referred to as the *expected value* of a sample estimate. For example, we may refer to the expected value of the estimated average income, and this will mean the arithmetic average of the sample estimates over all possible samples. In other words, the expected value of an estimate is the sum of the results from all possible samples divided by the number of possible samples if the possible samples are equally likely to be selected.*

In the illustration above, the expected value of the estimate of average income from samples of 2 is merely equal to the aggregate value over all 66 samples of the estimated averages given in Table 2, $176,550, divided by 66.

9. Bias due to sampling. Perhaps no one popular word that has been given an exact definition in mathematical statistics has created more of a

---

* If, however, the possible samples are selected with known probabilities but are *not* equally likely, then the expected value is a weighted average of the sample estimates, and the weight to be used for each sample is its probability of selection. See Vol. II, Ch. 3, Sec. 2, for the definition of mathematical expectation.

language barrier between the technician and the layman than the word *bias*. The primary confusion arises from the distinction between bias and measures of precision. The bias is simply equal to the difference between the expected value of the estimate and the true value being estimated. Whenever the bias is 0, the estimate is said to be *unbiased*. For example, in the illustration above, the expected value of the estimate of average income is $2675, which is identically equal to the population average income. Therefore, the estimate of average income based on samples of 2 is an unbiased estimate of the average income in the population. It will be shown later that the sample average is an unbiased estimate of the mean with simple random sampling, no matter what the size of sample is and no matter what the nature of the population is from which the sample is drawn.

To illustrate one way that a bias may arise, assume that a sample of 2 is drawn from the bowl of chips described in Sec. 5. Assume further that chips G, K, and L somehow become glued to the bottom of the bowl and have no chance of being drawn. It follows then that the sample of 2 can be drawn only from the 9 free chips, so that there are 36 possible samples of 2. The average over all these possible samples turns out to be $2622, and therefore the bias is equal to $2675 - $2622 = $53.

The type of bias indicated above might arise, for example, if one were choosing for his sample persons found at home during the daytime, and if G, K, and L were not at home during the day, whereas the remaining persons in the population were at home all the time. If a sample of 2 were drawn from those at home during the day, the sample would provide a biased estimate of the average income for the 12 individuals, although an unbiased estimate for the 9.

When an estimate is unbiased, it does not follow that it is without error. The estimate from the particular sample we happen to draw may differ greatly from the true value (the sample estimate based on C and K differed by $1275 from the true value) and still the estimate is unbiased (i.e., that *type* of estimate averaged over all possible simple random samples is equal to the true population average).

As we shall see later in this chapter, it is actually not important that an estimate be unbiased provided the bias, if any, is very small. In many situations, an estimation procedure with a very small bias may be considerably more reliable than the best available unbiased estimating procedure.

10. Precision of sample estimates increases with increasing size of sample: consistent estimates. If, for a given size of sample, practically every possible sample estimate of average income is close to the average income in the population, then we should not be taking much of a gamble if we depended on one sample selected at random.   If, however, a substantial proportion of the samples have average incomes very different from the average income of the population, we should be taking a big gamble in depending on a random selection of one sample.   We shall now illustrate how, as the size of sample is increased, the estimates will cluster closer around the average being estimated.

As indicated earlier, when the size of sample is 2, there are 66 possible samples and hence 66 possible estimates of average income.   Similarly,

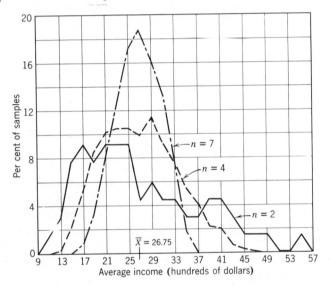

FIG. 1.   Distribution of estimates of average income from samples of various sizes drawn from population given in Table 1.

if samples of 3, 4, 5, 6, etc., are drawn, all possible samples of each size could be listed as was done for samples of 2 in Table 2 and the average incomes could be estimated from each.   The actual results of all possible samples of sizes 3–7, drawn from the illustrative population of 12 individuals, have been listed and the averages computed and summarized in Table 3 and Fig. 1.   It is obvious from a glance at this table and figure that the results cluster closer about the average of all possible samples as the size of sample increases.   Thus, the proportion of sample results falling between $2000 and $3400 is 47 per cent for samples of 2, is 58 per cent for samples of 3, is 69 per cent for samples of 4, is 78 per cent for samples of 5, is 87 per cent for samples of 6, and is 94 per cent for samples of 7.   Similarly, for any interval about the true average, the proportion of possible sample results that would fall in the interval would tend to increase as the sample size increases.

By taking samples large enough, the proportion falling within a designated interval about the expected value can be made as close to 100 per cent as may be desired. It can be seen from the chart that if it were desired that at least 95 per cent, say, of the sample results should fall

Table 3.   All possible estimates of average income from samples of various sizes drawn from population of individuals given in Table 1

Average income estimated from sample (dollars)	Number of samples having indicated estimate of average income with sample of size n						
	$n = 1$	$n = 2$	$n = 3$	$n = 4$	$n = 5$	$n = 6$	$n = 7$
800– 999	1						
1000–1199		1					
1200–1399	1	2	3	1			
1400–1599	1	5	10	11	7	1	
1600–1799		6	15	25	25	16	6
1800–1999	2	5	20	42	55	50	27
2000–2199	1	6	22	50	78	84	61
2200–2399	1	6	22	52	90	109	98
2400–2599		6	19	52	101	139	136
2600–2799	1	3	17	49	108	151	150
2800–2999		4	16	57	101	133	130
3000–3199	1	3	16	46	81	107	108
3200–3399		3	16	38	61	79	62
3400–3599		2	13	26	46	43	14
3600–3799	1	2	10	21	27	12	
3800–3999		3	7	11	10		
4000–4199		3	4	10	2		
4200–4399		2	6	3			
4400–4599		1	1	1			
4600–4799		1	2				
4800–4999	1	1	1				
5000–5199							
5200–5399							
5400–5599		1					
5600–5799							
5800–5999							
6000–6199							
6200–6399	1						
Number of samples	12	66	220	495	792	924	792
Average (expected value) (dollars)	2675	2675	2675	2675	2675	2675	2675

between $900 and $4500, a sample of only 2 would be necessary. On the other hand, if it were desired that 95 per cent of the sample results should fall in the smaller interval $2000–3400, a sample of 7 would nearly serve the purpose. Thus, if we draw a sample of 7 at random from this population and use the average income from the sample as an estimate of the true figure, we know we shall be within $700 of the true average about 95 per cent of the time.

This suggests, as is in fact the case, that we can achieve any desired precision by taking a large enough sample. Moreover, with a sample of a given size we can interpret the precision of the sample if we know the chances (or probability) that the sample estimate will lie within various distances from the result that would be obtained from a complete enumeration.

The increasing concentration of sample estimates around the value being estimated, with increased size of sample, illustrates *consistency*, a quality possessed by many types of sample estimates. We say that an estimate from a sample is a *consistent estimate* if the proportion of sample estimates that differ from the value being estimated by less than any specified small amount approaches 100 per cent as the size of sample is increased.* This means that if the sample size is sufficiently large one does not take a serious risk in using an estimate made from a sample drawn at random. An important characteristic of random sampling is that consistent estimates can be made from random samples.

> **Remark.** It may appear to the reader that the increase in concentration of sample estimates around the expected value shown in Table 3 and Fig. 1 arises from the fact that here, as we increase the size of the sample, we are taking a high percentage of the population. Actually, as will be seen shortly, the same kind of results will be observed when the size of sample is increased but only a small proportion of the population is included in the sample (see Sec. 12).

11. The standard deviation and variance of sample estimates. We have illustrated how one can determine how much confidence to place in a particular sample estimate by examining all possible estimates that might have resulted from the sampling procedure used. We cannot, of course, list all possible samples in a real situation; we must depend upon a single sample. Therefore, it is necessary to find some measure of the extent to which the sample results differ from the value being estimated; and this measurement, if it is to be useful, must be one that can be determined from the sample itself. The *standard deviation* is such a measure. We shall

---

* For a more precise definition of consistency, with special reference to finite populations, see Vol. II, Ch. 3, Sec. 7b.

illustrate the relation of the standard deviation to all possible estimates from samples of a given size, and show how it provides a measure of the precision of a sample estimate. Then we shall see that it can be computed from the original population without listing all possible samples, and, finally, that it can be estimated from a single sample.

The square of the standard deviation is the variance. The variance for the original population is equal to

$$\sigma^2 = \frac{(X_1 - \bar{X})^2 + (X_2 - \bar{X})^2 + (X_3 - \bar{X})^2 + \cdots + (X_N - \bar{X})^2}{N}$$

where $X_1, X_2, \cdots, X_N$ are the values associated with the N elementary units in the population, and $\bar{X} = (X_1 + X_2 + \cdots + X_N)/N$ is the average of the values. Similarly, the variance of the possible estimates for a given size of sample is the average value, over all possible samples, of the squares of the deviations of the sample estimates from their expected value. Thus, the variance of any variable is the expected value of the square of the individual deviations of that variable from the expected value of that variable. The variance is ordinarily indicated by the symbol σ^2, and a subscript may be added to indicate the variable to which it relates. Thus, if we let $\bar{x}$ stand for a sample mean based on a particular sample, $\sigma_{\bar{x}}^2$ is the variance of sample means for all possible samples of the same kind and size, and $\sigma_{\bar{x}}$ is the standard deviation or standard error.* The symbol σ^2 without a subscript designates the variance of the original population.

For samples of 1, the 12 possible deviations from the average income ($2675) are

− 1375	− 875
3625	25
425	− 1175
− 675	− 1775
925	2125
− 475	− 775

and the average of the squares of these deviations is

$$\frac{27,162,500}{12} = 2,263,542$$

Thus, the standard deviation for samples of 1 is $\sqrt{2,263,542} = \$1505$. This is the same as the standard deviation in the original population.

* Sometimes the term *standard deviation* is applied only to the original population, and the term *standard error* is applied to the distribution of sample estimates. We shall use the terms interchangeably.

If we compute the standard deviation of the estimated means given in Table 2, Sec. 5, for all possible samples of 2, it turns out to be $1015. The values of the standard deviation for estimated means based on samples of 1, 2, 3, 4, 5, 6, and 7 are given in Table 4.

Table 4. Standard deviation of estimate of average income
for various sample sizes

Sample of size n	$\sigma_{\bar{x}}$ (dollars)
1	1505
2	1015
3	786
4	642
5	537
6	454
7	383

The standard deviation thus computed is a measure of the extent to which the sample estimates differ from their expected or average value. Thus, from Table 3, Sec. 10, it can be seen that as the sample size becomes larger the sample estimates differ less and less from the expected value. At the same time the standard deviation becomes smaller and smaller, as is shown in Table 4. When the standard deviation of the sample estimates is small, most of the sample estimates are close to the average of all sample estimates; and when it is large the estimates are more widely spread. It can be shown that no matter what the population from which one is sampling, it is impossible for more than $\frac{1}{9}$ of the possible sample estimates to differ from the average of all estimates by more than 3 times the standard deviation of the sample estimates.*

In practical sampling problems where a reasonably large sample is used, the per cent of sample results that will differ from the average of all sample estimates by more than 3 times the standard deviation is very much less than $\frac{1}{9}$. It is in this connection that the *normal distribution* plays an exceedingly important role. This is the familiar bell-shaped distribution which has the property (among others) that about 95 per cent of the results differ from the average by less than twice the standard deviation. It also has the property that about 99.7 per cent of the results differ from the average by less than 3 times the standard deviation and

---

* This statement is an immediate consequence of the well-known Tchebycheff inequality. See Vol. II, Ch. 3, Sec. 7, Theorem 18.

about 68 per cent differ from the average by less than 1 standard deviation.* Although, in practical problems, the distribution of sample estimates over all possible samples is rarely, if ever, exactly normal, the approximation to a normal distribution is ordinarily very close for estimates based on samples that are moderately large, say 100 or more for populations which do not have exceedingly extreme or unusual items. This is true even though the original distribution from which the sample is drawn is far from normal. Thus, in practice, if we have a moderately large sample, we are often safe in assuming that the chance that our sample estimate, $\bar{x}$, will differ from its expected value by more than $3\sigma_{\bar{x}}$ will be less than 1 per cent, and we can be reasonably confident that the error in our estimate will be less than $3\sigma_{\bar{x}}$ ($\sigma_{\bar{x}}$ means here the standard deviation of the estimate). Similarly, there will be only about 1 chance in 20 that the error in our estimate will exceed $2\sigma_{\bar{x}}$, and about 1 chance in 3 that it will exceed $1\sigma_{\bar{x}}$.

The way in which the distribution of a sample estimate approaches the normal distribution as the size of sample is increased is illustrated by the example we have been following through. Note from Table 3 and Fig. 1 (pp. 19 and 18) that the original population used for the illustration is quite skewed; i.e., the population is not symmetric, but has a "long tail" to the right. With samples of 2 the skewness is still quite marked, but with samples of 7 the distribution of the estimated sample means already has become nearly symmetrical.

We find by examining the distributions of sample means for various sizes of samples, as given in Table 3 (p. 19), in relation to the corresponding standard deviations from Table 4, that even for the very small sizes of samples shown, and sampling from the fairly skewed population given in Table 1 (p. 13), one would not go very far astray by assuming that the probabilities associated with the normal distribution are applicable to samples of any size from this population. Actually, for each size of sample, the proportions of samples differing from the population average by more than 1, 2, and 3 times $\sigma_{\bar{x}}$ are as shown in Table 5. It can be seen that for samples of size 2 or more the proportions observed approximate roughly the normal distribution proportions.

We have illustrated for a very simple case what will be universally true —that the standard deviation of a distribution of sample estimates, if it is known, provides a measure of the precision of an estimate based on a single sample. Moreover, for samples of moderate size (say samples of

---

* The normal distribution is discussed in many texts; see, for example, James G. Smith and Acheson J. Duncan, *Fundamentals of the Theory of Statistics*, McGraw-Hill Book Co., New York, 1945, Vol. I, pp. 307–320, and also Paul G. Hoel, *Introduction to Mathematical Statistics*, John Wiley & Sons, New York, 1947, pp. 28–35.

more than 100 for many populations from which one may be sampling, i.e., for populations which do not have exceedingly extreme or unusual items) it usually provides a fairly precise measure.

In this illustration we have defined intervals $\bar{X} - k\sigma_{\bar{x}}$ to $\bar{X} + k\sigma_{\bar{x}}$, and have ascertained the proportion of the sample estimates included in such intervals determined by assigning different values to k. The particular values $k = 1$, 2, and 3 were used, although other values could have illustrated the point just as well.

Table 5. **Concentration of sample results around population mean**

Sample of size n	Per cent of sample results in Table 3 differing from the average of all samples by		
	Less than $\sigma_{\bar{x}}$	Less than $2\sigma_{\bar{x}}$	Less than $3\sigma_{\bar{x}}$
1	75	92	100
2	64	97	100
3	65	96	100
4	64	97	100
5	65	97	100
6	64	97	100
7	65	97	100
Normal distribution	68	95	99.7

If we computed, instead, intervals of $k\sigma_{\bar{x}}$ above and below each sample mean, such intervals, $\bar{x} - k\sigma_{\bar{x}}$ to $\bar{x} + k\sigma_{\bar{x}}$, would have encompassed the true mean in exactly the same proportion of cases as the intervals $\bar{X} \pm k\sigma_{\bar{x}}$ included the sample means.

Let us suppose now that we have drawn a simple random sample from a population and have computed the mean from that sample. Suppose, furthermore, that we know $\sigma_{\bar{x}}$, the standard deviation of means from all possible samples of this size. How can we infer the precision of this particular sample result? If we set an interval based on $\sigma_{\bar{x}}$ around the sample estimate, we can be fairly confident that $\bar{x} \pm \sigma_{\bar{x}}$ will give an interval such that one will be correct about two-thirds of the time if he assumes that the true mean will be within that interval. Similarly, $\bar{x} \pm 2\sigma_{\bar{x}}$ will give an interval for which the assumption will be correct 95 per cent of the time, and $\bar{x} \pm 3\sigma_{\bar{x}}$ more than 99 per cent of the time.

Thus, with a mean estimated from a sample and knowledge of the standard deviation of all sample means, one can evaluate the precision of the estimates. The precision is determined by and measured in terms of $\sigma_{\bar{x}}$, the standard deviation of the sample estimate.

Our next problem is to see how to compute $\sigma_{\bar{x}}$, the standard deviation of the sample means for a sample of size n, without obtaining the estimates from all possible samples of n. Obviously, if one were dealing with even a moderately large population, it would not be feasible, even if he knew the entire population from which he was sampling, to ascertain the estimated average income for each possible sample by listing all samples and obtaining the average income for each. With the little illustrative population of 12 individuals there were 792 different possible samples of 7 that could be drawn, and to list all of these is a good-sized job. But if one were considering, say, samples of only 100 from a population of 10,000, the number of possible samples would be astronomical. More-over, if one were in a position to list all possible samples, there would be no need to estimate $\bar{X}$ because it would be known.

The fact is, however, that it is not necessary to list all possible samples for the purpose of computing the standard deviation. From the theory of sampling we find that, for samples of n elements drawn with simple random sampling from a population of N elements, the standard deviation of all possible sample means is given by the formula:

$$\sigma_{\bar{x}} = \sqrt{\frac{N-n}{(N-1)n}}\, \sigma$$

where $\sigma_{\bar{x}}$ represents the standard deviation of the sample means with samples of size n, and σ represents the standard deviation of the original population (i.e., the standard deviation of the means of samples of size 1). This formula holds for simple random samples of any size and drawn from any kind or size of population. In the illustrative population, $\sigma = \$1505$ and N is equal to 12; so for samples of 2,

$$\sigma_{\bar{x}} = \sqrt{\frac{12-2}{(12-1)2}}\, 1505 = \$1015$$

which is the number given in Table 4.

Thus, if we know the standard deviation of the population from which we are sampling we can readily ascertain the standard deviation of a mean estimated from any given size of simple random sample.

Exercise 11.1. The reader should verify the accuracy of the formula by trying it for other sample sizes and for other small populations, listing all possible samples and computing the variance from the samples listed.

We have still one more problem and an important one. We have indicated that if we know the standard deviation of a population we can measure accurately the precision of an estimate based on a sample from that population. We shall not ordinarily know the standard deviation of a characteristic of the population, if we are drawing a sample to estimate the mean. However, just as we can obtain an estimate of a mean from a sample, we can also obtain an estimate of the standard deviation from the sample; and thus, with a moderately large sample, we can obtain not only the desired estimates from the sample but also measures of their precision. The measures of precision that are derived from the sample itself can be made as reliable as desired, since their precision again depends on the size of the sample. The evaluation of precision from the sample itself, with simple random sampling, is discussed in Ch. 4, Sec. 12–15.

12. Further illustrations of the principles already presented. All the illustrative results presented up to now have been based on very small samples drawn from a very small population, and at the same time on samples that constitute a fairly large proportion of that population. The sizes, both of the samples we have used for illustration and of the population from which the samples were drawn, are too small to be useful for practical sampling purposes. The succeeding two illustrations indicate that the same principles apply when we are drawing samples from a very large population.

Illustration with a larger population. Let us consider briefly a modification of the illustration already presented. In that illustration we assumed a population of 12 individuals. Now let us consider a population that has exactly the same form but which has 12,000,000 individuals in it instead of 12. Let 1,000,000 receive each of the incomes shown in Table 1 (p. 13).

> Note that the assumption that many individuals have the same income has no effect on the argument of this illustration, except to make the computations easier. Exactly the same type of results would have been obtained had many varying income values been assumed.

With this size of population it would be an impossible task to list all possible samples of even moderate size. The frequencies for the 1728 samples of 3 summarized in Table 6 are proportionate to what would be obtained by listing all possible samples of 3. To obtain approximate distributions for the larger sizes of sample, 2000 simple random samples of size 6 were drawn; these samples were consolidated at random to get 1000 samples of 12, and 500 samples of 24. The distributions of the means estimated from these samples are summarized in Table 6 and in Fig. 2.

It is seen from the table and figure that with increasing size of sample the sample estimates cluster more closely around the value being estimated, as occurred in the earlier illustration, and the spread of the samples in

Table 6.   Estimates of average income from samples of various sizes drawn from a population of 12,000,000 individuals with 1,000,000 having each of the incomes given in Table 1

Average income estimated from sample (dollars)	Number of samples having indicated estimate of average income with sample of size n			
	$n = 3$	$n = 6$	$n = 12$	$n = 24$
800– 999	1			
1000–1199	9	1		
1200–1399	37	3		
1400–1599	82	35		
1600–1799	132	81	9	
1800–1999	161	140	28	4
2000–2199	163	193	81	15
2200–2399	163	213	140	68
2400–2599	147	248	165	98
2600–2799	124	248	190	136
2800–2999	123	219	141	95
3000–3199	118	206	108	53
3200–3399	108	144	75	22
3400–3599	93	99	37	8
3600–3799	70	58	13	1
3800–3999	57	48	10	
4000–4199	33	23	1	
4200–4399	39	19	2	
4400–4599	15	9		
4600–4799	18	9		
4800–4999	19	1		
5000–5199	3	3		
5200–5399	6			
5400–5599	3			
5600–5799				
5800–5999	3			
6000–6199				
6200–6399	1			
Total	1728	2000	1000	500

each case is the amount that would be expected from the formula given earlier. (Note that σ is still equal to \$1505 as it was before, but that N is now 12,000,000 instead of 12.) The closer approach to a normal distribution with increasing size of sample is suggested by Fig. 2; Table 7 compares the proportions of samples exceeding $1\sigma_{\bar{x}}$, $2\sigma_{\bar{x}}$, and $3\sigma_{\bar{x}}$ with proportions expected from a normal distribution. Again, the reasonably close approximation of the results to the normal distribution is apparent.

Illustration with a more extreme population. Both the illustrations presented thus far have involved drawing samples from a skewed population, but not from one containing any very extreme incomes. It will be

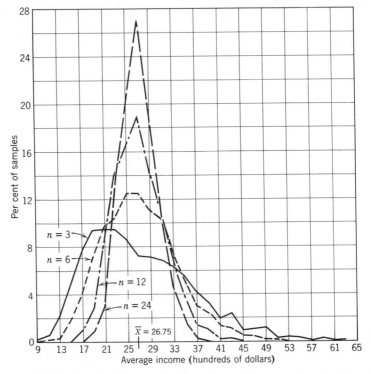

Fig. 2. Distribution of estimates of average income from samples of various sizes drawn from a population of 12,000,000 individuals, with 1,000,000 having each of the incomes given in Table 1.

Table 7.   Concentration of sample results around population average—
enlarged population

Sample of size n	Per cent of sample results in Table 6 differing from the average of all samples by		
	Less than $\sigma_{\bar{x}}$	Less than $2\sigma_{\bar{x}}$	Less than $3\sigma_{\bar{x}}$
3	67.7	96.2	99.4
6	66.6	95.2	99.3
12	68.3	95.8	99.7
24	68.2	95.2	99.8
Normal distribution	68.3	95.5	99.7

Table 8. Estimates for a highly skewed population of 12,000,000 individuals

Average income estimated from sample (dollars)	Number of samples having indicated estimate of average income with sample of size n			
	$n = 3$	$n = 6$	$n = 12$	$n = 24$
800– 1,199	10	1		
1,200– 1,599	119	38		
1,600– 1,999	293	221	36	2
2,000– 2,399	326	374	140	32
2,400– 2,799	268	320	107	24
2,800– 3,199	181	147	36	67
3,200– 3,599	87	37	98	65
3,600– 3,999	34	11	202	93
4,000– 4,399	9	3	78	58
4,400– 4,799	3	70	23	75
4,800– 5,199	1	212	62	30
5,200– 5,599		245	114	28
5,600– 5,999		111	30	11
6,000– 6,399		27	7	11
6,400– 6,799		7	24	
6,800– 7,199			28	4
7,200– 7,599	24	5	3	
7,600– 7,999	105	40	1	
8,000– 8,399	114	53	5	
8,400– 8,799	66	38	3	
8,800– 9,199	39	17	2	
9,200– 9,599	12	3		
9,600– 9,999	3		1	
10,000–10,399				
10,400–10,799		3		
10,800–11,199		7		
11,200–11,599		7		
11,600–11,999				
12,000–12,399		2		
12,400–12,799				
12,800–13,199				
13,200–13,599				
13,600–13,999	15			
14,000–14,399	12	1		
14,400–14,799	3			
14,800–15,199	3			
15,200–15,599				
15,600–15,999				
16,000–16,399				
16,400–16,799				
16,800–17,199				
17,200–17,599				
17,600–17,999				
18,000–18,399				
18,400–18,799				
18,800–19,199				
19,200–19,599				
19,600–19,999				
20,000–20,399	1			
Total	1728	2000	1000	500

of interest to examine what happens with the same population of 12,000,000 individuals as in the last illustration, but with the $6300 income changed to $20,000 income. In this instance, $\frac{1}{12}$ of the population accounts for about 44 per cent of the total income. In this illustration, again, the results presented are based on the samples used in the preceding illustration.

The distributions of the means estimated from these samples are summarized in Table 8 and Fig. 3. From Fig. 3 it is seen that the samples

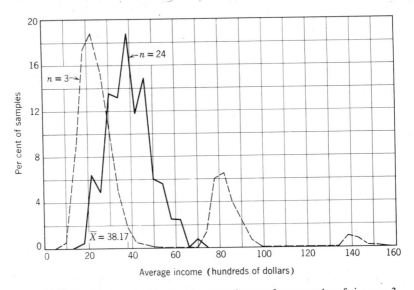

FIG. 3.   Distribution of estimates of average income from samples of size $n = 3$ and $n = 24$ for a highly skewed population of 12,000,000 individuals.

from this population are much farther from approximating the normal distribution than are samples of the same size from the two prior illustrations. But in this illustration, as in the others, the results coincide with what theory indicates would happen—the estimates appear to be (and in fact are) clustered more and more closely about the true mean of the population ($3817) as the sample size increases.

Notice that for samples of 6 and 12, even though the distribution is not unimodal, our use of the normal curve for interpreting the precision of the results is reasonably satisfactory, with not more than 1 per cent of the estimates exceeding $3\sigma_{\bar{x}}$ at these sample sizes. For larger samples, as is seen in Table 9, the agreement is still better; and for samples of 24 and larger the bimodal character of the distribution has disappeared. Although the approach to normality is slower with this more extreme population, it can be seen that even for relatively small samples the interpretation of the standard deviations on the basis of the normal curve provides a useful guide to the reliability of the estimate.

In these illustrations we have been dealing, for simplicity, with sample sizes that are smaller than would ordinarily be used or useful in practice. To achieve the higher precision that we usually desire from samples, we have only to make the samples big enough.   Moreover, whereas we have

Table 9.   Concentration of sample results for a more extreme population

Sample of size n	Per cent of sample results in Table 8 differing from the average of all samples by		
	Less than $\sigma_{\bar{x}}$	Less than $2\sigma_{\bar{x}}$	Less than $3\sigma_{\bar{x}}$
3	77.0	97.9	98.0
6	83.2	92.6	99.0
12	62.1	95.3	99.0
24	72.6	95.8	99.6
Normal distribution	68.3	95.5	99.7

been illustrating certain fundamental principles with simple random sampling, we shall ordinarily in practice use other sampling methods. The fundamentals of these other methods are, however, the same as those illustrated with simple random sampling, but are applied in somewhat more complex situations.

The principles that we have presented have operated as we should expect from the sampling theory, which will be developed in subsequent chapters.   The reader may find it helpful to construct other illustrations. The formula of Sec. 11 will be found to apply in every instance, without exception, where we have simple random sampling.   Thus, we have indicated a sample design that produces results of measurable precision.

13. Risks taken by depending on sample results.   One should recognize the meaning of "taking a risk," in the action one takes on the basis of the sample estimate.   The chance of an individual being killed through a home accident in one year (1943) in the United States was about 1 in 6500.*   Still, in everyday behavior one plans his routine activities as if nothing serious is going to happen.   If the consequence of failure is not serious, one may be willing to act as if there were no risk when the odds

* U.S. Bureau of the Census, *Vital Statistics Special Reports National Summaries*, Vol. 21, No. 7, Accident Fatalities in the United States, 1943.

are 20 to 1 in his favor.   If the consequence of failure is more serious, he may not wish to gamble even if the odds are as high as 100 to 1 or even 1000 to 1.

In designing a sample to serve a specific purpose, one must answer the questions:

(1) How large an error in the estimate can I tolerate before the inference drawn will lead me to the wrong action?
(2) What risk am I willing to take that the results of the sample are in error by more than that amount?

Before we can determine the size of sample required* in any particular instance, we must decide the "error risk" limits.   In many instances one might be willing to gamble with the results of the survey if the chance were 1 in 20 of getting a sample estimate that would be off by more than, say, 10 per cent from the true value.   In other instances, where the cost of an error is greater, one might require greater accuracy and also be afraid to gamble with odds such as these in his favor, insisting that he could tolerate being off by more than, say, 4 per cent in his estimate only 1 in 100 times, or perhaps 1 in 300 or 1 in 1000.

For an illustration of how one goes about setting the risks and establishing tolerable errors for actions, consider the following situation:

(1) The problem is to estimate the total number of unemployed persons in the United States and in each state during depression years when unemployment is large.
(2) Action is to be taken on the basis of the estimates, consisting of the appropriation of money by Congress for a work program, and the planning for the use of the funds appropriated.
(3) It is assumed that, if the figure is anywhere between 7,000,000 and 8,000,000 unemployed, a certain action will be taken.   A considerable change in the amount of the appropriation will be made if the figure is less than 4,000,000, and a quite different kind of change will be made if it is more than 12,000,000.   One might then be reasonably safe in assuming that, if the sample estimate were within about 10 per cent of the true figure, it would not appreciably change Congressional and administrative action.
(4) We assume that we shall behave as if the sample estimate is within 10 per cent of the true figure if the odds are 19 to 1 in favor of its falling within these limits.

---

* In other types of design, the sample size is only one of the factors to be considered.

Note that the error limits and the probability (or "risk") taken are related. The consequence of this fact is that if (a) the probability is 19 in 20 that the sample estimate will be within 10 per cent of the true figure, then (b) about 99 out of 100 times our estimate will be within 12½ per cent, and (c) about 997 out of 1000 times our estimate will be within 15 per cent. These are the figures which would follow from a given error limit on the assumption of normal distribution, which will be a safe assumption if we are dealing with a large enough sample. In other words, we would be extremely sure that the estimate would be within 15 per cent of the true figure.

The illustration above is typical of a very large class of problems where fairly wide bounds on the tolerable errors do not seriously affect the action to be taken. In other problems, the tolerable error has to be made smaller. As an illustration of this class of problems, consider the following:

(1) The problem. An estimate of the total population of each state.
(2) Action to be taken. Distribution of federal funds, on the basis of total population.
(3) Data available. The population of each state in the 1950 Census.

If large amounts of money are to be distributed on the basis of the population at some time subsequent to the 1950 Census, the estimate must be good enough to detect a comparatively small change. For example, a state that increases in population from 1,000,000 in 1950 to 1,100,000 in 1955 or decreases to 900,000 would be considered to have a highly significant change. Hence, we might decide that a shift of 3 per cent or more should be detected with relative certainty if the sample estimate is to be useful. This will be accomplished if the sample size is such that the standard deviation is only 1 per cent of the expected estimate. Then there will be about 997 chances in 1000 that the estimate is within 3 per cent of the true figure.

Having made up our minds what the tolerable error should be, and having determined the odds for the prescribed bounds, we can design the sample to meet these specifications. We determine the character and the size of the sample required to provide this amount of precision, and then, considering the various cost factors entering into the sample design, we compute the cost of the survey. If the cost is acceptable the design can be used as specified; if, however, the cost is excessive, then some balancing of precision against costs must be considered. It may be that some relaxation in precision will not invalidate the results, and that the available resources will suffice with this relaxation; or it may be possible to get an increase in the funds available. If, on the other hand, it is impossible to design a useful survey within the budget restrictions that have been imposed, the survey should be abandoned.

The methods used in designing samples to meet the required error limits, balanced against the required cost limits, are the main subject matter of this volume.

C. OTHER PRINCIPLES OF SAMPLE DESIGN
ILLUSTRATED

14. Other methods of controlling sampling error. The previous discussion has been based almost entirely upon the use of unbiased estimates derived from simple random samples of elements from the population under consideration.   For this type of sampling the size of sampling error (or the risk taken) can be controlled only by changing the sample size. The sampling error is, of course, dependent upon the population variance and to a limited extent upon the size of the population, but these factors are not controllable by the investigator if simple random sampling of elementary units is used.   However, there are other methods of controlling the sampling error, and in practical work the choice of a design involving proper application of these methods is of great importance. These methods may have a significant bearing on either the precision of sample results, or the cost of obtaining the desired precision, or both. They point to ways of making effective use of available resources.   The following sections are designed to give a summary introduction to some of the important topics, in order that the reader may achieve a better perspective of the whole subject before proceeding more intensively into specific phases of it in succeeding chapters.

We are often able to effect increases in efficiency in sample design by utilizing available resources in the form of maps, lists, census information, building permits, and other information; or by employing methods that cluster the units included in the sample, by the use of several stages of sampling or by other variations in method.   A sample design is said to be more *efficient* (or to have higher *efficiency*) than another if under specified conditions it yields more reliable results per unit of cost; i.e., if for a given cost it gives results of greater precision, or if results of specified precision are produced at lower cost.

It is important to note that the validity of a standard error is unrelated to the efficiency of the sample survey from which it was calculated.   The only requirement for the validity of a standard error and the interpretation described above is that every person, household, farm, or other unit have a known probability of being selected for the sample, and that appropriate estimation methods be used.   More complex methods of sampling are introduced merely to increase the efficiency of design.

15. Methods of estimation.   The discussion in previous sections has dealt with unbiased estimates.   For this type of estimate, the expected value of the estimate is equal to the value being estimated.   Actually, we are more concerned with the risk of error in making an estimate from a particular sample than with the error in the average of the estimates for all possible samples.   If the standard error is large, the fact that an estimate is unbiased is of little help.   With a large standard error the probability of drawing a sample with a large error is high.

Such a situation might be represented by a distribution of sample estimates such as A in Fig. 4.   Here the expected value of the sample

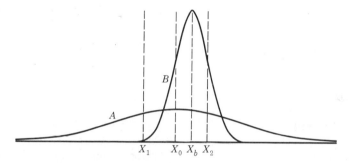

Fɪɢ. 4.   Two distributions of sample estimates: unbiased estimates in distribution A; biased estimates with smaller standard error in distribution B.

estimates is the true value X_0, but relatively few of these sample estimates are close to X_0, where we define "close" to mean falling in the interval (X_1, X_2).

Consider, on the other hand, a distribution of sample estimates such as B, in Fig. 4, where the mean of sample estimates X_b is *not* equal to the true value X_0.   Many more of the estimates represented by B are close to X_0, even though this estimating procedure is biased.   In such a case there is a better chance of getting a "good" sample from a biased set of estimates, represented by B, than from a set of samples (such as A) which is unbiased, but in which many of the samples have large errors.

As an example, let us consider a case in which we have a choice of two ways of estimating the same population characteristic.   We use the population of 12 individuals shown in Table 1 (p. 13) and assume that the purpose in sampling is to estimate the average income of this population. We shall demonstrate by taking a sample of 3 individuals.

The distribution of the simple unbiased estimate from samples of 3 (in this case the simple unbiased estimate is simply the sample mean) is shown in Table 3 (p. 19). Now, assume that we know, from a census of this population in an earlier year, that the average income of the 12 individuals in the census year was $2883 and that the income of each of the 12 individuals in that year (say 1950) was as shown in Table 10.

Table 10. Incomes of a hypothetical population of 12 individuals in the census year 1950

Individual	Income (dollars)	Individual	Income (dollars)
A	1100	G	2200
B	5500	H	3100
C	3500	I	2500
D	1700	J	1200
E	4000	K	5300
F	2400	L	2100
Total income	$34,600		
Average income	$2,883\frac{1}{3}$		

When we estimate average present income by selecting a sample of 3 individuals, say, and taking the average income of these 3, we make no use of the knowledge available from the prior census. Suppose, instead, that we estimate the average income of the population by computing the average present income of the sample divided by the average 1950 income of the same individuals, and multiply this ratio by the known average income of the population in 1950. For example, suppose that the sample happens to include individuals B, C, and J. From Table 1 we find that their present incomes are $6300, $3100, and $900, respectively, and their average income is $3433. Similarly, the average 1950 income for these same individuals is $(5500 + 3500 + 1200)/3 = $3400. The ratio estimate of present income from the sample would be $2883(3433/3400) = $2911.

It seems reasonable that such an estimate might be better than the sample mean of the present incomes. If our sample happens to over-represent individuals with high 1950 incomes, then the average may be expected to be too high in terms of present income, and with such an estimate we reduce the estimate of present average income by the relative amount that our sample of 1950 incomes is too high. To say the same thing in another way, we use the sample only to estimate relative change in average income, and not to establish the level. We may say that we have estimated from the sample the *ratio* of present average income to 1950 average income, and applied this estimated *ratio* to the known average income for 1950.

We can calculate this estimate for all possible samples of size 3. It turns out that the average of these estimates for all possible samples of 3 is $2658, whereas $2675 is the true population average; hence this estimate is a biased estimate. But the amount of the bias is small relative to the standard deviation of the estimate. The distribution of these ratio estimates compares with the distribution of the simple unbiased estimates as shown in columns 2 and 3 of Table 11. It can be seen that the ratio (biased) estimates not only vary among themselves considerably less than the simple unbiased estimates, but also tend to be closer to the true value $2675.

We can measure the variation of the ratio estimates from the true value by taking the square of each deviation *from the true value* (instead of from the average of the estimates) and getting the average of these squared deviations over all possible samples. This measure is known as the *mean square error*, or simply the MSE. It is distinguished from the variance in that the variance is measured by taking deviations from the expected value of the estimates. For unbiased estimates the mean square error is equal to the variance, but for biased estimates it will be different. For the biased estimate in this particular instance the mean square error for samples of 3 is 57,953, whereas the variance of the estimates (taken around their own expected value) is 57,648. There is little difference. This trivial contribution of the bias to the mean square error will not always be relatively small for samples of sizes as small as 3, but for large enough samples the bias of the ratio estimate will always be negligible relative to the standard error. What happens for such a ratio of sample means is that as the size of sample is increased the bias decreases, and so does the standard error, but the bias decreases at a faster rate than the standard error. Ordinarily, therefore, with such biased but consistent estimates we shall ignore the bias, because with almost any practical size of sample the square of the bias will be negligible in relation to the variance.

Such a ratio estimate is consistent, since the bias as well as the variance approaches zero as the size of sample is increased. The reader could verify this statement for the illustrative population by listing all possible samples of each size, computing the ratio estimate for each, and then computing the expected value, the variance, and the standard deviation of these estimates for each size of sample. Because of the negligible size of the bias of ratio estimates with reasonably large samples our measure of precision will be the standard error.

Table 11. Comparison of distributions of estimated average income based
on simple unbiased estimate (sample mean) and "ratio" estimate
from samples of 3

Estimated average income falling in the interval (dollars)	Per cent of samples based on		
	Simple unbiased estimate	Ratio estimate based on data in Table 10	Ratio estimate based on data in Table 12
(1)	(2)	(3)	(4)
1000–1199	.0		.5
1200–1399	1.4		3.6
1400–1599	4.5		3.6
1600–1799	6.8		4.5
1800–1999	9.1		6.8
2000–2199	10.0	1.8	8.6
2200–2399	10.0	13.6	8.2
2400–2599	8.6	28.2	9.1
2600–2799	7.7	30.9	9.1
2800–2999	7.3	16.4	8.2
3000–3199	7.3	8.6	9.5
3200–3399	7.3	.5	6.8
3400–3599	5.9		5.9
3600–3799	4.5		5.5
3800–3999	3.2		2.7
4000–4199	1.8		2.7
4200–4399	2.7		2.3
4400–4599	.5		.5
4600–4799	.9		1.4
4800–4999	.5		.0
5000–5199	.0		.5
Total	100.0	100.0	100.0
Average (expected value)	$2675	$2658	$2749
Standard error	$786	$240	$805
Root mean square error $= \sqrt{\text{MSE}}$	$786	$240	$808

It will be clear that a ratio estimate, in practice, frequently will be superior to the simple unbiased estimate.   However, this is not always the case.   If there were little or no correlation between the 1950 incomes and present incomes, the ratio estimate would be inferior to the unbiased estimate.   For example, if 1950 incomes of the 12 individuals in our population were as in Table 12, the distribution of the ratio estimate of the mean for all possible samples would be as shown in the last column of Table 11.

Table 12.   1950 incomes of 12 individuals, to indicate low correlation with present incomes shown in Table 1

Individual	Income (dollars)	Individual	Income (dollars)
A	500	G	2400
B	3000	H	2500
C	1100	I	3200
D	1700	J	1500
E	2000	K	1800
F	1000	L	1500

Here the variation from the true value is greater for the ratio estimate than it was for the simple unbiased estimate.   The root mean square error (square root of mean square error) of the ratio estimate is, in this case, $808, as compared with the standard deviation $786 of the simple unbiased estimate (sample mean).

The above illustrations indicate that the important fact to consider in making a choice between alternative estimates is not whether the estimate is unbiased.   The important fact is how close the estimate by one method or another is likely to be to the population characteristic being estimated. It is unimportant whether an estimate is unbiased so long as the bias is small.

The theory for dealing with ratio estimates will be given in Chapter 4 and subsequent chapters.   The purpose here was merely to indicate the role of alternative estimating procedures and to suggest how available data may be effectively utilized in improving a sample estimate.

Remark.   The use of the ratio estimate, the bias of which can be shown to be small for reasonably large sizes of sample, is to be distinguished from the use of biased methods of sample selection or estimation where the magnitude of the bias is unknown, and where this bias may not decrease with increase in sample size, and therefore may seriously affect the accuracy of the estimates, even with a large sample.

16. Stratification. One way of making effective use of available information was illustrated in the discussion of a ratio estimate. Stratification provides another method of utilizing supplemental information to get greater precision in our sample estimates.

Past data may be used to divide the population into groups such that the elements within each group are more alike than are the elements in the population as a whole. If a sample is drawn separately from each group by simple random sampling, we have *insured* the desired representation from each group, but still have a probability sample if the selections are at random within each group. Whenever a population is divided into such groups, and some kind of a random sample is taken in each group, the sample is called a *stratified* sample, the groups from which the sample is drawn are called *strata*, and the process of dividing this population into groups is called *stratification*.

We shall present some illustrations which show how stratification may increase the reliability of sample results for a given size of sample. We will use again the population given in Table 1 (p. 13).

Illustration 16.1. Assume that we know from a prior census the 1950 incomes of each member of the population, as shown in Table 10 (p. 36), and that a sample of 4 individuals is to be drawn to estimate the present average income. With the prior information the population can be divided into 4 groups of 3 persons each, so that the individuals in each group have 1950 incomes as much alike as possible. The groups (or strata) will be made up as follows: *AJD, LGF, IHC, EKB*.

If we then draw 1 person at random from each group, a proportionate stratified sample of 4 persons will be obtained. By *proportionate stratified sampling* we mean stratified sampling with a uniform fraction in the sample from each stratum. Let us examine how this type of sampling differs from simple random sampling.

In simple random sampling there are 495 possible samples of size 4 whose average present incomes are distributed as shown in Table 3 (p. 19). With proportionate stratified sampling there are only 81 possible samples, each of which is listed in Table 13. The average present income is also shown for each sample. A total of 414, or 84 per cent, of the samples possible under simple random sampling *have no chance of being drawn*, although each *individual still has the same chance* of being included in the sample and the sample estimate is unbiased. Samples such as *BCEK*, all having the highest incomes in 1950, or *ADJL*, all having the lowest incomes in 1950, are among the ineligibles.

Table 14 shows that for samples of 4 the chance of an error of more than 20 per cent is 44 out of 100 for simple random sampling and only 14 out of 100 for proportionate stratified random sampling. The comparison is also indicated by the standard deviations. With stratified sampling and samples of 4 the standard deviation of the estimates is $346, whereas with simple random sampling it is $642.

If stratification does not result in strata which are homogeneous with regard to the characteristic to be measured (*not* the characteristic employed in setting up the strata), there will be no gain from its use. This can be seen from Illustration 16.2.

Table 13. Eighty-one possible samples of 4 under stratification of Illustration 16.1

Sample	Mean (dollars)	Sample	Mean (dollars)	Sample	Mean (dollars)
ALIE	2075	JLIE	1975	DLIE	2250
ALIK	2375	JLIK	2275	DLIK	2550
ALIB	2750	JLIB	2650	DLIB	2925
ALHE	2375	JLHE	2275	DLHE	2550
ALHK	2675	JLHK	2575	DLHK	2850
ALHB	3050	JLHB	2950	DLHB	3225
ALCE	2475	JLCE	2375	DLCE	2650
ALCK	2775	JLCK	2675	DLCK	2950
ALCB	3150	JLCB	3050	DLCB	3325
AGIE	2050	JGIE	1950	DGIE	2225
AGIK	2350	JGIK	2250	DGIK	2525
AGIB	2725	JGIB	2625	DGIB	2900
AGHE	2350	JGHE	2250	DGHE	2525
AGHK	2650	JGHK	2550	DGHK	2825
AGHB	3025	JGHB	2925	DGHB	3200
AGCE	2450	JGCE	2350	DGCE	2625
AGCK	2750	JGCK	2650	DGCK	2925
AGCB	3125	JGCB	3025	DGCB	3300
AFIE	2150	JFIE	2050	DFIE	2325
AFIK	2450	JFIK	2350	DFIK	2625
AFIB	2825	JFIB	2725	DFIB	3000
AFHE	2450	JFHE	2350	DFHE	2625
AFHK	2750	JFHK	2650	DFHK	2925
AFHB	3125	JFHB	3025	DFHB	3300
AFCE	2550	JFCE	2450	DFCE	2725
AFCK	2850	JFCK	2750	DFCK	3025
AFCB	3225	JFCB	3125	DFCB	3400

Average income over all possible samples $= \dfrac{\$216{,}675}{81} = \$2675$

Standard error $= \$346$

Illustration 16.2. Assume that, instead of the 1950 incomes shown above, the 1950 incomes of the 12 individuals in our population were as shown in Table 12 (p. 39), and the population was divided again into 4 groups, each group consisting of individuals having similar 1950 incomes (i.e., *AFC*, *LJD*, *KEG*, and *HBI*). The comparison with simple random sampling, also displayed in Table 14, indicates that the risk of error has not been changed in any significant way by stratification.

Table 14.   Comparison of samples of 4 under 3 sampling schemes—
Illustrations 16.1 and 16.2

Relative error in estimate (per cent)	Per cent of all possible samples having given relative error		
	Simple random sampling	Proportionate stratified random sampling	
		Based on data in Table 10	Based on data in Table 12
More than 20	44.4	13.6	48.1
10–20	27.7	37.0	23.5
Less than 10	27.9	49.4	28.4

The very slight gain by stratification in this illustration is indicated by the fact that for samples of 4 the standard deviation of the estimated average income is $636 with proportionate stratified sampling and $642 with simple random sampling.

The difference between the results of the two stratifications in Illustrations 16.1 and 16.2 is due to the fact that, in Illustration 16.1, high 1950 incomes were very closely associated in the population with high present incomes and low 1950 incomes were associated with low present incomes. In Illustration 16.2, little relationship is apparent between 1950 income and present income. Thus, in Illustration 16.2, stratification did not give us homogeneous groups with respect to present income, and, consequently, no gain in precision was achieved.

Illustration 16.3. Another significant feature of stratified sampling deserves special mention. Consider the population of 12 individuals shown in Table 15, similar to the more extreme population described in Sec. 12. Note that there is one individual in this population whose income is very different from the incomes of all the remaining individuals. In practice, extreme values of income, sales, farm acreage, and many other characteristics tend to remain extreme over relatively long periods of time. The 1950 incomes for the individuals in this population are given in Table 15, as well as their present incomes.

Table 15. Hypothetical population of 12 individuals with
one extreme income item

Individual	Income (dollars)	
	Present	1950
A	1,300	1,100
B	20,000	10,000
C	3,100	3,500
D	2,000	1,700
E	3,600	4,000
F	2,200	2,400
G	1,800	2,200
H	2,700	3,100
I	1,500	2,500
J	900	1,200
K	4,800	5,300
L	1,900	2,100
Total income	45,800	39,100
Average income	3,817	3,258

Let us consider two possible stratifications of this population, based on 1950 incomes.

Stratification 1 is:

STRATUM	INDIVIDUALS	TOTAL PRESENT INCOME (dollars)
I	A, J, D	4,200
II	L, G, F	5,900
III	I, H, C	7,300
IV	E, K, B	28,400

Stratification 2 is:

STRATUM	INDIVIDUALS	TOTAL PRESENT INCOME (dollars)
I	A, J, D, L	6,100
II	G, F, I, H	8,200
III	C, E, K	11,500
IV	B	20,000

With stratification 1, there are 81 possible samples of 4; with stratification 2, there are 48. Stratification 1 is an illustration of proportionate stratified sampling.   Stratification 2 is an illustration of *disproportionate stratified sampling*.

The possible samples of 1 from each stratum, and the sample estimates of the population mean for each sample, are listed in Tables 16 and 17. For each sample resulting from stratification 2, two sample estimates of the population mean are listed.   The first estimate is the sample mean obtained by adding the values and dividing by 4.   The second estimate is a weighted average obtained by taking

$$\frac{4x_{\mathrm{I}} + 4x_{\mathrm{II}} + 3x_{\mathrm{III}} + x_{\mathrm{IV}}}{12}$$

Table 16.   Eighty-one possible samples of 4 under stratification 1 of Illustration 16.3

Sample	Mean (dollars)	Sample	Mean (dollars)	Sample	Mean (dollars)
ALIE	2075	JLIE	1975	DLIE	2250
ALIK	2375	JLIK	2275	DLIK	2550
ALIB	6175	JLIB	6075	DLIB	6350
ALHE	2375	JLHE	2275	DLHE	2550
ALHK	2675	JLHK	2575	DLHK	2850
ALHB	6475	JLHB	6375	DLHB	6650
ALCE	2475	JLCE	2375	DLCE	2650
ALCK	2775	JLCK	2675	DLCK	2950
ALCB	6575	JLCB	6475	DLCB	6750
AGIE	2050	JGIE	1950	DGIE	2225
AGIK	2350	JGIK	2250	DGIK	2525
AGIB	6150	JGIB	6050	DGIB	6325
AGHE	2350	JGHE	2250	DGHE	2525
AGHK	2650	JGHK	2550	DGHK	2825
AGHB	6450	JGHB	6350	DGHB	6625
AGCE	2450	JGCE	2350	DGCE	2625
AGCK	2750	JGCK	2650	DGCK	2925
AGCB	6550	JGCB	6450	DGCB	6725
AFIE	2150	JFIE	2050	DFIE	2325
AFIK	2450	JFIK	2350	DFIK	2625
AFIB	6250	JFIB	6150	DFIB	6425
AFHE	2450	JFHE	2350	DFHE	2625
AFHK	2750	JFHK	2650	DFHK	2925
AFHB	6550	JFHB	6450	DFHB	6725
AFCE	2550	JFCE	2450	DFCE	2725
AFCK	2850	JFCK	2750	DFCK	3025
AFCB	6650	JFCB	6550	DFCB	6825

where x_I is the value of the individual drawn for the sample from stratum I, x_{II} is the value of the individual sampled from stratum II, etc.

The samples listed for stratification 1 are similar to those listed in Table 13 (p. 41) for the population used in Illustration 16.1.

Table 17.   Forty-eight possible samples of 4 under stratification 2
of Illustration 16.3

Sample	Mean (dollars)	Weighted average (dollars)	Sample	Mean (dollars)	Weighted average (dollars)
AGCB	6550	3475.00	DGCB	6725	3708.33
AGEB	6675	3600.00	DGEB	6850	3833.33
AGKB	6975	3900.00	DGKB	7150	4133.33
AFCB	6650	3608.33	DFCB	6825	3841.67
AFEB	6775	3733.33	DFEB	6950	3966.67
AFKB	7075	4033.33	DFKB	7250	4266.67
AICB	6475	3375.00	DICB	6650	3608.33
AIEB	6600	3500.00	DIEB	6775	3733.33
AIKB	6900	3800.00	DIKB	7075	4033.33
AHCB	6775	3775.00	DHCB	6950	4008.33
AHEB	6900	3900.00	DHEB	7075	4133.33
AHKB	7200	4200.00	DHKB	7375	4433.33
JGCB	6450	3341.67	LGCB	6700	3675.00
JGEB	6575	3466.67	LGEB	6825	3800.00
JGKB	6875	3766.67	LGKB	7125	4100.00
JFCB	6550	3475.00	LFCB	6800	3808.33
JFEB	6675	3600.00	LFEB	6925	3933.33
JFKB	6975	3900.00	LFKB	7225	4233.33
JICB	6375	3241.67	LICB	6625	3575.00
JIEB	6500	3366.67	LIEB	6750	3700.00
JIKB	6800	3666.67	LIKB	7050	4000.00
JHCB	6675	3641.67	LHCB	6925	3975.00
JHEB	6800	3766.67	LHEB	7050	4100.00
JHKB	7100	4066.67	LHKB	7350	4400.00

From the listing of possible samples resulting from stratification 2, it can be seen that individual B (who had an income of $20,000) comes into every sample. In other words, his chance of being drawn is certainty. In stratification 2, individuals A, J, D, L and G, F, I, H have a chance of coming into the sample of 1 in 4 compared to a chance of 1 in 3 for stratification 1.

If we average the sample estimates for stratification 1, we get $3817, which is the population average. If we average the unweighted sample estimates for stratification 2, we get $6852. Thus, the unweighted sample average in stratification 2 is seriously biased. However, the weighted estimate for stratification 2 is unbiased and also has a much smaller sampling error than the proportionate stratified sample estimate. In Table 18, we compare the distribution of errors when the weighted estimate with samples of 4 drawn from stratification 2 is used, with the distribution of errors in samples of 4 drawn from stratification 1, and with simple random sampling.

Table 18.   Comparison of samples of 4, under 3 sampling schemes—
Illustration 16.3, more extreme population

Relative error in samples of 4 (per cent)	Per cent of all possible samples having given relative error		
	Simple random sampling	Stratification 1	Stratification 2— weighted average estimate
More than 20	95.6	100.0	.0
10–20	4.2	.0	18.8
Less than 10	.2	.0	81.2
Average	3817	3817	3817
Standard error	2127	1878	277

Remark. It might appear from Table 18 that stratification 1 gives worse results than simple random sampling since a larger proportion of estimates using stratification 1 are more than 20 per cent away from the true mean. Actually, both procedures are bad, as can be seen by examining their standard errors, in comparison with that for stratification 2 with weighting. Although the standard error for stratification 1 is somewhat less than that for simple random sampling, both are very large, and it would be unwise to use either of these sampling procedures for this population.

It is evident that we have a much smaller standard error with stratification 2 and a weighted average estimate than with either of the other two designs. This result is due to the fact that disproportionate stratified sampling can sometimes be used effectively to minimize the impact of unusual individuals, provided we have a way of identifying them in advance. Individual B had a much larger income than the other individuals in the population. Consequently, it would be inefficient sampling to give him the same chance of being drawn as any other individual. The subject of "optimum allocation," i.e., determining the relative sizes of samples to be drawn from each stratum in order to minimize the variance, is taken up in Chapter 5.

The illustrations point up the essential characteristics of stratified sampling, which are:

(1) Certain samples possible under simple random sampling are impossible with stratified sampling, and with effective stratification these tend to be the more extreme samples that contribute more heavily to the sampling variance.

(2) The variance is smaller when we are able to classify the units into groups so that the differences within each group are relatively small, while at the same time differences between groups (measured by the differences between their averages) are large.

(3) Stratification can be particularly effective when there are extreme values in the population which can be segregated into separate strata.

Not brought out by the illustrations is the fact that when costs differ greatly (e.g., between large and small establishments or between urban and rural households) it pays to consider costs also in setting up strata. Chapters 5 and 7 deal with cost considerations at some length.

Some points of similarity between simple random sampling and stratified sampling are:

(1) With proportionate stratified sampling, as with simple random sampling, each unit in the population has an equal chance of being included in the sample.

(2) The estimates from stratified sampling when properly constructed are consistent; it is necessary, if disproportionate sampling is used, that stratum weights be properly applied. Otherwise, serious biases may arise.

(3) The sampling error of the estimate can be evaluated from the sample results themselves provided the sample is sufficiently large. This fact has not been illustrated here but is treated in some detail in Chapters 4 and 5.

Past data, intuition, the judgment of experts in the field, or what one might think of as merely good guesses can all be used effectively in setting up strata. If judgment is exercised in determining the strata, the sample results will not be biased by this action, the variance may be reduced if the judgment is good, and the design will be a probability sample, provided the sampling within each stratum is carried out by a random process. To have a probability sample, one must only insure that every individual in the population has a chance of being drawn, and that this chance is known. In many fields, such as the study of retail sales, income data, and other highly skewed distributions, stratification is an exceedingly valuable tool. For estimating characteristics for less skewed distributions, such as for estimating proportions of units having specified characteristics, the importance of stratification can easily be exaggerated. This is illustrated in Sec. 19.

Stratification is only one of the aspects of sampling design which should be taken into account in order to increase the amount of information per unit of cost. Another method, and one which sometimes is more important in reducing costs, is the concept of cluster sampling.

17. Cluster sampling. We have illustrated in preceding sections that a change in sample design (including the estimating method) with no change in size of sample can result in changes in the precision of results. The implication might be drawn from the foregoing treatment that, of two designs using the same size of sample, the one having the smaller sampling error is the preferable one.

This would be true only if the cost per elementary unit were the same for both designs. What we should like to have is the maximum precision of results per unit of cost. If in one design the cost per elementary unit is much less than in another, we can afford to take a much larger sample in the former case than in the latter. The consideration of costs often leads to the use of "cluster sampling."

To assist in understanding cluster sampling we consider the following two ways of drawing a sample of households throughout the United States:

(1) A listing of every family in the United States is available, and a sample of 3000 families is drawn from the listing through simple random sampling. By this plan, households in the sample would be spread through most counties in the United States.
(2) A sample of, say, 50 counties is drawn, and a sample of 3000 households is taken from within the sample of counties.

As will be illustrated in this section, the sample in alternative 1 drawn by simple random sampling will have a smaller sampling error* than the sample in alternative 2, but it involves a much wider geographic spread and its cost may be considerably greater (since travel and supervisory costs may be much greater). The second method of sampling is an illustration of cluster sampling. If a population is divided into groups and a sample of groups is drawn to represent the population, the groups serve as

---

* Formulas for the sampling error with simple random sampling and with cluster sampling are compared in Chapter 6, and show that the clustering of units usually increases the sampling error.

sampling units, and the type of sampling is defined as cluster sampling. Once the clusters are drawn, one can proceed either to include in the sample all the elementary units in the selected groups or to take a sample of smaller clusters or elementary units from the sampled clusters. When a sample of elements is drawn from the groups, this type of design is called two- (or more) stage sampling or may be called subsampling. At both stages a probability sample is drawn.

To illustrate how cluster sampling works, assume that the population of 12 individuals listed in Table 1 (p. 13) is divided into the following 3 groups consisting of 4 persons each:

CLUSTER	INDIVIDUAL	INCOME (dollars)
I	A	1300
	D	2000
	J	900
	L	1900
II	F	2200
	G	1800
	H	2700
	I	1500
III	B	6300
	C	3100
	E	3600
	K	4800

Now assume that for our sample we draw a random sample of 1 cluster from this population and use the sample average of the 4 persons included in the sample as the estimate of the average income of the 12 individuals. There are, of course, only 3 possible sample estimates and these are:

I	$1525
II	2050
III	4450

The average over all possible samples is $2675, which is the average we are trying to estimate. In other words, the estimate is unbiased. The variance of the 3 possible estimates from cluster sampling shown above is 1,621,250 (the standard deviation is $1273), which is much larger than the variance for a simple random sample or stratified sample of the same size.

The variance for simple random samples of 4 persons is 411,553 (the standard deviation is $642). The variance for a stratified random sample of 4 drawn from this population, with the stratification shown in Illustration 16.1, is 119,861 (the standard deviation is $346). Thus, the variance of cluster sampling is 3.9 times that of simple random sampling and 13.5 times that of stratified sampling.   In other words, with the population of Table 1 (p. 13) we would need 3.9 times as large a sample of persons to obtain the same precision as with simple random sampling and 13.5 times as large a sample to obtain the same precision as with the better of the stratified samples illustrated.   As an explanation of why cluster sampling is so much worse, in this case, than either stratified sampling or simple random sampling, we notice that here the samples which are excluded tend to be the "better" ones.

It is possible to divide a population into clusters and get a sample with a variance just as small as or even smaller than that for simple random sampling or even for stratified sampling.   For example, suppose that the clusters were made up in the following way:

Cluster	Individual	Average income (dollars)
I	ECGJ	2350
II	AHKL	2675
III	BFDI	3000

Here the clusters are made up so that the individual incomes within each cluster are as different from each other as possible.   The average over all possible samples is the same as before, and the estimate is unbiased. However, if we measure how closely on the average each sample estimate approximates the true average, we find that now the cluster sampling has a variance of 70,417 (standard deviation $265), which is lower than that for simple random sampling or even for stratified sampling.

In the first illustration, the clusters consisted of persons having similar incomes, and the cluster sampling turned out to have a large sampling error.   In the second illustration, the clusters consisted of persons having dissimilar incomes, and the cluster sampling turned out to have a relatively small sampling error.

The very principles that make for efficient stratified sampling make for inefficient cluster sampling.   The more alike persons are within a cluster, the better our results will be if we use that cluster as a stratum in stratified sampling and the worse our results will be if we use it as a sampling unit.

Unfortunately, in practice, making the clusters heterogeneous may not be feasible or may be too expensive, and one may be forced to retain many features of the original population which may not be conducive to small sampling errors.   For example, persons of high income tend to live in the same blocks of a city, while those of extremely small incomes tend to appear together in other blocks.   If it were possible to draw a sample of households out of every block in a city, a good cross section of every type of neighborhood of the city could be assured.   However, this might mean preparing lists, by field canvass, of the dwelling units in every block in the city, and in a large city the cost might be prohibitive.

One way to reduce this cost would be to confine the sample to a sample of city blocks with several households in the sample from each selected block.   This would necessarily mean that the sample of blocks would contain proportionately more neighboring households than a simple random sample of households; and, therefore, we would get more families with similar incomes than we would if the same number of households were drawn through simple random sampling or stratified sampling of dwelling units.   However, the main purpose of cluster sampling is not to get the most reliable sample in terms of the number of elementary units included, but to get the most reliable results per unit of cost.   It may be considerably less costly to confine the whole sample of a certain size to selected blocks scattered throughout the city than to spread the sample over a much larger number of blocks.   Optimum design for this type of problem is discussed in Chapter 6.

18. Systematic sampling.   To draw a sample of, say, 1000 cards from a file containing 10,000 cards, one might select a random number between 1 and 10, and proceed by taking the card in the position indicated by this number, and every tenth card thereafter.   This type of sampling is called *systematic sampling*.   More generally, if the sample design calls for taking every kth element in the population, or some other specified pattern, the type of sampling is referred to as systematic sampling.   In the illustration above, the population consists of the 10,000 cards, and k is equal to 10.

Systematic sampling is used very widely.   For example, in a sample survey to estimate the average rental value of dwelling units in a city, one might take, say, every twelfth block within the city, and every fourth household within the selected blocks.

To illustrate the difference between systematic sampling and simple random sampling, assume that we took every fourth person from our original 12 individuals (Table 1, p. 13).

The possible samples are *AEI, BFJ, CGK, DHL*.   The net effect of systematic sampling, thus, is to set up 4 clusters.   The standard deviation of these 4 clusters is $510, which, in this instance, is less than $786, the standard deviation of simple random sampling for a sample of size 3. (The corresponding variances are 260,208 and 617,330, respectively.)

If, on the other hand, we had taken $k = 3$ and selected every third person, we should have set up the clusters *ADGJ, BEHK, CFIL*.   The standard deviation would then be $1216 (variance 1,478,750), which is greater than $642 (variance 411,553), the standard deviation for samples of 4 with simple random sampling. In this small population it is difficult to formulate any generalization concerning the precision of estimates made from a systematic sample. In a larger population, systematic sampling will frequently be found to yield results similar to those of proportionate stratified sampling. Systematic sampling is discussed in Ch. 11, Sec. 8.

19. Intuition without sampling theory may be misleading. One can see from the previous discussion that sampling theory agrees rather closely with common sense conclusions. It seems reasonable from purely common sense considerations that a sample drawn from each of a number of relatively homogeneous groups into which a population has been divided will be more efficient than one drawn indiscriminately. Again, it seems reasonable that the use of homogeneous groups or clusters as sampling units is likely to be inefficient. However, there are many situations where intuition is likely to be misleading if it is not bolstered by sampling theory.

For example, suppose that our problem is to estimate average wage or salary income for families receiving less than $5000 income and living in cities of population over 1,000,000, and that we are considering the following two alternative sampling plans:

(1) Take a sample of the cities and a large number of households in each city.
(2) Take the same total number of households as in (1) but spread the sample into all cities.

There were in 1939 five cities of more than 1,000,000 population, for which the average wage or salary incomes of families receiving less than $5000 were:*

Chicago	$1482
Detroit	1634
Los Angeles	1154
New York City	1446
Philadelphia	1305

The range of city averages is from $1154 to $1634, whereas within any city the families we are considering have wage or salary incomes ranging from none to $5000. The distribution for Chicago is shown in Table 19.

The variation between individuals in one city is about 10 times as big as the variation between the average incomes of the various cities. Our intuition tells us, and correctly so, that the variation between individual incomes in a city is very large compared with the variation between the

---

* See footnote to Table 19.

Table 19.   Distribution of family wage or salary income, Chicago, 1939*

Income (dollars) falling in the interval	Number of families	Per cent of families
0	175,740	19.0
1– 199	15,280	1.7
200– 399	27,060	2.9
400– 599	38,920	4.2
600– 799	46,740	5.0
800– 999	50,800	5.5
1000–1199	58,660	6.3
1200–1399	70,300	7.6
1400–1599	61,820	6.7
1600–1999	105,000	11.3
2000–2499	111,600	12.0
2500–2999	66,960	7.2
3000–4999	98,500	10.6
Total	927,380	100.0

city average incomes. What our intuition may fail to do is to warn us that even small differences among the city averages may have a very potent effect on increasing the sampling error if the cities serve as sampling units. (This is seen from previous discussions on cluster sampling and Chapter 6.) Thus, one should adopt the second alternative and take all cities into the sample. As is pointed out in Sec. 17 and in Chapters 6–9, it is only when there will be appreciable economies that we are led to cluster sampling.

One other faulty conclusion to which one may be led by a cursory examination of data is worth emphasis. Often it is assumed that, if a population is divided into a number of comparatively homogeneous groups (strata) on the basis of available data and if a sample is drawn from each of these groups, there will be a marked decrease in sampling error. A simple illustration will indicate that this is not always true. Assume that the problem is to estimate the per cent of persons completing 2 or more years of high school, and that the population is divided into strata as shown in Table 20.

Note that the per cent completing 2 or more years of high school ranges from 7.5 per cent in the male nonwhite 40-and-over class to 55.4 per cent in the female white 25–34 class. It turns out that the variance of a sample of 1000 with simple random sampling, completely ignoring

---

* Source: U.S. Bureau of the Census, *Census of Population: 1940*, Family Wage or Salary Income in 1939, Table 1a. Families with incomes of $5000 and over and families not reporting were excluded.

Table 20.   Persons over 25 years of age completing 2 or more years
of high school

Age, sex, and color	Number of people (thousands)		Per cent completing 2 or more years of high school
	Population over 25 years of age	Number completing 2 or more years of high school	
Male			
White			
25–34	9,465	4,792	50.6
35–49	12,092	4,031	33.3
50 and over	12,557	2,552	20.3
Nonwhite			
25–39	1,547	221	14.3
40 and over	1,802	136	7.5
Female			
White			
25–34	9,645	5,343	55.4
35–49	11,893	4,524	38.0
50 and over	12,348	3,006	24.3
Nonwhite			
25–39	1,710	319	18.7
40 and over	1,717	144	8.4
Total	74,776	25,068	33.5

Source: U.S. Bureau of the Census, *Census of Population: 1940*, Vol. IV, Characteristics by Age, Table 18.

strata, is .000223, whereas that of proportionate stratified sampling is .000203. Hence, simple random sampling would have required only 9 per cent more cases than proportionate stratified sampling to achieve the same accuracy. It would not be worth paying more than 9 per cent additional cost to obtain the additional precision possible through stratification. Of course, stratification should be used to obtain even this small increase in efficiency if stratification does not involve any added cost. However, it is quite clear that stratification has not been so effective as to remove all need for care in selecting the sample within groups.

20. More complex sample designs. Although we have illustrated simple random sampling, stratified sampling, cluster sampling, and systematic sampling as discrete methods of sampling, combinations of these methods and various estimating procedures are generally used for any one sampling problem. For example, the problem in sampling for an estimate of the labor force described in Case Study B, Ch. 12, involves the stratification of clusters, the sampling of clusters within strata, the sampling of small clusters within the selected larger clusters, and, in some instances, the sampling of dwelling units from the selected small clusters. Different types of probability samples are drawn at each stage. Ratio estimates are used. Thus, all methods described in this chapter are employed in a single problem.

The subsequent chapters will develop in more detail the sampling principles described briefly in this chapter. They will show how the results of sample surveys can be substantially improved by the expenditure of relatively small amounts of time and money to develop a "good" design for the particular sampling problem facing the investigator.

REFERENCES

(1) W. G. Cochran, *Sampling Techniques*, John Wiley & Sons, New York, 1953, Chapter 1.

(2) W. G. Cochran, *Recent Developments in Sampling Theory in the United States*, International Statistical Conferences, Washington, D.C., 1947.

(3) Tore Dalenius, *Bibliography on Sampling*, Swedish Employers' Confederation, Stockholm, 1950.

(4) W. Edwards Deming, *Some Theory of Sampling*, John Wiley & Sons, New York, 1950, Chapter 1.

(5) W. A. Hendricks, "Mathematics of Sampling," *Va. Agr. Exp. Stat. Spec. Tech. Bull.*, Blacksburg, 1948.

(6) Earl E. Houseman, "Design of Samples for Surveys," *Agr. Econ. Research*, **1** (1949), 3–10.

(7) H. Kellerer, "Elementare Ausführungen zur Theorie und Technik des Stichprobenverfahrens," *Mitteilungsblatt für mathematishe Statistik*, **1** (1949), 203–218 (first of series and continued in subsequent issues).

(8) P. C. Mahalanobis, "On Large Scale Sample Surveys," *Phil. Trans. Roy. Soc.*, Series B, **231** (1946), 329–451.

(9) Philip J. McCarthy, "Sampling—Elementary Principles," *N. Y. State School Indus. Labor Relations Bull.* 15, Cornell University, Ithaca, N.Y., 1951.

(10) H. Nisselson, *Aplicacion de los Metodos de muestreo en la Elaboracion de Censos*, Bogota, Contraloria General de la Republica de Colombia, 1950.

(11) H. Nisselson, *Anwendung von Stichprobenverfahren bei Zahlungen*, München, 1950.

(12) F. X. Schumacher and R. A. Chapman, *Sampling Methods in Forestry and Range Management*, Duke University School of Forestry, 1942.

(13) F. F. Stephan, "History of the Uses of Modern Sampling Procedures," *J. Amer. Stat. Assn.*, **43** (1948), 12–38.

(14) M. Thionet, *Méthodes statistiques modernes des administrations fédérales aux Etats-Unis*, Herman & Cie, Paris, 1946.

(15) F. Yates, *Sampling Methods for Censuses and Surveys*, Charles Griffin & Company, London, 1949, Chapters 1 and 2. (Readers of French may note that this book has recently been published in French.)

(16) F. Yates, "A Review of Recent Statistical Developments in Sampling and Sampling Surveys," *J. Roy. Stat. Soc.*, **109** (1946), 12–45.

CHAPTER 2

Biases and Nonsampling Errors in
Survey Results

A. SOME GENERAL REMARKS ON BIASES

1. The effect of biases in sample results. This chapter presents a discussion of biases in sample results: how they may arise and how they may be controlled or avoided. Nonrandom sampling methods and their possible biases, and biases with random sampling, are discussed briefly; and some consideration is given also to the problems of response and other nonsampling errors. The nature of errors in survey results is considered from the point of view that the ultimate problem of the investigator is, so far as possible, to design a sample survey in such a way that the total error in the results is minimized, and not just the random sampling error.

So long as the measurement or response recorded for each unit included in a sample is not in error, or is subject only to a negligible error, any difference between the expected value of the sample estimate and the value being estimated reflects only the bias due to sampling. The value being estimated is then the result that would be obtained from a complete census taken with the same methods of collection and the same care as the sample. However, there may also be errors in measurements or in the responses to a questionnaire that would lead to biases that would be present in a complete census as well as in a sample, and in the present chapter we want to consider all possible sources of bias.

We have suggested that biased methods are acceptable in some instances and not in others, and an attempt will be made now to indicate the circumstances under which biases should be avoided if possible and the circumstances under which they need not be.

2. The mean square error of a sample estimate. As suggested in Chapter 1, the standard error will be an unsatisfactory measure of the accuracy of an estimate whenever the bias is large relative to the standard error. This is so because the standard error measures the deviations of the possible sample estimates from their expected value, which, if the estimates are biased, is different from the value being estimated. A measure of the accuracy of the estimate when the bias is relatively large is the square root of the mean square error, where the mean square error is defined as the average of the squares of the deviations of the possible sample estimates from the value being estimated (the true value).

The mean square error of an estimate is simply equal to the variance of the estimate plus the square of the bias. Thus, the mean square error of a sample mean, $\bar{x}$, is given by:

$$\text{MSE}_{\bar{x}} = \sigma_{\bar{x}}^2 + (\bar{X} - \tilde{X})^2 \tag{2.1}$$

where $\bar{X}$ is the expected value of $\bar{x}$, and $(\bar{X} - \tilde{X})$ is the bias involved when $\bar{x}$ is used as an estimate of $\tilde{X}$. Obviously, whenever the methods of sampling and measurement used yield unbiased estimates, then $\bar{X}$ is equal to $\tilde{X}$, and $\text{MSE}_{\bar{x}} = \sigma_{\bar{x}}^2$.

If one is interested in the probability that $\bar{x} - \tilde{X} > k\sqrt{\text{MSE}}$ or the probability that $\bar{x} - \tilde{X} < -k\sqrt{\text{MSE}}$, the interpretation of the MSE (in the same way as the standard deviation) might be misleading except in the trivial case when one knows the direction and magnitude of the bias.

It appears from Table 1 that so long as the bias of an estimate is no greater than the standard error, and so long as one is interested only in the absolute magnitude of errors, and not in their direction, the probability that a particular sample estimate, $\bar{x}$, will differ from the value being estimated by more than $k\sqrt{\text{MSE}_{\bar{x}}}$ can, in practice, be interpreted in the same way as if the estimate were unbiased and $k\sigma_{\bar{x}}$ were used to set probability limits.

To illustrate, suppose that a biased sampling method is used and that $\bar{x}$ has an expected value of $\bar{X}$ and a standard deviation of $\sigma_{\bar{x}}$, and that $(\bar{X} - \tilde{X}) = .75\sigma_{\bar{x}}$ is the bias. Then

$$\sqrt{\text{MSE}_{\bar{x}}} = \sqrt{\sigma_{\bar{x}}^2 + (.75)^2\sigma_{\bar{x}}^2} = \sigma_{\bar{x}}\sqrt{1.5625} = 1.25\sigma_{\bar{x}}$$

Suppose, also, that the sample estimates are normally distributed, as they will be very nearly with reasonably large samples. It is seen from Table 1 that when the bias is equal to $.75\sigma_{\bar{x}}$ then

33 per cent of the time $\tilde{X}$ lies outside $\bar{x} \pm \sqrt{\text{MSE}_{\bar{x}}}$.

4.1 per cent of the time $\tilde{X}$ lies outside $\bar{x} \pm 2\sqrt{\text{MSE}_{\bar{x}}}$.

.9 per cent of the time $\tilde{X}$ lies outside $\bar{x} \pm 2.5\sqrt{\text{MSE}_{\bar{x}}}$.

.1 per cent of the time $\tilde{X}$ lies outside $\bar{x} \pm 3\sqrt{\text{MSE}_{\bar{x}}}$.

These results, for many practical purposes, agree with the interpretations based on the corresponding multiples of the standard deviation when an unbiased estimate is used. Table 1 shows corresponding values for other assumptions as to the magnitude of the bias relative to the standard deviation.

Table 1. Proportion of cases where the true value, $\tilde{X}$, is not included in the interval $\bar{x} \pm k\sqrt{\mathrm{MSE}_{\bar{x}}}$, for various levels of bias in $\bar{x}$

Bias in $\bar{x}$	$\dfrac{\sqrt{\mathrm{MSE}_{\bar{x}}}}{\sigma_{\bar{x}}}$	Proportion of sample estimates differing from $\tilde{X}$ by more than			
		$1\sqrt{\mathrm{MSE}_{\bar{x}}}$	$2\sqrt{\mathrm{MSE}_{\bar{x}}}$	$2.5\sqrt{\mathrm{MSE}_{\bar{x}}}$	$\cdot\,3\sqrt{\mathrm{MSE}_{\bar{x}}}$
0	1.000	.32	.046	.012	.0027
$.01\sigma$	1.00005	.32	.046	.012	.0027
$.1\sigma$	1.005	.32	.046	.012	.0027
$.25\sigma$	1.03	.32	.046	.012	.0027
$.5\sigma$	1.12	.32	.044	.011	.0022
$.75\sigma$	1.25	.33	.041	.009	.0013
1.0σ	1.41	.35	.034	.006	.0006
1.5σ	1.80	.38	.018	.001	..
2.0σ	2.24	.41	.007	..	..
3.0σ	3.16	.44	.0005	..	..
10.0σ	10.05	.48	..	..	..

We have indicated earlier (Ch. 1, Sec. 15) that in choosing a sampling method it is the mean square error that should be as small as possible, and not necessarily the variance of the sample estimate. Thus, if we have a choice between two methods, one of which is unbiased, and the other has a bias, but such that the mean square error of the second estimate is less than the variance of the unbiased estimate, then we shall regard the second method of estimation as better.

In actual practice the situation usually found is that, when we choose a biased method for which the mean square error can be measured or an upper limit can be placed on it, the bias will be negligible or small relative to the standard error, or can readily be eliminated. It is for this reason that the accuracy of the estimates, particularly of consistent estimates, has been given in terms of the standard error and little or no attention has been given to biases which are demonstrably small relative to the standard error. The second column of Table 1 shows that when biases can be shown to be relatively small, say, less than 25 per cent of the standard error of an estimate, they can be neglected without any serious effect on the interpretation of the results.

The primary purpose here is to point out that, if biased methods are used for which an upper limit can be placed on the bias, then the accuracy of the results is measurable by applying formula 2.1. But if the bias is unknown or cannot be reliably estimated from the sample, or if one cannot place some definite upper limit on the amount of the bias, then the bias term in the MSE will be unknown and the accuracy of the results cannot be evaluated. Before one uses a biased estimate it is important that he know that the bias is negligible or that a measurable upper limit can be found. An effort will be made in this chapter to indicate some common situations when the bias can be neglected and some when it cannot, and to point out how certain types of biases can be evaluated.

B. NEED FOR CARE IN SELECTION OF SAMPLE WITH VARYING PROBABILITIES

3. Biases may arise where sample units are selected with known but varying probabilities. A frequent source of bias in sample designs is the use of varying probabilities in selecting the sampling units. Often the design is such that these varying probabilities are known or can be readily ascertained. When this is true the bias can be eliminated by appropriate modification of the method of selecting the sample or of preparing estimates from the sample. We shall give some illustrations of biases of this type and indicate how they arise and how they may be avoided.

4. Illustration: Estimating the characteristics of "family units" from a sample of individual members. Suppose as an example that one wished to estimate the proportion of school families (i.e., families with children in school) in a given city that have a particular characteristic—say, the proportion of school families that own their homes. One might be tempted to draw a sample of school children, ascertain the tenure of the home for each child included in the sample, and compute directly from these returns the proportion of school families that own their homes. It would turn out that even though a perfectly good sample of school children were obtained by this procedure the result would be biased and perhaps very seriously so. As an illustration suppose that the school families were distributed according to the number of school children in the family and according to the tenure of the home as shown in Table 2.

Suppose that the sample is drawn from school records in such a way that each school child has the same chance of being included—perhaps by taking a simple random sample of the children enrolled in school. Notice from the table that 20 per cent of the children in school come from families that have 4 children in school. Therefore, if we have a reasonably good sample of children, approximately 20 per cent of the children in our sample will be from these families, and hence 20 per cent of the families in our sample will have 4 children in school, whereas only 10 per cent of all the school families in the city are of this type. At the other extreme, only about 20 per cent of the children in the sample will be from families with only 1 child in school, whereas 40 per cent of the families are of this type. Consequently, if the investigator computed the proportion of home ownership among the families of the children included in the sample, the expected value of such an estimate would be 35 per cent, whereas the true proportion of the school families that own their homes is 43 per cent. Thus, the bias in this instance is quite serious. It arises because families with 4 children, for example, have 4 times the chance of being represented in such a sample as families with 1 child; and each family has a chance of being included in such a sample that is proportionate to the number of school children in the family. Large families are over-represented, and smaller families are under-represented. In this illustration this means that the groups with low home ownership are over-represented, and the groups with high home ownership are under-represented, with the consequent downward bias in the estimate from the sample.

Table 2. Distribution of school families

Number of school children in family	Families				School children	
	Number	Per cent of total families	Owning home		Number	Per cent of total school children
			Number	Per cent of total families		
4	5,000	10	500	10	20,000	20
3	10,000	20	3,000	30	30,000	30
2	15,000	30	6,000	40	30,000	30
1	20,000	40	12,000	60	20,000	20
Total	50,000	100	21,500	43	100,000	100

A bias of the same sort would arise if we were estimating other characteristics of the school families from such a sample as, for example, the average size of family or the proportion of families with the head engaged in a certain occupation, etc. The bias would be small if the average value of the characteristic being estimated did not vary widely between the classes of families that had widely differing probabilities of being included in the sample, and the bias might be large if the average did vary widely between such classes of families.

We shall indicate three ways in which the bias introduced by the method outlined above can be avoided or eliminated.

(i) *Bias can be avoided by sampling families.* One way of avoiding the bias just considered is to compile an unduplicated list of school families, so that the sample can be drawn directly from a list of school *families* instead of from a list of the children in those families. In this instance, each school family will have the same chance of being drawn, and unbiased results will be achieved. The sampling theory corresponding to the method used for selecting the sample will be applicable for evaluating the reliability of such a sample. Thus, if a simple random sample of families is drawn, then the simple random sampling theory will be applicable, etc.

If the sampling is done in this way, by sampling families, both individual characteristics and family characteristics can be computed directly from the sample, and any estimates made from such a sample, if made in accordance with the appropriate theory as outlined in subsequent chapters, will be consistent.

(ii) *Bias can be eliminated by proper weighting.* Compiling the list of families, as suggested in (i), might be difficult, and it would not be necessary to do this to get an unbiased estimate. One could take the sample of school children that was assumed above and prepare consistent estimates from it. This could be accomplished by taking proper account of the probabilities the various families had of coming into the sample. Thus, suppose that a sample of n school children is drawn by a sampling method whereby each school child had an equal chance of being selected for inclusion in the sample (no matter whether the sampling method was simple random sampling, stratified sampling, or perhaps some system of cluster sampling). The effect of selecting families with varying probabilities may be reflected in the estimate if the investigator ascertains for the children that are included in the sample not only the tenure of the home (and any other characteristics that are to be measured by the sample) but also the number of other school children in the family (or, more generally, the number of members of the family that had an opportunity to be included in the sample of individuals that was drawn).

If we let x_i represent some characteristic of the family of the ith individual drawn into the sample, and a_i the number of members of that family that had an opportunity to be included in the sample, an unbiased estimate of the aggregate value of the characteristic for all families in the population is

$$x' = \frac{N}{n} \sum^{n} \frac{x_i}{a_i} \qquad (4.1)$$

where n is the number of school children in the sample (n is also the number of school families when at most 1 school child from a family is in the sample).

It should be observed that, in obtaining the estimate, the value of the family characteristic for an individual who is included in the sample is divided by a_i, the number of members of the family who had an opportunity of being included in the sample. The division by a_i is necessary in order to offset the fact that, for families with, say, 3 members who had an opportunity of being included in the sample, there will be 3 times as many individuals in the sample as would result had each family had an equal chance of being sampled. To illustrate with a very simple case how the estimate is prepared, suppose that a sample of 5 school children is drawn from a population of 20 school children and that the family characteristics of home tenure, family income, and number of children in school are obtained from the 5 individuals, as indicated in Table 3.

Table 3

Identification of child	Family characteristics		
	Home tenure 1 = owned, 0 = rented	Family income (dollars)	Number of school children in family a_i
1	0	6000	4
2	0	1500	1
3	1	3000	2
4	1	4000	1
5	1	2000	4

The estimate of the total number of families which live in homes that they own would be

$$x' = N \frac{\dfrac{x_1}{a_1} + \dfrac{x_2}{a_2} + \dfrac{x_3}{a_3} + \dfrac{x_4}{a_4} + \dfrac{x_5}{a_5}}{n} = 20 \frac{\dfrac{0}{4} + \dfrac{0}{1} + \dfrac{1}{2} + \dfrac{1}{1} + \dfrac{1}{4}}{5} = 7$$

This is an estimate of the number of families in the population being sampled (the families from which the 20 school children came) that own their homes. Similarly, the estimate of the total income of these families is

$$x' = 20 \frac{\dfrac{6000}{4} + \dfrac{1500}{1} + \dfrac{3000}{2} + \dfrac{4000}{1} + \dfrac{2000}{4}}{5} = \$36,000$$

If we wish to estimate the per cent of the families that are owners or the average income per family, we can do so by estimating the number of families in the population and dividing the appropriate estimated total by the estimated number of families. The estimated number of families in the population is given by:

$$w' = \frac{N}{n} \sum^{n} \frac{1}{a_i}$$

and the estimated average value per family is $r = x'/w'$. Thus, for the illustration

$$w' = \frac{20}{5} \left(\frac{1}{4} + \frac{1}{1} + \frac{1}{2} + \frac{1}{1} + \frac{1}{4} \right) = 12$$

wherefore the estimated per cent of the families that are owners is $\frac{7}{12} = 58$ per cent, and the estimated average income per family is $\$36,000/12 = \$3000$.

The estimated average per family is a ratio of random variables, and the estimated ratio will be a consistent estimate. If *two* members of the same family are selected in the sample, the family must be included *twice* in the tabulation. The estimate of the precision of any of the above estimates is readily obtained from the theory presented in subsequent chapters by simply calling

$$\frac{x_i}{a_i} = y_i$$

and

$$\frac{1}{a_i} = z_i$$

Then the estimated total becomes simply

$$\frac{N}{n} \sum^{n} y_i \tag{4.2}$$

and the estimated average becomes

$$\frac{\sum\limits^{n} y_i}{\sum\limits^{n} z_i} \tag{4.3}$$

and the appropriate variance estimate to be applied is one of those presented in later chapters for the variance of an estimated total or of an estimated ratio as the case may be. The appropriate formula to use will depend on the method followed in drawing the initial sample of school children.

(iii) *Bias can be avoided by associating family data with a unique member of the family.* Another method of avoiding bias in the problem we are considering would be to specify that the characteristics of a family be associated with a unique member of the family from among those members who have a chance of being included in the sample. Thus, we might specify that the family data will be associated with the oldest school child in the family. Since every school family has one and only one "oldest school child," each family will have the same chance of being drawn as the oldest school child. Family data then would be compiled only for the families of those children in the sample who are the oldest school children in their respective families. In compiling family data all other members of the sample would be ignored. In order to carry out this sampling method it would be necessary to ascertain for each child originally drawn into the sample whether or not he is the oldest child in school from that family. If not, then no further use would be made of the information for that child in connection with estimating the characteristics of families. If he is the oldest, then the family data would be obtained and used. Family information for the children so selected would then constitute a sample that could be used in the normal way. Thus, if the sample of children were a simple random sample, the sample of oldest children would be a simple random sample of all the oldest children; and since there is one and only one oldest child for a school family, we would have a simple random sample of families. The estimate of an average or ratio would be prepared from such a sample in the way usual for a simple random sample, and the precision of the sample results would be evaluated in the usual way. (See Chapter 4 for a method of evaluating the precision of sample results.)

Let us illustrate briefly how this method would work. Going back to the very simple illustration given in the preceding paragraphs, suppose that the additional information in the accompanying table was ascertained for each child.

CHILD	OLDEST SCHOOL CHILD (Yes or No)
1	Yes
2	Yes
3	No
4	Yes
5	No

In this instance the family incomes would be compiled and used only for the children in the sample designated by 1, 2, and 4. These are the oldest children in their respective families.

We now have a sample of $n = 3$ instead of 5 for purposes of compiling family estimates, and each family has had the same chance of being included in the sample so no special weighting is necessary. The estimate from this sample of the proportion who own their homes will be 33 per cent [equals $(0 + 0 + 1)/3$], and similarly the average income per family estimated from this sample is $(\$6000 + \$1500 + \$4000)/3 = \$3833$. These estimates differ rather widely from the earlier estimates, as would be expected from such a small sample. The variance of the estimated mean or percentage is given by the usual formula for the variance for the particular method of sampling used—simple random sampling, stratified sampling, stratified cluster sampling, etc., as given in subsequent chapters.

The estimated aggregate value of some characteristic for all families in the population requires special consideration. An estimate of this aggregate is given by x/f, where f is the sampling fraction used in the selection of school children, and x is the aggregate value of the characteristic for the families included in the sample. Another estimate that can be used in some instances and that will have a smaller variance is xN/n, where N is the total number of school families in the population, and n is the number in the sample. The variance for each of these estimates is given in Sec. 9, Ch. 4.

Remark. Note that if one were trying to get a sample of all families in a city the methods described in (i), (ii), and (iii) would lead to a bias, since families without school children would have no chance of being selected.

5. General applicability of these principles. The situation where a single family, farm, business establishment, or other unit for which information is desired may have multiple chances of being selected, is commonly encountered. Each of the methods suggested for dealing with the problem has practical applicability, and other similar methods can be devised. See, for example, the method of selecting farms from a sample of areas, discussed in Sec. 14. The case for using one or the other of the types of methods for avoiding or eliminating the bias depends on the circumstances in the particular problem.

6. Biases that may arise in estimating individual characteristics where families are sampled and one individual (or a fixed number of individuals) is included in a sample from a family. It is not uncommon in surveys such as opinion or attitude polls to draw a sample of adult persons for interview by including in the sample one person per family in a sample of families. This use of only one person per family may be introduced, at additional cost, to avoid conditioning of respondents (see Sec. 24 of this chapter) or for other reasons. If a single individual is drawn at random within each sample family and the estimate is computed without proper weighting, then again the sample estimates will be subject to a more or less serious bias. The bias would arise because a member of a family containing three adult members would have only one-third as much

chance of being included in the sample as would a member of a family with only one adult member; or, more generally, a member of a family with a adult members would have only $1/a$ as much chance of being in the sample as would a member of a family with only one adult member. The estimate could be made an unbiased one by ascertaining for each individual in such a sample the number of members in the family that would have been eligible to be included in the sample (in this instance the number of adult members in the particular families) and using this number as a weight in preparing estimates from the sample.   An estimate which avoids the bias, the variance of this estimate, and the estimate of the variance are given in Ch. 7, Sec. 12.

The type of bias just described arises in the same way if one takes a sample of one family or of a fixed number of families per block, or of a fixed number of farms or of stores per area for areas that vary in the number of farms or stores they contain, or for similar designs.   Serious biases will sometimes result unless appropriate recognition of the probabilities of selection is carried into the estimating procedures, or unless the original selection of the primary units has been with probability proportionate to size (see Ch. 8, Sec. 14).   Appropriate weighting is accomplished by weighting the returns for a particular individual (or other unit for which statistics are being compiled) by the reciprocal of the probability that the particular unit had of being selected.   This can be done only if appropriate data on size are available or are obtained for the sampled units, thus providing information on the probabilities of selection of the elements included in the sample.

A method by which a sample that does not require special weighting is obtained, and for which it is appropriate to include in the sample only one person from a family, would be to ascertain before drawing the sample of families the number of individuals in each family that are members of the population being covered by the survey.   If these numbers are known, then the families can be sampled with probability proportionate to the number of members, and one member included in the sample from each family.   This method is sometimes useful where only one interview is wanted per family (to avoid conditioning other members of the family; see Remark in Sec. 24) provided the necessary information on size of family is known either exactly or approximately in advance.   Then the procedures of Chapter 8 can be applied.   Ordinarily such a method will be economical, however, only if measures of size are readily available or the cost of ascertaining such measures is very small.

7. Bias introduced by selecting units nearest to randomly selected points. A method of sampling that has sometimes been used and that provides another illustration of a biased method follows a pattern somewhat as follows. A sample of farms or of families or of stores or of other units is wanted for an area. A detailed map of the area is obtained on which a random sample of points is designated.*

Then an interviewer is given the map and told to obtain his sample by including the dwellings (or the farms or other units) that are nearest to the selected random points. Let us examine how this method of selection may affect the probability that a particular dwelling will have of being included. Assume that the map, Fig. 1, shows the distribution of dwellings in a part of the area. Suppose that a point is selected at random

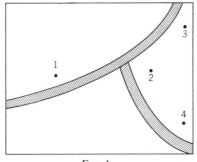

Fig. 1.

within this area and that the dwelling nearest to the point selected is to be included in the sample. Notice that, if the random point happens to fall anywhere in the left-hand half of the rectangle, the dwelling numbered 1 will be the nearest to the point and will be in the sample. Now the point has an equal chance of falling anywhere in the right-hand half of the rectangle, in which case one of the dwellings 2, 3, or 4 will be nearest and will fall in the sample. Thus, point 1 has a greater chance of selection than do any of the other points. Moreover, a higher proportion of the points within the right-hand part of the rectangle is nearer to dwelling number 2 than to either 3 or 4. It is apparent, therefore, that this method of selecting the sample will give the dwelling numbered 1 the greatest chance of being selected, the dwelling numbered 2 the second greatest chance, and the dwellings numbered 3 and 4 the least chance. If the dwellings were disposed over the area in a different manner, the probabilities would change but remain unequal. The chance that a particular dwelling would have of being selected depends upon the density of the dwellings in the neighborhood.

---

* The random sample of points may be designated by regarding the map as plotted on rectangular coordinates. Then random coordinates are selected, and these designate a set of random points.

With such a sampling method it might be possible to unravel the probabilities that each dwelling included in the sample had of being included, and from these probabilities one would be able to avoid biases in the sample estimates.   However, to determine the probabilities would be, at best, a very complicated job, and a better way of avoiding this bias is ordinarily to choose a method of selection for which the probabilities are more readily determined.   There are variations of the random point method that give unbiased results.   For example, one can cover *all* the dwellings within a fixed radius around the random point.   Then each unit so selected will have an equal chance of selection, provided the random point is allowed to fall *outside* the physical boundaries of the area being sampled by a distance at least equal to the radius.   Such a method would be used if other considerations pointed to it as desirable, but in any event this would be a way of varying the random point method to achieve results of measurable precision.

8. Possible bias with stratified disproportionate sampling.   The method of drawing a disproportionate stratified sample and the conditions where it is desirable are discussed in Chapter 5.   With disproportionate stratified sampling the estimating procedure usually involves weighting the results from each stratum by the reciprocal of the sampling fraction (the probability of selection) for that stratum.   However, if through oversight or by design one does not use this weighting procedure but simply merges the sample returns and aggregates them without weighting, a bias may be expected.

C.   BIASES WHEN SAMPLE IS SELECTED WITH UNKNOWN PROBABILITIES

9. Nonrandom sampling methods—bias introduced when sample units are selected with unknown probabilities.   Sections 5–8 have illustrated a very common type of bias introduced in sampling where the probabilities of selecting units for the sample are variable, and where the estimating procedures do not take account of this variability.   These illustrations have for the most part pointed to methods of avoiding the bias by obtaining certain additional information for the selected units that makes it possible to ascertain the probability of selection for each unit in the sample.

When the probabilities of selection are unknown and cannot be estimated, the investigator is faced with a difficult problem.

The following paragraph is quoted from Deming:*

The insidious thing about biases is their constancy and the consequent difficulty of detecting them.   Tests conducted to demonstrate the absence of bias are ofttimes only experimental demonstrations of remarkable ability to repeat the same mistake.   To be specific, if the results of a large survey are divided into ten piles at random, or are divided according to the geographic locations of the regions whence they originate, intercomparisons are incapable of detecting a bias in the over-all procedure because the results in each pile may *all be wrong by the same amount*.   Similarly, agreement year after year does not demonstrate the absence of a bias.   It should also be remarked that most biases are not removed or diminished simply by increasing the size of the sample.

Some illustrations of situations where the biases are beyond the control of the investigator are given below.

10. Voluntary response to a mailed questionnaire.   An investigator planning a survey sometimes uses reasoning like the following: "I don't see how this method of selecting these stores, these families, or these persons will have any bearing on the characteristics to be estimated from the sample—there is no reason to believe that those selected are different from those not selected, and therefore there will be no bias."   Such reasoning is common, for example, in connection with the use of respondents who happen to reply to mail questionnaires.   It is argued that, since there is no *apparent reason* why any of those who respond will differ from those who do not, the ones who do happen to respond constitute a random sample of the population.   The dangers of this reasoning are illustrated by many survey experiences.

For example, in 1937 a "census of unemployment" was authorized by the Congress, and funds were appropriated; but the provisions for the census specified, in effect, that it should be a voluntary registration, and the method for carrying it through was a mail questionnaire procedure. The President appealed to all unemployed and partially unemployed to respond, and a nation-wide publicity campaign attempted to achieve full cooperation.   Then the Post Office Department undertook to leave a form at every door in the United States (with the exception of certain areas that did not receive postal delivery service).

The technicians responsible for the "census" were aware of the difficulties frequently encountered in interpreting voluntary mail survey results and undertook, immediately after the mail canvass, to take a scientific sample of the population and cover it completely with an enumerative survey in order to provide a basis for evaluating the response to the much more widespread mail returns.

---

* Deming (1), p. 17.

With the tremendous impetus to respond in this survey, the return was very high. As evaluated by the check sample, approximately 67 per cent of those who should have responded actually did so, but still there were significant and substantial biases in the returns.* The biases differed widely between men and women and between age groups and other classes. Moreover, they differed for varying characteristics within a given class. Thus, WPA workers, the fully unemployed, and the partially unemployed responded in different ways within a given age-sex group.

It should be pointed out that the mail survey in this instance was tremendous in size, with more than 11,000,000 responses. Nevertheless, the errors in the summary figures from the mail returns were many times as large as the possible sampling errors of a reasonably well-designed random sample of only a small fraction of this size. In fact, the check survey covered less than 2 per cent of the population and involved only a fraction of the cost of carrying out the extensive mail canvass. Not only did it provide results of greater precision but also the precision could be evaluated objectively.

Other illustrations of voluntary mail surveys are surveys of production, employment, sales, and other characteristics of manufacturing or business establishments carried out currently or periodically on a sample basis by the government. Sometimes, in such surveys, a response is obtained from a very high proportion of the establishments in the sample, accounting for perhaps 95 per cent or more of the total of the characteristic that is being estimated for the establishments designated for the sample, and in such instances reliable results may be expected. There is little room for serious bias to arise. However, it is necessary to have substantially complete coverage if confidence is to be placed in such methods.

The risk of bias may be reduced, but cannot be avoided, by dealing separately, for example, with separate age-sex groups, particular occupational groups, or other classes of the population that are presumably more homogeneous in their reactions to a questionnaire than the general population. In some instances the seriousness of the problem may be reduced by such methods, but the core of the difficulty still remains: when the probabilities of including each member of the population in the sample are not known, one is unable to insure results of known precision, and biases of unknown and often of unsuspected character may distort the survey estimates.

For discussion of the effective application of mail survey methods, and

---

* Calvert L. Dedrick and Morris H. Hansen, *Census of Partial Employment, Unemployment, and Occupations: 1937*, Vol. IV, The Enumerative Check Census, U.S. Government Printing Office, 1938.

of methods for making joint use of voluntary responses to a mail questionnaire and of other sampling methods that will insure unbiased or consistent sample estimates, see Ch. 11, Sec. 3, and Case Study A, Ch. 12.

11. Selection of a convenient sample. If one who is interested in a
sample of the total population draws a sample of telephone subscribers in
a city, there will be unknown biases with respect to the characteristics
desired, and no matter how large a sample is taken of telephone subscribers in the city—even if the size were increased so as to include all the
telephone subscribers—one could not expect to get results of known
precision for all families in the city.   More than that, as already suggested,
it would not be sufficient to subdivide the sample into groups that appear
to be homogeneous with respect to the characteristic being measured and
weight the groups separately.   Such a procedure may or may not reduce
the bias, but it provides no insurance that the bias will be eliminated or
reduced to a negligible level, and again the magnitude of the bias cannot
be measured.

The so-called "quota controlled" sampling method, which has been
widely used, is essentially a sample of convenience but with certain controls
imposed that are intended to avoid some of the more serious biases
involved in taking those most conveniently available.   With this method
quotas are set up, for example, by telling an enumerator to take a specified
number of interviews in a given age group, and of a particular sex, and
perhaps in a roughly defined income group, with possibly other specifications with regard to fairly specific localities or areas within which these
quotas are to be filled.   This method is similar to a stratified sampling
method except that a nonrandom sample more or less conveniently
available is used within the strata, rather than the method of random
selection.

The restrictions imposed on the convenience of the interviewer by this
method may possibly considerably reduce the biases.   However, they may
also be completely ineffective.   What is worse, there is no way to determine the biases except by a sample properly drawn and executed.

12. Purposive sampling. A method of selecting a sample often employed in place of random sampling is to choose a sample which is
"representative" with respect to certain known characteristics of the
population.   Thus one might attempt to choose for the sample that single
county which agrees most closely with United States averages in respect
to such selected characteristics as the per cent of the population engaged
in agriculture, the per cent engaged in manufacturing, trade, and other
industry groups, the proportion white and the proportion native-born.

The same approach is sometimes used in choosing a sample of several counties by the device of first classifying the counties into groups, or strata, and then selecting a "representative" county from each stratum. The method is sometimes applied in sampling business establishments, families, or other units.   It differs from stratified random sampling in that the actual selection of the units to include in the sample in each group is done purposively rather than by a random method.

The purposive approach to sampling may be useful where it is necessary to include a very small number of units in the sample.   Thus, if one were faced with the task of finding one county, or even five or perhaps a dozen counties, to represent all the United States, purposive selection might be the best approach.   Of course, neither a sample of one county nor a sample of five counties can ordinarily be found that will represent the United States on a number of characteristics, unless the investigator is extremely fortunate, or unless the answer to the problem is known for all practical purposes before the sample is selected, or unless there is no variability between areas in the desired characteristics.   A method based on purposive selection is biased, but the biases probably would be smaller for a sample of one county selected purposively to represent the United States, than the random errors would be in a measurable method that depended on a random selection of a single county.   On the other hand, if the sample is to include a considerable number of units, then the biases of these purposive methods often will be more serious than the random errors introduced by the methods discussed in this book, in which random or chance selection rather than purposive selection is used.

13. The role of purposive and other nonrandom sampling methods.   An experiment described by Yates* illustrates the inadequacy of judgment selection in a rather striking fashion.   A collection of about 1200 stones was spread out on a table, and each of 12 persons was asked to select 3 samples of 20 stones, which should represent as nearly as possible the size distribution of the whole collection.   The results showed a consistent tendency, common to nearly all observers, to overestimate the average size of the stones; in fact, only 6 of the 36 estimates were smaller than the true average weight, and 3 of these estimates were made by a single observer.   Another interesting aspect of such a purposive selection is the consistent tendency to underestimate the variance of the distribution; the observers select stones as near their concept of the average size as possible,

---

* F. Yates, "Applications of the Sampling Technique to Crop Estimation and Forecasting," *Transactions of the Manchester Statistical Society Session 1936–1937.*

with a much smaller proportion of extreme sizes than would be obtained in a random selection.

Since we know of no statistical theory for measuring the reliability of sample results by purposive or other nonrandom sampling methods, such methods are automatically excluded if the criteria of good sample design described in Chapter 1 and adopted in this book are followed. But this presumes that a probability sampling method is feasible. In some instances a probability sample may be practically impossible, as in drawing a sample of fish from the sea, or of some types of wildlife. In such instances, if data are to be collected, a nonprobability sample must be used. Also, there may be instances where a probability sample can be designated, but only incomplete responses are available, as where there is refusal to cooperate in a survey and persuasion is unsuccessful in getting cooperation from a substantial fraction of the designated sample. In such instances it is, nevertheless, important to designate a probability sample as a basis for evaluating the possible importance and effect of the noncooperation.

Whenever a nonrandom method is used, the same principles for efficient sample design developed throughout this volume will be applicable, but with the substitution of some purposive or other nonrandom method of final selection, where a reasonably satisfactory one appears available, instead of a random selection. One should keep clearly in mind, however, that in using such methods he is obtaining results whose accuracy must be based on assumptions and judgments that cannot be measured objectively.

Although the facts would be difficult to establish, it may happen, in a case where a probability sample is feasible, that a nonrandom method would yield more reliable results per unit of cost than the optimum method chosen through the application of the criteria and sampling theory we have considered.

How, then, is one to know which type of method to use? A suggested answer to this question is the following: If it is important that reliable results be obtained, and if a fairly heavy loss may be involved if the wrong action or decision is taken as a consequence of having depended on results that actually turn out to have larger errors than are considered tolerable, then a method for which the risk of error can be controlled should be used if possible. On the other hand, if conditions are such that only fairly rough estimates are required from the sample, and important decisions do not hinge on the result, then only a small sample is required, and the price to be paid for using a sample whose accuracy can be measured may not be justified. Under these conditions it may be that the biases of a low-cost nonrandom method will be considerably less important than the random errors resulting from the small size of the sample, and thus such methods may be expected to produce results of sufficient reliability more economically than would more rigorous alternative methods. However, it appears reasonable to assume that, in most instances in which a fairly precise estimate is desired, and for which, therefore, a fairly large sample is used, the possible biases of nonrandom methods may be sufficiently serious to make them less efficient in terms of precision of results per unit of cost than an appropriate probability sampling method.

14. Biases that arise when a sample is not carried out in accordance with specifications. A fundamental criterion of good sampling discussed in Chapter 1 was that the specifications of the procedures to be followed must involve only simple workable steps that can be actually carried through in practice. An approach must be rejected as impracticable unless one can assure himself that, with the resources and facilities at his disposal for carrying out the sample, the procedures specified can and will in fact be carried out exactly or substantially as specified. Thus, one must assure himself, in designing a sample, that any procedures specified are practicable and workable under the particular circumstances in which he expects to use them. If such is not the case, a sample selected with unknown probabilities is likely to be the result.

Some of the biases that may arise in connection with methods or procedures that are difficult to carry out in practice will now be discussed. Some problems that need particular attention have to do with making administrative or procedural errors in the use of maps, lists, or other facilities, and in other steps involved in designating the sample and obtaining the desired information from the units that are to be included in the sample.

Suppose that an interviewer in a city were instructed simply to get a random sample of 50 people. Few interviewers would know what is meant by a random sample or how to select one; and, given such an instruction, an interviewer would almost necessarily end up with some sort of convenient sample. If a random sample is to be obtained, the investigator must break the problem down into simple routines and spell out the various steps and specifications in such a way that the interviewer will know exactly what to do. Moreover, it is not sufficient that the staff taking the survey know what to do. They must be able to do it. Thus, if a sample of automobiles in an area is desired, it is conceivable that the sample could be designated by specifying a sample of small areas, and associating an automobile with a particular area on the basis of its location within that area at a particular instant of time. It is probable that in practice such a sample could not be followed through, at least without the extensive resources needed for coverage of all areas simultaneously, together with the authority of a police force to stop and detain all automobiles in the designated areas. Without such resources, one would probably be doomed to serious administrative errors if he tried to apply such a method. Therefore, in accordance with the criterion of using only workable methods, the procedure would have to be rejected.

Again, suppose that the problem is to take a survey of farms, and that an area sampling method is to be used whereby the farms in designated sample areas are to be covered. One might conceive of designing a sample of areas by specifying the boundaries of the areas in terms of latitude and longitude, and if the farms in such areas were correctly enumerated the sample might be entirely satisfactory. But most persons employed as interviewers who were given such specifications would find it difficult if not impossible to locate the areas accurately. The situation is little better if a sample of areas is designated, say, on maps that are too small to be read or that are poor and that cannot be followed in the field operations. The problem of clearly designating areas is solved by providing reasonably accurate and detailed maps so that an interviewer with a moderate amount of training in map-reading can locate and cover the area indicated.

The problem of designating uniquely the particular farms to be included in the sample would still not be solved by specifying the areas on an accurate and detailed map. Some farms may be partly inside and partly outside a designated area, and one would have to formulate rules that determine whether or not a particular farm is to be regarded as associated with a given area. Various rules may be used to do this. For example, one may first specify some unique way of determining who is the operator of the farm, and then designate the farm as in a given area provided the operator lives in that area; or another approach may be to designate a principal farm dwelling if there is a dwelling on the farm, and assign the farm to the area that contains the principal farm dwelling; if there is no dwelling on the farm, the location of, say, the northwest "corner" of the farm may determine its location. If the farm has no dwelling other rules can be found. The problem is not easily solved, and in fact is a problem in taking a census as well as a sample, because a census too is taken by assigning an area to an enumerator to canvass with instructions to include in the census all the farms in the specified area.

Although the problem of associating units with areas occurs in a census as well as in a sample, it may be more serious with a sample. Thus, in a census of agriculture, the Bureau of the Census establishes enumeration areas that usually contain from 50 to 200 farms. The proportion of farms that will be near the border or cross over the border of such areas will be considerably smaller than for areas with, say, 4 farms, as may be seen in Fig. 2.

In this illustration, 100 points were selected at random in the large square, which measures 50 units on each side. The 100 points may be taken to represent the location of 100 farms. We note that 8 of the farms (8 per cent) lie within 1 unit of the boundary. Now let us look at the

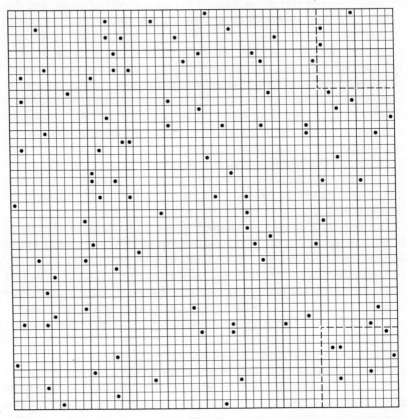

Fig. 2.

smaller squares, say, squares that measure 10 units on a side. In the small square at the upper right, 3 out of 3 points (100 per cent) are within 1 unit of a boundary, and in the small square at the lower right, 2 out of 6 points (33 per cent) are within 1 unit of a boundary. In this illustration, on the average, 8 per cent of the points in the large 50 × 50 square would be within 1 unit of a boundary, whereas 36 per cent of the points in the 10 × 10 squares would lie within 1 unit of a boundary. Since points near a borderline are more likely to involve difficulties in regard to their exact location, it is clear that such difficulties will occur less frequently in general when the areas are larger.

Even so, if good maps are available and simple rules are spelled out for associating farms with areas, and if reasonably well-trained interviewers are available, considerable experience has shown that the use of small areas is feasible and that farms, dwellings, and business establishments can be associated with small areas satisfactorily.

The discussion in Chapter 6 indicates that small clusters are more efficient sampling units than large ones if the entire unit is to be included in the sample (i.e., no subsampling). However, where maps are poor and boundary problems are frequent and difficult to handle with small areas, it may be necessary to use larger areas and thus reduce the number of boundary problems. Often, under these circumstances, subsampling will be desirable, as discussed in connection with block sampling in Chapter 3.

Many other illustrations could be given of problems involved in designating workable procedures, but the general conclusion would be the same in each instance. The investigator must adapt the procedures used in a survey to the particular circumstances that he encounters. The only acceptable procedures are those that can be carried out with the resources and personnel available. They should also be verifiable, so that administrative controls can be established for insuring that the work has been done substantially as specified.

> **Remark.** A good illustration of how errors may result when sampling units are too small is given by Sukhatme,* in a report on biases which arise in using very small areas as sampling units in estimating the yield of wheat. When the area was a circle of radius 2 ft., he found an overestimation of yield of about 40 per cent, due chiefly to the inclusion of border plants. Errors of this magnitude are obviously unacceptable in the administration of a national food program.

D. POSSIBLE BIASES WHEN DECISIONS ON SAMPLE DESIGN ARE BASED ON SAMPLE RESULTS

15. Biases sometimes introduced if decisions on sample method are made on the basis of results from the sample. In making decisions on further methods to be followed, it is sometimes desirable to make use of knowledge gained from an examination of a part of a sample already drawn.

---

* P. V. Sukhatme, "Bias in the Use of Small-size Plots in Sample Surveys for Yield," *Nature*, **157** (1946), No. 3993, p. 630.

However, such a procedure may be the cause of serious biases in sample results. For example, one may make a decision to increase the size of the sample after an examination of partial sample returns. This procedure when properly used may be highly desirable and effective, but when improperly used may cause serious biases. Similarly, one may make a decision as to the particular kind of sample estimate to employ after the sample returns have been obtained and examined. Properly used, such a procedure may be a way of improving the reliability of estimates from the sample. When improperly used, however, this procedure may introduce serious errors.

It is difficult to state general principles for determining when it is acceptable to base further sampling decisions on partial returns, but some specific rules and illustrative cases can be presented. The basic rule to follow is that the making of decisions on further sampling procedures on the basis of partial returns from the sample should be avoided except in cases where it can be demonstrated that no significant biases will be introduced. The next seven sections discuss several common practices and indicate some conditions under which it is permissible to use partial returns as a guide for further decisions. The theory of sequential sampling, which deals with a general approach to increasing the size of sample on the basis of an examination of initial sample results, is not treated in this book.

16. Decision to select another sample after looking at sample results. A fairly obvious and flagrant way of arriving at biased results is to examine the returns from an initial sample to determine whether they appear acceptable to the investigator; if they do, he uses the results as they are; if they do not, he discards the sample results and draws a new sample, perhaps by a different method, in the hope that he will obtain a result more nearly like the one he expected. Such an approach can be utilized to obtain almost any results desired, or can "prove" any point even when unbiased or consistent methods of selecting the sample and making the individual estimates are used if the initial results are subject to relatively large sampling errors.

This is not to suggest that the investigator should refrain from questioning the results when he finds that they are contradictory or inconsistent with other data. Often the results of compilations, either from samples or censuses or from other sources, are in error due to various causes. The errors may have arisen from blunders in compilation, errors in interviewing, or other sources, and obviously the results should then be checked thoroughly. So far as possible, of course, administrative controls should be established to avoid such errors; verification procedures and the correction of errors should be carried through whether or not the results appear to show what the investigator expected.

Verification by drawing a second sample may be acceptable, but until one has isolated any sources of significant error other than random sampling error in the initial result, any effort at verification by drawing a new sample is likely to be subject to the same errors that caused difficulty in the first sample.

17. Determination of sample size after looking at initial sample results. It can be shown that significant biases are less likely to arise if the investigator sets out to achieve a specified degree of precision, draws a sample, increases the sample size if the estimated variance of the item being estimated from the sample is too large to be within the bounds of error that have previously been specified as acceptable, and stops when the variance comes within the previously specified magnitude. Note that the increase of sample size under such conditions may sometimes result in a significant bias if the initial sample size is so small that it gives an unreliable estimate of the variance and the estimate of the variance is correlated with the estimate of the item. But if the initial sample size is large enough so that the estimate of the variance is subject to a coefficient of variation of no greater than, say, 15 per cent, then one may be able to use this approach with reasonable assurance that if biases result they will be small relative to the standard error of the sample estimate. Such a method will lead to an under-estimate of the variance, but this bias is made small if the coefficient of variation of the initial variance estimate is small.

18. Determination of method of estimation after looking at the sample returns. Another acceptable way in which an investigator can use a sample result for determining how to proceed is in the choice of the estimating method. This can be done if he specifies, in advance of making his sample estimates, several alternative types of estimates that will be considered. He then computes from his sample the estimates of the variances for the respective estimating procedures and chooses that method of estimation which has the least estimated variance. For example, one may wish to estimate a certain total from the sample. One method of estimation might be to use the simple unbiased estimate, obtained by multiplying the sample total by the reciprocal of the sampling fraction. Another method might be to use a ratio estimate, perhaps the ratio to total population from the sample applied to a known total population of the area. Then, if large enough samples were taken to yield reasonably reliable estimates of the variances, it would be a reasonably safe procedure to estimate from the sample itself the variance of each of these estimates, and choose the form of estimate that has the smallest estimated variance. Although this procedure will lead to an underestimate of the variance, the understatement will be trivial for sufficiently large samples.

> This is very different from the situation in which the investigator examines the results from possible alternative procedures and chooses the one that looks to him to be the most reasonable or the closest to what he had expected in advance. The latter procedure is subject to serious biases, particularly when the variances of the estimates compared are relatively large. The consideration that distinguishes acceptable from unacceptable procedures of choosing the best estimate is whether the search for different methods arises out of one's dissatisfaction with the magnitudes of the estimates that have already been examined, or out of a desire to obtain the estimate with minimum variance.

19. Rejection of atypical or "unrepresentative" observations. Another procedure which may lead to more or less serious biases is to examine the observations drawn by a random process and then to discard those that, in the judgment of the investigator, are unrepresentative or atypical. In an extreme case, when most of the observations must pass the test of being representative in the eyes of the investigator or else be rejected, the whole selection operation is reduced to one of a judgment or purposive selection. In a less extreme case the investigator may accept practically all observations but reject occasional unusual ones as atypical. This problem is given some further attention in Ch. 8, Sec. 9.

20. Substitutions for sample selections that are out of business, vacant dwellings, or otherwise not members of the population that is being sampled. A special and often misunderstood problem arises when one finds a unit in the sample that is not a member of the population that is being sampled, although it lies in the area or is on the listing from which the sample is being taken. Thus, suppose that one is sampling from a list of retail stores, selecting one at random from each successive set of 20 stores on the list. Suppose, now, that one of those chosen is found, after selection, to be out of business. A procedure sometimes followed is to substitute another store for the one that was out of business, perhaps by taking the next store on the list, or the store next door, or by taking another one at random from the set of 20 in which the out-of-business store was found. Such a procedure is ordinarily biased and should not be used. If the list from which the sample is drawn has on it stores that are out of business, the sample will include approximately the proper proportion of such stores.   Stores on the list adjoining the ones that are out of business may well be of a different character from the remaining stores, and if they are, such a substitution procedure may introduce serious biases.

The situation is the same, of course, if one is sampling dwellings or people and makes substitutions for members falling in the sample who are not eligible for the population being sampled.   The right action in such instances is merely to reject those not to be covered, without substitution. The total size of sample may have to be increased by a supplemental sample in order to get enough eligibles of the desired class.   However, increasing the total size of sample is quite different from substituting neighbors for particular persons or dwellings that are rejected as not being eligible for the survey.

21. Subsampling and double sampling.   Some sampling procedures are designed specifically to take advantage of the sample returns in deciding on efficient further methods to follow in completing the survey.   Subsampling methods and double sampling methods especially have this characteristic.   In subsampling, for example, there is no risk of bias whatever if one draws an initial set of sampling units consisting of clusters of elements and then subsamples from these selected units by examining the particular unit selected and then choosing whatever random methods may be most convenient for subsampling.   This approach makes it possible, in designing the subsample, to take full advantage of any special features of the particular primary units selected.   This is discussed in Ch. 9, Sec. 12.

In double sampling, also, the objective of the whole method is to examine an initial sample as a basis for drawing a subsample from it. The use of this method is described in Ch. 11, Sec. 3.

22. Pretesting as a basis for planning a sample design.   Another highly desirable method of obtaining partial sample results, examining them, and making decisions as to further sampling methods and the ultimate sample size is through the use of a pretest sample.   In this instance, an initial sample is drawn as a basis for obtaining experience in the use of a questionnaire and on the cost of various operations, and for estimating the variances of the sample method or alternative methods that are being considered.   After the initial evidence is obtained the final survey is designed and carried through.   In this type of situation no bias whatever is involved, and this procedure is a widely used and often highly efficient one in the design of statistical surveys, not only for obtaining an efficient sample design but also in clarifying instructions, improving the design of questionnaires, etc.

E. RESPONSE AND OTHER NONSAMPLING ERRORS IN SURVEYS

23. Nature and sources of nonsampling errors. We have referred to the sampling error of a sample estimate as the difference between the estimate computed from the particular sample and the result that would be obtained from a complete census if the same interviewing and other procedures involved in collecting the data were followed. The reason for defining sampling error in this way was to concentrate attention on variations due to sampling and not to have these confounded with other types of errors in surveys that are present whether the coverage is complete or is on some kind of sample basis. It needs to be recognized, however, that even if a presumably complete census were taken instead of a sample, there might be more or less serious errors in the results arising from errors in response to the questionnaire or from other causes; the nature of such errors and ways of controlling them need attention in survey design.

In the 1940 Census of Population, for example, statistics were collected and compiled on the number of people who were employed on work relief programs, while at the same time information concerning the number on the program payrolls was available from the emergency agencies themselves. It was found that the complete census did not classify as on emergency work programs all of those who were known to be receiving emergency work relief. The net discrepancy amounted to approximately 25 per cent. The problem here was primarily a response-error problem. The process of asking a person certain questions and recording the answers to those questions does not insure that the answers recorded are the correct answers, if there are any, to those questions.

As an illustration of the way response errors may arise let us consider the problem of ascertaining the number of persons having a particular characteristic in a city, say the number of persons between 18 and 44 years of age, inclusive. This seems like a relatively simple characteristic to measure.

First, suppose that a canvass—a presumably complete canvass—were made of the entire city. Should we expect to come out with exactly the true value? To answer this question we must determine what we mean by "true value," and the first step in making this determination is to formulate a more specific definition of what it is that is to be measured. Thus, we may want to count all persons in the city between 18 and 44 years of age at a particular instant of time, including anyone who happens to be traveling through the city at that time, and excluding anyone who normally lives there but happens to be elsewhere at that instant. This definition, although clear, might be hard to apply with precision in an actual canvass, especially since there would be difficulty in conducting the canvass in such a way that it could be completed instantaneously.

Instead, we might want to cover those who "usually live here." If so, what do we mean by "usually live here"? Shall we consider that people live in an area who maintain a home there but are away on a two-month or perhaps a six-month or longer vacation? If so, how can they be interviewed? Perhaps they are abroad. Suppose that someone who maintains a home in an area has accepted employment elsewhere and spends only his weekends at home, or suppose that he maintains a home in each of two different areas and divides his time between the two places. In which of the two places shall we say he lives? Or a person may have no home anywhere but may be staying in the area temporarily, or he may be simply passing through in a trailer that is his only home. One can readily see many problems in defining accurately the apparently simple population we set out to measure. Once the true value is defined, it is apparent that there are many problems of applying the definition accurately in an actual canvass. Consequently, errors may be made through omissions of people who should be covered, or inclusion of people who should not be covered, or there may be duplications in the enumeration of some people.

We see, therefore, that in taking a census to ascertain the number of persons 18–44 years of age more or less serious errors may occur in determining whom to enumerate in a particular community as part of a census of the area. Moreover, once one has determined that a particular person is to be interviewed, there is still the question of getting an accurate report on that person's age. Some people do not know their age exactly. Others tend to respond in round numbers or may even purposely report their ages incorrectly. The problem of getting an accurate response might be considerably more serious if we were inquiring whether the individual were employed, or whether he held a particular opinion, or if we were interested in other more complex types of information.

A complete catalogue of all the sources of error in a survey is beyond the scope of this volume. However, an examination of the major phases of a survey or census indicates that some of the more important possible errors other than sampling errors arise from the sources listed below. The sources of error indicated are not mutually exclusive or exhaustive.

a. Errors due to faulty planning or definitions. In planning a survey the purposes of the survey are made explicit. The purposes are then translated into a set of definitions of the characteristics for which data are to be collected and into a set of specifications for collecting, processing, and publishing. The possibilities of error arise where the statistician fails to understand the purposes of the survey, where the definitions that are set up may not be pertinent to the purposes, where the specifications (for the sample, the questionnaire, the method of collecting the data, the methods of selection and training of personnel, processing methods, etc.) would lead to error even if followed exactly.

b. Response errors. Response errors may be accidental or may be introduced purposely, or they may arise from lack of information. A respondent may misunderstand a question and give an improper answer unintentionally, or may respond incorrectly because of a belief that an incorrect answer may increase his prestige, or for some other reason. Similarly, the interviewer may affect the accuracy of response by the way he asks questions or records them. One source of error common to most methods of collecting information is that of *recall.* Many of the questions in surveys refer to happenings or conditions in the past, and there is a problem both of remembering the event and of associating it with the correct time period.

c. Errors in coverage. One can conceive of a true number of residents in an area, according to some definition, at a point in time. When we take a census of population we will miss some persons and duplicate or enumerate others in error. The net error is the difference between those missed and those enumerated that should not have been. Such errors are often larger than would be commonly expected. Similarly, in an agriculture or business census, there is a question of under- or overcoverage, but here the problem is more difficult because of the lack of clarity of the definition of a farm or an establishment for borderline cases. Errors in applying a definition may affect coverage, as well as errors in location. Samples drawn from such populations may be subject to coverage limitations, also, if the sample is so designed that certain classes of the population have no probability of being included or inappropriate probabilities of being included. Errors in coverage may be regarded as a type of response error, as was implied in the illustration given earlier in this section.

d. Errors in classification. The statistical classification of data, such as classifying persons by occupation, business establishments by industry, deaths by cause, and illnesses by diagnosis, is fundamental to most statistical operations. Some classifications are straightforward, but many systems of classification are not unique or are very difficult to apply, and conceptual problems of actual applications of the classification system lead to misinterpretations and to error. These errors, too, may be regarded as a form of response error.

e. Compiling errors. Errors may be introduced in the various processes involved in tabulating and summarizing the original observations made in the survey.   Compiling errors are subject to control through verification, consistency check, etc.   Any operation such as editing, coding, punching, tabulating, transcribing is a potential source of error.   One of the important decisions to be made in large-scale censuses and surveys is *how much control* in the sense of verification, consistency checks, etc., is required to maintain the desired level of accuracy.   Case Study E, Ch. 12, illustrates an approach to this problem.

f. Publication errors.   Here there are two sources of error to be considered.   One has to do with the mechanics of publication—with proofing errors and the like.   The other, potentially much more serious, lies in the failure of the survey organization to point out the limitations of the statistics.   Errors here can run the gamut from faulty labeling of tables to failure to state known sampling and other types of errors and to point out more general limitations involving definitions and purposes.   A report which conveys an erroneous impression either of the survey statistics themselves or of their accuracy may contribute more to the error of a statistic-in-use than any other phase of the survey.

We shall give principal attention to the evaluation and control of response errors of various types.

24. Definition of expected survey value.   Results expected on the average from a sample survey or from a complete canvass of a population, based upon any specified set of procedures and conditions for obtaining the information, may be referred to as the *expected survey value*.   The expected survey value may vary with the particular approach used to obtain the information.   As an example, let us return to the illustration mentioned above, in which it is desired to ascertain the number of persons 18–44 years of age in an area through a presumably complete census. The specification might be to include in the survey all people who live in the city, i.e., whose "usual place of residence" is in the city.   Let us consider two possible sets of conditions for taking the canvass.

(*a*) One method of taking the canvass might be to divide the city into relatively small areas and to employ interviewers and assign one to carry out the canvass in each such area.   This method might involve a simple listing sheet as a questionnaire on which each address is to be listed, and the interviewer might be instructed to inquire of some responsible person at each address, "How many people live at this address who are between 18 and 44 years of age, inclusive?" and to enter the response obtained on the listing sheet.   He might be instructed to make as many calls as necessary in order to obtain an interview at each address, or to assure himself through sufficient inquiry of neighbors that no one lives at a particular address, or, where it is extremely difficult to find someone at home, even after repeated calls, to obtain the desired information from a neighbor if possible.

(b) A second method of taking the canvass might involve dividing the city into the same small areas, making similar assignments of interviewers to carry through the canvass, and providing for an interview of a responsible person at each address, as before. But, let us assume that the second method involves the use of a questionnaire in which every individual residing at an address is to be listed separately by name, by his relationship to the head of the family, and by age and sex. Suppose that this questionnaire also calls for the date of birth of each individual and provides for further inquiry concerning the individual's age whenever the date of birth and the age as originally reported are inconsistent, and that it provides for specific inquiries to be made about persons who live at the address but who may be temporarily away from home, and about possible lodgers or others at the address who might have been overlooked in the initial listing of the persons resident at the address.

Suppose that the two methods of canvass just described were carried out under conditions that were essentially identical in all other respects, i.e., the same types of interviewers, similar quality of supervision, similar weather conditions, same time of the year, and other essential conditions the same.

Would one expect the two presumably complete censuses just outlined to yield the same results if independent canvasses by the two methods were taken of the same area? Actually, differences in results may often be expected from what appear to be relatively minor variations in the survey method. Thus, the expected survey value will depend upon the particular procedures followed and other conditions surrounding the survey. Many other variations in method could be introduced with corresponding variations in the results expected: variations in the training of the interviewers or the qualifications they possess, or in their supervision, or in other factors having an effect on the results to be expected from a census.

The idea of an expected survey value does not imply that a fixed result is achieved by the use of a specified method of taking a complete census. It does imply that, with a large enough experience through repeated samples or censuses taken by means of a particular method and under similar conditions, the results of the aggregate of the experiences would converge to a fixed value. This is an assumption that is made in the hope that it will yield a helpful approach to measuring response error. Thus, under the assumption of the existence of an expected survey value, if two independent canvasses of a population are carried out, using the same methods each time, there will be some differences between the results of the two canvasses. A respondent will not always give an identical answer to the same question; or if personal interviews are involved, the question may be posed slightly differently for a given respondent at different interviews. For these and many other reasons differences will arise in repeated samples or with a complete census carried out at different times under the same specified conditions. However, if the population under consideration is large, the differences in averages, aggregates, or other derived measures arising from carrying out two independent complete censuses under the same essential conditions will be of a trivial order of magnitude.

It may and often will be feasible to exercise greater care in collecting data on a sample basis than might be practicable in taking a complete census, so that the essential conditions surrounding a sample may be quite different from the essential conditions surrounding a complete canvass that it would be practicable to conduct. In this instance the expected survey value for the sample procedure may be considerably different and perhaps closer to the true value than would be the result of a complete census taken under less adequately controlled circumstances. (See Case Study B, Ch. 12.) On the other hand, it is not difficult to imagine, or unusual to find, a sample survey that has been taken under less stringently controlled conditions than ordinarily would be imposed if the larger sum of money involved in a complete census were being expended.

Certain types of conditions can surround a complete census which it may be impossible to introduce into a sample survey. Thus, it is common practice in a population census in the United States, after the canvass of an area is completed, to announce publicly the total population of the area as obtained from the canvass and to ask anyone who believes he was not covered by the census to cooperate by getting in touch with the census representatives. In addition, local officials and civic groups who have an interest in seeing that the official population figures do not reflect an undercount may undertake to locate people who might have been missed by the census and to stimulate such persons to take steps to insure that they are included. In practice it has ordinarily been found that many of the people picked up in this way who believed they were not included actually were, and usually only small differences are introduced into the census results from such activity whenever the original census has been taken with reasonable care. This type of activity would not be practicable if one were taking a sample of the city instead of a complete census.

Often the reduction of response errors is achieved only by intensive and often expensive measurement or questionnaire or interviewing methods, whose costs would be prohibitive in a complete census. On the other hand, significant decreases in response errors can sometimes be achieved at slight increase in expenditure, perhaps by a change in wording or by one or two additional questions on a questionnaire that may add little to the time of each interview. Thus, in connection with migration studies, the Census Bureau recently investigated alternative methods of obtaining information on place of residence of the respondent at some prior date. Previous experience with the question had shown that there was a strong tendency for the respondent to give a post office address rather than actual place of residence, or, if he lived in a suburb of a city, to give the name of the central city as his place of residence instead of the suburb. This caused rather significant errors in the results; in the test made it was found that the expected survey error was about 10 per cent when a single question was asked as compared with the result obtained by using several questions that brought out the facts more clearly. In this instance, a few additional questions resulted in a slightly increased time for interviewing, but it appeared that they were essential if the information was to be reasonably reliable.

Many other illustrations can be found where it has been demonstrated that the accuracy of response depends on the form of questionnaire, the method of interview, the ability and training of the interviewer, or related factors, and where the proper expenditure of additional effort may be expected to increase the accuracy of the response. In other instances, however, additional effort may bear but little fruit in the form of increased accuracy, especially in instances where the information that is wanted is vague in nature.

   Remark. Effect of conditioning of respondents. Often the responses of one interviewee have an effect on those of another interviewee. Thus suppose that one were to interview a husband and wife together, and ask them about any instances of infidelity or, for that matter, about their voting intention in the next election. Some of the responses obtained when husband and wife were interviewed together might differ from those that would result if they were interviewed separately and under circumstances in which they placed confidence in the investigator. The responses might be affected by a joint interview, and therefore might differ from the responses to a privately and confidentially conducted interview. Similarly, on many types of questions, if one member of a family were interviewed one day and another the following day, intervening conversations might condition the responses on the second interview. Further, the response to a mailed questionnaire, filled out by the respondent, might differ from that obtained if an interviewer were present and asked the questions and recorded the responses. The interview or response situation conditions the response in many instances.

   Such conditioning is a circumstance that would be present in a complete census in the same way as in a sample survey. In a sample, however, it may be feasible to avoid certain types of conditioning that could not be avoided in a complete census. In a sample, for example, it can be specified that the interview shall be conducted with only one member from a family. This latter specification could not be followed in a complete census.

It is not the purpose here to suggest that such conditioning is undesirable. One may in some circumstance obtain more useful answers when a joint interview is held than when separate interviews are conducted. The purpose here is merely to point to the nature of conditioned responses and to the fact that often certain types of conditioning can be controlled if desired with appropriate survey design.

Response bias and response variance. The discrepancy between the "true value" that is being measured and the expected survey result is called the "response bias." The magnitude of such a response bias will depend on the particular interviewing and related procedures that are followed, the form of the questionnaire, the training of the personnel that carry out the project, etc. The response bias may or may not be large; the procedures specified for taking the survey should be such as to insure that it is not large enough to make the results misleading. The collection of information is purposeless unless procedures of interviewing and canvassing or other methods of obtaining information can be found for which such biases are small enough that the results will be useful. Only when this is true is it worth while to proceed to the problem of sample design.

> **Remark.** When response errors as well as sampling errors are under consideration, the response bias discussed in this section may be distinguished from biases that arise from the sampling procedures by referring to the latter as sampling biases. However, in the sections of this book where the meaning is clear from the context or where only errors due to sampling are being considered, the sampling bias will be referred to simply as the bias.

Once the idea of an expected survey value has been accepted, one can consider the total response error in any particular instance to be divided into two major parts: first, the response bias, and, second, the remaining response error, which may be thought of as the contribution due to response variation or "response variance." It is obvious that the errors in some responses may be offset by errors in a different direction in other responses. Response variance is a measure of the variability of those contributions to response errors that tend to be "compensating" with large enough samples.

25. The measurement of response errors. The measurement of response bias usually requires the existence of information external to the sample itself—involves, in fact, the existence of data from which the true value to be measured may be estimated more closely than from the survey data. In many cases, there are no such external data, and collecting them may be an expensive and difficult process. The measurement of response variance, on the other hand, presents a much simpler problem than the measurement of response bias. Like other variances, response variance can be estimated from an appropriately designed sample.

To the extent that response errors reflect differences in the way a question is worded, or in the skill exercised and the time spent by an interviewer, methods may be devised to aid in determining the existence of such errors. For example, the effect of different questionnaires can be measured by directing them to different random samples of the same population, and, if interviewers are to be employed, by random assignments to interviewers. This type of approach has been widely used.

Similarly, in order to evaluate the variation between interviewers one can assign a random sample of interviews to each interviewer instead of giving him a compact assignment of work within a single part of an area. Then the variation between the results obtained by the different interviewers can be compared with the variation to be expected if all interviewers did uniform work. If some of the interviewers are poorly trained or do poor work for other reasons, the differences between interviewers will be large relative to the expected random sampling errors between the samples, and the magnitude of the differences provides a measure of the inconsistency of the work done. With this evidence, one can evaluate the contribution of interviewers to the response variance.*

The lack of significant interviewer or questionnaire differences in an experiment does not demonstrate that there are no response errors. On the other hand, the presence of such differences in the experiment is a clear indication of the existence of response errors. Suppose, for example, that an interviewer was attempting to obtain information on egg production, and that his method of approach was to ascertain the number of chickens on hand at the time of the interview, and to multiply this number by some standard figure on the probable number of eggs laid per year, per chicken. Suppose, furthermore, that through meetings and discussion this method was communicated among the interviewers working on the survey and all were using the same approach. In this instance an analysis of the survey would show no differences whatever in egg production per chicken, and would thus fail to detect response errors although they might be exceedingly serious.

An important method for studying the effect of response errors in a survey is through the use of data available from other sources and independent of the survey. In a population study, for example, it may

---

* Such a scheme was used, for example, by P. C. Mahalanobis (2) and also by J. Stevens Stock and Joseph R. Hochstim (3).

be possible to check the accuracy of age reporting by matching the returns against birth certificates, and thus accurately to evaluate errors of response. The use of a more intensive questionnaire or interview may be an effective way of obtaining data of higher accuracy, and thus provides a means for evaluating the quality of the responses in the original survey. Such methods may aid in measuring both response bias and response variance.

Response variance, whether it is associated with the interviewer, the respondent, or other aspects of the survey design, will be reflected in the sampling variance as estimated from the sample results if appropriate methods of computing the sampling variance are used. When the compensating response errors associated with the individual sampling units are independent, the sampling errors computed in accordance with the various formulas given throughout this book will reflect the effect of response errors. In other instances, where the response errors are not independent for independently selected sample units, the compensating response errors can be reflected in the sampling variance as estimated from the sample by appropriate modification of the sampling variance formulas.

The response bias, as distinguished from the response variance, will not be reflected in the formulas for the sampling variance and can be estimated only by intensive measurement or by comparison of the survey results with other data which make it possible to evaluate the magnitude of the bias.

26. Minimizing the total error in survey results. The primary consideration in survey design is to allocate the appropriate resources to the control of response errors, sampling errors, and other sources of errors.

In the control of response errors, it is often important to be particularly concerned with the response bias and to allocate enough of the resources to keep the response bias relatively small. The contribution of response bias to the total error cannot be decreased simply by increasing the size of sample or the number of interviewers. The response variance, however, in its effect on the total error, plays a role similar to that of the variance due to sampling, and where the compensating response errors are independent for different sampling units, the response variance is simply one component of the sampling variance. In other cases, the response variance can be analyzed in terms of an interviewer contribution and other contributions, to determine how much of the available resources should be used to reduce these sources of errors in the same way as sampling variance can be analyzed into within-cluster components, between-cluster components, etc. One can examine whether it would pay to increase the number of interviewers so as to decrease the interviewer contribution, or whether the resources would be better spent if they were diverted to more effective training of a small number of interviewers.   It may be pointed out that the latter procedure may have the effect of also reducing response bias, which often is the more serious of the two types of errors.

A double sampling method, in which an intensive method of measurement is used on a small subsample of a larger sample on which less intensive and much less expensive methods of measurement are employed, is sometimes an effective way of reducing response bias in survey results. This approach to sample design is discussed in Sec. 3, Ch. 11.   Chapter 12, Vol. II, gives some theory that makes possible the further consideration of methods of measuring and reducing response errors and that provides guides for the appropriate allocation of resources to the various phases of survey design.

REFERENCES

(1) W. Edwards Deming, *Some Theory of Sampling*, John Wiley & Sons, New York, 1950, Chapter 2.
(2) P. C. Mahalanobis, "Recent Experiments in Statistical Sampling in the Indian Statistical Institute," *J. Roy. Stat. Soc.*, **109** (1946), 325–370.
(3) J. Stevens Stock and Joseph R. Hochstim, "A Method of Measuring Interviewer Variability," *Public Opinion Quarterly* (Summer 1951), pp. 322–334.
(4) Gertrude Bancroft and Emmett Welch, "Recent Experience with Problems of Labor Force Measurement," *J. Amer. Stat. Assn.*, **41** (1946), 303–312.
(5) H. Cantril, *Gauging Public Opinion*, Princeton University Press, 1944.
(6) Gabriel Chevry, "Control of a General Census by Means of an Area Sampling Method," *J. Amer. Stat. Assn.*, **44** (1949), 373–379.
(7) J. Cornfield, "On Certain Biases in Samples of Human Populations," *J. Amer. Stat. Assn.*, **37** (1942), 63–68.
(8) J. Durbin and A. Stuart, "Difference in Response Rates of Experienced and Inexperienced Interviewers," *J. Roy. Stat. Soc.*, **CXIV**, 163–206.
(9) A. Ross Eckler and L. Pritzker, "Measuring the Accuracy of Enumerative Surveys," *Proceeding of the International Statistical Conferences*, New Delhi, India, 1951.
(10) J. J. Feldman, Herbert Hyman, and Clyde W. Hart, "Interviewer Effects on the Quality of Survey Data," *Public Opinion Quarterly* (Winter 1951–52), pp. 734–761.
(11) Eli S. Marks and W. Parker Mauldin, "Problems of Response in Enumerative Surveys," *Amer. Sociological Review*, **15** (1950), 649–657.
(12) O. Morgenstern, *On the Accuracy of Economic Observations*, Princeton University Press, 1950.
(13) J. Neyman, "On the Two Different Aspects of the Representative Method: The Method of Stratified Sampling and the Method of Purposive Selection," *J. Roy. Stat. Soc.*, **109** (1934), 558–606.
(14) Gladys L. Palmer, "Factors in the Variability of Response in Enumerative Studies," *J. Amer. Stat. Assn.*, **38** (1943), 143–152.

CHAPTER 3

Sample Designs for Some Common Sampling Problems

A. FREQUENTLY ENCOUNTERED SAMPLING PROBLEMS

1. Use of this chapter. The purposes of this chapter are to outline a few sampling problems commonly encountered, to indicate some simple rules for sample design for selected problems, and to indicate where to look in the remaining chapters for a fuller description of the methods and for the theory for such problems.

Some "rules of thumb" are given in this and other chapters for choice of sample design that may prove to be reasonably near the optimum in dealing with some common types of sampling problems. The investigator who is engaged in large-scale or continuous sampling operations may well find such rules useful for suggesting approaches to consider, but should not rely on the suggestions without further investigation of the theory and alternative methods. The "rules of thumb" may be close enough to the optimum procedures for occasional small-scale problems which parallel closely the types of problems described.

It should be clear that, although some rules for selecting a sample can be given that can be carried out in a simple and straightforward manner, the determination of the necessary size of sample, and the evaluation of the precision of the results from a sample, are technical problems calling for careful study and application of available sampling theory, as referred to in other chapters.

2. Important distinctions between types of sampling problems. The principal distinctions made between types of sampling problems in this chapter have to do with the distribution of the population being sampled and with the resources available for drawing the sample.

Two aspects of the distribution of a population are of particular importance in their effect on sample design. The first is whether or not the population is highly skewed, i.e., whether or not a small proportion of the units in the population account for a high proportion of an aggregate or average value being measured. The second aspect which needs to be considered is the geographic distribution of the population. A population that is widely dispersed geographically may call for different sampling methods (but not different fundamental principles) from one located in a limited geographic area, although whether or not geographic distribution has an important effect on sample design depends on the resources available for sampling and the method of measurement or of obtaining a response.

A particularly important consideration in choosing an efficient sample survey design is whether there is a complete list, a partial list, or no reasonably satisfactory list of the elementary units of the population that can be used in selecting the sample.

These distinctions and certain others are important in determining the approach to efficient sample design. They are introduced in the remaining sections of this chapter, which describe some commonly occurring problems and identify sampling principles which are appropriate to these problems.

B. SAMPLE DESIGNS WHEN THE POPULATION IS NOT HIGHLY SKEWED

3. A sample from a card file or a set of existing records. *Problem:* A file of cards is available indicating the personal characteristics of the employees in a manufacturing plant. The problem is to determine the proportion of the employees having a particular characteristic, say the proportion who have completed high school. Information on education is in the card records, and there is one and only one card in the record for each employee. The information could be compiled by tabulating the total file, but it may be obtained more quickly and more economically by tabulating only the sample. The method of sampling suggested is to choose a systematic sample by taking every kth card from the file (see Ch. 11, Sec. 8), in whatever order the file happens to exist. It will not usually be necessary to take any steps to stratify or control the sample in any other way for this type of problem. More specifically, the procedure is as follows:

Step 1. Determine the accuracy needed in the sample results. The size of sample needed to achieve this accuracy can be ascertained as indicated in Sec. 8–11, Ch. 4, and in particular from Eq. 11.2 or 11.3 of Sec. 11. Suppose the decision is that the estimate is needed with a relative error (coefficient of variation) of approximately 5 per cent, and

that on the basis of advance knowledge and speculation the proportion
of high school graduates is presumed to be in the neighborhood of 40 per
cent. Then the values to use in Eq. 11.3 in order to estimate the size of
sample required are:

$$P = .40 \qquad\qquad k = 1$$
$$D = .05 \qquad\qquad V^2 = Q/P = 1.5$$

We find that this calls for a sample size of approximately 600.

Step 2. Suppose that it is decided that a sample of $n = 600$ is to be
taken, and that the number of cards in the population is $N = 6000$.
Then the sampling fraction will be $f = n/N = \frac{1}{10}$. We can select this
size of sample by choosing 1 in N/n or 1 in 10. Here $1/f = N/n = 10$ is
referred to as the sampling interval.

To draw the sample we take a starting number at random between
1 and 10 inclusive. Suppose that this number is 4. Then we take the
cards numbered 4, 14, 24, 34, · · ·, 94, 104, · · ·, 5994. The cards to be
drawn in the sample are determined by successively adding the sampling
interval to the starting number.

Step 3. The methods of estimating the desired means or totals from
the sample, and of determining the precision of the sample estimates and
the size of sample required for any desired degree of precision, are given
in Chapter 4 and in Sec. 8, Ch. 11.

Treatment of ineligible cards. If the card file contains a number of
ineligible cards, as, for example, blank cards, we *should not substitute*
eligible cards for them. Thus, suppose that the cards contain information
for employees no longer on the rolls. This means that, if we draw a
sample of 600 cards from the file, some of the cards will be for persons
no longer employed, and we will not have 600 cards in the sample for
persons currently employed.

If a sample of approximately 600 cases is wanted of present employees,
we can proceed as follows. Guess at the proportion of cards for present
employees that are in the file. Assume that this proportion is $\frac{2}{3}$. Reduce
the sampling interval that would be applied to a file containing only
eligible cards by this fraction to obtain, in this case

$$\tfrac{2}{3} \times 10 = \tfrac{20}{3}$$

To obtain 1 in $\frac{20}{3}$ cards from the file, we can find a pattern that spreads
3 units out over a set of 20, take each of these as a starting number, and
take every 20th unit thereafter. An example would be to take the 4th,
11th, and 18th units as starting numbers from the first set of 20. Then
the 24th, 31st, 38th, 44th, etc., units would be included in the sample.

In this way, if there are 6000 cards in the population, we will end up with 900 cards in the sample of all employees, about 600 of which ($\frac{2}{3} \times 900$) will refer to present employees.

If one does not know even approximately what proportion the cards for present employees are of the total, he can draw an initial small sample from the cards, estimate the proportion, and then follow the procedure outlined above. The only purpose of the initial small sample is to estimate the total size of sample required in order to get the appropriate size of sample of present employees.

If the card file contains some cards that are not eligible for the sample, then the number eligible for and included in the sample will be subject to a sampling error, and not simply an error in selection or an error due to rounding (see Sec. 9–13, Ch. 4, for standard error of a proportion and of a total frequency).

Treatment of duplicates. In using a card file, one should be sure that 1 and only 1 card refers to an individual in the population. For example, assume that certain of the persons had 5 cards representing them, others 3, and others only 1; then the expected representation in the sample of such classes will be in the ratio of 5 to 3 to 1. This will mean that the sample will have over-representation of the first 2 classes compared to the last, and the results may be seriously biased. To avoid this bias, all duplications must be removed from the file *or* a special technique must be used. Consideration is given to such problems in Ch. 2, Sec. 4–5.

Use of numbers on records in selecting sample. If the cards in the file are numbered serially, then the serial numbers often can be used to speed up the sample selection process. The cards ending in specified digits or sequences of digits can be selected. When cards are not numbered serially, there may sometimes be other numbers that can serve as a basis for selecting the sample. For example, if each card represents a person and has on it his Social Security number, a 5 per cent sample may be chosen by selecting each card with a Social Security number ending in, say, 14, 34, 54, 74, and 94 or in any other set of digits that accounts for 5 per cent of the digits from 00 through 99. When using serial numbers for selecting the sample one should be relatively sure that there is no systematic tendency for any class of cards to have a greater or lesser representation of the particular digits to be used in selecting the sample. (See Sec. 8, Ch. 11, for further precautions to be taken when drawing a systematic sample.)

Modification in method if cost of drawing sample is high. The method described above for sampling from a file was based on the assumption that, with a file on hand, the cost of sampling by this method will be very low. If the cost of drawing the sample by such a method is in fact high as compared with the cost of summarizing the information from the sample, then, even with a file on hand containing the information, it may pay to resort to other methods of sampling, such as cluster sampling from the file. For example, when the cards are not serially numbered, but there is a complete list of file drawers in which they are contained, one can take a sample of drawers and select a subsample from the selected drawers. Cluster sampling, however, is likely to be desirable only in the case where there is very little or no correlation in the characteristic or characteristics being estimated in succeeding cards. When clusters are used, the theory of cluster sampling applies, as given in Chapters 6 and 7.

4. A sample from existing records that do not contain the desired information. The situation described in the preceding section is to be distinguished from one in which the record merely provides a list from which the sample is to be drawn and does not have the factual information required for the survey. Thus, it may be true that a list of the addresses of every household in a community may be available from a recent directory or a local census. Similarly, lists of establishments for a trade may be available from the files of a trade association. In some places every family or every person in a community must be registered. Such lists may provide the means of selecting the sample, but often the required information must be obtained by methods such as direct field interviewing, mail canvassing, and telephoning.

In such cases, the method of drawing the sample described above for sampling from a file of cards may be satisfactory, but often alternative methods can be found that are more efficient. For example, cluster sampling may introduce very large economies, particularly if a small sample is selected from a large geographic area.

If the records are in geographic sequence, a geographically clustered sample can be drawn very readily. For example, suppose that it is desired to draw a sample in such a manner that clusters of $\bar{n} = 5$ units are chosen, with a specified sampling fraction, f; i.e., f is the proportion of the population to be included in the sample.

A procedure that may be convenient in drawing the sample from a list that is in a geographic sequence is to regard the cards of the file as clustered or grouped into sets of $\bar{n}$, and take 1 in k of such clusters. Thus, suppose that $\bar{n} = 5$ and $f = \frac{1}{20}$. If the cards are numbered serially, the cards numbered 1–5 are grouped together; and, similarly, cards numbered 6–10, 11–15, 12–20, $\cdot$ $\cdot$ $\cdot$, etc., are regarded as clusters. We then choose 1 in 20 of these clusters, following the procedure described earlier for the choice of individual cards.

When there are a large number of cards and the cards are filed in drawers geographically, it may be more efficient to take a sample of drawers and subsample the selected drawers. Such a procedure would be advantageous when there are many more drawers than the desired size of sample.

For more details on cluster sampling in local areas see Chapters 6 and 7.

The need for clustering becomes much more marked when a sample is to be drawn for estimates for a large geographical area where the efficient design calls for multi-stage sampling. Assuming that the file is geographically arranged, one may select, say, counties or some other similar large areas in the manner described in Chapter 9 and then sample from the cards for each of these first-stage units in the manner described above. If the records are not grouped geographically, it may be necessary to ignore them and use area sampling methods described in Chapter 9.

5. A sample of persons, families, or dwelling units from a local area. *Problem:* To take a population or dwelling unit sample of a city or local community when there are no reasonably adequate or up-to-date lists of people, heads of families, or dwelling units for the city that can serve as the list from which to draw the sample. For example, the problem might be to estimate the proportions of persons using certain products or having specified opinions, incomes, reading habits, employment status, or other characteristics.

A very simple probability sample. Even in the circumstance of having very few materials to use as a basis for drawing a sample, the actual selection of a random sample can be relatively simple. It is not essential to have a great deal of information or to introduce complicated processes in order to obtain a random sample of persons or dwelling units. We might have only a reasonably up-to-date map of the city which shows the street boundaries. The city map might be a published map or an aerial photograph or a sketch of the block boundaries within the city. The only requirement is that the map be sufficiently accurate that individual blocks or other small areas can be identified, numbered, and sampled, and that field workers can locate and identify the areas that are selected.

To obtain a probability sample of dwelling units or persons one needs only to draw a random sample of blocks and then take a census of the selected blocks. The steps are given as Procedure I in Sec. 4, Ch. 6. Where this whole-block method is used, the very large blocks, say those having 3 or 4 times the average population per block, or more, should be subdivided into parts which will be treated as separate blocks. Each part should have roughly the same population as an average block.

To make estimates from the sample and to estimate the precision of results from the sample see Chapter 4, Sec. 6 and 7 of Ch. 6, and Sec. 8 of Ch. 11.

Although the simple procedure just described will yield results of measurable precision, it will ordinarily not be the best approach. Usually it will be worth while to spend the time and effort to design a more efficient procedure that will more nearly approximate the optimum survey design.

Subsampling small compact clusters. The sampling efficiency will usually be increased by decreasing the average size of the units to be included in the sample. Procedures II and III, described in Sec. 4, Ch. 6, are alternative methods for using smaller clusters as sampling units. Procedure II is essentially the same as the method just described except that blocks in the sample are subdivided into segments. Optimum sample design considerations for this approach are given in Sec. 28, Ch. 6.

Procedure III involves listing and subsampling within the selected blocks. This use of more than one stage of sampling is commonly referred to as subsampling. In a subsampling procedure one may list all the dwellings or other units to be subsampled in the sample of blocks, and select for interviewing a sample of the units listed. Thus, if a sample of 10 per cent of the persons is desired, one might select every fifth block and interview the persons living at every second address or dwelling within the selected blocks. A given size of sample drawn in this manner ordinarily yields considerably more reliable results than will a sample of blocks completely enumerated. It will also be more costly, but if the total size of such a sample is reduced to a size that gives equivalent cost, the results may be considerably more reliable.

When such a subsampling procedure is used, one must keep the method of listing the units within the sample blocks as simple and economical as possible. In determining the kind of subsampling units to be listed, one need only remember that they should be readily identifiable, that they should be small, and that every person (or other elementary unit) in the block must be in one of the listed units. Sections 25 and 26 of Ch. 6 give some considerations involved in the definition of listing units.

The "best" or optimum determination of the proportion of blocks to be drawn into the sample from the various strata and the subsampling fractions to be used in the selected blocks is given in Chapters 6 and 7. However, it is not necessary to adhere rigidly to the optimum allocation of the sample. One may depart moderately from the optimum values without significantly increasing the cost or the sampling error. Thus, the investigator has considerable latitude in the design when he prescribes the block sampling and subsampling fractions so as to simplify the operations and processing of the sample. One simplification that is satisfactory for most population samples for estimating multiple characteristics, as well as for many individual characteristics that are widely dispersed, is to impose the condition that the sample be self-weighting; i.e., that every element of the sample have the same probability of being selected, so that an estimate of the proportion of employed persons is simply the ratio of the number of employed persons in the sample to the total number of persons in the sample. This is accomplished by making the product of the block sampling fraction and the subsampling fraction the same for all blocks in the population. An approximation to the optimum sampling fractions will often be accomplished by merely selecting an average of, say, 5 households per sampled block if the item being estimated has a low internal homogeneity, and an average of 2–3 households if the internal homogeneity is moderately high (see Sec. 8, Ch. 6). Illustrations of the first class are items such as the per cent of the total population in the labor force, or the per cent of the total persons registered as Democrats or Republicans, or the per cent of persons who would buy a nationally advertised brand of razor blades. Illustrative of the second class are items such as rent, income, and race. Illustrations are given in Sec. 8 of Ch. 6, and in Case Study D of Ch. 12. Sections 12–13, Ch. 8, provide a guide to approximating optimum sample design with a uniform over-all sampling fraction.

Estimation of totals. It should be emphasized that the preceding discussion of methods of sampling from a local area such as a city has been concerned with the problem of estimating averages, proportions, ratios, percentage distributions, or other average characteristics from the sample and not with the problem of estimating the total number of persons in the population, the total number of users of a product, the total number of employed persons, or other similar aggregates that will be highly correlated with the total population. The principal difficulty in estimating such totals from cluster samples as described above arises from the sensitivity of such estimates to wide variations in the number of families per block. Estimated ratios are affected less severely by the variation in size of block when both the numerator and the denominator of the ratio tend to vary together.

Special considerations for sample design for estimating totals are given in Chapter 8.

6. Population or dwelling unit sampling in a local area when there is an incomplete list of dwelling units. Sometimes a relatively recent city directory or other moderately complete listing of dwelling places in an area is available. Even though it is not complete, such a listing, especially if it lists individual dwelling units within large structures, may be used effectively, in such a way that it will not bias the sample results, provided it does not contain duplicate listings for the same address.* This type of resource can be used by proceeding in the following way:

The dwellings in the city may be regarded as divided into two major strata for sampling purposes: (*a*) the dwellings that are listed in the directory; and (*b*) the dwellings that are not listed in the directory. The sample from the stratum consisting of those listed in the directory is to be selected from the list. In some instances these dwellings may be sampled in small clusters from the list if evaluation of costs and sampling variance points to this approach (see Sec. 16–29, Ch. 6). In a sample drawn from such a list some addresses may no longer represent dwellings. This is the case if a building has been converted to nonresidential use, has been torn down or destroyed, or has otherwise disappeared. No substitution should be made for these, since the sample of addresses should reflect such disappearances.

The sample of the remaining dwellings in the city—those that do not appear in the directory—should be drawn by a cluster sampling procedure similar to the one outlined in Sec. 5, and here whole blocks are likely to be efficient sampling units, without segmenting or subsampling. The procedure for this stratum of dwellings not in the directory will be to make a check in each sample block of the completeness of the directory for that block and to include in the sample those dwellings in the block that do not appear in the directory. If there are in the city some new large residential structures or housing developments, or blocks that have clusters of new housing units, it will be desirable to define these as constituting another special stratum, and to sample this special stratum by the regular block sampling method described in Sec. 5, disregarding any sample from the directory that falls in these particular structures or blocks. Chapter 7 gives the theory for optimum design for this sampling method.

7. Small samples from large areas. The discussion in the preceding section has centered on the problem of making estimates for local areas such as cities or counties, or for large samples from large areas, or other situations where travel costs or costs of designating the elementary units in the sample do not constitute the major costs of the survey. When estimates are desired for a large geographic area (a large state or nation) with a small fraction of the population in the sample, other considerations must be taken into account. Factors which are relatively unimportant

---

* In certain instances such a listing can be used effectively even with duplicate listings of the same address, but special procedures are required. See, for example, Ch. 2, Sec. 3–8.

in sample design for local areas may now become more important, and conversely. For example, in nationwide surveys the convenient or the optimum primary sampling unit to be used may often contain as many as 10,000 or even 100,000 or more persons, whereas in local area surveys primary units with as few as 200 persons may be considered large. Stratification may have a more important role in designs for national than for local surveys. Travel costs, mapping costs, the use of past information, all have a more prominent part in the design of such samples. The general approach is one of drawing an initial sample of large primary units, and then subsampling within the selected primary units, using methods such as those for small area sampling. Chapter 9 presents the methods and theory for problems of this type.

C. SAMPLE DESIGNS FOR HIGHLY SKEWED POPULATIONS

8. General nature of problem.   The sampling of farms, business establishments, etc., to estimate magnitudes such as aggregate or average production, stocks, sales, and employment, or absolute or relative changes in such magnitudes, or sampling for certain types of data for individuals or families, such as average or aggregate income where a few individuals or units contribute a considerable part of the total, calls for emphasis on sampling procedures that have not been treated in the preceding sections of this chapter. In these problems, for example, stratification and the use of special lists assume especially important and significant roles. Mail survey methods are particularly important in sampling business establishments and can be supplemented by other methods in order to yield results of known precision.

It is desirable in such sampling problems to identify in advance the units that are large in size and include in the sample a higher proportion of these than of the smaller units. The device of getting a listing of large establishments and including all or a high proportion of these in the sample will generally yield important gains in efficiency when the population is highly skewed. See Ch. 5, Sec. 6–17, for fuller discussion of the problem and Case Studies A and C in Ch. 12.

9. Sampling from a highly skewed population: complete lists are available, and needed data are in the records.   This problem is essentially the same as that described in Sec. 3 except for the fact that here the population is highly skewed. It is assumed that the information to be compiled is in the records, and could be compiled by using all the records. In this instance, the important new principle is to identify one or more separate strata consisting of the larger units and to take higher sampling fractions from these strata.   Often the higher sampling fraction that should be taken is 100 per cent for the stratum consisting of the largest units.   The sample can be drawn from within the strata following procedures described in Sec. 3.   The theory, illustrations, and practical approaches to survey design for this type of problem are discussed in Ch. 5, Sec. 6–17.

10. Sampling from a highly skewed population: complete lists are available, but desired information is not in the records.   The problem here is the same as that described in Sec. 9 so long as the list contains a satisfactory measure of size that makes it possible to identify and sample separately the large units, and so long as the cost of collecting the information is not too high, either because the needed information can be collected by mail or other low-cost procedures, or because the sample is confined to a comparatively small area so that travel does not make an exceedingly important contribution to the cost.   If the list does not contain a measure of size, such a measure must be obtained by the procedures described in the next section or perhaps by the procedure described in Ch. 11, Sec. 3.   For the principles and procedures involved in determining how large the special list should be, the number of strata into which the population should be divided, and the appropriate sampling fractions, see Ch. 5, Sec. 6–17.

If the area to be covered is very large, travel may be an important factor in the cost.   If the list is arranged geographically, the procedures of Chapter 9 can be applied, using the lists for subsampling from within the selected primary sampling units.   If the list is not arranged geographically, then the subsampling procedure within selected areas can follow the lines described in the next section.

11. Sampling from a highly skewed population: partial lists or no lists are available.   The procedures will be illustrated with the problem of estimating the sales of retail establishments in a local area.   They will be similar for related problems.

Ordinarily, whenever relatively few establishments contribute a high proportion of the magnitude being measured, and there are no complete or substantially complete lists of establishments, steps similar to those indicated below should be followed in sampling from a local area.

Step 1.   Determine the major strata, sample size, and allocation to strata.   Determine the number of different major strata that will be used in selecting the sample (i.e., the number of different size classes of establishments for which different sampling fractions will be used), the boundaries of the strata, the approximate size of sample, and its allocation to the

major strata.   The size of sample will be determined jointly by the requirements of accuracy and by the available resources.   It is probably
satisfactory at this stage in planning the sample to assume that the
sampling process will be one-stage, with the elementary unit as the
sampling unit, even though in some of the strata the final selection may
involve cluster sampling and two or more stages of sampling.   The unit
costs assumed, however, should reflect the costs of the actual methods to
be used.   Chapter 5 gives the appropriate theory for one-stage sampling
of elementary units in all strata, along with some rules for defining the
strata and for approximating the optimum allocation of the sample to
strata.   It also gives the formulas for estimating the precision of estimates
from different sizes of samples.

   *Step 2.   Prepare a list of large establishments and draw the sample from
the establishments listed.*   The list of large establishments should include
all size classes of establishments that are identified as separate major
strata (i.e., requiring separate sampling fractions), except the class of
smallest establishments, or perhaps the two smallest size classes if a
substantial proportion of establishments are included in the next to the
smallest class.   The list of large establishments does not have to be 100
per cent complete, and the identification of size does not have to be exact,
but it will pay to exert a great deal of energy, if necessary, in making sure
that the list is complete for at least the very large establishments.   One
should, of course, first take advantage of all easily accessible sources.
The large stores in a community are often well known to chambers of
commerce, trade associations, and residents of a community.   Such
sources can be tapped with very little expense.   In preparing the list of
large establishments, the information to be obtained is:

   (i) An exact identification of the location of the establishment.   Ob-
       taining telephone numbers will be helpful in future follow-up.
   (ii) A rough measure of size, using any one of a number of measures.
       One relatively simple index is the number of employees.   Another
       may be the sales of the establishment in a previous month or year.

   Step 3.   Sample small stores.   An area sample can be used to obtain
a sample of the small stores.   Proceed by obtaining a map or maps of
the area showing individual city blocks or other small areas and other
geographic details.   The blocks or sections of the city, and villages if
rural areas are involved, in which establishments of the class that is to be
sampled are likely to be located should be separately outlined and distinguished on the map from blocks where few, if any, will occur.   We
shall refer to blocks where such establishments are likely to be found as
class A, and to others as class B.

We may draw the same over-all sampling fraction of stores from class A and class B blocks. But from the class A blocks we will begin by taking a higher proportion of blocks in the sample and subsample, whereas from the class B blocks we will simply include in the sample all the establishments located in the sample of blocks that is selected. The procedures for drawing the area sample are described in Ch. 6, Sec. 4. The average size of subsample per block to be taken from the A blocks should be small, perhaps 1–5 stores of the type being surveyed. The optimum sampling principles of Chapters 6 and 7 provide the theory for determining the optimum average size of the subsample. These chapters also give formulas for estimating from the sample the precision of sample results.

It is important, in obtaining the area sample, to exclude from it *all* stores on the large-store list, whether such stores are in the sample drawn from the large-store list or not.

The principles described above may readily be extended to large-area sampling. A complete description of an application of these principles to large-area sampling for business statistics is given in Case Study A, Ch. 12. The theory and practical considerations for large-area sampling are presented in Chapter 9.

> **Remark. Cut-off methods.** Sometimes the concentration of activity in a few establishments is so great that a small proportion of the establishments accounts for 90 or 95 per cent or more of the aggregates being estimated. In such instances, it may be sufficient to use a complete coverage of such large establishments without any sample at all from the smaller ones. This approach, which is described in Sec. 6, Ch. 11, is sometimes satisfactory in certain manufacturing and other industries where the concentration of activity is particularly marked.

D. MISCELLANEOUS PROBLEMS

12. Some special aspects of agriculture sampling. There are points of emphasis in certain types of agriculture sampling that differ from other types of sampling problems, and some of these will be indicated briefly here.

One type of agriculture survey procedure is to obtain information from the operator as to the crops, livestock, etc., on the holding that he operates. This type of problem is similar to that of sampling establishments (as described in Sec. 8–11). In such surveys, the principles involved are so closely parallel to those for the sampling of establishments that no further elaboration is necessary. Section 14, Ch. 2, deals with some special problems in avoiding biases in farm sampling.

There are other methods of survey where the information is obtained by direct observation and measurement without depending on responses from the operator of the holding. Response errors may be reduced considerably by such methods. Illustrative of these procedures are some surveys conducted to estimate yield or total acreage under crop. In India, for example, estimates of total crop acreages (but not identified with type of holding) have been made by obtaining a sample of plots or fields, identifying by personal observation the crops on the sampled plots, measuring the area of the plots, and compiling estimates from these sample data without depending upon the process of asking questions of the operator or farmer. This method has been particularly efficient in India because of the availability of detailed maps that show the individual plots or fields so accurately that the plots on the ground can be identified from the maps, and the areas of the plots can be measured on the maps. The sampling principles to apply in such a method are the same as those for other sampling problems. The sampling may involve one, two, or more stages, depending upon whether the area is to be covered intensively or a small sample is being drawn from a large area. The reader interested in this type of problem is referred particularly to Mahalanobis.*

An extension of this approach can be used to estimate yield per unit of area through crop-cutting samples. Thus, yield can be estimated without dependence on the operator's knowledge or memory. A substantial amount of research work has been done that provides a guide for survey design.† The procedure is to obtain a sample of fields or plots (using several stages of sampling if the density of the sample is light, and perhaps only one stage if it is heavy). Once the sample of plots is obtained, a random point or points are selected in the sample plot, a small area is delimited, and the crop is actually harvested for a sample of such small areas. Substantial border biases are likely to arise (see Sec. 14, Ch. 2) if areas are not carefully delimited, and if sampling is not at random in the total area to which the yield figures are to apply. Obviously, such a survey must be carried out just before harvesting, when the crop is nearly ready. Such a survey, if conducted without bias, would give an unbiased estimate of the harvest if the harvesting were performed under the same harvesting conditions as the sample. The results may lead to a biased

---

* P. C. Mahalanobis, "A Sample Survey of the Acreage under Jute in Bengal," *Sankhyā*, **4** (1940), 511–530.

† For example, P. C. Mahalanobis, "Recent Experiments in Statistical Sampling in the Indian Statistical Institute," *J. Roy. Stat. Soc.*, **109** (1946), 325–370; P. V. Sukhatme, "The Problem of Plot Size in Large-Scale Surveys," *J. Amer. Stat. Assn.*, **42** (1947), 297–310; F. Yates, "Some Examples of Biased Sampling," *Annals Eugenics*, **6** (1935), 202–213; A. J. King, D. E. McCarty, and M. McPeek, "An Objective Method of Sampling Wheat Fields to Estimate Production and Quality of Wheat," *U.S. Dept. Agr. Tech. Bull.* 814, 1942.

estimate of the actual harvesting, since harvest losses in the sample method may be different from those in the actual harvesting.

The theory given throughout this book is directly applicable to such crop or yield sampling. The theory in Chapters 6 and 7 will be applicable, and, in some cases, also that of Chapters 8 and 9.

13. Sampling for rare items. When the proportion of units in a population that are of a specified type is small, it may be exceedingly expensive to draw a sample that will provide an estimate of high relative precision of the number or characteristics of such units. Some guiding principles can be given that may aid in increasing the efficiency of the design for such a problem.

A few more words are in order to describe the nature of the problem under consideration. Suppose, for example, that one wants an estimate of the number of physicians in the United States, or the average income of physicians, or the proportion or number working in a particular specialty. If a list of the physicians in the country and their addresses is available, it will not be a "rare item" problem, because the population is directly accessible. Suppose, on the other hand, that no reasonably adequate list of physicians is available, and that one wishes to estimate either the total number of physicians or the number having a specified characteristic by interviewing a sample of the general population, ascertaining for each member of the population whether he is a physician, and, if so, determining any other characteristics desired. Now the particular population under consideration is buried in a very much larger population, and at best it will be an expensive proposition to obtain a sample that will give estimates for physicians that will be of high relative precision. There are many similar illustrations.

Often there are partial but not nearly complete lists of the members of the desired group, and it may be important to make use of these lists in designing a sample for such a rare item.

The problem is not difficult when it is only necessary, as is often the situation, to be able to demonstrate from the sample that the number or proportion of cases having the property in the population is small. For example, a simple random sample of 800 cases would be sufficient if one were required merely to state with approximately a 95 per cent probability of being correct that the proportion of the population having a characteristic was less than 3 per cent, when in fact the true proportion was 2 per cent. Note that this is a relative range of error of 50 per cent, although only 1 percentage point. On the other hand, if one wished to estimate with the same confidence the number (or proportion) having the characteristic within 5 per cent of the actual number in the population, the required sample size would be about 80,000 cases. When samples as large as this are needed, it usually is worth while to divert some of the resources available for the survey to special devices which will make it possible to obtain the required results with a smaller sample.

Several different situations will be considered. The situations that may have a particular effect on the sample design involve the way the rare item is distributed in the population, and the extent to which a list of members of the rare class is available or can be prepared.

Case I. Let us assume, first, that no list of a substantial proportion of the members of the rare population is available and one cannot be readily prepared, and that the rare item is distributed rather evenly throughout the population. It follows that no strata accounting for a small part of the total population can be identified in which a high proportion of the members of the rare population will be found. This implies that the members of the rare population are not highly clustered in particular blocks or subgroups of the total population. In this case, about the only thing to do to reduce costs is to sample in large clusters. If the multistage sampling theory of Chapters 6–9 is applied to this case, it will be found that (if the population is actually as we have assumed) the measure of homogeneity within clusters will be comparatively small, and one should draw a sample of large clusters and enumerate them completely.

This method has been used by the Bureau of the Census in sampling for dwelling unit vacancies in areas where the vacancy rate is very low (say less than 2 or 3 per cent), and the occasional vacant units are not clustered, but appear to be well scattered. An efficient basic design is to draw a sample of blocks and to canvass them completely in order to identify the occasional vacant units. In practice, this method has been modified to take account of the fact that many of the vacancies are widely distributed as assumed, but in some instances large structures containing many apartments have just been constructed and are not yet rented or are in the process of being rented, and these have been identified and sampled separately.

Case II. A second case arises when a partial list is available identifying the members of the population that is to be measured. If such a list covers perhaps one-third or more of the population to be surveyed, its use may reduce considerably the costs of obtaining a sample that will yield estimates of specified precision. The method of joint use of a list with area sampling described in Sec. 6 and 11 of this chapter is directly applicable, and the theory is given in Sec. 10 and 11 of Ch. 7 if a mixed sample design involving both one- and two-stage sampling is used, or in Chapter 5 if a single-stage sample is used.

Case III. Sometimes no list is available, but the rare class of the population is quite unevenly distributed throughout the larger population from which it must be sampled, with a large proportion of the rare population concentrated in a relatively small proportion of the area being surveyed. For example, in the problem of estimating the total number, proportion, or characteristics of persons in a minority racial or ethnic group in a city, it is frequently found that a high proportion of the minority population resides in a small proportion of the residential area of a city. The approach to sampling in this case involves separating the population into geographic strata, on the basis of the degree of concentration of the rare population. This approach is illustrated in Sec. 11 of Ch. 7. It is sometimes true, in such situations, that the stratum of lowest concentration is known to have such a small part of the rare population in it that this whole stratum, which may be large in total population, can be excluded from the population to be surveyed without serious damage to the survey results. Where this can be done without seriously impairing the value of the results, it may substantially reduce the cost of the survey. This suggestion is a special case of the use of the *cut-off* (Ch. 11, Sec. 6).

Case IV. This case is the same as Case III except that here a partial list is available or can be prepared. It is often true that minority group organizations, or organizations of farmers or business establishments handling or producing a certain class of items, have lists covering an important part of the members of the group, or on the basis of personal knowledge can prepare such lists at low cost. In this event, the list sampling method is combined with the one- or two-stage cluster sampling method, using the theory given in Sec. 10–11 of Ch. 7.

14. Treatment of not-at-homes and nonresponses. The importance of obtaining the desired measurements or responses for all or virtually all units designated for inclusion in the sample, without making substitutions of other units, has been emphasized in the preceding chapters. However, often it is necessary to proceed with some small amount of nonresponse. The problems of initial nonresponses, not-at-homes, and ultimate non-interviews have a number of facets. These are discussed and methods are presented or illustrated for their treatment in a number of places. Economical methods of obtaining representation in the sample of persons not responding to questionnaires or not at home on initial visits are discussed in Sec. 3, Ch. 11. Often a small remaining proportion of nonrespondents is handled by a system of substitution that has the effect of weighting. Methods for doing this are discussed in Remark 4, Sec. 16, Ch. 5.

Methods for handling ultimate nonrespondents after collection of data is completed are discussed and illustrated in Ch. 12, Case Studies A and B.

CHAPTER 4

Simple Random Sampling

A. DEFINITIONS AND NOTATION

1. Definition of simple random sampling. A procedure of sampling will be called *simple random sampling* if, in a sample of size n, all the possible combinations of n elementary units that may be formed from the population of N elementary units have the same probability of being included. (See Ch. 1, Sec. 4.)

2. Reasons for discussing simple random sampling. There are three reasons for introducing simple random sampling at this point: (*a*) many of the fundamental principles of sampling may be explained in terms of simple random sampling and then adapted to more complicated designs; (*b*) the theory of simple random sampling may, under certain conditions, provide a useful guide to the precision that is to be expected from certain other designs whose formulas are more complicated (e.g., a systematic selection); (*c*) simple random sampling is actually used without modification in some problems, although examples are confined largely to problems like the sampling of records.

Examples of simple random sampling or of designs that approximate simple random sampling are frequent, even though they form only a small portion of all the sampling that is carried out. An outstanding example of a method that approximates simple random sampling is the use of sampling in connection with a census. For example, in taking the national Censuses of Population in the United States in 1940 and 1950, and in Canada in 1951, it was found desirable to take a sample from the complete list of the population, and to make certain tabulations from the sample instead of for all persons, with the aim of speeding up these tabulations (e.g., of the labor force). In addition, the sample was used as a part of the census itself, in the interests of economy, with certain information collected from only a subset of the persons enumerated in the complete census. Similarly, a company may wish to obtain information for a sample of its employees, or a business establishment may desire

110

to obtain information for a sample of its customers.   In such instances, there is often a complete listing, and simple random sampling can be carried out, although even in these circumstances simple random sampling is often not the best procedure.   In the sampling of physical materials and property for appraisal and inventory, complete lists of items are often kept up to date, from which simple random samples may be drawn.

In this chapter we shall describe the procedures to be followed in (a) drawing a simple random sample from a finite population; (b) computing estimates of averages, percentages, and totals from the sample and evaluating the precision of the sample estimates; and (c) determining the size of sample necessary to obtain results of specified precision.   The problems of estimating and evaluating the precision of simple percentages, averages, and totals from the sample will be considered first, and the problems of making certain more complex types of estimates and of evaluating their precision will be examined later.

We shall assume that the aims of a survey have already been well defined, so that we may proceed with the steps that are to be followed in drawing a simple random sample of size n and in preparing estimates from it.   For the present we shall ignore the problem of determining the correct size of sample, and shall assume that simple random sampling is possible and desirable.   We shall learn later how one determines in advance the approximate size of sample that would be necessary, with simple random sampling, to achieve a specified degree of precision.   The problem of the choice of a particular sample design is a more complex one and is dealt with in other chapters of the book.

3. Notation and terminology.   We shall assume that we are sampling from a population (or universe) containing a total of N elementary units on which measurements are to be made, and that we wish to draw into the sample a total of n elementary units by a simple random sampling procedure.   It will be assumed that each elementary unit has been assigned a serial number and that these serial numbers run from 1 to N; the particular serial number of any individual elementary unit will be designated by the symbol i.   That is, i takes on the values from 1 to N, and any particular value of i designates a particular elementary unit in the population.   We shall let X represent a characteristic (or variable or variate) that is measured.   More specifically, let:

X_i be the value of some particular characteristic for the ith elementary unit in the population of N elementary units.   Thus, if X_i is used to designate the income of the ith individual, then X_1 is the income of the individual in the population that has been assigned the serial number 1, X_2 is the income of the second individual, etc., and X_N is the income of

the individual having serial number N.   Similarly, let Y_i be the value of
a second characteristic for the ith individual.   Additional symbols Z_i, W_i,
etc., will be introduced as needed for other characteristics.

Also let

$$X = \sum_{}^{N} X_i = X_1 + X_2 + X_3 + \cdots + X_N \qquad (3.1)$$

be the aggregate value of the specified characteristic over all members of
the population.

The symbol $\sum^{N}$ merely indicates a sum of N values, in this case the N
values of X_i.   Thus, if X_i designates the income of the ith individual,
then $\sum^{N} X_i$ would designate the sum of the income of all individuals in the
population, or, in other words, the aggregate income of the entire population under consideration.   Note that a capital letter with a subscript
(X_i) has been used to denote the ith elementary unit in the population,
and a capital letter without the subscript has been used to denote the sum
over the entire population, i.e., over the entire N elementary units or individuals in the population.   Thus, if $N = 3$, $X = \sum^{N} X_i = X_1 + X_2 + X_3$.

Now suppose that we draw a sample of n elementary units from a
universe of N elementary units and number these units from 1 to n, in the
order in which they are selected.   We use small letters to designate
sample numbers; thus, we shall adopt the notation x_1 for whatever the
value of X_i that appears as the first elementary unit of the sample, x_2 for
the value of X_i that appears as the second elementary unit of the sample,
etc.   Now the first elementary unit of the sample may be any one of the
N elementary units, and hence x_1, the value of the first elementary unit
selected, may be X_1, or X_2, or X_3, $\cdots$, or X_N.   Similarly x_2, the value
of the second elementary unit selected, may be any of the values X_1, X_2,
X_3, $\cdots$, X_N.

If a sum of some particular characteristic (such as rent) is taken over
the n elementary units that are included in a sample, the sum will be
denoted by a small letter.   In the notation to be used,

$$x = \sum_{}^{n} x_i \qquad (3.2)$$

is the aggregate of the characteristic for the n units included in the sample.
Thus, if $N = 3$ and $n = 2$, and X_3 and X_1 are selected for the sample, in
that order, then $x_1 = X_3$, and $x_2 = X_1$, $x = \sum^{n} x_i = x_1 + x_2 = X_3 + X_1$.

The distinction between the mean of the population and the mean of a
sample will be indicated also by the use of a capital letter for the former
and a small letter for the latter.   Thus,

$$\bar{X} = \frac{\sum\limits_{i}^{N} X_i}{N} = \frac{X}{N} \qquad (3.3)$$

is the average or mean of the characteristic per elementary unit in the *population*, and

$$\bar{x} = \frac{\sum\limits_{i}^{n} x_i}{n} = \frac{x}{n} \qquad (3.4)$$

is the average or mean of the characteristic per elementary unit in the *sample* for a sample of n families.

Often the characteristic that we are trying to measure is not a quantitative one. We may instead wish to indicate the presence or absence of a particular characteristic, or to ascertain the number or proportion of elementary units in the population that do or do not have the characteristic specified. In such instances, the above notation is still used, but the value assigned to X_i is 1 if the individual under consideration has the specified characteristic, and is 0 if the individual does not have the characteristic. Thus, if we want to consider the number of people or the proportion of the population with incomes within a particular income group, we may use the symbol X_i to indicate the presence or absence of this characteristic for each individual. Then X_i will have the value 1 if the ith individual's income is within the specified income interval and will have the value 0 if it is not. It follows for such a characteristic that

$$X = \sum\limits^{N} X_i \qquad (3.5)$$

is the total number of elementary units in the population that have the specified characteristic (i.e., individuals having incomes within the designated income group).

For example, assume that $N = 3$ and that the first individual has an income of $6000, the second $2000, and the third $3000. If we wish to express the number of persons in this population having incomes over $2500, we can assign to X_i the value 1 for those individuals having incomes over $2500 and the value 0 for those with incomes of $2500 or less. The number 1 is assigned to the first and third individuals since they have incomes over $2500, and the number 0 to the second individual. Then, $X_1 = 1$, $X_2 = 0$, $X_3 = 1$, and $\sum\limits^{N} X_i = 1 + 0 + 1 = 2$, the number of persons having incomes over $2500. Similarly,

$$x = \sum\limits^{n} x_i \qquad (3.6)$$

is the total number of elementary units in a particular sample of n that have the specified characteristic;

$$P = \frac{X}{N} \qquad (3.7)$$

is the proportion of the population having the specified characteristic;

$$Q = 1 - P$$

is the proportion of the population not having the characteristic; and

$$p = \frac{x}{n} \qquad (3.8)$$

is the proportion of the elementary units in a sample of n that have the specified characteristic, and, again, $q = 1 - p$.

Note that $P = \bar{X}$ and $p = \bar{x}$ for variates that have only the value 1 or 0; i.e., P and p are special cases of $\bar{X}$ and $\bar{x}$.

The same type of notation would be used if we were considering another characteristic, as, for example, the number of males in the population. Then we would assign to X_i the value of 1 if the ith individual were male, and the value 0 if not. The sum of the X_i, i.e., X, in this instance would be equal to the total number of males in the population; and X/N would be the proportion male.

With this notation we shall usually designate an estimate from a sample by the same symbol as that used for the population characteristic being estimated, except that the sample estimate will be denoted by a small letter instead of by a capital letter. If we are estimating a population total from a sample, however, the notation needs modification, for here x represents the total for the sample and cannot be regarded as an estimate of X, the total for the population. In such an instance we will use x' to denote the estimate of X from the sample.

We shall also need measures of variability, for which we shall use the notation:

$$\sigma^2 = \sigma_X^2 = \frac{\sum\limits^{N}(X_i - \bar{X})^2}{N} \qquad (3.9)$$

is the variance of the X_i in the population and sometimes will be referred to as the population variance. Note that here the $\sum\limits^{N}$ indicates the sum of the quantities $(X_i - \bar{X})^2$ in the universe. Thus, if $N = 3$, $\sum\limits^{N}(X_i - \bar{X})^2 = (X_1 - \bar{X})^2 + (X_2 - \bar{X})^2 + (X_3 - \bar{X})^2$. The subscript X on σ^2 will be omitted unless it is needed for clarity.

For simplification of both discussion and formulas we shall also refer to S^2 as the variance of the X_i, where

$$S^2 = S_X^2 = \frac{N}{N-1}\sigma^2 = \frac{\sum\limits^{N}(X_i - \bar{X})^2}{N-1} \qquad (3.10)$$

It should be noted that $N/(N-1) \doteq 1$ for any population of reasonable size, i.e., for N moderately large, and S^2 and σ^2 are essentially the same numerically.*   Similarly,

$$\sigma \doteq \sigma_X = \sqrt{\frac{\sum\limits^{N}(X_i - \bar{X})^2}{N}} \quad \text{or} \quad S = S_X = \sqrt{\frac{\sum\limits^{N}(X_i - \bar{X})^2}{N-1}} \quad (3.11)$$

will be referred to as the standard deviation of the characteristic X in the population.

We define

$$s^2 = s_X^2 = \frac{\sum\limits^{n}(x_i - \bar{x})^2}{n-1} \quad (3.12)$$

as the variance of the characteristic x_i in a particular sample of size n, and

$$s = s_X = \sqrt{\frac{\sum\limits^{n}(x_i - \bar{x})^2}{n-1}} \quad (3.13)$$

as the sample standard deviation of the characteristic.

Note that, although we distinguish between σ and S in the formulas, we refer to both as the standard deviation, and to both σ^2 and S^2 as the variance. The more precise distinctions in the formulas usually make little difference, but where (in certain instances in subsequent chapters) the difference between σ^2 and S^2 is important, the formula will contain the appropriate value.

The term *standard error* is ordinarily used only in referring to the standard deviation of all possible sample estimates of a percentage, mean, total, or other summary measure estimated from samples.   The standard error of such estimates will be indicated by the notation $\sigma_{\bar{x}}$, σ_p, etc., where the subscript denotes the particular statistic to which the standard error relates.   When the standard error is estimated from the sample itself, the estimate of $\sigma_{\bar{x}}$ will be denoted by $s_{\bar{x}}$, with similar notation for the estimated standard error of other statistics, such as σ_p, denoted by s_p and $\sigma_{\bar{y}}$, denoted by $s_{\bar{y}}$.

The fraction of the universe that is included in the sample is n/N, but since we shall frequently use this ratio it will be convenient to assign a symbol

$$f = \frac{n}{N} \quad (3.14)$$

for the *sampling fraction*. Then the proportion of the population not included in the sample is $(1-f)$.

Certain additional notation will be introduced as it is needed.

---

* The equal sign with a dot over it ($\doteq$) is to be read as "is approximately equal to."

4. An illustration. We shall consider the problem of obtaining a sample of the adult population (over 14 years of age) in a community that has a total adult population of 5000. We shall assume that from this sample we desire estimates of such items as the proportion of the population male and female, and the corresponding totals; and the average wage and salary income for the persons who earned less than $5000 during the prior year.

For this illustration, let us assume that a complete and up-to-date list of the adult population is at hand, from which a simple random sample may be drawn in order to estimate various characteristics not given in the complete listing. The symbols X_i, Y_i, Z_i, etc., will be used to indicate various characteristics of the same person. Thus, if we wish to consider the proportion of males in the population, we would let $X_i = 1$ if the ith person is male and let $X_i = 0$ if the ith person is female. On the other hand, if we wish to consider the proportion of females in the population, we would let $Y_i = 1$ if the ith person is female and let $Y_i = 0$ if the ith person is male. Similarly, if we are considering the average age, Z_i can indicate the age of the ith individual, etc.

Now let us consider the problem of drawing a sample of 400 individuals from this population and preparing, from the sample, estimates of the characteristics of the entire population. We shall discuss the operations of drawing such a sample from a finite population by the use of simple random sampling, of computing estimates from the sample, and of evaluating the precision of these estimates.

5. Drawing a simple random sample. It was pointed out earlier that a practical method of drawing a simple random sample is to use a table of random numbers, which has been constructed through a process analogous to that of drawing chips from a bowl. A replica of some random numbers is shown on p. 117.

A simple random sample of n elementary units may be drawn from a population of N elementary units by proceeding as follows:

(*a*) Number the N units in the population serially, in any order. Each serial number should have as many digits as the number of digits in N. For example, in our illustration $N = 5000$, and the required number of digits is 4. The first unit is assigned the number 0001; the second, 0002; the 203rd unit, 0203; up to 5000 for the last one.

(*b*) Select a page from the table of random numbers. As the numbers are random, any arbitrary selection of a page will do, just so that one does not always begin at the same point, and does not permit the numbers on the page to influence his selection of the page. In practice, one may well begin on the first page of random numbers, mark lightly in pencil the last number used on a page, and proceed onward from that point when the next random number is needed.

Table of random numbers*

Eleventh thousand

	1–4	5–8	9–12	13–16	17–20	21–24	25–28	29–32	33–36	37–40
1	20 17	42 28	23 17	59 66	38 61	02 10	86 10	51 55	92 52	44 25
2	74 49	04 49	03 04	10 33	53 70	11 54	48 63	94 60	94 49	57 38
3	94 70	49 31	38 67	23 42	29 65	40 88	78 71	37 18	48 64	06 57
4	22 15	78 15	69 84	32 52	32 54	15 12	54 02	01 37	38 37	12 93
5	93 29	12 18	27 30	30 55	91 87	50 57	58 51	49 36	12 53	96 40
6	45 04	77 97	36 14	99 45	52 95	69 85	03 83	51 87	85 56	22 37
7	44 91	99 49	89 39	94 60	48 49	06 77	64 72	59 26	08 51	25 57
8	16 23	91 02	19 96	47 59	89 65	27 84	30 92	63 37	26 24	23 66
9	04 50	65 04	65 65	82 42	70 51	55 04	61 47	88 83	99 34	82 37
10	32 70	17 72	03 61	66 26	24 71	22 77	88 33	17 78	08 92	73 49
11	03 64	59 07	42 95	81 39	06 41	20 81	92 34	51 90	39 08	21 42
12	62 49	00 90	67 86	93 48	31 83	19 07	67 68	49 03	27 47	52 03
13	61 00	95 86	98 36	14 03	48 88	51 07	33 40	06 86	33 76	68 57
14	89 03	90 49	28 74	21 04	09 96	60 45	22 03	52 80	01 79	33 81
15	01 72	33 85	52 40	60 07	06 71	89 27	14 29	55 24	85 79	31 96
16	27 56	49 79	34 34	32 22	60 53	91 17	33 26	44 70	93 14	99 70
17	49 05	74 48	10 55	35 25	24 28	20 22	35 66	66 34	26 35	91 23
18	49 74	37 25	97 26	33 94	42 23	01 28	59 58	92 69	03 66	73 82
19	20 26	22 43	88 08	19 85	08 12	47 65	65 63	56 07	97 85	56 79
20	48 87	77 96	43 39	76 93	08 79	22 18	54 55	93 75	97 26	90 77
21	08 72	87 46	75 73	00 11	27 07	05 20	30 85	22 21	04 67	19 13
22	95 97	98 62	17 27	31 42	64 71	46 22	32 75	19 32	20 99	94 85
23	37 99	57 31	70 40	46 55	46 12	24 32	36 74	69 20	72 10	95 93
24	05 79	58 37	85 33	75 18	88 71	23 44	54 28	00 48	96 23	66 45
25	55 85	63 42	00 79	91 22	29 01	41 39	51 40	36 65	26 11	78 32

(c) On the selected page of random numbers use a vertical guide to demarcate the required number of columns of digits.   Thus, if $N = 5000$, we shall need 4 columns.   On the replica above, the first 4 random numbers of 4 digits are

2017

7449

9470

2215

---

* M. G. Kendall and B. Babington Smith, *Tracts for Computers*, No. XXIV, Cambridge University Press, second edition, 1946.

Move the eye downward on these 4 columns until you encounter a number less than 5000; all others are counted as blanks. The first number less than 5000 is 2017; this is the serial number of the first item that is to be drawn into the sample. For the second item, we proceed onward— 7449, 9470, 2215, which is the serial number of the second item that is drawn into the sample. The numbers 7449 and 9470 are ignored, since they are larger than 5000, the size of the population. As no item may be drawn twice, duplicate random numbers are to be counted as blanks.

When we arrive at the bottom of the page of random numbers, we demarcate the next 4 columns and use them. The second column yields 4228, 0449, etc.; and proceeding in this manner through the successive columns, we select the required 400 individuals to be included in the sample.

Often in a sampling problem one will use many pages of random numbers; he may even exhaust the entire set, in which case he turns back to the beginning of the table. Some people would then demarcate columns 2, 3, 4, 5, for 4 digits, to avoid traveling over the same ground twice, or read down instead of across, etc.

6. Obtaining the desired information. The sampling procedure just outlined has identified the individual elements of the universe that are to be in the sample. The next step in a statistical survey is to obtain the information desired from each of the individuals that was designated for the sample. The method of collecting this information will vary, depending on the problem. It may involve arranging interviews with the selected individuals and recording their responses on a carefully designed questionnaire; it may involve merely assembling information from sources already available, as, for example, if a company has information in its records for the entire universe that is to be surveyed, but wants to make certain special tabulations with the aid of a sample of the records. Collection of the information may involve a testing procedure, as where the elements in the universe consist of a batch of goods, perhaps a carload of bricks, that is being purchased, and one wants to test a sample of them to determine whether they conform with specifications, or to ascertain the quality of the lot or its weight, or whether to accept the lot or to reject it.

In the illustration we are considering we shall assume that wage and salary income during the preceding year will be ascertained for each individual in the sample having an income up to $5000. For those in the sample with incomes of more than $5000 there will be merely an indication that their incomes are over that level. (This assumption is made because the source of information from which the illustration is drawn was collected on that basis.)

If we wish to obtain from the sample estimates to which statistical theory is completely applicable, it is essential that the information be collected for each of the individuals originally designated for inclusion in the sample. The data might be assembled from each of the 400 persons designated for the sample, and summarized as shown in Table 1.

Table 1.   Information obtained from 400 sample individuals

Individual number in sample $i = 1$ to n	Sex		Age	Wage or salary income (dollars)
1	M		19	1,274
2	M		46	692
3		F	28	863
.	.		.	.
.	.		.	.
.	.		.	.
399	M		24	2,281
400		F	39	0
Total	218	182	16,370	210,428

B.   SAMPLE ESTIMATES AND THEIR PRECISION— SIMPLE MEANS, PERCENTAGES, AND TOTALS

7. The computation of estimates from the sample. We shall consider, now, three simple types of characteristics of the population and methods of estimating them from the sample. The characteristics of the population whose estimates we shall consider here are, first, the average value $\bar{X}$ of some characteristic; second, the proportion P of the population having a certain characteristic; and third, the aggregate or total X for some characteristic. Although the estimation of a proportion is a special case of the estimation of an average, it will be considered separately because in the evaluation of the precision of proportions some relationships hold that do not hold for averages in general.

Estimates of $\bar{X}$, P, and X from the sample are obtained by computing $\bar{x}$ from Eq. 3.4, p from Eq. 3.4 or 3.8, and x' from Eq. 7.1 or 7.2.

$$x' = N\bar{x} = \frac{1}{f} x \tag{7.1}$$

is an estimate from the sample of X, the aggregate value of the specified characteristic for the N units in the population, where $\bar{x} = x/n$ is the sample estimate of $\bar{X} = X/N$, and x is the aggregate value of the characteristic for the n units in the sample, or

$$x' = Np = \frac{1}{f}x \tag{7.2}$$

is an estimate of X, the total number of elements or individuals in the population having a specified characteristic, where $p = x/n$ is the sample estimate of $P = X/N$, and where x is the number of units in the sample having a specified characteristic.

In estimating X the forms $N\bar{x}$ and $(1/f)x$ given above will yield identical results except for rounding errors, but sometimes one form is more convenient than the other.

Each of the above estimates is unbiased; i.e., the expected value of $\bar{x}$ is equal to $\bar{X}$, the expected value of p is equal to P, and the expected value of x' is equal to X, the population total.* As already indicated in Sec. 12 of Ch. 1, this means that, on the average over all possible samples, the estimate will be precisely equal to the population value that is being estimated. An estimate obtained from Eq. 3.4, 3.8, 7.1, or 7.2 is called a *simple unbiased estimate*. The unbiased estimates in this book will be referred to as simple unbiased estimates unless specifically indicated otherwise. The exceptions in general make use of supplemental information not involved in determining the probability of selection.

Remark. Estimating means or totals for subgroups. If we take a simple random sample of units from a population, then we also have a simple random sample of any subgroup of the units in that population.† When the average or percentage to be estimated is for a subgroup of the population, Eq. 3.4 or 3.8 applies, but n in these equations is the number of units in the subgroup n_g instead of the total sample. There is little opportunity for confusion in this case, but special care is needed in defining $\bar{x}$ or p in Eq. 7.1 or 7.2 in estimating totals for a subgroup. Suppose, for example, that one is estimating the aggregate value of a characteristic, X, for males in the population. A simple random sample of n persons is selected. If the total number of males in the population is known one would have a choice between two estimates.

(*a*) For the first estimate (given by Eq. 7.1) one can either multiply x, the aggregate value for males, by the reciprocal of the sampling fraction, or multiply $\bar{x} = x/n$ by N, where x is the aggregate value of the characteristic for males in the sample, and n is equal to the total number of persons in the sample (not the total number of males). Thus $\bar{x}$ in this instance is not the average value per male, but is the average value per person included in

---

* For proof, see Vol. II, Ch. 4, Sec. 1.
† For proof, see Vol. II, Ch. 4, Sec. 10.

the sample.   (*b*) If the total number of males is known from another source, a better estimate of *X* is given by

$$x' = \bar{x}_g N_g = \frac{x}{n_g} N_g \qquad (7.1a)$$

where $\bar{x}_g$ now is the average value per male in the sample and N_g is the number of males in the population.   This is a special case of Eq. 7.1 but with $\bar{x}_g$ substituted for $\bar{x}$ and N_g substituted for N.   If one were estimating the total number of males having a certain characteristic, Eq. 7.1a would be used, with $\bar{x}_g$ now equal to p_g, where p_g is the proportion of males in the sample having the characteristic.   In general, for simple random sampling, whenever we are estimating the aggregate value for a subset of the population, it is desirable when N_g is known to use Eq. 7.1a, with N_g equal to the number in the subset for the population, and n_g equal to the number in the subset for the sample.

Going back to our illustration of the sample of individuals, we may compute estimates of the per cent male, and the average and aggregate wage and salary income of individuals.   The totals needed are shown at the foot of Table 1, Sec. 6.   The desired estimates are as follows:*

$$\frac{218}{400} = .545 = \text{estimated proportion male (using Eq. 3.8)}$$

$$\frac{\$210,428}{400} = \$526 = \text{estimated average income (using Eq. 3.4)}$$

$$5000(\$526) = \$2,630,000 = \text{estimated total income (using Eq. 7.1)}$$

Some further illustrations with estimates of average and percentage for subsets are given in Sec. 15.

Although we know that these are unbiased estimates, this tells us nothing about how reliable they are.   Our next step, therefore, is to evaluate the precision of these estimates.

8. Standards of precision of sample estimates.   We have seen in Ch. 1, Sec. 11, that the standard error of a sample estimate provides a measure of its precision.   If the standard error of an estimate is known, we can set bounds around the estimated value in such a way that the true value that is being estimated will almost certainly (or with any desired probability) lie within these bounds.

We shall adopt the standard of three standard deviations as entitling us to say that we are "practically certain."   For a "normal" universe the chances for 3σ are 997 in 1000, but we shall apply the term "practically certain" to the chances that are associated with 3σ whatever the distribu-

---

* In this illustration, the estimated average income and total income are defined to exclude that part of any individual's income in excess of $5000.

tion of the statistic being estimated. For most characteristics and for reasonably large samples, the chances of a consistent sample estimate deviating from the true value by more than 3σ are negligible.

9. Absolute precision of sample estimates. The variances (the standard error squared) of the three estimates we have given, if the estimates are based on simple random samples, are as follows:*

The variance of p, the proportion of individuals in the sample having a certain characteristic, is

$$\sigma_p^2 = (1-f)\frac{N}{N-1}\frac{PQ}{n} \doteq (1-f)\frac{PQ}{n} \qquad (9.1)$$

the variance of $\bar{x}$, a mean estimated from the sample, is

$$\sigma_{\bar{x}}^2 = (1-f)\frac{S^2}{n} \qquad (9.2)$$

and the variance of x', an estimated total from the sample, is

$$\sigma_{x'}^2 = N^2(1-f)\frac{S^2}{n} = (1-f)\frac{nS^2}{f^2} \qquad (9.3)$$

where

$$S^2 = \frac{\sum\limits^{N}(X_i - \bar{X})^2}{N-1} \qquad (9.4)$$

and the other terms are defined in Sec. 3.

We have seen earlier that a proportion is merely a special case of a mean. It follows, then, that the two formulas for the variance should be the same; i.e., Eq. 9.1 is equivalent to Eq. 9.2. Actually, this is so because the variance in the population of a characteristic taking on only the value 1 or 0 is equal to $P(1-P)$. To see this, let us define

$Y_i = 1$ if the ith individual has a particular characteristic;
$\quad = 0$ if it does not.

Then
$$\bar{Y} = P$$

and

$$S_Y^2 = \frac{\sum\limits^{N}(Y_i - \bar{Y})^2}{N-1} = \frac{\sum\limits^{N}(Y_i - P)^2}{N-1} = \frac{N}{N-1}\left(\frac{\sum\limits^{N}Y_i^2}{N} - P^2\right)$$

But, if $Y_i = 0$ then $Y_i^2 = 0$, and if $Y_i = 1$ then $Y_i^2 = 1$. Therefore $Y_i^2 = Y_i$, and

$$\frac{\sum\limits^{N}Y_i^2}{N} = \frac{\sum\limits^{N}Y_i}{N} = P$$

* For proof, see Vol. II, Ch. 4, Sec. 2.

so that

$$S^2 = \frac{N}{N-1}(P - P^2) = \frac{N}{N-1}P(1-P) = \frac{N}{N-1}PQ \qquad (9.4a)$$

So we see that the variance of p can be written in exactly the same manner as the variance of a sample mean, and indeed it is a special case of the variance of the sample mean. This special case has been treated separately because some simplification can be introduced for it, since σ^2 need not be computed by application of formula 3.9 but is readily obtained in simple random sampling from a knowledge of P alone.

It should be noted, also, that a very simple relationship holds between the variance of $\bar{x}$ and that of x'. Since we can compute x' by multiplying $\bar{x}$ by the known number N, it follows that $\sigma_{x'}$ will be equal to $N\sigma_{\bar{x}}$, and then the variance of x' will be $N^2\sigma_{\bar{x}}^2$, which is the relationship between formulas 9.1 or 9.2 and 9.3. The general rule or theorem applied here is that, if σ_x^2 is the variance of a sample estimate or other variate, and if k is a known number or constant (i.e., a number that is known independent of the sample and not subject to any sampling error), then the variance of the product kx is equal to $k^2\sigma_x^2$. Similarly, the variance of $k\bar{x}$ is equal to $k^2\sigma_{\bar{x}}^2$.

The variances given in Eq. 9.1, 9.2, and 9.3 differ from those shown in some statistics books by the factor of approximately $(1 - f)$, which results from sampling from a finite population and is referred to as the *finite multiplier*. The finite multiplier is merely the proportion of the population not included in the sample. Thus, some show

$$\sigma_{\bar{x}}^2 = \frac{\sigma^2}{n} \qquad (9.5)$$

as the variance of the mean of n observations, and $\sigma_{\bar{x}} = \sigma/\sqrt{n}$ as the standard error of the sample mean. Actually, however, because of the effect of the finite multiplier, the precision of a sample estimate is determined not only by the absolute size n of the sample, but also to some extent by the proportion of the population that is included in the sample. For example, if $n = N$, i.e., if we take 100 per cent of our finite population as the sample so that $f = 1$, then the finite multiplier $(1 - f)$ is equal to 0 and we have no sampling error at all, which we know must be true because we have covered the entire universe. This result is different from that obtained by using Eq. 9.5, which, with 100 per cent of the population covered, would indicate a sampling error equal to $\sigma/\sqrt{N}$, although the error due to sampling is actually 0.

Equation 9.5 is correct on the assumption that the total number of elements in the universe being sampled is infinitely large, or if the sampling is carried out with replacement, which amounts to the same thing. Sampling with replacement means that after a unit is selected it is replaced and has a chance of being selected again.

When a small percentage of a finite universe is included in the sample, say 5 per cent or less, the reduction of the variance due to the finite multiplier can be ignored, and Eq. 9.5 provides a simple and acceptable approximation. However, the effect of the finite multiplier is significant in cases where as much as 25–50 per cent or more of the population is included in the sample, and we should then be careful to use Eq. 9.2 and 9.3.

10. Relative precision of sample estimates. We can talk about the precision of a sample estimate in either absolute or relative terms. For example, the error made by using p as an estimate of P can be regarded in absolute terms as measured by $(p - P)$, or in relative terms as measured by $(p - P)/P$. The standard error (square root of the variance), as obtained from Eq. 9.1, is a measure of the absolute error, i.e., it is the standard deviation of the distribution of $(p - P)$ over all possible samples. A measure of average relative error is obtained merely by computing the standard deviation of the distribution of the relative errors, $(p - P)/P$. We call this the coefficient of variation of p. We shall denote the coefficient of variation of a variable by the symbol V, and thus designate the coefficient of variation of p by the symbol V_p.* We shall call the square of the coefficient of variation the *rel-variance* in order to avoid the long expression "coefficient of variation squared." The term rel-variance is, of course, a shortening of "relative variance."

In general, then, the coefficient of variation of any sample estimate is equal to (standard error of the estimate)/(the value being estimated), and the coefficient of variation of an original variate, X_i, is $V = S/\bar{X}$. The corresponding rel-variances are the squares of these expressions. Then we have as the rel-variances of X_i, $\bar{x}$, x', and p:

$$V^2 = \frac{S^2}{\bar{X}^2}, \quad \text{or} \quad V_X^2 = \frac{S_X^2}{\bar{X}^2} = \frac{\sum\limits_{i}^{N}(X_i - \bar{X})^2}{(N - 1)\bar{X}^2} \tag{10.1}$$

$$V_{\bar{x}}^2 = \frac{\sigma_{\bar{x}}^2}{\bar{X}^2} = (1 - f)\frac{S^2}{n\bar{X}^2}, \quad \text{or} \quad = (1 - f)\frac{V^2}{n} \tag{10.2}$$

and

$$V_{x'}^2 = \frac{\sigma_{x'}^2}{X^2} = N^2(1 - f)\frac{S^2}{nX^2} = (1 - f)\frac{S^2}{n\bar{X}^2}, \quad \text{or} \quad = (1 - f)\frac{V^2}{n} \tag{10.3}$$

---

* It should be noted particularly that this use of V is different from that in many texts in which V denotes a variance.

It is seen from Eq. 10.2 and 10.3 that $V_{x'} = V_{\bar{x}}$, which follows because x' equals a constant times $\bar{x}$, and such constant multipliers drop out of the coefficient of variation and rel-variance because they appear in both the numerator and denominator.

Note that in sampling to estimate the proportion of the total population having a specified characteristic

$$V^2 = \frac{N}{N-1}\frac{Q}{P}$$

or $V^2 \doteq Q/P$, and therefore

$$V_p^2 = (1-f)\frac{V^2}{n} \doteq (1-f)\frac{Q}{nP} \tag{10.4}$$

It should be emphasized that V_p measures the relative precision of p as an estimate of P and not the absolute precision of P.   Confusion sometimes arises because σ_p^2 is the variance of a set of relative numbers, and V_p^2 is the rel-variance of the set of relative numbers.

As with the absolute measures of precision, where the proportion of the population included in the sample is small, say less than 5 per cent, the factor $(1-f)$ is approximately 1, and the formulas above are approximately

$$V_{\bar{x}}^2 \doteq \frac{V^2}{n}, \quad V_{x'}^2 \doteq \frac{V^2}{n}, \quad V_p^2 \doteq \frac{Q}{nP} \tag{10.5}$$

The probability that the *relative* error of a sample estimate is less than some specified multiple of its coefficient of variation is exactly the same as the probability that the *absolute* error of a sample estimate is less than that same multiple of its standard error.   Thus, we can say that we are practically certain that the relative error in a sample estimate will not be greater than 3 times its coefficient of variation, and that the chances are only 1 out of 3 that the relative error will exceed the coefficient of variation.

Remark.   When $\bar{x}$ or p is an estimated average or percentage for a subgroup of the population (see Remark in Sec. 7), then Eq. 10.2 or 10.5 applies, but is approximate, although the approximation will be close if the number of members of the subgroup expected in the sample is not too small, say equal to 20 or more.   In applying these equations V^2 is the rel-variance among the units in the subset of the population, and n is the number of members of the subset expected in the sample.   Thus, if a sample of persons is drawn and the average value of a characteristic is computed for the males in the sample, then V^2 in Eq. 10.2 is the rel-variance of the characteristic among males and not for the total population, and n is the number of males expected in the sample.   Similarly, if the characteristic being estimated is the proportion of the subset (males in this case) having a characteristic, then the $V^2 = Q/P$, where P is the proportion of the subset having the characteristic, and $Q = 1 - P$.

When x' is an estimated total for a subset obtained as described in part (a) of the Remark in Sec. 7, the rel-variance of x' is given by Eq. 10.3. However, the rel-variance is now based on *all* units in the population, and *not* just the subset. Thus, if the population consists of both males and females, and if the total income of the males is estimated with Eq. 7.1 (and not Eq. 7.1a), then

$$\bar{X} = \frac{\sum\limits^{N} X_i}{N}, \quad \text{and} \quad S^2 = \frac{\sum\limits^{N} (X_i - \bar{X})^2}{N - 1}$$

Here X_i has the value 0 for all units that are not members of the subset. Also, N is the total size of the population from which the simple random sample is drawn, and not the number of males in the subset.

It is often useful to state the variance of such an estimated total in another form.* Equation 10.3 is very nearly equal to

$$V_{x'}^2 \doteq (1 - f) \frac{V_g^2 + Q}{Pn} \tag{10.6}$$

where now P equals the proportion of elementary units having a certain characteristic in the subset and $Q = 1 - P$, and where

$$V_g^2 = \frac{\sum\limits^{N_g} (X_i - \bar{X}_g)^2}{(N_g - 1)\bar{X}_g^2} \tag{10.7}$$

is the rel-variance for the members of the subset, and $\bar{X}_g$ is the average value per element in the subset.

If N_g, the total number in the subset, is known, the estimate of the total for the subset is given by Eq. 7.1a, and the rel-variance of the estimate is approximately

$$V_{x'}^2 \doteq (1 - f) \frac{V_g^2}{Pn} \doteq (1 - f) \frac{V_g^2}{n_g} \tag{10.8}$$

and the approximation will be close if, again, n_g is equal to 20 or more. By comparing Eq. 10.6 with Eq. 10.8, we see that an estimate based on Eq. 7.1a has a smaller variance than when Eq. 7.1 is used. Equation 10.6 is a convenient formula for estimating $V_{x'}^2$ when V_g^2 is known or has already been estimated.

In the special cases when x' is an estimate of the number of elementary units in the subset, then V_g^2 (Eq. 10.7) is very nearly

$$V_g^2 \doteq \frac{Q_g}{P_g} \tag{10.9}$$

where P_g is the proportion of the subset having the characteristic, and $Q_g = 1 - P_g$.

11. The size of sample necessary to obtain results of specified precision.
The problem to be solved in determining the size of sample necessary to achieve results having a specified degree of precision may be stated as follows. We wish to have a satisfactory degree of certainty that the

---

* For proof, see Vol. II, Ch. 4, Sec. 17.

sample estimate of a particular characteristic is in error by no more than a specified amount, or that the error made is no more than a specified proportion of the value being estimated.   For example, we may wish to be practically certain that the coefficient of variation of the sample estimate does not exceed, say, .04 or 4 per cent.

Since we are assuming for the present that the method of sampling to be used is simple random sampling of the elementary units, our only choice in the sample design is in regard to the size of sample required. When the precision required is specified, all that remains is to set the coefficient of variation equal to the average error that one is willing to tolerate, or to set the coefficient of variation of the sample estimate equal to one-third of the maximum error that one wants to be practically certain not to exceed, and solve for the sample size required.   For example, if we want to be practically certain that the relative difference between the estimated mean from a sample and the true mean will be no greater than D, we set

$$3V_{\bar{x}} = D, \quad \text{or} \quad V_{\bar{x}} = \frac{D}{3}$$

and from Eq. 10.2 or 10.3 we get

$$\left(\frac{D}{3}\right)^2 = (1-f)\frac{V^2}{n} = \frac{N-n}{N}\frac{V^2}{n}$$

or

$$n = \frac{9NV^2}{ND^2 + 9V^2} \tag{11.1}$$

We can then compute the size of sample necessary by substituting the appropriate values for D, V^2, and N in Eq. 11.1.

We see, then, that to ascertain the size of sample required to achieve a specified precision we must have a reasonable approximation to V in advance.   A knowledge of the approximate size of V may be available from past experience.   If not, some pretesting and preliminary study may be necessary in order to obtain an approximate value for it.

The value for n as given in Eq. 11.1 is for the specific situation in which the precision desired is such that 3 times the coefficient of variation of the estimate is equal to D.   In general, one might wish to have a degree of precision such that k times the coefficient of variation would be equal to D.   Then the size of sample necessary is given by substituting k^2 for 9 in Eq. 11.1, and we have

$$n = \frac{k^2NV^2}{ND^2 + k^2V^2} \tag{11.2}$$

The value selected for k determines the probability that the sample result will have a relative error no greater than $\pm D$. Formula 11.2 is applicable with simple random sampling whether the characteristic being estimated is a mean, a total, or a percentage.

In the usual case where the population is large relative to any size of sample that may be considered, the computation to determine the size of sample needed is somewhat simpler. In such instances, as we have already seen (Eq. 10.5), the rel-variance of an estimated mean, percentage, or total is given approximately by V^2/n. If we wish to have a result of such precision that k times the coefficient of variation of the estimate is equal to D, then we have

$$\frac{k^2V^2}{n} = D^2$$

whence

$$n = \frac{k^2V^2}{D^2} \tag{11.3}$$

The decision on the level of accuracy required, i.e., on the value of D, is an important one.* We see from Eq. 11.3 that, if we are willing to double an expected relative error, we shall require a sample only about one-fourth as large. For example, if

$$D = .04, \ k = 3, \text{ and } V = \tfrac{1}{2}$$

then the necessary sample size is

$$n = \frac{9}{4(.0016)} = 1406$$

But, if we are satisfied with $D = 8$ per cent instead of 4 per cent, the sample size required is reduced to $n = 9/.0256 = 352$, a sample only one-fourth as large as 1406.

It is important, therefore, to make D as large as can be tolerated, in order to avoid paying a very high price for results of greater precision than required.

One further point should be mentioned in connection with the calculation of the size of sample that is needed. Thus far we have dealt with the estimation of a single characteristic. Usually, however, one estimates many characteristics from the same sample, and the size of sample necessary to achieve the desired precision for one characteristic may be larger or smaller than the size of sample necessary to achieve the desired precision for others. This problem is ordinarily settled by taking a

---

* See Ch. 1, Sec. 13.

sample large enough that each of the most important characteristics is estimated with sufficient precision. Then, for the characteristics of secondary importance, one accepts whatever precision is attained. Some of the characteristics of secondary importance will be estimated with greater precision than the purposes of the survey require, whereas others will be estimated with less than the desired precision. In either case, the various results of the sample must be interpreted in the light of the precision actually attained.

12. Estimates of variances from the sample.   Equations 9.1, 9.2, and 9.3 give the variances of the sample estimates p, $\bar{x}$, x', and Eq. 11.2 and 11.3 show how these variances can be applied to determine the size of sample needed for a specified precision of results. The use of these formulas, however, requires a knowledge of certain population values. The variance of p, for example, can be computed with Eq. 9.1 if we know P, but P is the unknown value that we are trying to estimate. If P were known, we should not be trying to estimate it from a sample. Similarly, in computing the variance of $\bar{x}$ or x' with Eq. 9.2 or 9.3, we need to know S^2, the variance of the universe. In many instances S^2 may be known approximately from prior experience. As an estimate of S^2 from the sample itself, we can compute s^2, the variance of the sample observations, where s^2 is given by Eq. 3.12. To estimate the variance of $\bar{x}$ or x' we substitute s^2 for S^2 and have as our estimate, from Eq. 9.2,

$$s_{\bar{x}}^2 = (1-f)\frac{s^2}{n} \tag{12.1}$$

and from Eq. 9.3,

$$s_{x'}^2 = N^2(1-f)\frac{s^2}{n} = (1-f)\frac{ns^2}{f^2} \tag{12.2}$$

It turns out* that s^2 is an unbiased estimate of S^2, and therefore that Eq. 12.1 and 12.2 represent unbiased estimates of the variances of $\bar{x}$ and x'. Similarly,

$$v^2 = \frac{s^2}{\bar{x}^2} \tag{12.3}$$

is an estimate from the sample of V^2 (as given in Eq. 10.1), and this sample estimate may be substituted for V^2 in the equations that give the precision of sample estimates or the size of sample required. The estimate, v^2, is a consistent (although not unbiased) estimate of V^2, and for reasonably large samples the bias will be trivial.†

---

* For proof, see Vol. II, Ch. 4, Sec. 4.
† For proof, see Vol. II, Ch. 4, Sec. 15, 20, and 21.

Similar considerations apply to the estimate of the variance of p. We have already seen (Sec. 9) that, for a variate that takes on only the value 0 or 1, $S^2 = NPQ/(N-1)$. Similarly, it can readily be seen that $s^2 = npq/(n-1)$, and we can substitute $npq/(n-1)$ for $NPQ/(N-1)$ in Eq. 9.1 to obtain an unbiased estimate of the variance of p. Consequently, we have as our estimate of σ_p^2

$$s_p^2 = (1-f)\frac{pq}{n-1} \tag{12.4}$$

Equations 12.1, 12.2, and 12.4 will be good approximations provided the estimate of p or of s^2 is based on a sufficiently large sample. But how large must the sample be to allow us to rely upon the estimated variance when that variance is estimated from the sample? The answer to this question is different for different problems, although a very simple answer can be given for many of the problems that we encounter in our experience.

By now it should be clear to the reader that the variance estimated from the sample will vary from sample to sample, and the estimated variance, too, will have a standard deviation over all possible samples. Also, as with the sample mean, the coefficient of variation over all possible samples of the estimated variance provides a measure of the relative precision of the estimate from a particular sample.

We shall assume that the estimate of a standard deviation is sufficiently reliable if it has a coefficient of variation no greater than 10 or 15 per cent. This coefficient of variation is not to be confused with the precision required for the estimate of the mean or total. The precision that is required in an estimate of a standard deviation is, of course, a matter of personal preference, and it will depend on circumstances. As a working rule, we shall adopt 10 per cent, except where otherwise stated.

To illustrate how the variability in the estimate of the standard deviation will affect the sample size, let us suppose that, as in the illustration in Sec. 11, $D = .04$, $k = 3$, and $V = .5$. Suppose that we do not actually know $V = .5$, but that we estimate it with a coefficient of variation equal to 10 per cent. However, since the unknown $V = .5$, about 19 times in 20 we shall have the estimate v in the interval $.4 \leq v \leq .6$. Using Eq. 11.3 to determine the sample size, we find $900 \leq n \leq 2025$. If now V is actually equal to .5, then $n = 900$ will lead to a value of $D = .05$, and $n = 2025$ will lead to $D = .033$, so that the precision obtained will lie in the range $.033 \leq D \leq .05$, the limits corresponding to sample sizes of 2025 and 900, respectively, instead of being exactly equal to .04, as specified above. Thus, such a variation in the advance estimate of V may lead to somewhat greater precision (and higher cost) than necessary, or to lower precision than desired, or may necessitate a further sampling operation to increase the sample size if the accuracy actually achieved is deemed not sufficient.

Some simple rules for determining size of sample needed for reliable estimate of variance.   If a simple random sample is to be drawn from an original universe that is approximated by the normal distribution, then 50 observations are enough to yield a reasonably reliable estimate of the standard error of a mean or total.   Simple approximate rules are also available if we are estimating, from a simple random sample of elementary units, the proportion of the elements or the total number of elements in the population having a specified characteristic.   These rules are as follows:*

Rule I.   If p, the sample proportion, is between 30 per cent and 70 per cent, and if the denominator on which the percentage is based is 60 or more, then the coefficient of variation, V_s, of the estimated standard error will be less than 10 per cent.

Rule II.   Whether or not p or q is less than 30 per cent, if *both* np and nq are greater than 35, then, again, the V_s will be less than 10 per cent.

The two rules cover much actual practice.   Cases not covered by these rules will require the worker to turn to the theory of confidence intervals referred to in Sec. 13.

Illustration 12.1.   Precision of the estimate of the standard error of a proportion.   Suppose that we want to estimate the proportion of the families having incomes in each of the income groups shown in Table 2, and that a simple random sample of 200 families has been drawn from a

Table 2.   Family income—hypothetical example

Income group (dollars)	Number in sample	Per cent of families as estimated from sample
Under 500	68	34
500–1499	72	36
1500–2999	40	20
3000 and over	20	10
Totals	200	100

* For proof, see Vol. II, Ch. 4, Sec. 8 and 9.

population of 2000. The results of this sample are summarized in Table 2.

First, suppose that we wish to estimate the proportion of families having incomes under $500 and also the standard error of this estimate. The estimated proportion is 68/200 = .34 or 34 per cent. The estimated standard error of this proportion (from Eq. 12.4) is

$$s_p = \sqrt{(.9)\frac{(.34)(.66)}{200-1}} = 3.2 \text{ percentage points}$$

Because the numerator (68) of the proportion 68/200 is greater than 35, and also because the denominator minus the numerator (200 − 68 = 132) is greater than 35, the estimated standard error can be used with confidence, according to Rule II given above. For similar reasons the percentage estimated to have incomes between $1500 and $3000 also has an estimated standard error that can be used with confidence. On the other hand, the precision of the estimated percentage receiving $3000 or more income will not be estimated so reliably.

Moreover, we cannot get from the sample a reliable measure of the precision of the proportion estimated to earn less than $3000, even though there are more than 35 persons in the sample in this group. The percentage in this group (90 per cent) is not between 30 per cent and 70 per cent, and the denominator minus the numerator of the proportion is less than 35, so that neither Rule I nor Rule II applies.

Now, among the families having $1500 or more income, suppose that we wish to estimate the proportion which received more than $3000 income, and wish to estimate the standard error of this estimate. The estimated proportion is 20/60 = 33 per cent, which is between 30 and 70 per cent. Also, the denominator is 60, so that Rule I is met, and, therefore, our estimated standard error can be used with confidence.

Exercise 12.1. The occupancy and tenure of dwelling units in a certain city are estimated by a sample of 160 dwelling units as follows:

OCCUPANCY AND TENURE	NUMBER IN SAMPLE	PER CENT OF DWELLING UNITS AS ESTIMATED FROM THE SAMPLE
(1)	(2)	(3)
All dwelling units	160	100
Owner-occupied	48	30
Tenant-occupied	104	65
Vacant	8	5

Assume that the population is large enough that the finite multiplier can be neglected.   What is the standard error, as computed from the sample, of each of the percentages in column 3?   Which standard errors can be used with confidence?

Precision of the estimate of the standard error for estimates other than proportions.   If the variate being measured for each elementary unit takes on values other than 1 or 0, the problem is more difficult, unless the variate is approximately normally distributed; a great many populations to be sampled will have far from normal distributions.

If we are sampling from a population that has no extremely large or small items, a sample of 100 will be sufficient to provide a reliable estimate of the standard deviation, even if the original distribution does not approximate the normal distribution.   On the other hand, with populations having some very extreme items (a small proportion of them but a higher proportion than would be expected with the normal distribution), much larger samples may be required in order to get reliable measures of precision from the sample itself.   In practice, however, when the population has some exceedingly extreme items, it is desirable *not* to use simple random sampling, and ordinarily one finds it possible to avoid that method.   Instead, as will be indicated in detail in Chapter 5, it may be possible to take advantage of the large differences between the very extreme items and the remainder of the population, to increase the precision of the results much beyond that which could be achieved with simple random sampling from such a population.

A reasonable question to ask at this point is: How do we know the kind of population from which we are sampling?   The evidence concerning extreme items provided by the sample itself, unless the sample is very large, may not be sufficient to indicate the nature of this population and the probable reliability of our estimates of precision from a sample of a given size.   Consequently we may not know the approximate size of sample necessary to make reasonably accurate measures of precision from the sample itself.   In sampling for a percentage or a total number in the population having a specified characteristic, there is no problem.   As long as we are dealing with percentages, the rules given earlier hold for any kind of population, so long as the elementary unit whose characteristic is being measured is the sampling unit and so long as simple random sampling is used.   For other characteristics, however, the answer is not so simple, and one must depend on prior knowledge and other investigations as to the nature of the population being sampled.   For large samples (say 500 or more) it is necessary to have only a very general knowledge that the population is not extremely skewed or otherwise peculiar.

Coefficient of variation of the sample estimate of the standard deviation.

The relative precision (coefficient of variation) of the estimated standard deviation, s_X, with simple random sampling is given approximately by*

$$V_s \doteq \sqrt{\frac{\beta - 1}{4n}} \qquad (12.5)$$

or, if n is very small or if β is close to 1, a better approximation is

$$V_s \doteq \sqrt{\frac{\beta - \dfrac{n - 3}{n - 1}}{4n}} \qquad (12.6)$$

where n is the size of sample,

$$\beta = \frac{\mu_4}{\sigma^4}, \quad \text{and} \quad \mu_4 = \frac{\sum\limits^{N} (X_i - \bar{X})^4}{N} \qquad (12.7)$$

is referred to as the fourth moment about the mean.†

We can use Eq. 12.5 to ascertain the relative precision of s, if we know the approximate value of β. Conversely, if β is known approximately, we can solve Eq. 12.5 for n to ascertain the size of sample necessary to achieve any specified precision in our estimate of S. Solving for n, we have

$$n \doteq \frac{\beta - 1}{4V_s^2} \qquad (12.8)$$

for the size of sample necessary in order to estimate the standard deviation from the sample with a coefficient of variation of V_s. Now, if we adopt the standard, mentioned earlier, that we will regard s as a reliable estimate of S if we have a coefficient of variation of no more than 10 per cent, we substitute $V_s^2 = .01$ in the above equation to obtain

$$n \doteq \frac{\beta - 1}{.04} \qquad (12.9)$$

For the normal distribution β is equal to 3, and we can now examine the basis for the statement made earlier that a sample of 50 or more is

---

* The formula assumes a population large relative to sample size, or sampling with replacement, and is a good approximation for sizes of sample such that V_s is less than .15; i.e., V_{s^2} is less than .30. Limits of sampling variation for $s_{\bar{x}}$ can be obtained by the method given in Sec. 7, Ch. 4, Vol. II. For sampling from a finite population, where a large proportion of the population is included in the sample, this formula will overstate the sampling error. Section 5, Ch. 4, Vol. II, gives the formula for the rel-variance of s^2, for sampling without replacement. For proofs see Vol. II, Ch. 4, Sec. 6 and 7.

† β is the well-known Pearson measure of kurtosis or peakedness.

adequate to provide a reliable measure of reliability from the sample itself.   If we are doing simple random sampling from a normal distribution, we have $n = (3 - 1)/.04 = 50$.

Formula 12.9 does not provide a good approximation for distributions if β is much less than 3, but for these distributions a size of sample of less than 50 is sufficient to provide a reliable estimate of the standard deviation. For distributions that have a higher proportion of very extreme values than the normal distribution, β will be found to take on large values.

We see from formula 12.9 that, as β increases, the size of sample necessary to be able to place confidence in our standard deviation estimated from the sample will increase.   Thus, for a 10 per cent coefficient of variation in the estimated standard deviation (from Eq. 12.9), the following sizes of sample are needed for the indicated values of β:

$$\beta = 6, \qquad n = 125$$
$$\beta = 11, \qquad n = 250$$
$$\beta = 41, \qquad n = 1000$$
$$\beta = 101, \qquad n = 2500$$

Populations with values of β as high as those shown are not unusual. One frequently encounters populations with very large values for β, but for many of these it is particularly inefficient to use simple random sampling or a method that is substantially equivalent.   For many such populations one can find alternative and more efficient sampling methods (discussed in Chapter 5).

13. Exact confidence limits for sample estimates.   We have discussed the interpretation of the precision of an estimate in terms of its standard error, and the procedure for estimating from a sample the standard error of an estimated mean, total, or percentage.   With respect to the interpretation of the standard error, we have indicated that, if an estimate is normally distributed and if its standard error is known, then one can obtain precisely the probability that the estimate will be subject to errors of more than any specified multiple of its estimated standard error.   But there are two reasons in the types of problems with which we shall deal why such probability statements will not be exact.   The first reason is that the sample estimate, although it may be distributed approximately according to the normal distribution, may not be exactly so; the probabilities will consequently be approximate.   The second reason is that we do not ordinarily know the standard error of our estimate exactly but must estimate the standard error itself from the sample.

Although the probabilities are not exact for the methods of setting limits of sampling variability that we have given, we believe that they will be reasonably close for most practical purposes whenever the sample is large enough that V_s is less than 10 per cent.

Methods exist for setting "confidence limits," which may be used under certain circumstances for computing limits of sampling error, and with which it is possible to make exact probability statements. Confidence limits are ranges of sampling variability which can be computed under certain circumstances from the sample itself and for which exact probabilities can be associated with the statement that the upper and lower confidence limits will include the true value being estimated. Such probabilities will be exact when one is using simple random sampling from a normal distribution, or for a variate that takes on only the value 1 or 0,* or from certain other distributions. [See, for example, Deming (1), Chapters 9 and 16, and S. S. Wilks, *Elementary Statistical Analysis*, Princeton University Press, 1949.] Confidence limits cannot be computed with exact probabilities for sampling in general from populations of unknown distribution.

We shall not discuss here the use of confidence limits because they are presented in other literature and because we are not ordinarily sampling from a normal distribution or even from a known type of distribution other than where the variate has only the value 0 or 1.

When a simple random sample is used with a variate that takes on only values 0 and 1, the treatment in Sec. 12 is adequate provided the conditions on precision indicated in the rules given are met. When these conditions are not met, available tables will provide more accurate limits of sampling errors.†

14. Some illustrative populations. We shall now examine a few populations that have been encountered in actual sampling work in order to illustrate for different types of populations the sizes of sample necessary, with simple random sampling, to achieve results of a given precision in estimating the standard deviation as well as in estimating means, totals, or percentages.

In 1944 the Bureau of the Census estimated the total population of

---

* A variate having the value 0 or 1, when the sampling is simple random sampling with replacement, yields the binomial (or Bernoulli) distribution. When the sampling is *without* replacement, the distribution of sample values (means or totals) will be approximately binomial unless the sample size, n, is large relative to the size of the population, N. When both N and n are very large, with n small relative to N, the distributions of means and totals approach normal distributions.

† See, for example, National Bureau of Standards, Applied Mathematical Series 6, *Tables of the Binomial Probability Distribution*, U.S. Government Printing Office, Washington, D.C., 1950.

each of certain designated cities from a sample.*   Each of the cities had had a very large influx of population since the most recent census. To obtain the estimate, a list of the dwelling places was made in each of the designated cities, a sample of dwelling places was taken, and the people in these sample dwelling places were enumerated. The estimated total population of an area was then obtained by computing the average number of persons per dwelling place from the sample and multiplying this average by the known total number of dwelling places in the area. We shall not review here how the sample was drawn or how a dwelling place was defined except to say, first, that the sampling method in some of the cities was approximately equivalent to simple random sampling, and, second, that a dwelling place was usually an entire structure provided the structure did not appear to contain four or more families. It will be useful to examine the distribution of dwelling places by number of persons for one of these cities, and to compute the size of sample needed to achieve estimates of specified precision from the sample.

Table 3 and Fig. 1 show the distribution of the population in dwelling places in the city of Charleston, S.C.†   The reader will do well to examine carefully Fig. 1 along with the other figures and tables that follow in order to perceive the consequences of doing unrestricted random sampling from populations such as these, and to appreciate that different types of populations may call for varying treatment.

Computations from the data in Table 3 show that for Charleston the coefficient of variation of the distribution of persons per dwelling place was .73.   With this information, and with the further knowledge that the total number of dwelling places in the Charleston area was about 20,000, we can readily ascertain the size of sample necessary to achieve any specified precision in our estimate of the average population per dwelling place. Suppose, for example, that we wish to estimate the population with a coefficient of variation of 4 per cent. From Eq. 11.2, with $V^2 = .73^2 = .533$, $D = .04$, and $k = 1$, we have

$$n = \frac{(20,000)(.533)}{(20,000)(.0016) + .533} = 328 \qquad (14.1)$$

Thus, a sample of approximately 330 dwelling places is required.

---

* Reported in *A Chapter in Population Sampling*, Sampling Staff, U.S. Bureau of the Census, U.S. Government Printing Office, Washington, D.C., 1947.

† Actually the information here summarized is based on a sample of dwelling places from the city of Charleston, but for our purpose it is just as well to regard it as representing precisely the total population; i.e., we want to consider the sampling problems for a population that is described by the distribution shown in Fig. 1.

Table 3. Number of persons per dwelling place in city of Charleston, S.C.: 1944

Number of persons per dwelling place X_i	Per cent of dwelling places having X_i inhabitants	Number of persons per dwelling place X_i	Per cent of dwelling places having X_i inhabitants
0	.8	10	1.9
1	7.7	11	3.8
2	13.1	12	2.7
3	12.3	13	1.2
4	15.4	14	1.5
5	11.5	15	2.7
6	9.2	18	.4
7	6.9	21	.8
8	3.1	23	.4
9	4.2	24	.4

Source: A sample of 260 blocks from the *Survey of Congested Production Areas of 1944*, conducted by the U.S. Bureau of the Census at the request of the Committee for Congested Production Areas.

$$\bar{X} = 5.69$$
$$\sigma = 4.15$$
$$V = .73$$
$$\beta = 5.94$$

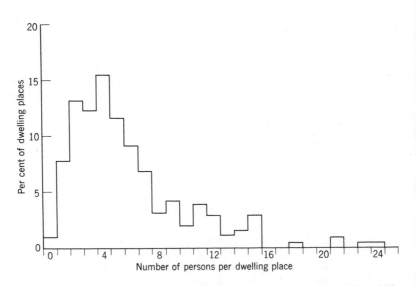

FIG. 1. Number of persons per dwelling place in city of Charleston, S.C.: 1944.

Now, if we are sampling from such a population, and if we use a sample of 330 dwelling places, how much reliance can we place on the standard error of our sample estimate when the standard error is computed from the sample itself?   Computations based on Table 3 show that β is equal to 5.94.   Substituting this value into Eq. 12.5, we have

$$V_s = \sqrt{\frac{5.94 - 1}{4(330)}} = .06 \text{ or 6 per cent} \tag{14.2}$$

In other words, from a sample of approximately 330 dwelling places we not only shall have achieved the required accuracy in the estimated total population or estimated average population per dwelling place, but also shall have evaluated accurately the precision of our sample estimate from the sample returns themselves, because the coefficient of variation of the estimated standard deviation would be only 6 per cent.   This would be more than sufficient accuracy if we accept the suggestion made earlier that for most problems a 10 per cent coefficient of variation in our estimate of the standard error is small enough.

Of course, in advance of planning a sample, we would not ordinarily know the value of V or of β or the exact nature of the distribution from which we are sampling.   If the distribution of the population per dwelling place were known, we would not even need the sample, because we should then know also the average size of dwelling place.   However, we may know from prior experience and from preliminary investigation that the population is distributed roughly as shown in Table 3 and Fig. 1, and from such knowledge we would be able to infer that the coefficient of variation is in the neighborhood of perhaps .6–.9 and that β is in the neighborhood of 5–10.   Such information may be adequate for designing a sample by which to estimate the population per dwelling place.

Thus, rough approximations often provide a useful and accurate guide for fixing a suitable sample design and the size of sample required.   The sample itself will then provide objective estimates of the population per dwelling place or of the aggregate population of the area or of whatever characteristics are desired, as well as of the precision of these estimates, and will indicate whether there is a need for increasing the size of the sample.

It is of interest to examine what modifications in the illustrative distribution of the population per dwelling place already shown would have led to marked changes in the coefficient of variation and β.   This type of examination provides a guide in speculating on the possible range in magnitude of the coefficient of variation or of β.   A sample estimate is sensitive to the relative magnitude and frequency of extreme items, so let us see how a change in these might affect the coefficient of variation and β.

Suppose, for example, that the actual distribution is as shown in Table 3 except that about 4 out of 1000 dwelling places contained 40 people each. Then the coefficient of variation would increase from .73 to .8, and β would increase from 5.94 to 15. Thus, changes in the frequencies of extreme items can have a substantial effect on the precision of the estimate of the variance. Yet, with this modification, the sample of 330 dwelling places would have a precision of about $4\frac{1}{2}$ per cent, which is not far from the 4 per cent precision aimed at, and the estimated variance would still be of acceptable precision—10 per cent.

It is interesting to note that, even with $V = .73$, $\beta = 15$, and a sample of only $n = 150$, the precision of the estimate of total population is 6 per cent and the precision of the estimated standard error is 15 per cent, which are still accurate enough for many purposes.

From the above remarks, it is clear that moderate errors in original assumptions concerning the nature of the population from which a sample is to be drawn will not lead to serious difficulties in specifying the size of sample required. It hardly needs pointing out, though, that *without* reasonable care in these original speculations one can easily be led into very serious errors in the sample design or in the size of sample required, and in the final conclusions from the sample.

The effect of more extreme variations in the distribution of the population being sampled will be indicated in the further examples that follow. These examples illustrate some of the other types of populations that have been encountered in practical sample surveys.

Figures 2–7 show* (a) the distribution of blocks in Los Angeles by number of dwelling units in 1940; (b) the distribution of farms in the United States by size (in acres) in 1940; (c) the distribution of sales of retail trade establishments in the United States in 1939; (d) the family income distribution of the population of Atlanta, Ga., in 1933; (e) the age distribution of the population of the United States in 1940; and (f) the distribution of weights of bales of cotton in Marshall County, Ala., for 1945. Let us examine these distributions from the point of view of drawing simple random samples from each.

The distribution of blocks by size in the city of Los Angeles, Table 4 and Fig. 2, shows the effect of a somewhat more extreme tail on a distribution than that for the distribution of dwelling places in Charleston. The use of a simple random sample from this population to estimate total dwellings in the city or average dwellings per block would call for rather

---

* Tables 4-9 show the data on which the figures are based. The values $\bar{X}$, σ, V, and β were computed with smaller intervals, in some cases, than are shown in the tables, and consequently they will differ somewhat from the results obtained by computing with the data shown.

Table 4.   Number of dwelling units per block in city of Los Angeles: 1940

Number of dwelling units per block X_i	Per cent of blocks having X_i dwelling units	Number of dwelling units per block X_i	Per cent of blocks having X_i dwelling units
0– 4	25.44	70– 79	2.04
5– 9	9.52	80– 89	1.73
10–14	8.60	90– 99	1.29
15–19	7.76	100–149	2.95
20–24	7.62	150–199	.86
25–29	7.01	200–249	.36
30–39	10.66	250–299	.16
40–49	6.42	300–399	.11
50–59	4.47	400+	.05
60–69	2.95		

Source: A sample of blocks from U.S. Bureau of the Census, *Census of Population and Housing: 1940*, Supplement to the First Series Housing Bulletin for California, Los Angeles Block Statistics.

$$\bar{X} = 29.0$$
$$\sigma = 37.9$$
$$V = 1.3$$
$$\beta = 26.5$$

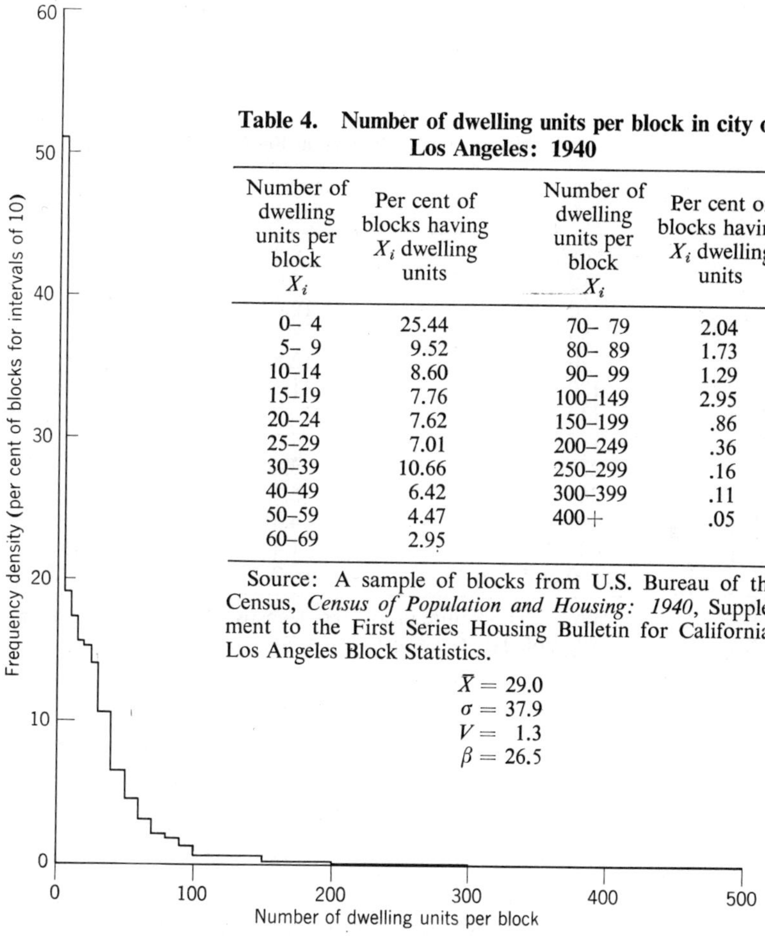

FIG. 2.   Number of dwelling units per block in city of Los Angeles: 1940.

Table 5.   Farms by size in the United States: 1940

Size of farm (acres)	Per cent of farms	Per cent of total acreage
Under 10	8.3	.3
10– 29	16.6	1.7
30– 49	12.6	2.8
50– 69	8.4	2.8
70– 99	12.8	6.0
100– 139	11.3	7.5
140– 179	10.2	9.2
180– 219	4.6	5.2
220– 259	3.4	4.6
260– 379	5.3	9.5
380– 999	4.9	16.1
1000–4999	1.4	15.4
5000 and over	.2	18.9

Source: U.S. Bureau of the Census, *Census of Agriculture: 1940*, Vol. III, *General Information.*

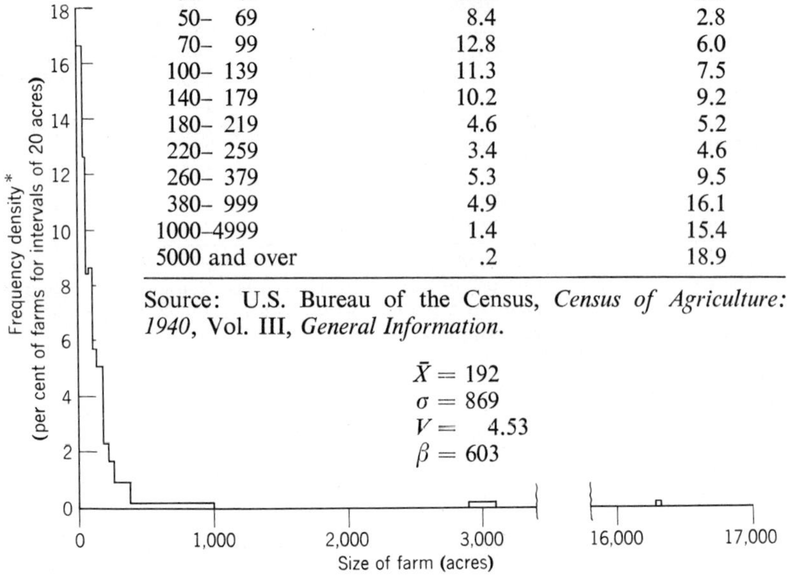

$$\bar{X} = 192$$
$$\sigma = 869$$
$$V = \quad 4.53$$
$$\beta = 603$$

FIG. 3.   Farms by size in the United States: 1940.

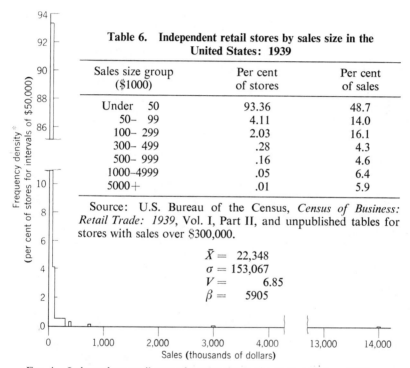

Table 6.   Independent retail stores by sales size in the United States: 1939

Sales size group ($1000)	Per cent of stores	Per cent of sales
Under 50	93.36	48.7
50– 99	4.11	14.0
100– 299	2.03	16.1
300– 499	.28	4.3
500– 999	.16	4.6
1000–4999	.05	6.4
5000+	.01	5.9

Source: U.S. Bureau of the Census, *Census of Business: Retail Trade: 1939*, Vol. I, Part II, and unpublished tables for stores with sales over $300,000.

$$\bar{X} = \ \ 22{,}348$$
$$\sigma = 153{,}067$$
$$V = \ \ \ \ \ \ 6.85$$
$$\beta = \ \ \ 5905$$

Frequency density *
(per cent of stores for intervals of $50,000)

Sales (thousands of dollars)

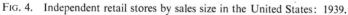

FIG. 4.   Independent retail stores by sales size in the United States: 1939.

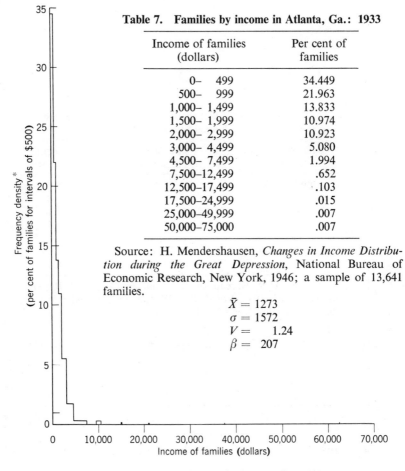

Table 7.   Families by income in Atlanta, Ga.: 1933

Income of families (dollars)	Per cent of families
0– 499	34.449
500– 999	21.963
1,000– 1,499	13.833
1,500– 1,999	10.974
2,000– 2,999	10.923
3,000– 4,499	5.080
4,500– 7,499	1.994
7,500–12,499	.652
12,500–17,499	.103
17,500–24,999	.015
25,000–49,999	.007
50,000–75,000	.007

Source: H. Mendershausen, *Changes in Income Distribution during the Great Depression*, National Bureau of Economic Research, New York, 1946; a sample of 13,641 families.

$$\bar{X} = 1273$$
$$\sigma = 1572$$
$$V = 1.24$$
$$\beta = 207$$

(Vertical axis label) Frequency density* (per cent of families for intervals of $500)

(Horizontal axis label) Income of families (dollars)

FIG. 5.   Families by income in Atlanta, Ga.: 1933.

Table 8.   Population of the United States by age: 1940

Age of the population (years)	Per cent of persons in given age group	Age of the population (years)	Per cent of persons in given age group
Under 1	1.53	50–54	5.51
1– 4	6.47	55–59	4.44
5– 9	8.12	60–64	3.59
10–14	8.92	65–69	2.89
15–19	9.37	70–74	1.95
20–24	8.80	75–79	1.14
25–29	8.43	80–84	.59
30–34	7.78	85–89	.21
35–39	7.25	90–94	.05
40–44	6.68	95+	.01
45–49	6.27		

Source: U.S. Bureau of the Census, *Census of Population: 1940*, Vol. IV, Part I, *Characteristics by Age*.

$$\bar{X} = 31.6$$
$$\sigma = 20.2$$
$$V = .64$$
$$\beta = 2.37$$

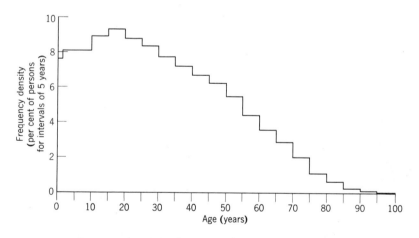

FIG. 6.   Population of the United States by age: 1940.

Table 9.   Cotton bales by weight in Marshall County, Ala.: 1945

Weight of bales (pounds)	Per cent of bales	Weight of bales (pounds)	Per cent of bales
Under 390	.13	520–529	14.79
390–399	.13	530–539	12.01
400–409	.20	540–549	9.12
410–419	.10	550–559	6.07
420–429	.30	560–569	3.89
430–439	.34	570–579	2.35
440–449	.57	580–589	1.34
450–459	1.04	590–599	.47
460–469	1.61	600–609	.34
470–479	2.98	610–619	.23
480–489	5.50	620–629	.20
490–499	7.41	630–639	.13
500–509	13.18	640–649	.07
510–519	15.39	650 and over	.10

Source: Sample of 2982 Bales of Cotton, Marshall County, Alabama, from U.S. Bureau of the Census (unpublished report on cotton ginned before November 1, 1945).

$$\bar{X} = 521$$
$$\sigma = 31.4$$
$$V = .060$$
$$\beta = 5.38$$

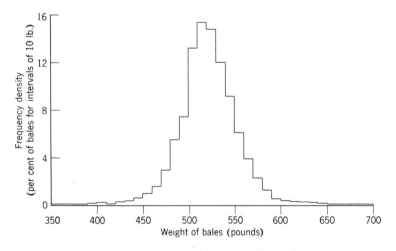

FIG. 7.   Cotton bales by weight in Marshall County, Ala.: 1945.

large samples, if any reasonably high degree of precision were wanted in estimating the total. Moreover, samples of more than 600 would be required to yield reliable estimates of the standard deviation from the sample. These results suggest that it would be desirable to use a method of sampling other than unrestricted random sampling of blocks if one wanted to make a simple unbiased estimate of the total number of dwelling units in the city.

From Fig. 3 and 4, we see that for the distributions both of size of farm and of retail sales there is an exceedingly heavy concentration of small establishments and then a very, very long tail in the distribution. The large establishments are tremendously large in comparison with the small ones. There are only a few of them, but they account for a substantial part of total acres or total sales. In the case of farms, for example, farms of 1000 acres or more constitute only 1.6 per cent of all farms but account for more than a third of all land in farms; and the situation with retail trade is even more striking. The consequence is a very large coefficient of variation for each of these distributions. In using a simple random sample from such distributions, exceedingly large samples would be required to achieve reasonably reliable estimates of average size of farm or of average sales per establishment or of the corresponding totals. The figures show more clearly than do the tables that the distributions are exceedingly skewed with a high proportion of the farms or establishments in the small size groups and a small proportion of exceedingly large ones.

Not only is the coefficient of variation very large for these distributions, but also β is so large that, with simple random sampling, large samples would have to be used to obtain a reliable estimate of the standard deviation. In sampling from the farm distribution, the average number of acres per farm estimated from a simple random sample of 1000 farms would have a coefficient of variation of about 14 per cent. Further, if we estimated the standard deviation from the sample, it would have a coefficient of variation of nearly 40 per cent. It is clear that one would hardly be able to place any reliance at all in such an estimate, even with a sample as large as a thousand.

The distribution of retail sales is still more extreme if one is considering using simple random sampling. The coefficient of variation of the estimated total sales, estimated from a simple random sample of 1000 establishments, would be greater than 20 per cent, and the coefficient of variation of the estimated standard deviation of this estimate would be more than 100 per cent.

These results are rather striking, but perhaps not unusual. Such types of distributions are often encountered in dealing with economic data. Actually, the use of simple random sampling from such distributions gives results that might have been anticipated. The proper approach to follow (as we shall see in Chapter 5) with such distributions is to make special provision for sampling the extreme elements of the population.

The situation involved in the family income distribution shown in Fig. 5 is only slightly different. Here it turns out that the 2.5 per cent of the families which have the highest incomes receive about 15 per cent of the total income. The extreme incomes shown in the long tail of the distribution have a marked effect in considerably increasing the variance of the estimate. However, this is somewhat less serious than the case of the retail sales or size of farm distribution.

In this instance, a simple random sample of about a thousand families is required to provide an estimate of aggregate or average income with a coefficient of variation of 4 per cent. For a sample of 1000, the coefficient of variation of the estimated standard deviation is greater than 20 per cent. Thus, this estimate of the standard deviation is still too unreliable to be satisfactory for measuring precision. One would need a simple random sample of between 4500 and 5500 families in order to have what we have agreed to regard as an accurate estimate of precision from the sample itself. In this instance, too, the error can be reduced considerably by avoiding unrestricted random sampling or a method that approximates it.

The age distribution of the population and the distribution of weights of bales of cotton, shown in Fig. 6 and 7, provide a very different picture. Both these distributions lack the unusually extreme items present in the distributions just described. For the two populations now under consideration, as for the distribution of persons per dwelling place first introduced, simple random sampling may or may not be the most efficient sampling method, depending upon the resources available for designing the sample. In any event, samples of moderate size will lead to sound conclusions regarding the precision of the sample estimates made from the sample and will provide reasonably reliable estimates of means and totals. In both these instances samples of 50–100 will be quite adequate for evaluating precision from the sample results alone.

We cannot infer from the fact that a distribution is skewed that it will have a high value of β, and thus that a small sample will necessarily give poor estimates of means or standard deviations. Nevertheless, in practice it is often found that difficulties with simple random sampling are associated with badly skewed distributions (with a long tail of extreme values). Finally, although simple random sampling is very unsatisfactory for such distributions, methods of sampling are available that turn the peculiar nature of the distribution to advantage in improving the efficiency of the sample.

15. Computations for an illustration, with some supplemental remarks.
Let us now examine an illustrative sample survey of a city: Ashland,
Ohio. The sample for this illustration was drawn from 1940 Census of
Population schedules for Ashland. A 5 per cent simple random sample
of 498 adults (persons 14 years of age and over) was selected from the
population. The information for the members of the sample was obtained
from their 1940 census schedules.

We shall carry through at this point some computations that can be
made in order to estimate different items from the sample. We shall then
show the computations for estimating measures of precision (variances,
standard errors, and coefficients of variation) of the estimates.

The items for which we shall assume that estimates are wanted are
listed in Table 10. The figures shown in this table are the aggregate
values of the specified characteristics for the individuals in the sample.
The table contains the raw data needed from the sample to estimate the
desired averages or totals and their variances.

Table 10.   Raw data from a sample of the adult population of
Ashland, Ohio: April 1940

Item	Total	Male	Female
Number of persons	498	232	266
Number receiving wage and salary income	249	168	81
Total wage and salary income* (dollars)	242,717	204,724	37,993
Sum of squares (Σx_i^2)	380,418,813	354,742,266	25,676,547
Number receiving wage and salary income but less than $1000	141	63	78
Number having less than $50 income from sources other than wages or salaries	371	167	204
Number receiving wage and salary income but with less than $50 income from other sources	215	140	75
Total wage and salary income (dollars) of persons having less than $50 income from other sources*	191,049	156,320	34,729
Sum of squares (Σx_i^2)	254,509,813	231,102,762	23,407,051

*Excluding the wage and salary income in excess of $5000 received by any
individual.

Source: Data from a 5 per cent sample of returns in the 1940 Census of
Population.

The estimates computed from the data in Table 10 are given in Table 11. The estimated averages and percentages were computed by Eq. 3.4 or 3.8. The estimated total for a characteristic is equal to $1/f$ multiplied by the sample total for the characteristic (see Eq. 7.1 or 7.2). Thus, the estimated proportion of males in the adult population of Ashland is

$$p = \frac{\sum\limits_{i}^{n} x_i}{n} = \frac{232}{498} = .466$$

or 46.6 per cent, and the estimated total number of males is

$$x' = \frac{1}{f} \sum\limits_{i}^{n} x_i = 20(232) = 4640$$

Table 11.   Estimates of selected characteristics of the adult population of Ashland, Ohio

Based on data presented in Table 10

Item	Total	Male	Female
1. Number of persons	9960	4640	5320
2. Per cent of total persons	100.0	46.6	53.4
3. Total wage and salary income* (dollars)	4,854,000	4,094,000	760,000
4. Average wage and salary income (dollars) per adult person*	487	882	143
5. Average wage and salary income* (dollars) for those receiving wage or salary income	975	1219	469
6. Number receiving wage and salary income but less than $1000	2820	1260	1560
7. Per cent of those receiving wage and salary income with income less than $1000	56.6	37.5	96.3
8. Number having less than $50 income from sources other than wages or salaries	7420	3340	4080
9. Number receiving wage and salary income but with less than $50 income from other sources	4300	2800	1500
10. Total wage and salary income (dollars) of individuals having less than $50 income from other sources*	3,821,000	3,126,000	695,000
11. Average wage and salary income (dollars) of individuals receiving such income and having less than $50 income from other sources*	889	1117	463

* Excluding the wage and salary income in excess of $5000 received by any individual.

Table 12.   Estimated standard errors of the estimates given in Table 11

Item	Total	Male	Female
1. Number of persons	..	217	217
2. Per cent of total persons	..	2.2	2.2
3. Total wage and salary income (dollars)	316,000	321,000	93,000
4. Average wage and salary income (dollars) per adult person	32	56	17
5. Average wage and salary income (dollars) for those receiving wage or salary income	47	60	34*
6. Number receiving wage and salary income but less than $1000	196	145	158
7. Per cent of those receiving wage and salary income with income less than $1000	3.1	3.7	2.1*
8. Number having less than $50 income from sources other than wages or salaries	190	206	214
9. Number receiving wage and salary income but with less than $50 income from other sources	216	196	156
10. Total wage and salary income (dollars) of individuals having less than $50 income from other sources	263,000	263,000	89,000
11. Average wage and salary income (dollars) of individuals receiving such income and having less than $50 from other sources	42	53	35*

* Sample not large enough to give reliable estimates of the standard error for these items.

In Table 12 are given the estimated standard errors of each of the estimates given in Table 11.   We shall illustrate the computation of some of them.

(a) The estimated per cent male is 46.6, and the estimated standard error of this estimate is obtained by substituting in Eq. 12.4 (or substituting sample estimates in Eq. 9.1) to obtain

$$s_p = \sqrt{\frac{(1 - .05)(.466)(.534)}{497}}$$
$$= .022$$

Actually, in this illustration, the finite multiplier $(1 - f)$ is close enough to 1 so that for all practical purposes it could have been assumed to be equal to 1, and its effect ignored.   This holds for the computation of all the standard deviations shown in Table 12.

(b) The situation is slightly different in estimating the standard deviation of the proportion of a subgroup that has a characteristic.   Thus, the estimate of the proportion of the population receiving less than $1000 income, from the subgroup of those receiving wage or salary income, is .566.   But now, in applying Eq. 12.4, we must remember that the size of sample, n, is in this instance the number of persons in the sample who receive wage or salary income.   The estimate of the standard deviation of the proportion of persons with wage and salary income of less than $1000 is

$$s_p = \sqrt{(1-f)\frac{p_g q_g}{n-1}} = \sqrt{.95\frac{(.566)(.434)}{248}} = .031$$

where p_g is the proportion of the subgroup having the specified characteristic, and $q_g = 1 - p_g$.

To estimate the variance of a mean, $\bar{x}$, or total, x', where the characteristic takes on values other than 0 and 1, we need the terms indicated in

$$s^2 = \frac{\sum_{i}^{n}(x_i - \bar{x})^2}{n-1} = \frac{\sum_{i}^{n}x_i^2 - n\bar{x}^2}{n-1} \qquad (3.12)$$

Therefore, we need $\sum_{i}^{n}x_i^2$ from the sample for each such characteristic, and these values are also given in Table 10.

(c) For the average wage and salary income of the total adult population, as an example, we find from Table 10 that $n = 498$, $\bar{x} = 487$, and $\sum_{i}^{n}x_i^2 = 380{,}418{,}813$.   From Eq. 3.12,

$$s^2 = \frac{380{,}418{,}813 - 498(487)^2}{497} = 527{,}784$$

$$s_{\bar{x}} = \sqrt{(1-f)\frac{s^2}{n}} = \sqrt{.95\frac{527{,}784}{498}} = 32$$

(d) For an average of a subgroup the procedure is the same as was illustrated above for the proportion of a subgroup having a specified characteristic, except that $\sum_{i}^{n}x_i^2$ is now the sum of squares of the income or other characteristic of those individuals in the particular subgroup, and $\bar{x}$ is for the subgroup.   Thus, for estimating the standard deviation of the average income of males receiving wage or salary income:

$$n = 168, \quad \bar{x} = 1218.60, \quad \sum_{i}^{n}x_i^2 = 354{,}742{,}266$$

$$s^2 = \frac{\sum_{i}^{n}x_i^2 - n\bar{x}^2}{n-1} = \frac{354{,}742{,}266 - 168(1{,}484{,}986)}{167} = 630{,}327$$

and

$$s_{\bar{x}} = \sqrt{(1-f)\frac{s^2}{n}} = \sqrt{.95\frac{630,327}{168}} = 59.70$$

Here, n is the number of males in the sample who receive wage and salary income.   Note that

$$s = \sqrt{630,327} = 793.9$$

$$v = \frac{793.9}{1219} = .6513$$

and

$$v_{\bar{x}} = \frac{59.7}{1219} = .0490$$

Remark 1. The standard errors of estimated totals can be estimated from Eq. 12.2 (p. 129), or, if the estimated total is for a subgroup, Eq. 10.6 may be more convenient.   The estimate of the rel-variance for a total of a subgroup from Eq. 10.6 is obtained by substituting sample estimates for V_g^2, P, and Q in this equation, and the estimate of the variance is then equal to this result multiplied by x'^2.   We shall illustrate the estimation of the standard error of an estimated total of a subgroup with each formula. The advantages of using Eq. 10.6 were indicated in the remark in Sec. 10.

(e) To estimate the standard error of estimated total income for males, using Eq. 12.2, we have

$$n = 498, \quad \bar{x} = \frac{204,724}{498} = 411, \quad \overset{n}{\sum} x_i^2 = 354,742,266$$

$$s^2 = \frac{354,742,266 - 498(168,921)}{497} = 544,506$$

$$s_{\bar{x}} = \sqrt{.95\frac{544,506}{498}} = 32.23$$

and

$$s_{x'} = 9960(32.23) = 321,000$$

(f) To estimate the standard error of estimated total income for males, using Eq. 10.6, we shall assume that the subgroup refers to males receiving (wage and salary) income.   In this case from Table 10 we find that $n = 498$, $n_g = 168$.   From illustration d, we find that

$$v_g = .6513, \quad v_g^2 = .4242$$

$$p = \frac{168}{498} = .3373, \quad q = 1 - p = .6627$$

$$x' = 4{,}094{,}000$$

$$s_{x'} = x' \sqrt{(1-f)\frac{v_g^2 + q}{np}}$$

$$= 4{,}094{,}000 \sqrt{.95\left(\frac{.4242 + .6627}{168}\right)}$$

$$= 4{,}094{,}000(.0785) \doteq 321{,}000$$

Alternatively the estimate based on Eq. 10.6 can be stated in the form

$$x' \sqrt{v_{\bar{x}_g}^2 + (1-f)\frac{q}{pn}} = 4{,}094{,}000 \sqrt{.00240 + .00375} = 321{,}000$$

where $v_{\bar{x}_g}^2 = (1-f)v_g^2/pn = (.0490)^2$ from illustration d.

(g) Now, let us assume that the subgroup referred to is total males, instead of males receiving wage and salary income, as was the situation in f. In this case, n is still 498 but n_g is 232.

$$\bar{x}_g = \$882 \text{ from Table 11}$$

$$p = \frac{n_g}{n} = \frac{232}{498} = .4659$$

$$q = 1 - p = .5341$$

Then

$$s_g^2 = \frac{354{,}742{,}266 - \frac{(204{,}724)^2}{232}}{231} = 754{,}389$$

$$v_g^2 = \frac{s_g^2}{\bar{x}_g^2} = .9697$$

$$v_{x'} = \sqrt{(1-f)\frac{v_g^2 + q}{np}} = .0785$$

and

$$s_{x'} = x'v_{x'} = 321{,}000 \text{ as illustrated in } e \text{ and } f$$

(h) To estimate the standard error of estimated number of males receiving wage and salary income, but less than \$1000, using Eq. 12.2, we have

$$n = 498, \quad f = .05$$

$$p = 63/498 = .1265, \quad q = 1 - p = .8735$$

and from Eq. 12.2

$$s_{\bar{x}'}^2 = (1-f)\frac{ns^2}{f^2} = .95\,\frac{(498)(.1107)}{(.05)^2} = 20,956$$

or

$$s_{\bar{x}'} = 145$$

Remark 2. The reader should compute the standard errors shown in Table 12. He should then convert these to coefficients of variation, remembering that the coefficient of variation of each estimate is simply equal to the standard error of the estimate given in Table 12 divided by the corresponding estimated quantity given in Table 11.

Remark 3. If N_g for the particular subgroup under consideration were known in e, f, g, and h, above, then we could estimate the subgroup total with Eq. 7.1a instead of Eq. 7.1. The variance of the estimate based on Eq. 7.1a is smaller than that based on Eq. 7.1. In estimating the total with Eq. 7.1 we are, in effect, estimating both the proportion in the subgroup and the average value of the characteristic for the subgroup, whereas with Eq. 7.1a we are estimating only the average value for the subgroup. The comparison between Eq. 10.6 and 10.8 makes it possible to see the reduction in variance that results from making use of a known number in a subgroup. The reader should estimate both these variances for some of the items given in Tables 10, 11, and 12.

Exercises

15.1.   In a certain city a sample of 1000 households provides the following information on number of persons per household:

TENURE AND RACE	NUMBER OF HOUSEHOLDS n	NUMBER OF PERSONS $\sum x_i$	AVERAGE NUMBER OF PERSONS $\bar{x}$	$\sum x_i^2$
All households	1,000	3,323	3.32	15,318
White	766	2,442	3.19	10,380
Nonwhite	234	881	3.76	4,938
Owner-occupied				
White	350	1,177	3.36	5,138
Nonwhite	57	245	4.30	1,466
Tenant-occupied				
White	416	1,265	3.04	5,242
Nonwhite	177	636	3.59	3,472

If the sampling fraction used in selecting the sample was 1 in 16, what are the estimates from this sample of (*a*) the number of households in the city, (*b*) the number of white households, (*c*) the number of nonwhite households, (*d*) the number of owner-occupied households, etc.? What is the estimated total number of persons, number of persons in white households, number of persons in tenant-occupied households, etc.?

15.2.   Using the data in Ex. 15.1, estimate the per cent of dwelling units of white families that are owner-occupied; also the per cent of owner-occupied dwelling units that are occupied by white families.

15.3.   Find the standard deviations of the per cent of households in each category in Ex. 15.1, and also the standard deviations of the percentages in Ex. 15.2.

15.4.   Find the variances and standard deviations of the estimated average number of persons (a) in all households, (b) in white households, and (c) in nonwhite owner-occupied households.

15.5.   Compute the coefficients of variation for the estimates whose standard deviations were found in Ex. 15.3 and 15.4.

15.6.   Using the rules of Sec. 12, determine which of the standard deviations of the percentages in Ex. 15.1–15.3 are estimated reliably from the sample.   If the value of β for the distribution of family size is not more than 12, determine which of the standard deviations of the averages in Ex. 15.4 are estimated reliably (coefficient of variation less than 10 per cent) by the sample.

Remark 4.   Additional comments on above computations.   (1) In Table 12 the standard error of the per cent male as estimated from the sample is exactly the same as for the per cent female.   This will always be true of two proportions, p and q, where $p + q = 1$.   The maximum possible value of the standard error of p or q for any given size of sample occurs when $P = Q$, and the absolute standard error decreases for either larger or smaller values of either P or Q.   On the other hand, the relative precision of p and q may be quite different, since the relative coefficient of variation of p is σ_p/p $= \sqrt{Q/nP}$, whereas that of q is $\sqrt{P/nQ}$.   From this it is clear that the coefficient of variation, for a given size of sample, is smaller for large values of P than for smaller ones.   It is equal to $\sqrt{1/n}$ when $P = Q$.   When P becomes small, Q becomes close to 1, and it is a quite satisfactory approximation to take the relative error of the proportion or total as $\sqrt{1/nP}$. Thus, since $nP = x$, the frequency in the sample, the coefficient of variation of a percentage or total in a class which constitutes a small proportion of the total population under consideration is approximately equal to $\sqrt{1/x}$.

(2) Certain items in Table 12 are footnoted to indicate that for these items the sample is not large enough to yield a reasonably reliable estimate of the standard deviation.   Where the estimate to which the standard deviation relates is a simple percentage or the estimated total number of elements having a characteristic, the confidence in a reliable estimate of the standard deviation of the estimate is determined by applying the rules given in Sec. 12.   Where the estimate involved is an average or total of a characteristic that takes on values different from 1 or 0, the decision as to whether the estimated standard deviation is reliable is not so obvious.   It was indicated earlier that this decision depends on the distribution of the population from which the sample was drawn, and of course this distribution is not ordinarily known to us.   In this particular instance, however, the problem is not especially difficult because the incomes being considered are only the wage and salary incomes up to $5000.   Any incomes in excess of $5000 are recorded as incomes of $5000 in this anaylsis.   The reader can readily ascertain, by a little manipulation of reasonable alternatives, that, whatever shape the tail of this distribution may be, so long as incomes

in excess of $5000 are not allowed, the value of β is probably no greater than 5–10. If β is no larger than 10, then samples of 250 or more are adequate for this purpose. Smaller samples are subject to some question—but not too serious question unless the sample is less than 150.

(3) In carrying through computations we did not apply formula 3.12 as first written down, but manipulated it into a very commonly used and simple form. The reader should expect to do this in carrying through computations for most formulas that have been or will be presented. The particular form that is most convenient for computation depends upon whether one is computing by hand or with a calculating machine, slide rule, tabulating machine, computer, or other facilities, and we shall not attempt to present the most convenient form for actually carrying through computations of formulas but shall leave this step to the reader.

(4) All the formulas in this chapter have been presented for computing from ungrouped data instead of from frequency distributions. Where the original data are given by a frequency distribution, or where the amount of computation can be reduced by converting the data into frequency distributions, the modification of the formulas to make them applicable to frequency distributions is direct. Thus, wherever ΣX_i or $\Sigma (X_i - \bar{X})^2$ or any similar type of sum is shown for the original observations, the appropriate form for grouped data is obtained by thinking of each observation in a group as a separate observation. Thus, for a frequency distribution of two classes with a frequency of 4 in the first class and of 3 in the second, with X_1 the mean or midpoint of the first class, and X_2 the mean or midpoint of the second class, we would have

$$\sum^{7} X_i^2 = X_1^2 + X_1^2 + X_1^2 + X_1^2 + X_2^2 + X_2^2 + X_2^2$$

Thus, our sum contains X_1^2 4 times and X_2^2 3 times. We may therefore write $\sum^{7} X_i^2 = \sum^{2} N_i X_i^2$

More generally, we may write

$$\sum^{N} X_i^2 = \sum^{C} N_g X_g^2$$

where there are C classes or groups in the frequency distribution, and N_g is the number in the group, and X_g the midpoint or average value for the group. Then N is equal to $\sum^{C} N_g$ and

$$\bar{X} = \frac{\sum^{C} N_g X_g}{\sum^{C} N_g}$$

Also,

$$\frac{\sum^{N} (X_i - \bar{X})^2}{N} = \frac{\sum^{C} N_g (X_g - \bar{X})^2}{\sum^{C} N_g} ; \quad \frac{\sum^{N} (X_i - \bar{X})^4}{N} = \frac{\sum^{C} N_g (X_g - \bar{X})^4}{\sum^{C} N_g}$$

Similar modifications are called for in computing other values from the sample or for the population. The use of grouping in such computations will give satisfactory results provided the group intervals are not too large. Usually at least a dozen or more groups are desirable.

Exercises

15.7. According to the 1945 Census of Agriculture, there were in the United States 15,954 farms classified as "horticultural—specialty." These farms were distributed by value of farm products sold or used by the farm households as shown below.

VALUE (dollars)	NO. OF FARMS	MEAN VALUE OF FARM PRODUCTS SOLD (dollars)
Under 250	240	162
250– 399	547	318
400– 599	875	489
600– 999	1,243	768
1,000–1,499	1,203	1,193
1,500–2,499	1,726	1,931
2,500–3,999	1,666	3,131
4,000–5,999	1,668	4,856
6,000–9,999	1,804	7,620
10,000 and over	4,982	39,982

Compute the variance of the population of farms having less than $10,000 value of products, using the mean values of the classes.

Remark. Because of the large variability in value of products of farms over $10,000, the computation of the variance by the method of Ex. 15.7 for all farms would lead to an understatement of the variance, since the contribution due to the farms over $10,000 would not be well approximated by the mean value for these farms. Moreover, as will be seen in Chapter 5, simple random sampling of farms would be inefficient. Improved methods of sampling such a population will be discussed in that chapter.

15.8. What would be the variance of the estimated mean based on a simple random sample of 1000 farms drawn from the farms having less than $10,000 value of products?

C. SAMPLE ESTIMATES AND THEIR PRECISION— RATIOS OF RANDOM VARIABLES

16. Ratios of random variables. We now wish to consider estimates that involve the ratio of two random variables, i.e., ratios whose numerator and denominator are both subject to sampling errors. The need for such estimates arises frequently.

In some instances, the sample estimates, their variances, and the estimates of variances presented in the preceding sections are directly applicable, and no theory beyond that already presented is necessary. Ratios of random variables have already been introduced in the earlier sections of this chapter in estimating averages for subgroups. For example, in the illustration given earlier we computed the percentage of the male population that earned less than $1000 income. The numerator of this expression was the number of males earning less than $1000 income in a sample of n cases from the adult population. The denominator was the number of males in the sample. Thus, both the numerator and the denominator were subject to random sampling errors, since we had a random sample of the whole adult population. This ratio, then, was the ratio of two random variables. Its sampling variance could be computed as though it were a simple percentage, however, because the following three conditions were met:* (1) the sample was a simple random sample of elementary units; (2) the denominator of the ratio was the number of elementary units of a specified class in the sample; and (3) the numerator was the aggregate value of some characteristic for the units included in the denominator. Thus the theory in the earlier sections can be applied whenever we deal with the estimation of an average value per element for a subset of elements provided the elements are drawn with simple random sampling.

For many ratio estimates used in practice the conditions just stated are not met. For example, suppose that we have a simple random sample of n families and obtain information on the number of people in each family, by sex. If we compute the proportion of the total persons enumerated in the sample that are male, we again have a ratio of random variables. Both the total number of persons and the number of males in the sample depend on the particular set of n families that happens to be selected. In this instance, although the denominator is a count of the number of the people in the sample, these people are not a simple random sample of people, and therefore the formulas in the preceding sections cannot be used. This type of sampling is called *cluster sampling* and is considered in Chapters 6–9. As another illustration of a situation where the formulas of the previous sections do not apply, suppose that we estimate from our sample the ratio of aggregate rent to aggregate income. Here the denominator is a random variable and refers to a characteristic of a simple random sample, but the denominator is not the *size* of a simple random sample of elementary units.

We need now to develop formulas to evaluate the precision of such types of estimates. The formulas given later in this section apply to all types of ratios. They involve more computation than the formulas given in the preceding sections, and hence it is desirable to recognize the instances

---

* If we consider the average sampling error over all possible samples of size n, the answer is a little different, but the difference is of no importance if the expected number in the subgroup is not too small, or if we are evaluating the precision of an estimate from a particular sample. For proof, see Vol. II, Ch. 4, Sec. 17. See also Deming (1), pp. 449–454.

when the simpler computations of the last section are applicable.   The class of problems considered in the previous section occurs so frequently in practice that there may be considerable wasted effort if the more general formulas of this section are applied when the simpler formulas will give the same answers.   It may, however, be pointed out that, if it is not immediately apparent which formula should be used, the safer formulas are the more general ones, since the formulas in the preceding sections are special cases of those which follow.

A question that may arise in the reader's mind is: Why use estimates that involve the ratio of random variables?   At least a part of the answer should be fairly obvious.   As suggested earlier, if we want to find the proportion of the population that is male, or the proportion of family income that goes for rent, and if we have a simple random sample of families, the simplest estimate will be the ratio of the sample totals.   In fact, often we have no feasible alternative to the use of the ratio of random variables, as would be the case, for example, if we were estimating the ratio of rent to income and total income was not known from independent sources.

But even if we knew from independent sources the total that could be used in the denominator we might still wish to estimate the ratio from the sample.   Suppose, for example, that we consider the alternatives of estimating the ratio of rent to income (a) by computing the ratio of rent to income for the sample families, or (b) by estimating the total rent from the sample and dividing it by a known independent total income.   Which way should be prefer to estimate the ratio?

First, let us suppose that we estimate the percentage of income paid for rent by estimating the total rent from the sample and dividing this estimate by the known total income.   How reliable would this estimate be?   If the average rent paid by the sample of families is higher than the average for the whole population, the total rent bill estimated from this sample would be correspondingly high; and, if we divide this total by the known total income, we obtain an overestimate of the percentage of income paid for rent.   Conversely, if our sample happened to be too low in average rent, then we should expect our percentage estimated from the sample to be too low.

But, now, suppose that instead of estimating the ratio in this way we took the income from those families included in the sample as the denominator of the ratio and the rent paid by those families as the numerator. It is often true that there is a fairly high correlation between rent paid and family income, so that if we have families in our sample that pay above-average rentals we shall probably also have families with above-average incomes.   If the average rent bill is overestimated, the average income is likely to be overestimated also; and the ratio of the two, which is the proportion of income paid for rent, may be relatively much closer to the true figures.   Similarly, if the average rent in the sample is low, the average income is likely to be low also, and the percentage of income spent for rent may again be relatively much closer to the true ratio being estimated.   Thus, if there is a high correlation between rent and income, we may be able to do a good deal better in estimating the percentage of income that goes for rent if we compute the ratio from the sample, even though we know the total income from independent sources.

If, on the other hand, there is only a low correlation or no correlation between rent and income, this would not be true at all.   In this case, if we had a known independent figure for income we would want to use it in estimating the ratio because that estimate would be likely to be the more reliable one.   Often, however, we do not have the choice of employing known independent totals for our ratios; and we must use the data from the sample because independent information is not available. The purpose of these remarks is merely to give an intuitive basis for understanding how ratio estimates behave and how they might be utilized by choice in some instances even though it were not necessary to use a ratio of random variables.

If supplementary information is available for the denominator of the ratio, the investigator often has other alternatives that make effective use of this independent information, and that will yield results at least as good as or better than the simple ratio estimates discussed here.   Thus, other techniques of introducing supplementary information to increase the reliability of sample results include the use of regression or difference estimates (Ch. 11, Sec. 2), stratification (Ch. 5), and varying probabilities of selection (Ch. 8, Sec. 14).

17. Estimates of totals derived from estimates of ratios.   There is another application for a ratio estimate; this occurs where we are interested, not in the ratio itself, but rather in an estimated total.   Suppose, for example, that for a particular population we want, not an estimate of the percentage of income paid for rent, but rather an estimate of the total rent bill of the community.   One way we might estimate this total rent bill would be to compute the unbiased estimate of the total by the procedures already described earlier in this chapter (Sec. 7).   But now suppose that the total income of the population is known.   We are likely to get a more reliable estimate of the total rent in the community from a sample of a given size, if, instead of computing the simple unbiased estimate indicated earlier, we compute the ratio of rent to income for our sample of families and then apply this ratio to the known total income of the population. If there is a high correlation between rent and income, this total is likely to be estimated more accurately from a sample of a given size in this way than by multiplying the average rent from the sample by the known number of families (using Eq. 7.1).

There are other ways of estimating total rent for the population under consideration. For example, we might have for a recent earlier year a complete housing census with information on the rental value of each dwelling unit as well as the total of these rental values for the entire area.* Then, for the dwelling units in the sample, we could find the ratio of current rental value to rental value at the date of the census and apply this ratio to the total rental value of dwellings in the population of the previous census. If there were a very high correlation between rental value of a dwelling unit at the time of the census and rental value when the sample survey was being made, as might be expected, this latter estimate might be a more reliable one than a simple unbiased estimate (Eq. 7.1 or 7.1a).

There are many other illustrations of how ratio estimates and other special types of estimates may be introduced to improve estimates of totals. Some of these will be brought out in subsequent examples in this chapter.

Although such approaches often make it possible to improve the reliability of totals estimated from a sample, sometimes they may lead to a less reliable estimate of a total. As will be seen later, whether a ratio estimate will be more accurate depends in part on the correlation between the estimate of the numerator of the ratio and the estimate of the denominator and in part on the variability in the numerator as compared with that in the denominator.

18. Ratio estimates and their precision. Let us examine the ratio of two random variables more carefully, indicate how to evaluate its precision, and ascertain when we should use it in preference to the simple unbiased estimate given in Eq. 3.4 or 7.1.

Consider a population of N individuals or elementary units. Each unit in this population may have many different characteristics. We shall let X_i stand for one of the characteristics of the ith unit, and Y_i for another characteristic of that same unit. For example, X_i might be the rent paid by the ith family and Y_i the income of that family, or X_i might be the sales of a particular business establishment in one month and Y_i the sales

---

* We shall assume, for present purposes, that no dwellings were built or none destroyed during this period, to simplify the illustration, although with certain modifications in the sampling and estimating procedures one could avoid making these assumptions (as illustrated in Ch. 3, Sec. 6).

of the same establishment in a prior month.   If we assume as an illustration that X_i is the rental paid by the ith family and Y_i is the income of that same family, then:

$Y = \sum\limits^{N} Y_i$ is the total income of all families in the population under consideration.

$X = \sum\limits^{N} X_i$ is the total rent paid by all families in that population.

$R = X/Y$ is the proportion of income paid for rent in this population.

Since $X/Y = N\bar{X}/N\bar{Y} = \bar{X}/\bar{Y}$, R is the ratio either of the means or of the totals.   We shall assume that we want to estimate the characteristic X/Y from a sample of size n, i.e., from a sample of n families.   We can compute the ratio of rent to income in the sample as an estimate of this ratio in the population; thus:

$r = \bar{x}/\bar{y} = x/y$ is an estimate from the sample of R; where

$\bar{x}$ is the average rent paid by the families in the sample and is the estimate from the sample of the average rent paid. Similarly,

$\bar{y}$ is the average income of the families in the sample and is the estimate from the sample of the average income received.

We want to know something about the reliability of r as an estimate of R.

Although r is not an unbiased estimate of R, it is a consistent estimate, and with simple random sampling and a moderately large sample the bias of r will be negligible in relation to its standard error.*   Consequently, for most practical purposes one can and should ignore the bias.

The variance of r is approximately†

$$\sigma_r^2 \doteq R^2(1-f)\left(\frac{V_X^2 + V_Y^2 - 2\rho V_X V_Y}{n}\right) \qquad (18.1)$$

and the rel-variance of r is approximately

$$V_r^2 = \frac{\sigma_r^2}{R^2} \doteq (1-f)\left(\frac{V_X^2 + V_Y^2 - 2\rho V_X V_Y}{n}\right) \qquad (18.2)$$

where, as before, V_X (Eq. 10.1) and V_Y are the coefficients of variation of the X_i and Y_i, respectively, and

$$\rho = \frac{\sum\limits^{N}(X_i - \bar{X})(Y_i - \bar{Y})}{N\sigma_X\sigma_Y} = \frac{\sum\limits^{N}(X_i - \bar{X})(Y_i - \bar{Y})}{(N-1)S_X S_Y} \qquad (18.3)$$

* For proof, see Vol. II, Ch. 4, Sec. 15 and 21.
† For proof see Vol. II, Ch. 4, Sec. 13.

is the coefficient of correlation between the X_i and Y_i.

In applying the formula for the standard error or coefficient of variation of r there is no assumption that the average relationship between X_i and Y_i can be represented approximately by a straight line or that it has any other particular form. These formulas are good approximations, whatever the nature of the distributions of the original populations, provided large enough samples are used. However, for certain distributions larger samples may be required for the approximations to be good than for others. An approximate rule* as to what is a large enough sample for these relationships to hold with simple random sampling, for any kind of population, is that the sample be large enough that the coefficient of variation of $\bar{y}$, the denominator of the ratio, should be less than .05, i.e., that

$$V_{\bar{y}}^2 = (1-f)\frac{V_Y^2}{n}$$

should be less than $(.05)^2 = .0025$. If for the population under consideration $\rho \doteq V_Y/V_X$, then the approximations will be reasonably good if the coefficient of variation of $\bar{y}$ is less than .15. The condition that $\rho = V_Y/V_X$ will be approximately met whenever the average relationship between the X_i and Y_i, when plotted on a scatter chart, can be reasonably well represented by a straight line through the origin.

> **Remark.** The rel-variance of the ratio of two sample means is similar in form to the variance of the difference between two sample means. Thus, $\bar{x}$ has a variance of $\frac{S_X^2}{n}(1-f)$ and $\bar{y}$ has a variance of $\frac{S_Y^2}{n}(1-f)$; if the correlation between X_i and Y_i is equal to ρ, the variance of the difference between $\bar{x}$ and $\bar{y}$ is equal to
>
> $$\sigma_{\bar{x}-\bar{y}}^2 = (1-f)\left(\frac{S_X^2 + S_Y^2 - 2\rho\,S_X S_Y}{n}\right) \qquad (18.4)$$
>
> This is the same form as that for the rel-variance of the ratio of the sample means, except that here we have S_X and S_Y instead of V_X and V_Y.

If the correlation between X_i and Y_i is zero, then the rel-variance of the ratio becomes merely the sum of the rel-variances of the numerator and denominator. Thus, when there is no correlation, the coefficient of variation of a ratio of random variables will be larger than that of either the numerator or the denominator of the ratio; but when there is a high positive correlation it may be very much smaller.

Each of the above formulas 18.1–18.4 is based on the assumption that $\bar{x}$ and $\bar{y}$ are computed for an identical sample. This, of course, is not

* For proof, see Vol. II, Ch. 4, Sec. 12.

necessary—$\bar{x}$ might be computed from one sample of, say, size n, and $\bar{y}$ might be computed from an independent sample of, say, size m. Then we should have as the rel-variance of the ratio (ignoring the finite multipliers, although they could be readily introduced if the proportion of cases in the sample were large enough)

$$V_r^2 \doteq \frac{V_X^2}{n} + \frac{V_Y^2}{m} \qquad (18.5)$$

It is obvious that, if feasible, there is an advantage in using an identical sample for the estimate of the numerator and denominator of the ratio provided there is a positive correlation between X_i and Y_i.

The variance and rel-variance of the ratio $r = \bar{x}/\bar{y}$ can be stated in other forms that may be helpful in visualizing what the sampling error of a ratio of means or totals may be when sampled from various kinds of populations. It is easily shown that

$$R^2(V_X^2 + V_Y^2 - 2\rho V_X V_Y) = \frac{\sum\limits_{i}^{N} Y_i^2(R_i - R)^2}{(N-1)\bar{Y}^2}, \quad \text{where } R_i = \frac{X_i}{Y_i} \quad (18.6)$$

and also

$$= \frac{\sum\limits_{i}^{N}(X_i - RY_i)^2}{(N-1)\bar{Y}^2} \qquad (18.7)$$

and, therefore, if $\bar{x}$ and $\bar{y}$ are means of two different characteristics based on an identical sample, then

$$\sigma_r^2 \doteq (1-f)\frac{\sum\limits_{i}^{N} Y_i^2(R_i - R)^2}{(N-1)\bar{Y}^2 n} \qquad (18.8)$$

or

$$\doteq (1-f)\frac{\sum\limits_{i}^{N}(X_i - RY_i)^2}{(N-1)\bar{Y}^2 n} \qquad (18.9)$$

or, if we define

$$Z_i = X_i - RY_i$$

then

$$\sigma_r^2 = (1-f)\frac{S_Z^2}{n\bar{Y}^2} \qquad (18.10)$$

where

$$S_Z^2 = \bar{X}^2(V_X^2 + V_Y^2 - 2\rho_{XY}V_X V_Y) = S_X^2 + R^2 S_Y^2 - 2R\rho_{XY}S_X S_Y \qquad (18.11)$$

In Eq. 18.8 we have the variance of the ratio, r, stated in terms of the deviations of the ratios of the individual observations around the ratio of the population means. Each deviation from the over-all ratio is weighted by the square of the denominator of the individual ratio.

We also see from Eq. 18.9 that the variance of the ratio can be stated in terms of the variance of the deviations of the X_i from RY_i. Let us see what this means by considering a scatter chart in which the X_i and Y_i are plotted as points. First, it should be noted that $X = RY$ describes a straight line through the origin on the chart, and the amount by which the X_i for any specified Y_i fails to fall exactly on this straight line is equal to $Z_i = X_i - RY_i$. This is illustrated in Fig. 8. If the ratios $R_i = X_i/Y_i$

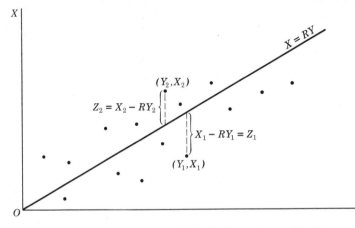

FIG. 8.   Scatter chart of Y_i, X_i, illustrating graphically
the meaning of $X_i - RY_i = Z_i$.

were all exactly equal to R, all the points on the scatter chart would fall on the line. It is the deviations of these ratios from R that determine the deviations of the X_i from RY_i, and the variance of r is approximately equal to the variance of these deviations divided by $n\bar{Y}^2$.

As indicated by Eq. 18.6 and 18.7, each of these formulas for the variance of r is identical with that given by Eq. 18.1, and they can be used interchangeably. In sampling from any particular population, some advantage may be found in each one in studying sources of contribution to the variance of the ratio of two sample means or totals.

In general, the rel-variance of u/w, the ratio of two random variables, is approximately*

$$V^2_{(u/w)} \doteq V^2_u + V^2_w - 2\rho_{uw}V_uV_w = V^2_u + V^2_w - 2V_{uw} \quad (18.12)$$

The results already given are special cases of this more general formula.

---

* For proof, see Vol. II, Ch. 4, Sec. 11.

Thus, Eq. 18.2 is the variance when we have a simple random sample of n observations, have measured two characteristics, X_i and Y_i, for each observation, and have computed the ratio $\bar{x}/\bar{y}$. The rel-variance of $\bar{x}$ (which takes the place of u in Eq. 18.12) is given by $(1 - f)V_X^2/n$; the rel-variance of $\bar{y}$ (indicated by w in Eq. 18.12) is $(1 - f)V_Y^2/n$; and the correlation between $\bar{x}$ and $\bar{y}$ turns out to be exactly the same as the correlation between X_i and Y_i.* Similarly, in Eq. 18.5, we have the rel-variance of the ratio of sample means, $\bar{x}$ and $\bar{y}$, but here the means are from independently selected samples and the correlation between them is zero, so that the third term involving $\rho_{\bar{x}\bar{y}}$ disappears. Ordinarily we shall deal with one of these two special cases, i.e., identical samples or independent samples; but other cases can arise and Eq. 18.12 can be applied in general. It is necessary, in general, to evaluate $\rho_{\bar{x}\bar{y}}$ or $V_{\bar{x}\bar{y}}$ whereas in the simpler cases presented $\rho_{\bar{x}\bar{y}}$ is equal to ρ in the original population (Eq. 18.3), and $V_{\bar{x}\bar{y}}$ is then simply equal to $\rho V_{\bar{x}}V_{\bar{y}}$.

Remark. It should be pointed out that the variance of the ratio of random variables can be obtained very readily in cases where the ratio is based on a sample of 1, i.e., based on a single observation. In this instance the sample estimate is $r = x_i/y_i = r_i$, which can be regarded as an estimate of R. The variance in this instance is simply

$$\frac{\sum_{i}^{N}(R_i - \bar{R})^2}{N - 1}$$

where

$$\bar{R} = \frac{\sum_{i}^{N} R_i}{N}$$

The bias in this instance is $(\bar{R} - X/Y)$, which may be large.

19. Conditions under which supplementary data with ratio estimates are useful in improving estimates of totals and ratios. Let us consider further the question of choosing (when a choice is available) between the estimate given by Eq. 7.1 and the ratio estimate of Eq. 19.1 below.

Suppose that we want to estimate the total rental value for all dwellings in a particular population. We have seen that one way to estimate this total is to compute the simple unbiased estimate

$$x' = N\bar{x} \tag{7.1}$$

if $\bar{x}$ represents the average rent per family in the sample. But if we know $\bar{y}$, the average income per family in our sample, and also know from

---

* For proof, see Vol. II, Ch. 4, Sec. 3.

independent sources the value of Y, the total income of the families in the population, then we might compute

$$x'' = \frac{\bar{x}}{\bar{y}} \, Y = x \, \frac{Y}{y} = x' \, \frac{Y}{y'} \tag{19.1}$$

as another estimate of X.

How can we determine which is the better estimate? One would want to choose the estimate having the smaller expected error, which we will measure by the coefficient of variation (or the standard error).

We have already seen that, if a total is estimated by multiplying a sample mean by N, a figure which is known, then the estimated total has the same coefficient of variation as the sample mean, and the variance of the total is N^2 times the variance of the sample mean. This is a special case of the rule given in Sec. 9, p. 123. The application of this rule makes it a simple matter to arrive at the variance or the coefficient of variation of totals or ratios that are derived by multiplying or dividing a sample estimate by some known total or average.

Thus, if Y is known, without sampling error, and if $x'' = Yr$, then

$$\sigma_{x''}^2 = Y^2 \sigma_r^2 \tag{19.2}$$

and

$$V_{x''}^2 = V_r^2 \tag{19.3}$$

Similarly, if we compute the ratio $\bar{x}/\bar{Y}$, where $\bar{Y}$ is known, then

$$\sigma_{(\bar{x}/\bar{Y})}^2 = \frac{\sigma_{\bar{x}}^2}{\bar{Y}^2} \tag{19.4}$$

and

$$V_{(\bar{x}/\bar{Y})}^2 = V_{\bar{x}}^2 \tag{19.5}$$

We shall now compare the sampling error of an estimated total such as x'', based on the estimate of a ratio of random variables, with that of x', in which a simple expansion of the sample total is made, multiplying x by $1/f$, the reciprocal of the sampling fraction.

We have seen that

$$V_{x'}^2 = (1-f) \frac{V_X^2}{n} \tag{10.3}$$

and

$$V_{x''}^2 \doteq (1-f) \frac{(V_X^2 + V_Y^2 - 2\rho V_X V_Y)}{n} \tag{19.6}$$

and we can examine these to see under what circumstances one will be smaller than the other. If we take $T = V_{x''}^2/V_{x'}^2$, we have

$$T \doteq 1 + \frac{V_Y^2}{V_X^2} - 2\rho \, \frac{V_Y}{V_X} \tag{19.7}$$

and x' will have the smaller variance whenever this expression is greater than 1, and will have the larger variance when it is less than 1. This expression will always be greater than 1 unless ρ, the correlation between

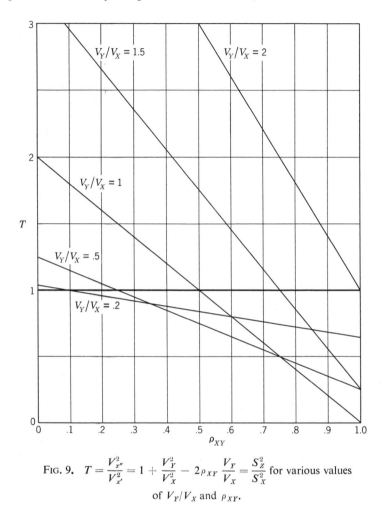

FIG. 9. $T = \dfrac{V^2_{x''}}{V^2_{x'}} = 1 + \dfrac{V^2_Y}{V^2_X} - 2\rho_{XY}\dfrac{V_Y}{V_X} = \dfrac{S^2_Z}{S^2_X}$ for various values

of V_Y/V_X and ρ_{XY}.

X_i and Y_i, is equal to or greater than $V_Y/2V_X$.* Since the correlation coefficient cannot be greater than 1, the ratio estimate will have a larger coefficient of variation than the unbiased estimate, even with perfect correlation, whenever V_Y is greater than $2V_X$.

Figure 9 shows the value of $T = 1 + (V^2_Y/V^2_X) - 2\rho(V_Y/V_X)$ for

* For proof, see Vol. II, Ch. 4, Sec. 19.

several different values of V_Y/V_X and for different levels of the correlation, and makes it readily apparent for a number of different values of V_Y/V_X whether a particular ratio-type estimate (of the form x'') or the unbiased estimate (x') will have a smaller variance.

From Fig. 9 it is clear that when $V_X = V_Y$ the ratio estimate will have a smaller variance than the unbiased estimate if the correlation between X_i and Y_i is greater than .5, and will have a *larger* variance if it is less than .5. Moreover, with V_X equal to V_Y the ratio estimate has a substantially smaller variance if the correlation is high, and in this case (i.e., $V_X = V_Y$) its variance approaches zero as a perfect correlation is approached. The chart shows, as has already been indicated, that for V_Y/V_X greater than 2 there will be a loss in using the ratio estimate as compared with the unbiased estimate, even with perfect correlation. With smaller values of V_Y/V_X there will be a gain in using the ratio estimate provided the correlation is high enough.

Figure 9 also shows that for very small values of V_Y/V_X, i.e., where the coefficient of variation of the denominator is quite small compared with that of the numerator of the ratio being estimated, some gain results from using the ratio estimate, as compared with the unbiased estimate, even with a very low correlation.

But when V_Y/V_X is small, the gains are not very striking even with a high correlation. Thus, if $V_Y/V_X = .2$, and at the same time the correlation is zero, only a very slight loss will be taken; but, on the other hand, even with a perfect correlation one can reduce the variance of the unbiased estimate by only about a third when $V_Y/V_X = .2$. Thus, with very small values for V_Y/V_X, it can make little difference whether the ratio estimate or the unbiased estimate is used.

When the correlation is negative, a loss will always be taken by using the ratio estimate; a ratio estimate should be avoided if possible under these conditions.

Let us now return to the illustrative problem of determining which estimate to choose in estimating X, the total rental value of dwellings in a community, when Y, the total family income, is known. Figure 10 shows roughly the kind of relationship between rent and income that sometimes might be found.

With the data shown in this figure there is a noticeable increase in rental paid, on the average, as income increases, until a certain level of income is achieved, after which the increase in rental value with increasing income is not very consistent or very marked. Clearly, such a population can be so distributed that V_X will be less than half of V_Y, in which event there is no chance of gaining by using the ratio estimate—one can only lose.

Suppose that for the data shown in the chart

$$V_X = .65, \quad V_Y = 1.9, \quad \rho = .8$$

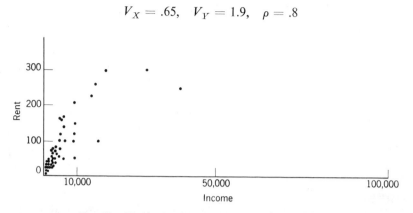

FIG. 10.   Family income and family rent (hypothetical data).

Since V_Y is more than $2V_X$, we would lose by using x'' as our estimate even were ρ as large as .99.   But, if those families with incomes of more than \$10,000 were excluded, then we might find that, say,

$$V_X \doteq .5, \quad V_Y \doteq .8, \quad \rho \doteq .90$$

and since ρ is greater than $V_Y/2V_X = .8$, we would gain, in this instance, by using the ratio estimate, and in fact would reduce the variance of the estimated total rental value to about 70 per cent of what it would be if we had used the simple unbiased estimate.

Remark.   Figure 9 and the illustration above point to the need for finding ways of reducing the coefficient of variation of the denominator when it is larger than that of the numerator.   One way of accomplishing this is to use stratification.   In the income illustration above, for example, stratification by size of income might have the effect of reducing the variance of the denominator more than that of the numerator.   Sometimes a transformation such as $Z_i = \sqrt{Y_i}$ for the variable in the denominator of the ratio estimate will achieve the desired result.   Thus, whereas $x'' = (x/y) Y$ may lose over the unbiased estimate, the ratio estimate

$$\frac{x}{\sum\limits_i^n \sqrt{y_i}} \sum\limits_i^N \sqrt{Y_i}$$

may gain over the unbiased estimate.   Fortunately the common situation in the use of ratio estimates is one where the coefficient of variation of the denominator is smaller than that of the numerator, and the need for such precaution is not great.

One important point should be brought out in distinguishing between the use of a ratio of sample means as an intermediate step in estimating a total and its use in estimating a ratio from a sample for the sake of obtaining the ratio itself. If one wants an estimate of a particular ratio, say $X/Y = R$, he may use $\bar{x}/\bar{y} = r$ from the sample as the estimate; or, if $\bar{Y}$ is known, he may use $\bar{x}/\bar{Y}$ as the estimate. But the only condition under which one has the choice of using an estimate of the form $\bar{x}/\bar{Y}$ occurs when the specific characteristic, $\bar{Y}$, is in fact known for the total population and is not merely a related characteristic. This is very different from what happens when the objective is to estimate the total, X. Then we have a choice of $N\bar{x}$, $(\bar{x}/\bar{y})Y$, $(\bar{x}/\bar{z})Z$, or any other similar type of estimate for which the necessary data from the sample and from independent sources are available, and should choose the one that has the smallest expected error.

To illustrate this principle let us consider a sample design planned for Haiti that was worked out at the request of a consultant to the Haitian government a few years ago. Although at that time Haiti had never had a population census, it was desired to work out a sample design that would provide a reliable estimate of the total population and of certain characteristics of the population. The proposed design indicates how available resources can be put to work in arriving at a sample design, and at the same time provides an excellent illustration of the principle just mentioned: that data which may be more or less seriously in error can be effectively utilized in a ratio estimate to improve the efficiency of an estimated total.

In the case of the proposed Haiti sample, discussion brought out the fact that there were no accurate maps of Haiti that could be used to divide the country into small areas that might serve as sampling units. But it was also learned that the country was divided into approximately 500 administrative units, referred to as sections, and that each of these administrative units had a head man or chief who knew the territory fairly well and whose duties included, among other things, periodically visiting each family in the unit. In addition, although no satisfactory maps were available showing the boundaries of these units, it was stated that the head of the section knew which families were in his section (such an assumption would need further investigation before its final acceptance). Although the section chiefs were often illiterate, it was thought that a little careful working with the head of a section, perhaps with the assistance of a priest or teacher in the area, would make it possible to get an approximate estimate of the total number of families in the section (based on local knowledge without any field work). If such estimates were not too wild, and if they were available for all sections in the country, it would be possible to make use of them to increase greatly the precision of estimates from a sample. Moreover, a person or persons traveling around the country could visit the sections and obtain such an estimate of the total families in the section at a small fraction of the cost of taking a census of the section. Thus, it was expected that in a period of about four months four or five people could cover the country, obtain various data that were desired as background information for other purposes, and obtain the estimates of the numbers of dwellings in each section throughout the country. The sample design proposed provided for obtaining such estimates of the numbers of families in every section in the country.

Now, let us suppose that a simple random sample of 20 per cent of the sections is drawn, i.e., $N/n = 1/f = 5$, and a complete census is taken in each of these sampled sections. We will then have the following information:

(a) The estimated number of families living in each section in the country. Let us designate this figure for the ith section by the symbol Y_i. In addition, we will have $y = \sum_{}^{n} y_i$, the total estimated families in the sections included in the sample, and $Y = \sum_{}^{N} Y_i$, the total estimated families for all sections in the country.

(b) For each section included in the sample we will have the total population, obtained by actual enumeration of the section. We will designate this figure for the ith section by the symbol X_i. We will also have $x = \sum_{}^{n} x_i$, i.e., the total population enumerated in the sections included in the sample.

The simple unbiased estimate of the total population is obtained by computing (Eq. 7.1)

$$x' = \frac{N}{n} x$$

But, since the section chiefs' estimates would be known both for the sections included in the sample and for the entire country, we could also use as our estimate:

$$x'' = \frac{x}{y} Y \qquad (19.1)$$

This estimate would have the smaller variance provided there was a fairly high correlation between the X_i and Y_i, as was anticipated.

There will undoubtedly be biases, perhaps very serious ones, in the advance estimates of the numbers of families in the sections, and the question arises whether the biases in the advance estimates used to obtain an "expansion factor" for arriving at our final estimate introduce a bias into the final estimate. Actually, a little examination will show that they do not. Suppose, as a very simple illustration of this, that each Y_i was in fact 10 per cent larger than the true number of families in the ith section, which we will call Z_i. Then $Y_i = 1.1Z_i$, $y = 1.1z$, and $Y = 1.1Z$, and from these $X'' = (x/y)Y = (x/1.1z)\,1.1Z = (x/z)Z$, and the consistent overestimates of the numbers of families made by the section chiefs have in no way biased the final estimate of X. Of course, in practice, errors such as in the section chiefs' estimates will not be consistent. In any event, since we have a random sample of the sections, $N\bar{y}$ is an unbiased estimate of Y. Consequently, if Y is greater than the true number of families, then, on the average over all possible samples, $\bar{y}$ will be too high in exactly the same proportion; and if Y is too low, then, on the average, $\bar{y}$ will be too low in the same proportion. Therefore, any biases in the Y_i will appear in both the numerator and denominator of the expansion factor, Y/y, and will cancel out and not affect the value of the whole expansion factor. Thus, no matter what the bias in the original estimates used in obtaining the expansion factor, such biases will not introduce similar biases in the final estimate. This latter statement will be true even though the original estimates had *no* correlation with the final population enumerations. However, in such an instance the use of an estimate without the ratio adjustment would be preferable.

Of course, the gain, if any, that will be achieved through the use of the ratio estimate will depend in part upon the reliability of the advance estimates. In designing the Haiti sample, a fairly high correlation of the advance estimate of families with the actual enumerated populations was anticipated because it was known that there was a large variability in the sizes of the sections, and it was felt that the advance estimate would roughly but effectively indicate the approximate sizes of the sections. If this were so, then V_Y would probably be roughly equal to V_X, and it was anticipated that a correlation of perhaps .9 with the actual populations enumerated would be achieved. Under these circumstances, we find that the ratio estimate has about 20 per cent as large a variance, or less than one-half as large a standard deviation, as the unbiased estimate. If the conditions outlined above hold, we will have achieved the effect of a much larger sample by the introduction of the ratio estimate based on the estimated numbers of households.

Another principle involved in this illustration needs emphasis. It would be essential, in carrying out the above design, not to select the sample sections *before* the work was carried through of obtaining estimates from the section chiefs for all sections in Haiti. If the sample selection were made first, the knowledge of which sections were included in the sample might affect the character of the advance estimates for these particular units. In this event, the estimates for these units would *not* constitute an unbiased sample of the estimates for all sections, and as a consequence biases of a more or less serious sort would be introduced into the final estimated totals.

20. Certain lessons for original design of samples. Some of the results we have obtained have very important implications in connection with the original design of samples. Thus, suppose that one is interested in estimating relative changes in the sales of retail stores from one year to the next. One way of sampling for this relative change would be to obtain a sample of establishments the first year and obtain the estimated average sales per establishment from this sample for that year; then another independently selected sample might be taken the following year and the average sales estimated from this sample for the second year; and the relative change in sales could be estimated by computing the ratio of these two sample averages. The rel-variance of this ratio would be $V_u^2 + V_w^2$, where V_u^2 represents the rel-variance of the estimated total sales in the first year, and V_w^2 represents the rel-variance of the estimated total sales in the second year. But now suppose that instead we include the same stores in the sample for each year, and obtain the average sales each year for these identical stores. Then the sample estimates for the two years would not be independent; in fact, in this particular instance a very high correlation between them would be expected. Moreover, V_u would be approximately equal to V_w. Consequently, the coefficient of variation of the ratio would be *very* much smaller with the identical sample. Thus, in this instance, the theory points to the practice commonly followed of using an identical sample for estimating changes.

Let us consider, however, another and quite different illustration. Suppose that we are estimating unemployment from a sample of families. We might have a sample of, say, 3000 families at one date and estimate the number of unemployed from this sample; then perhaps a year later we might take the same sample of 3000 families and again estimate unemployment from this sample. Now, if our primary interest is in measuring change in unemployment, it might be expected by some that the sample of identical households would be much superior to an independent sample taken at each date. However, when the rate of unemployment is relatively low, it turns out, in our experience, that the individuals unemployed at one date are not, for the most part, the individuals who were unemployed, say, a year earlier. Consequently, the correlation of unemployment is so low between successive periods that both methods are equally good.

21. Evaluation of the precision of ratio estimates from the sample. A consistent* estimate of σ_r^2 or V_r^2 is obtained by making estimates from the sample of exactly the same form as the values we want for the population, i.e., by computing (from Eq. 12.3)

$$v_X^2 = \frac{s_X^2}{\bar{x}^2}, \quad v_Y^2 = \frac{s_Y^2}{\bar{y}^2} \tag{21.1}$$

$$\rho' s_X s_Y = s_{XY} = \frac{\sum_{i}^{n}(x_i - \bar{x})(y_i - \bar{y})\dagger}{(n-1)} \tag{21.2}$$

or

$$\rho' v_X v_Y = \frac{s_{XY}}{\bar{x}\bar{y}}$$

and

$$r = \frac{\bar{x}}{\bar{y}}$$

and, by putting these together, obtain

$$s_r^2 = (1-f)r^2 \frac{(v_X^2 + v_Y^2 - 2\rho' v_X v_Y)}{n} \tag{21.3}$$

Just as σ_r^2 can be stated in several different ways, we find that s_r^2 can also be stated in several ways, e.g.,

$$s_r^2 = (1-f)\frac{\sum_{i}^{n} y_i^2(r_i - r)^2}{(n-1)n\bar{y}^2} \tag{21.4}$$

which can also be written as

$$s_r^2 = (1-f)\frac{\sum_{i}^{n}(x_i - ry_i)^2}{(n-1)n\bar{y}^2} = (1-f)\frac{s_Z^2}{n\bar{y}^2} \tag{21.5}$$

where $z_i = x_i - ry_i$. These equations for s_r^2 all give identically the same results.

They aid in determining the circumstances under which one may expect a reasonably reliable estimate of the s_r^2 from the sample. To indicate the reliability of the estimate we write, as before (Sec. 18), $Z_i = X_i - RY_i$. Since $R = \bar{X}/\bar{Y}$, the mean of Z_i is equal to zero.

* For proof, see Vol. II, Ch. 4, Sec. 21.
† We use ρ' to distinguish the correlation computed from sample data from the ρ for the population.

An approximation to the rel-variance of s_r is given by*

$$V_{s_r}^2 \doteq \frac{\beta_Z - 1}{4n} + \frac{V_Y^2}{n} - \frac{\rho_{Z^2Y}\sqrt{\beta_Z - 1}\; V_Y}{n} \tag{21.6}$$

where

$$\beta_Z = \frac{\sum\limits^{N} Z_i^4}{N\sigma_Z^4}$$

i.e., β_Z is the ratio of μ_4 of the Z_i to σ_Z^4, and ρ_{Z^2Y} is the coefficient of correlation between Z_i^2 and Y_i.

Formula 21.6, when solved for n, provides a guide in determining the size of sample required to obtain a satisfactory estimate of σ_r or V_r from the sample. In order to evaluate the size of sample required to achieve, say, no more than a 10 per cent coefficient of variation in the estimate s_r, we set $V_{s_r}^2 = .01$ and solve for n. In order to obtain an answer we need to be able to speculate roughly on the values of β_Z, V_Y, and ρ_{Z^2Y}, and often this can be done on the basis of past knowledge and experience or of pretesting and experimentation. The plotting of a scatter chart (such as Fig. 8, p. 166) based on data available from past experience, showing the approximate relationship between X_i and Y_i, may be helpful, with the line approximating $X = RY$ drawn on it.

The following rules may prove useful in speculating on the accuracy of s_Z as an estimate of S_Z. If the relationship between X_i and Y_i as indicated on the scatter chart is such that a line through the origin and through the point $(\bar{Y}, \bar{X})$ is a pretty good fit to the data, i.e., if there are no exceedingly atypical values of Z_i shown on the chart or reasonably likely to exist in the population, then the size of sample required probably will be small, perhaps no more than 50–100. On the other hand, if a few highly atypical values of Z_i may reasonably occur, a considerably larger sample may be required to provide from the sample itself a reliable estimate of the precision of an estimated ratio.

Where exceedingly atypical values of the Z_i may be expected, then the presumed distribution of the Z_i can be compared with the distributions of other characteristics discussed in an earlier section (see Sec. 14), and this examination may provide a basis for speculating on reasonable values of β_Z.

It should be pointed out, also, that the fact that the distributions of X_i and Y_i are badly skewed does not necessarily mean that Z_i will or will not be well behaved. A very badly skewed distribution with respect to X and Y may be well approximated by a line through the origin, and Z may be nicely distributed with a relatively small value for β_Z.

---

* For proof, see Vol. II, Ch. 4, Sec. 18.

REFERENCES

(1) W. Edwards Deming, *Some Theory of Sampling*, John Wiley & Sons, New York, 1950, Chapter 4.
(2) W. G. Cochran, *Sampling Techniques*, John Wiley & Sons, New York, 1953, Chapters 2, 3, and 4.
(3) F. Yates, *Sampling Methods for Censuses and Surveys*, Charles Griffin and Company, London, 1949.

CHAPTER 5

Stratified Simple Random Sampling

A. NOTATION, AND SELECTION OF A STRATIFIED SAMPLE

1. Some notation and general considerations. This chapter deals with stratified sampling in the case when the selection of the sample within each stratum is accomplished by simple random sampling of specified sampling units. Ordinarily those specified sampling units will be the elementary units. Chapter 7 and subsequent chapters cover the more general case of stratification with cluster sampling.

Notation. Some of the extensions or modifications in notation that will be needed in dealing with stratified sampling are as follows:

The number of strata into which the population under consideration is divided will be designated by L. N will represent the total number of elementary units (or sampling units) in the entire population, and N_h will represent the number in the hth stratum. Therefore,

$$N = \sum_h^L N_h = N_1 + N_2 + \cdots + N_L$$

Similarly, the size of the sample drawn from the hth stratum will be designated by n_h, and

$$n = \sum_h^L n_h$$

is the total size of the sample drawn from all strata.

This notation is similar to that for simple random sampling except that the subscript h indicates a particular stratum. The subscript i will designate the individual sampling unit, but the sampling units will be regarded as numbered separately within each stratum instead of throughout the population. Thus, the value of a characteristic X of the ith sampling unit in the hth stratum will be designated by X_{hi}. For example, if families are the units being sampled and the incomes of families are under consideration, and if we have a population consisting of 10 families grouped into 3 strata, with 2 of the families in the first stratum, 4 in the second, and 4 in the third, then:

$$N = 10$$
$$N_1 = 2$$
$$N_2 = 4$$
$$N_3 = 4$$

In addition, X_{11} and X_{12} represent the respective incomes of the 2 families in the first stratum; X_{21}, X_{22}, X_{23}, and X_{24} represent the respective incomes of the 4 families in the second stratum; and X_{31}, X_{32}, X_{33}, and X_{34} represent the respective incomes of the 4 families in the third stratum.

Now the total income of the families in the first stratum is

$$X_1 = X_{11} + X_{12}$$

and, using the summation notation in which we drop a subscript to indicate a summation, we may write this total as

$$X_1 = \sum_i^{N_1} X_{1i}$$

Notice that to indicate the sum of the items in the first stratum we have merely dropped the subscript i, which amounts to saying that we have summed over all the elements that have "1" as the stratum designation.

Similarly, the total income for the second stratum is

$$X_2 = X_{21} + X_{22} + X_{23} + X_{24}$$

which, again, is indicated by

$$X_2 = \sum_i^{N_2} X_{2i}$$

and similarly

$$X_3 = \sum_i^{N_3} X_{3i}$$

More generally, if the subscript h designates the hth stratum, then the total of a characteristic added over all units in that stratum will be

$$X_h = \sum_i^{N_h} X_{hi}$$

Thus, as in Chapter 1, a summation is indicated by dropping the subscript over which the sum is taken. When the sum is taken over all units in a population (or in a stratum), it will be indicated by a capital letter, and the sum over the units in a sample will be indicated by a small letter. Thus:

X_{hi} is the value of some characteristic for the ith unit in the population within the hth stratum, and x_{hi} is the value of the characteristic for the ith unit in the sample from the hth stratum, so that

$$X_h = \sum_i^{N_h} X_{hi}, \quad \text{and} \quad x_h = \sum_i^{n_h} x_{hi}$$

Similarly,

$$X = \sum_h^{L} X_h = \sum_h^{L} \sum_i^{N_h} X_{hi}$$

represents the sum of the stratum totals over all strata, or the sum over all units in the entire population; and

$$x = \sum_h^{L} x_h = \sum_h^{L} \sum_i^{n_h} x_{hi}$$

is the total value of the characteristic under consideration for all the units in a sample of size

$$n = \sum_h^{L} n_h$$

Sometimes, to distinguish whether a summation is over strata, or over units within a stratum, the summation sign will have a subscript placed under it.   Thus:

$\sum_i^{N_h} X_{hi}$ designates that the summation is over the units within the hth stratum.   Often the subscript under the summation will not be necessary because the symbol at the top of the summation will indicate what is included in the summation.   Thus, the fact that $\sum^{N_h} X_{hi}$ is the sum over all the units within the hth stratum is clear because N_h designates the total number of units in the hth stratum.   Similarly:

$\sum^{n_h} x_{hi}$ denotes the sum over a sample of n_h units from the hth stratum. The symbol at the top of the summation may be omitted when the limits of summation are obvious.

With this notation $\bar{X}$, as before, represents the mean over the entire population, so that

$$\bar{X} = \frac{X}{N}$$

The mean within the hth stratum will be designated by

$$\bar{X}_h = \frac{X_h}{N_h}$$

and the mean of a sample of n_h units from that stratum will be designated by

$$\bar{x}_h = \frac{x_h}{n_h}$$

The variance of the characteristic between elementary units within the hth stratum will be designated by σ_h^2, so that

$$\sigma_h^2 = \frac{\sum\limits_{i}^{N_h}(X_{hi} - \bar{X}_h)^2}{N_h} \qquad (1.1)$$

and

$$S_h^2 = \frac{N_h}{N_h - 1}\sigma_h^2 = \frac{\sum\limits_{i}^{N_h}(X_{hi} - \bar{X}_h)^2}{N_h - 1} \qquad (1.2)$$

The corresponding rel-variance is

$$V_h^2 = \frac{S_h^2}{\bar{X}_h^2} \qquad (1.3)$$

Also, the variance over the entire population without regard to strata is

$$\sigma^2 = \frac{\sum\limits_{h}^{L}\sum\limits_{i}^{N_h}(X_{hi} - \bar{X})^2}{N}, \quad \text{or} \quad S^2 = \frac{\sum\limits_{h}^{L}\sum\limits_{i}^{N_h}(X_{hi} - \bar{X})^2}{N - 1} \qquad (1.4)$$

and the rel-variance is

$$V^2 = \frac{S^2}{\bar{X}^2} \qquad (1.5)$$

which are exactly the same variance and rel-variance as for simple random sampling, but now a summation over two subscripts is indicated to get the total over the entire population, because the observations are regarded as numbered first by strata and then serially within strata.

Exercise 1.1. Suppose that a population of 12 elementary units is divided into 3 strata, with 5 units in the first stratum, 3 in the second, and 4 in the third, and with values as indicated in the table below.

STRATUM 1	STRATUM 2	STRATUM 3
$X_{11} = 6$	$X_{21} = 9$	$X_{31} = 20$
$X_{12} = 10$	$X_{22} = 18$	$X_{32} = 26$
$X_{13} = 2$	$X_{23} = 12$	$X_{33} = 16$
$X_{14} = 4$		$X_{34} = 26$
$X_{15} = 8$		

Show that the means of the strata are respectively 6, 13, and 22, and the mean of the population is 13.08.   Show that

$$\sigma_1^2 = 8, \quad \sigma_2^2 = 14, \quad \text{and} \quad \sigma_3^2 = 18$$

and that

$$S_1^2 = 10, \quad S_2^2 = 21, \quad \text{and} \quad S_3^2 = 24$$

and finally

$$\sigma^2 = 60.24, \quad S^2 = 65.72$$

The role of stratification.   We have already seen in Chapter 1 that stratification can be used to increase the reliability of sample results. We shall now explore stratified sampling more fully, to find out how to draw a stratified sample and how to prepare estimates from such a sample. We shall also consider the precision of results that can be expected from stratified samples, and the guiding principles in the choice of a stratified sample to achieve maximum precision per unit of cost.

The amount of increase in precision of sample estimates accomplished by stratification will depend on the degree of homogeneity that is achieved within strata, or, saying the same thing in another way, on how much of the variability in the characteristic being estimated is reflected in the differences among the strata.   This in turn depends on how effectively the strata have been defined.

In establishing stratum boundaries, use should be made of all information that helps classify members of the population into groups which differ from one another with respect to the characteristic being measured, or with respect to the cost of collecting data.   But, within each stratum, the sample must be a probability sample; we do not permit judgment to enter into the selection of the individual sampling units.

Judgment in establishing the strata used in selecting a sample is a mark of good sampling procedure.   Such a sample must be distinguished from a judgment sample, in which the units included are selected in some purposive fashion, with the result that it is impossible to attach a probability of selection to the units that come into the sample.

There seems to be some belief that the method of stratification that is used is the only factor that determines whether a sample is good or bad, and that sampling without stratification is never good.   However, as was suggested in Chapter 1, there are many instances where stratification, even though carried through with great care, can have only a trivial effect in increasing the reliability of the results from a sample.   On the other hand, there are important instances in which stratification is a highly effective and important device for obtaining a reliable sample at a minimum cost.

Besides presenting the general theory of stratified sampling, we shall in this chapter attempt to distinguish between cases where stratification is important and where it is not.   We shall indicate the principles to be followed where stratification is important, in order to make it as effective as possible.   It should be pointed out, also, that even where trivial gains are to be expected, stratification is often used because it can be introduced at little or no cost.

Important topics to be discussed in stratified simple random sampling. The important topics to be discussed are: (*a*) defining the strata to be used; (*b*) determining the size of sample to be taken from each stratum; (*c*) selecting the sample from the strata as defined; (*d*) preparing the estimates from the sample; and (*e*) evaluating the reliability of the sample estimates.   We shall postpone consideration of the first two topics to a later section of this chapter, since the problem involved there can be considered more adequately after the theory of stratified sampling has been examined.

2. Selection of a stratified sample.   Once the strata have been determined and the size of sample to be taken from each stratum has been specified, the sample is selected in exactly the same way as a simple random sample, except that the sampling is done independently within each stratum; i.e., each stratum is treated as a population from which a simple random sample is selected.   Thus, if simple random samples of $n_1, n_2, \cdots, n_h, \cdots, n_L$ units are drawn from the L strata, respectively, we have a stratified simple random sample.   Sometimes the sample is drawn from the strata in such a way that the sampling fraction is the same for all strata, in which event we say that we have a proportionate stratified sample.   It is not necessary, however, that the same proportion be included from each stratum.   The proportion in the sample from the hth stratum is equal to $f_h = n_h/N_h$, and in any particular problem this fraction in the sample may vary slightly, widely, or not at all, from one stratum to the next.

B.   SAMPLE ESTIMATES AND THEIR PRECISION

3. Simple unbiased estimates of means, percentages, and totals.   In this chapter we shall again consider first the computation of simple unbiased estimates of means, percentages, and totals, after which we shall consider the use of ratio estimates.

Preparing estimates from the sample.   The mean of the population, $\bar{X}$, is

$$\bar{X} = \frac{X}{N} = \frac{\sum\limits_{}^{L} N_h \bar{X}_h}{\sum\limits_{}^{L} N_h} \tag{3.1}$$

and, thus, is the weighted average of the stratum means where the weight used in the hth stratum is N_h, the number of units in the stratum.

Since we are assuming that simple random sampling is used within each stratum, we know from Ch. 4, Sec. 7, that

$$\bar{x}_h = \frac{x_h}{n_h}$$

is a consistent (and unbiased) estimate of $\bar{X}_h$, the true stratum mean. Consequently, our estimate of the mean for the entire population will be the weighted average of the estimates for the individual strata

$$\bar{x} = \frac{\overset{L}{\sum} N_h \bar{x}_h}{\overset{L}{\sum} N_h} \qquad (3.2)$$

and will be an unbiased estimate of $\bar{X}$. The proof that $\bar{x}$ is an unbiased estimate of $\bar{X}$ follows from the fact that $N_h \bar{x}_h$ is an unbiased estimate of $N_h \bar{X}_h$ and from the fact that the expected value of the sum, $\Sigma N_h \bar{x}_h$, is equal to the sum of the expected values of the individual terms. It will be unbiased no matter what sampling fractions are used in the various strata, provided at least some sample is taken from each stratum and provided, of course, that the estimate used is that given by Eq. 3.2 and is not merely a simple mean of the sample observations.

Exercises

3.1.   Using the data in Ex. 1.1, with a sample of 1 element from each stratum, compute the 60 possible sample estimates of the true mean and show that their average is 13.08, i.e., that the estimate is unbiased.

3.2.   Show that a sample of 2 elements from each stratum will lead to 180 possible sample estimates.

3.3.   Suppose that the sample again has 6 elements as in Ex. 3.2, but now that there are 2 observations in stratum 1, 3 in stratum 2, and 1 in stratum 3. Find all possible sample estimates, and show that the sample estimate is unbiased.

The estimated total for a stratum is

$$x'_h = N_h \bar{x}_h$$

and the estimated total for the population is

$$x' = \overset{L}{\sum} N_h \bar{x}_h = N\bar{x} \qquad (3.3)$$

If we have a proportionate sample with a uniform sampling fraction for each stratum, i.e., $f_h = f$, where $f_h = n_h/N_h$ and $f = n/N$, then

$$\bar{x} = \frac{\sum\limits^{L} N_h \dfrac{x_h}{n_h}}{N} = \frac{\sum\limits^{L} x_h}{n} = \frac{\sum\limits^{L} \sum\limits^{n_h} x_{hi}}{n} \tag{3.4}$$

and, therefore, with proportionate sampling, the estimate of the mean is merely the simple unweighted mean of all the observations included in the sample.   This is important because the process of applying different weights to different strata is sometimes laborious and expensive, but with proportionate sampling the use of a stratified sample calls for the same procedure for making estimates from the sample as does simple random sampling.   Proportionate stratified sampling is one of a class of designs which lead to *self-weighting samples*.   The identifying characteristic of self-weighting samples is that each element of the population has the same chance of selection.

If the sampling fraction is not uniform, one must take the weighted average of the sample means for the respective strata or the estimate will be biased.   The magnitude of the bias depends on how widely the weights actually used differ from the correct weights, and on how widely the stratum means differ from each other.   If the means of the different strata are all alike, then the bias will be zero no matter what weights are used in arriving at the average.

Remark.   In practice we seldom have exactly the same proportion included from all strata with proportionate stratified sampling, but treat the results as though proportionate sampling were actually accomplished.

Ordinarily the total number of units in a stratum is not an even multiple of the sampling fraction, and it is not possible to draw a sample that is exactly proportionate from each stratum.   Thus, a population might be divided into 5 strata as indicated below, and an effort made to draw a 5 per cent sample from each stratum.   This might lead to results such as the following:

STRATUM	No. OF UNITS IN STRATUM	No. ACTUALLY SELECTED FOR SAMPLE	ACTUAL PROPORTION IN SAMPLE
Total	4523	226	.04997
1	550	27	.04909
2	1517	76	.05010
3	912	46	.05044
4	420	21	.05000
5	1124	56	.04982

The actual sampling ratios obtained vary from .04909 in the first stratum to .05044 in the third stratum.   In practice it is usually acceptable to disregard small departures from uniformity and to use a uniform factor equal to the over-all sampling fraction for the entire population.

Exercise 3.4. Suppose that the data in the table above refer to tenant-occupied households, and that the 5 strata have aggregate rents as shown in column 4 below.

STRATUM	No. of HOUSEHOLDS IN STRATUM	No. of HOUSEHOLDS IN SAMPLE	AGGREGATE RENT FROM SAMPLE (dollars)
(1)	(2)	(3)	(4)
Total	4523	226	8695
1	550	27	1325
2	1517	76	4532
3	912	46	1917
4	420	21	570
5	1124	56	351

(*a*) Compute the estimated average rent from the sample, using the exact sampling fraction in each stratum (Eq. 3.2).

(*b*) Compute and compare the estimated average rent on the assumption that the sampling fraction was uniform and equal to 226/4523 in all strata, i.e., using Eq. 3.4 to estimate the average.

Precision of simple unbiased estimates. Applying the formula from Ch. 4, Eq. 9.3, for the variance of an estimated total, we see that the variance of x'_h, the estimated total for a stratum, is

$$\sigma^2_{hx'} = N^2_h (1 - f_h) \frac{S^2_h}{n_h} \tag{3.5}$$

where f_h is the sampling fraction in the hth stratum and S^2_h is given by Eq. 1.2.

Two simple and widely used theorems will enable us to put together the variance of a simple unbiased estimate of a total or a mean from a stratified sample.*

(1) The first of these theorems is that the variance of the sum of independently selected samples is the sum of their variances. In stratified sampling (with simple random sampling within strata) the sample drawn in one stratum is entirely independent of that drawn in another stratum. The sampling from each stratum is carried out as a separate simple random sampling process, and the fact that an overestimate or an underestimate is made in one stratum has no influence on whether the estimate for another stratum is an over- or underestimate. Consequently, the sample estimates from the various strata are independent, and therefore the variance of the estimated total over all strata is simply the sum of the variances of the estimated totals within each of the strata separately. Thus,

$$\sigma^2_{x'} = \sum^L N^2_h (1 - f_h) \frac{S^2_h}{n_h} \tag{3.6}$$

_____

* Given in Theorem 11, Corollaries 1 and 4, Sec. 4, Ch. 3, Vol. II.

Now suppose that we have used proportionate sampling so that $f_h = f$, then $n_h = fN_h$, and

$$\sigma_{\bar{x}'}^2 = N^2(1-f)\frac{S_w^2}{n} \tag{3.7}$$

where

$$S_w^2 = \frac{\sum\limits^{L} N_h S_h^2}{N} \tag{3.8}$$

and where S_h^2 is given by Eq. 1.2.

(2) The second theorem referred to is that, if a random variable is multiplied by a constant, the variance of the product is the constant squared multiplied by the variance of the variable. In the case of stratified sampling we multiply the estimated total for all strata combined by $1/N$ to obtain the estimated mean. Since N is known and not obtained from the sample, and not subject to any sampling error, the variance of the mean is $1/N^2$ times the variance of the estimated total.

Thus the variance of the sample mean estimated from a stratified sample is given by*

$$\sigma_{\bar{x}}^2 = \frac{1}{N^2}\sum\limits^{L} N_h^2(1-f_h)\frac{S_h^2}{n_h} \tag{3.9}$$

and with proportionate sampling this becomes simply

$$\sigma_{\bar{x}}^2 = (1-f)\frac{S_w^2}{n} \tag{3.10}$$

Note (from Eq. 9.4a, Ch. 4) that, if the mean or total being estimated is the proportion of the population having a specified characteristic or the total number having the characteristic, then

$$S_h^2 = \frac{N_h}{N_h - 1} P_h Q_h \tag{3.11}$$

and if the N_h are even moderately large (perhaps 20 or more)

$$S_h^2 \doteq P_h Q_h \tag{3.12}$$

and

$$S_w^2 \doteq \frac{\sum\limits^{L} N_h P_h Q_h}{N}$$

Similarly, if f_h is not large, i.e., if the proportion of the population included in the sample is less than, say, 5 per cent for all strata, the finite

---

* For proof, see Vol. II, Ch. 5, Sec. 1.

multipliers $(1 - f_h)$ in Eq. 3.5–3.10 can be regarded as equal to 1, and we have, for the variance of the sample mean,

$$\sigma_{\bar{x}}^2 = \frac{1}{N^2} \sum_{}^{L} N_h^2 \frac{S_h^2}{n_h} \tag{3.13}$$

and with proportionate sampling this becomes simply

$$\sigma_{\bar{x}}^2 = \frac{S_w^2}{n} \tag{3.14}$$

In measuring the precision of the result from a stratified random sample the only assumption involved was that the sampling within strata was simple random sampling. There was no assumption as to how the strata were made up. The gains that we get depend entirely on how effectively the stratification is accomplished, no matter whether it is done by grouping the units into strata on the basis of some objective criteria, or on a judgment basis.

Exercise 3.5.　Using the income data in Table 1, Sec. 5, Ch. 1, set up one of the possible stratifications of the 12 incomes into 3 strata of 4 elements each (different from that illustrated in Ch. 1), show that a simple random sample of 1 elementary unit from each stratum provides an unbiased estimate of the mean, and find the variance of your estimate. Review illustrations in Sec. 16, Ch. 1.

4. Ratio estimates.　The reasons for computing an estimate based on a ratio of random variables were summarized in Ch. 4, Sec. 16 and 17, in connection with simple random sampling. The same considerations apply to stratified sampling. We shall now present some methods for making estimates from a stratified sample where ratios of random variables are involved, and shall consider how to evaluate the reliability of such estimates.

As an illustration, suppose that the problem is to estimate the ratio of rent paid to income, for families in a particular area, from a stratified random sample of families. If X_{hi} is the rent paid by the ith family in the hth stratum, and Y_{hi} is the income of that family, then X_h is the total rent paid by all families in the hth stratum, and Y_h is their aggregate income. Similarly, X is the aggregate rent paid by all families in the entire population and Y is the aggregate income.

Then the desired ratio of rent to income for all families in the area is $R = X/Y$. We want to obtain an estimate of this ratio from a stratified sample of families. We shall consider two ways of estimating the ratio from the sample: one involves taking the ratio of estimated totals or averages computed from a stratified sample; the second involves computing a ratio of random variables for each stratum, and then obtaining a weighted average of these.

Ratio of estimated totals or averages. One estimate of R is obtained by computing the ratio

$$r = \frac{\bar{x}}{\bar{y}} = \frac{x'}{y'} = \frac{\sum\limits^{L} \dfrac{N_h}{n_h} \sum\limits^{n_h} x_{hi}}{\sum\limits^{L} \dfrac{N_h}{n_h} \sum\limits^{n_h} y_{hi}} \qquad (4.1)$$

where, as has already been seen, $\bar{x}$ and $\bar{y}$ are the averages estimated from Eq. 3.2, and x' and y' are the simple unbiased estimates of the totals X and Y, obtained from Eq. 3.3. This estimate has the same form as the estimate if simple random sampling is used, except that now the totals or averages from which the ratio is computed are from a stratified sample.

The variance is obtained by applying Eq. 18.12, Ch. 4, as follows:

$$\sigma_r^2 \doteq R^2(V_{\bar{x}}^2 + V_{\bar{y}}^2 - 2\rho_{\bar{x}\bar{y}} V_{\bar{x}} V_{\bar{y}}) \qquad (4.2)$$

where

$$\left.\begin{aligned} V_{\bar{x}}^2 &= V_{x'}^2 = \frac{\sigma_{\bar{x}}^2}{\bar{X}^2} \\[2mm] V_{\bar{y}}^2 &= V_{y'}^2 = \frac{\sigma_{\bar{y}}^2}{\bar{Y}^2} \end{aligned}\right\} \qquad (4.3)$$

are the rel-variances of $\bar{x}$ and $\bar{y}$, respectively; $\sigma_{\bar{x}}^2$ and $\sigma_{\bar{y}}^2$ are the variances (as given by Eq. 3.9) of $\bar{x}$ and $\bar{y}$ from a stratified simple random sample; and

$$\begin{aligned} \rho_{\bar{x}\bar{y}} &= \frac{\dfrac{1}{N^2} \sum\limits^{L} N_h^2 \dfrac{1-f_h}{n_h} \dfrac{\sum\limits^{N_h}(X_{hi} - \bar{X}_h)(Y_{hi} - \bar{Y}_h)}{N_h - 1}}{\sigma_{\bar{x}} \sigma_{\bar{y}}} \\[4mm] &= \frac{\dfrac{1}{N^2} \sum\limits^{L} N_h^2 \dfrac{1-f_h}{n_h} \rho_{hXY} S_{hX} S_{hY}}{\sigma_{\bar{x}} \sigma_{\bar{y}}} \end{aligned} \qquad (4.4)$$

is the coefficient of correlation between $\bar{x}$ and $\bar{y}$ in stratified simple random samples. Equation 4.2 for the variance of r (Eq. 4.1) can be restated to show the contributions of the various strata as follows:*

$$\sigma_r^2 \doteq \frac{1}{N^2 \bar{Y}^2} \sum\limits^{L} N_h^2 \frac{1-f_h}{n_h} S_{hZ'}^2 \qquad (4.5)$$

where

$$S_{hZ'}^2 = S_{hX}^2 + R^2 S_{hY}^2 - 2R\rho_{hXY} S_{hX} S_{hY} \qquad (4.6)$$

---

* For proof, see Vol. II, Ch. 5, Sec. 2.

where S_{hX}^2 and S_{hY}^2 are given by Eq. 1.2, and ρ_{hXY} is the correlation between X_{hi} and Y_{hi} in the hth stratum.

Remark. The expression $\rho_{hXY} S_{hX} S_{hY}$ in Eq. 4.6 is the covariance between X_{hi} and Y_{hi} in the hth stratum. If we let the covariance between X_{hi} and Y_{hi} be equal to S_{hXY}, then

$$\rho_{hXY} = \frac{S_{hXY}}{S_{hX} S_{hY}}$$

The variance is a special case of the covariance. Thus,

$$S_{hXY} = \frac{\sum\limits^{N_h}(X_{hi} - \bar{X}_h)(Y_{hi} - \bar{Y}_h)}{N_h - 1}$$

and when X_{hi} is substituted for Y_{hi}, we have $S_{hXY} = S_{hX}^2$ as given by Eq. 1.2. Similarly, when Y_{hi} is substituted for X_{hi}, we have S_{hY}^2. It follows that $S_{hXX} = S_{hX}^2$ and $S_{hYY} = S_{hY}^2$.

Equations 4.2 and 4.5 are algebraically identical. One form or the other may be more convenient to use in a particular situation. Equation 4.5 is of the same form as Eq. 3.9, with $S_{hZ'}^2/\bar{Y}^2$ replacing S_h^2. Equation 4.5 becomes identical with Eq. 3.9 when all Y_{hi} are equal to 1. Then $\bar{Y}^2$ is equal to 1, and the terms involving Y in Eq. 4.6 are equal to 0.

When the sample over all strata is sufficiently large so that $\bar{x}$ and $\bar{y}$ are approximately normally distributed, and when $\rho_{\bar{x}\bar{y}}$ is approximately equal to $V_{\bar{y}}/V_{\bar{x}}$, the approximation to the variance of r is a good approximation provided $V_{\bar{y}}$ is no greater than .15. It will be a good approximation when $V_{\bar{y}}$ is less than .05 for any value of $\rho_{\bar{x}\bar{y}}$. (For a fuller statement of the conditions when the approximation is good, see Vol. II, Ch. 4, Sec. 12.) The variance of r given above in Eq. 4.2 or 4.5 applies whether a proportionate or disproportionate sample is taken from the strata.

If a proportionate sample is taken so that $f_h = f$ is constant for all strata, the approximation to the variance of r becomes

$$\sigma_r^2 \doteq R^2 \frac{1-f}{n}(V_{wX}^2 + V_{wY}^2 - 2\rho_{wXY} V_{wX} V_{wY}) \tag{4.7}$$

where

$$V_{wX}^2 = \frac{\sum\limits^{L} N_h S_{hX}^2}{N\bar{X}^2} = \frac{S_{wX}^2}{\bar{X}^2} \left.\begin{array}{c} \\ \\ \\ \\ \\ \\ \end{array}\right\}$$

$$V_{wY}^2 = \frac{\sum\limits^{L} N_h S_{hY}^2}{N\bar{Y}^2} = \frac{S_{wY}^2}{\bar{Y}^2} \tag{4.8}$$

are rel-variances based on the average within-stratum variances; and

$$\rho_{wXY} = \frac{\sum_{}^{L}N_h \dfrac{\sum_{}^{N_h}(X_{hi} - \bar{X}_h)(Y_{hi} - \bar{Y}_h)}{N_h - 1}}{NS_{wX}S_{wY}} = \frac{\sum_{}^{L}N_h S_{hXY}}{NS_{wX}S_{wY}} \qquad (4.9)$$

is the average coefficient of correlation within strata. The subscript w on the variances, coefficients of correlation, and coefficients of variation denotes an "average within strata."

From Eq. 4.2 it follows that the coefficient of variation of·the ratio estimate with stratification will be smaller than $V_{\bar{x}}$, the coefficient of variation of the unbiased estimate of a mean or total from the same stratified sample when $\rho_{\bar{x}\bar{y}} > (V_{\bar{y}}/2V_{\bar{x}})$, or, if a proportionate sample is taken from each stratum, when* $\rho_{wXY} > (V_{wY}/2V_{wX})$, and thus that the occasions for using the ratio estimate of a total in preference to the simple unbiased estimate of the same total are essentially the same as when simple random sampling is used (see Sec. 19, Ch. 4).

Weighted sum or average of ratios. Instead of computing the ratio of the averages $\bar{x}$ and $\bar{y}$ (or of the totals x' and y'), we might as an alternative method of estimating the ratio R compute the ratio $r_h = \bar{x}_h/\bar{y}_h = x_h/y_h$ as an estimate of $R_h = X_h/Y_h$, for each stratum, and then take the weighted average of these individual stratum estimates. Thus, returning to the illustration of estimating the ratio of rent to income, if the total rent paid by all families in the sample from the hth stratum is x_h and the aggregate income of these families is y_h, then r_h is the estimate of the ratio of rent to income for the hth stratum, and

$$x_h'' = Y_h \frac{x_h}{y_h} = Y_h r_h$$

is the estimated total rent for that stratum. Consequently,

$$x'' = \sum_{}^{L} x_h'' = \sum_{}^{L} Y_h r_h \qquad (4.10)$$

is an estimate of the total rent based on the ratio estimates for the respective strata. Similarly,

$$r' = \frac{x''}{Y} = \frac{\sum_{}^{L} Y_h r_h}{Y} \qquad (4.11)$$

is the estimate of the ratio of rent to income obtained from the sample by taking the weighted average of the estimated ratios in the respective strata.

* The reader can verify that these follow directly from Eq. 4.2 or 4.7.

The variance of this estimate of the ratio (Eq. 4.11) is approximately*

$$\sigma_{r'}^2 \doteq \frac{1}{N^2 \bar{Y}^2} \sum^{L} N_h^2 \frac{1-f_h}{n_h} S_{hZ}^2 \tag{4.12}$$

where

$$S_{hZ}^2 = S_{hX}^2 + R_h^2 S_{hY}^2 - 2R_h \rho_{hXY} S_{hX} S_{hY} \tag{4.13}$$

where $R_h = X_h / Y_h$, and where the remaining terms in this expression are defined as for Eq. 4.6. Equations 4.6 and 4.13 are identical except for R_h in Eq. 4.13, which replaces R in Eq. 4.6.

Remark. In Eq. 18.10 of Ch. 4 the variance of r was expressed in terms of the variance of Z_i, where $Z_i = X_i - RY_i$. Similarly, with stratified sampling, if we define $Z_{hi} = X_{hi} - R_h Y_{hi}$ we have within the hth stratum the variance of Z_{hi} equal to S_{hZ}^2, i.e.,

$$S_{hZ}^2 = \frac{\sum_{i}^{N_h}(X_{hi} - R_h Y_{hi})^2}{N_h - 1}$$

Also, the $S_{hZ'}^2$ defined by Eq. 4.6 can be put into the related form

$$S_{hZ'}^2 = \frac{\sum^{N_h}(Z_{hi}' - \bar{Z}_h')^2}{N_h - 1}$$

where

$$Z_{hi}' = X_{hi} - RY_{hi}$$

and

$$\bar{Z}_h' = \frac{\sum Z_{hi}'}{N_h}$$

The approximation to the variance is good with large enough samples in each stratum. The sample is large enough for the variance approximation to be good for each stratum separately provided the coefficient of variation of the denominator of the ratio in each stratum does not exceed .05–.15. Values up to .15 are all right if $\rho_{hXY} \doteq V_{hY}/V_{hX}$.

Two points that have been mentioned in connection with ratio estimates are to be emphasized in dealing with this particular estimate of the ratio: first, the fact that the ratio of random variables r_h is a biased estimate of R_h; and, second, the fact that formulas for the variance as given by Eq. 4.12 and 4.13 are approximations and do not hold exactly, being good approximations only under certain conditions. We shall examine these points more fully.

The bias of ratio estimates from stratified samples. In the discussion until now we have dismissed the bias of a ratio estimate as trivial if a

---

* For proof, see Vol. II, Ch. 5, Sec. 3.

moderately large total sample is used. This will be so with an estimate based on a ratio of averages or totals (Eq. 4.1) but may not be so with an estimate based on a weighted sum or average of ratios as given by Eq. 4.10 or 4.11.

The bias of estimate 4.1 is given approximately by

$$\text{Bias} \doteq R(V_{\bar{y}}^2 - V_{\bar{x}\bar{y}}) \tag{4.14}$$

where

$$V_{\bar{x}\bar{y}} = \rho_{\bar{x}\bar{y}} V_{\bar{x}} V_{\bar{y}}$$

The bias of estimate 4.11 is given approximately by

$$\text{Bias} \doteq \frac{1}{Y} \sum_{h}^{L} X_h \frac{1-f_h}{n_h} (V_{hY}^2 - \rho_{hXY} V_{hX} V_{hY}) \tag{4.15}$$

When there are no strata ($L = 1$) both reduce to

$$\text{Bias} \doteq R \frac{1-f}{n} (V_Y^2 - \rho_{XY} V_X V_Y) \tag{4.16}$$

the bias for simple random sampling without stratification. If the sample from each of the strata is reasonably large, say 50–100 or more units, then for most populations ordinarily encountered the bias of either estimate is indeed trivial, and no further attention need be given to it than formerly. But if the stratification is carried to such a point that only a few units are included in the sample from each stratum, and then the stratum-by-stratum ratio estimates are made and weighted up to obtain an estimated total, average, or ratio, there is a danger that the bias in each stratum will be relatively large and that it will be more or less consistent from stratum to stratum, and therefore that the increase in the size of sample resulting from combining the sample over the strata will not have the effect of reducing the bias to a negligible size.*

Illustration 4.1. To illustrate the bias which may arise when we use the stratum-by-stratum estimate with a small sample in some or all of the strata, let us consider a hypothetical population that consists of 100 strata; 50 strata are exactly alike and are of type 1, and the other 50 are also exactly alike and are of type 2. In each stratum there are 4000 elementary units, 1000 of each class, a, b, c, and d, as shown in the accompanying table. Each elementary unit has an x value and a y value, and these values are as shown in the table.

---

* For proof, see Vol. II, Ch. 5, Sec. 4.

Class of unit	Type of stratum					
	Type 1			Type 2		
	Number of units	x	y	Number of units	x	y
a	1000	10	20	1000	10	40
b	1000	10	5	1000	10	10
c	1000	20	10	1000	20	20
d	1000	5	10	1000	5	20
Totals	4000	45	45	4000	45	90
	$R_1 = 1.0$			$R_2 = .5$		

These strata have the following properties: for strata of type 1, the ratio $R_1 = X_1/Y_1 = 1$; for strata of type 2, $R_2 = X_2/Y_2 = .5$; for both types of strata, $V_X^2 = V_Y^2 = .2346$ and $\rho = -.003$.

Suppose that we sample by selecting 2 units at random from each stratum. There are 10 possible sample types, with the relative frequencies shown in the table.

Possible sample value	Expected relative frequency	Ratio $x_h/y_h = r_h$	
		Stratum of type 1 r_h	Stratum of type 2 r_h
aa	$\frac{1}{16}$	.5	.25
ab	$\frac{2}{16}$	.8	.40
ac	$\frac{2}{16}$	1.0	.50
ad	$\frac{2}{16}$	.5	.25
bb	$\frac{1}{16}$	2.0	1.00
bc	$\frac{2}{16}$	2.0	1.00
bd	$\frac{2}{16}$	1.0	.50
cc	$\frac{1}{16}$	2.0	1.00
cd	$\frac{2}{16}$	1.25	.625
dd	$\frac{1}{16}$	.5	.25
Average of sample estimates	1.00	1.13125	.565625

In each stratum the sample of 2 units gives, on the average, an overestimate of the true ratio R_h with a bias of 13 per cent. Hence the estimate from all 100 strata, $r' = \Sigma Y_h r_h/Y$, will be an overestimate of R, and the relative bias will be 13 per cent, even with an over-all sample of 200 cases.

If, however, we use the ratio of estimated totals $r' = x'/y'$, the bias is of the order of .09 per cent, or about one-hundredth as large.

Let us now consider the variances for the two types of ratio estimates. In this illustration the ratios of the stratum totals vary between the types of strata, being equal to 1 in half the strata, and being equal to 1/2 in the remaining strata. This is the case in which we may expect to gain when using the stratum-by-stratum estimate; and indeed we do, the standard

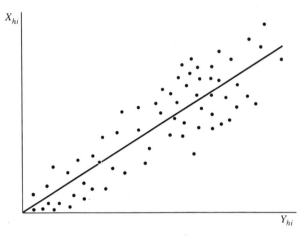

Fig. 1.   A stratum for which the relationship between X
and Y is represented approximately by a straight line
through the origin.

error for this estimate being 5.1 per cent from the total sample of 200, as compared with a standard error of approximately 5.6 per cent for the ratio of estimated totals or estimated means. The true ratio over all strata is .6667, so that the coefficient of variation of either type of estimate is about 8 per cent. The relative bias of the stratum-by-stratum estimate is considerably larger than this coefficient of variation. This illustrates the danger of a stratum-by-stratum estimate when a relatively few cases are taken from each stratum, no matter how large the over-all sample size. On the other hand, the bias in the ratio of estimated totals depends on the over-all sample size.

There will be no bias or only a trivial bias in an estimate of r_h, no matter how small the sample, if the stratum population from which the sample is being drawn is such that the X_{hi}/Y_{hi} and Y_{hi} are uncorrelated. This will be approximately true when $\rho_h \doteq V_{hY}/V_{hX}$, i.e., when the regression of X_{hi} and Y_{hi} is reasonably well represented by a straight line through the origin.* Thus, if the relationship between X_{hi} and Y_{hi} within each stratum has approximately the form shown in Fig. 1, so that a line through the origin is a roughly good fit, there need be little concern

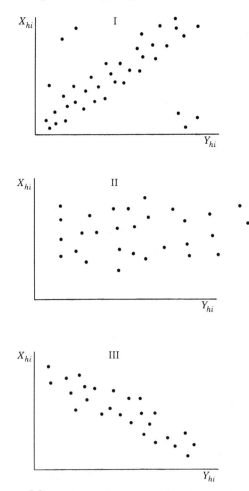

FIG. 2. Three strata for which the relationship between X and Y is not represented by a straight line through the origin.

about the bias, even with small samples from each stratum and an estimate based on a weighted sum or average of ratios. But, if the relationship is something like one of those shown in Fig. 2, or one of

---

* For proof, see Vol. II, Ch. 5, Sec. 4.

many other possible relationships where the line of relationship departs in a significant way from going through the origin, then the ratio estimates for individual strata based on small samples may have a serious bias.

Exercises

4.1. (*a*) Compute the approximation to the variance and to the bias for the data given in Illustration 4.1 for both types of estimates illustrated. Compare the approximation to the bias for the stratum-by-stratum estimate (Eq. 4.15) with the actual variance and bias given in Illustration 4.1, which were obtained by listing the possible samples. The data for the ratio of the estimated totals quoted in the illustration were based on the approximations to the bias and to the variance (Eq. 4.14 and 4.2). Verify these results.

(*b*) Plot the data from Illustration 4.1, separately for each type of stratum, and indicate which of the charts in Fig. 1 and 2 they most closely resemble.

4.2. Look at the income data in Table 15, Sec. 16, Ch. 1, and plot these data; which of the charts in Fig. 1 and 2 do the data most nearly resemble? Compute the variance and exact bias for a sample of 2 units and the approximations to them.

4.3. Using the data in Table 15, Ch. 1, compute the exact bias and variance for a sample of 10 elements; compute also the approximations to them.

4.4. If the 1950 incomes for individuals B and K were \$500 and \$300, respectively, what would the chart look like? Compute the bias and variance, and the approximations to them, for a sample of 2 elements, using the 1950 incomes for B and K given in this exercise.

Which ratio estimate to use. It can be readily shown that, for populations for which the bias of the ratio estimate based upon the weighted average of stratum-by-stratum ratios is negligible, the estimate will have a variance as small as or smaller than that of the ratio of averages or of totals over all strata combined.* However, the difference between the two will be trivial unless the stratification is sufficiently effective to produce a very wide variability in the ratios R_h from stratum to stratum. Highly effective stratification may mean that these ratios will vary widely, but the more usual situation in practice is that the variation in the R_h is sufficiently small that one method will be about as reliable as the other. In Illustration 4.1 given earlier even considerable differences between the stratum ratios do not have a striking effect. Thus, the rules for choice between the two methods should be:

(1) If the sample taken from each stratum is relatively small, then the ratio of estimated totals (Eq. 4.1) should be used unless there are wide differences between the strata in the ratios R_h. In the event that there are such differences, it will ordinarily be possible to group the strata in advance into sets of strata for which the ratio within each group will not differ too widely from stratum to stratum, and such that each group has a

---

* For proof, see Vol. II, Ch. 5, Sec. 5.

large sample size.   The estimates can be made for these groups of strata.

(2) If there is a reasonably large number of units in the sample from each stratum, the method of taking an average of the ratio estimates stratum by stratum (Eq. 4.10 or 4.11) is to be preferred unless it involves extra work.   If it does, then one should be reasonably sure of gaining considerably by this estimate before he actually uses it;   otherwise the gain may not offset the extra work involved.

(3) If the sampling units are the elementary units, and the denominator of the ratio is simply the number of units in the sample, for a subgroup, both methods yield unbiased estimates, and the choice of estimate is determined by consideration of the variances of the estimate, and the work involved in preparing them (cf. Ch. 4, Sec. 16).   This special case is one for which $\rho_h = V_{hY}/V_{hX}$, and each stratum estimate is unbiased.

(4) The method of averaging the ratio estimates stratum by stratum (Eq. 4.10 or 4.11) may be used as a method of estimation only provided that the Y_h are known independently or provided the $Y_h = N_h$, in which event the weighted sum or average of ratios becomes equivalent to the ratio of estimated totals or averages, and there is no problem of bias from the stratum estimate.

An experience often encountered is that the difference between the variances of the two estimates is trivial.   However, the reader should be aware of the differences in the two and be able to detect the conditions where one is likely to be unreliable compared with the other.   Thus, in sampling to estimate change in sales of business establishments, either method is satisfactory, as the ratio for the stratum of large stores does not usually differ by more than perhaps 20 per cent from the ratio for medium-sized or small stores.   We customarily use the ratio of estimated totals, as it is easier to compute.   The variance with this type of estimate is ordinarily not measurably greater, and we avoid any danger of a substantial bias from any of the strata.

In contrast, in a quarterly survey of employment in state and local governmental units,* the estimate of total employment is made by using a weighted average of the ratios of present employment in the reporting units to the employment in the same units in a previous base period, stratum by stratum.   The governmental units are stratified by type of employment (school, nonschool, and higher education), by type of unit (state, city, county, township, special district), and by size of unit.   The ratio of present employment to employment in the previous period varies from .6 to 2.4, a sufficiently wide variation to suggest that the

---

* U.S. Bureau of the Census, *Public Employment in* ———— (quarterly), (Government Employment), Washington, D.C.

stratum-by-stratum estimate is preferable. Moreover, the number of cases in each stratum is very large. This method yields separate estimates for different types of governmental units as a by-product, since each type of unit is a separate stratum.

5. Gains by using proportionate stratified sampling as compared with simple random sampling. We have already seen (Ch. 4, Eq. 9.2) that the variance of a sample mean, $\bar{x}$, based on a simple random sample is equal to

$$(1-f)\frac{S^2}{n} \tag{5.1}$$

and with proportionate stratified sampling the variance of the sample mean is equal to

$$(1-f)\frac{S_w^2}{n} \tag{3.10}$$

Therefore, the absolute reduction of the variance of the sample mean due to stratification with proportionate sampling is obtained by subtracting formula 3.10 from formula 5.1, which gives

$$(1-f)\frac{S^2 - S_w^2}{n} \tag{5.2}$$

and this is approximately equal to*

$$\frac{1-f}{n}\left(\sigma_b^2 - \frac{S_w^2}{\bar{N}}\right) \tag{5.3}$$

where $\bar{N} = N/L$, and

$$\sigma_b^2 = \frac{\sum\limits_{}^{L} N_h(\bar{X}_h - \bar{X})^2}{N} \tag{5.4}$$

is the variance between the stratum means, $\bar{X}_h = X_h/N_h$.

The relative gain for a simple unbiased estimate achieved through proportionate stratified sampling is obtained by dividing the absolute gain as given in Eq. 5.2 or 5.3 by the variance of the estimate from a simple random sample (Eq. 5.1). This gives a relative gain due to stratification of

$$\frac{\sigma_b^2 - (S_w^2/\bar{N})}{S^2} \tag{5.5}$$

which, in turn, is approximately equal to the measure of homogeneity within strata, δ, discussed in Chapter 6.†

It is easily shown, also, that‡

---

* See Vol. II, Ch. 5, Sec. 7.
† See Ch. 6, Sec. 8, for a discussion of this measure of homogeneity.
‡ For proof, see Vol. II, Ch. 5, Sec. 6.

$$\sigma_b^2 + \sigma_w^2 = \sigma^2 = \frac{N-1}{N} S^2 \qquad (5.6)$$

where

$$\sigma_w^2 = \frac{1}{N} \sum^{L} \sum^{N_h} (X_{hi} - \bar{X}_h)^2 \qquad (5.7)$$

and that

$$S_w^2 \doteq \frac{\bar{N}}{\bar{N}-1} \sigma_w^2 \qquad (5.8)$$

will be a good approximation whenever the N_h are large enough or very nearly equal so that $(N_h - 1)/N_h \doteq (\bar{N} - 1)/\bar{N}$.

We see from Eq. 5.4 and Eq. 5.6 that, in sampling from any particular population, the larger the differences between the means of the various strata, the larger will be the variance between strata and the smaller will be the average variance within strata.   Thus, if we can group the units of the population into strata such that the differences between the stratum means are large and account for most of the variation of the characteristic being measured, then we can gain quite a lot by stratification.   On the other hand, Eq. 5.5 shows that, unless the variance between stratum means is large relative to the total variance, not very much will be gained by stratification.

If the strata were made perfectly homogeneous with respect to the characteristic being measured so that all elements within a stratum were exactly alike with respect to that characteristic, then the variance within strata would be equal to zero, the variance between strata would account for all the variability of the characteristic being measured, and there would be no sampling error from such a stratified sample.   If we knew enough about the population to stratify so effectively as to have perfect homogeneity within strata, however, we would know enough about the population in advance that there might be little need to take a sample.

The reader may find it profitable to examine some populations stratified on the basis of different characteristics, and observe how the differences between the stratum means affect the gains due to stratification.   It will be found that, unless exceedingly large differences are accomplished between the strata and only small amounts of variation remain within the strata, the gains will be only moderate or perhaps barely noticeable.

Exercises

5.1. Suppose that it is desired to estimate the value of farm products in the United States, and data are available from which farms may be classified by size, by type, or by tenure of operator.   Using the information shown below, determine which of the three methods of stratification is most effective.   Compare the variance of a sample of 1000 farms, using proportional sampling and the most effective stratification, with that of a simple random sample of 1000 farms.

Stratification	Number of farms N_h	Average value of product (dollars) $\bar{X}_h$	Variance (thousands) S_h^2
All farms	5,858,889	3,472	47,393*
I. Size of farm (acres)			
Under 10	593,937	1,137	17,910
10– 29	944,379	1,471	12,709
30– 49	707,544	1,734	13,891
50– 69	472,598	2,007	15,179
70– 99	685,146	2,425	16,631
100–139	634,611	3,100	24,821
140–179	566,248	4,145	33,118
180–219	283,091	5,081	51,362
220–259	210,058	6,288	63,914
260–499	473,923	7,719	97,223
500–999	173,547	10,875	180,767
1000 and over	113,807	17,366	394,343
II. Type of farm			
Not classified by type	106,929	398	1,125
Fruit and nut	132,873	8,557	222,300
Vegetable	93,646	5,351	143,303
Horticultural—specialty	14,841	14,378	424,325
All other crops	1,860,644	3,659	41,571
Dairy	558,667	4,727	48,739
Poultry	273,129	3,850	69,594
Livestock	809,817	5,971	90,392
Forest products	30,645	1,916	8,807
General farms	688,807	3,748	24,502
Subsistence	1,288,891	488	146
III. Tenure of operator			
Full owners	3,292,063	2,736	35,683
Part owners	661,156	6,904	106,153
Managers	47,357	18,420	509,610
Tenants			
Cash	410,091	2,690	36,205
Share—cash	137,330	5,725	48,164
Share	682,561	4,223	40,052
Croppers (South only)	446,850	1,736	2,696
Other and unspecified	181,481	2,753	29,438

* This is approximately the variance of value of product for simple random sampling without stratification.

5.2. Determine which of the following stratifications is the most efficient with proportionate sampling for estimating the proportion of stores with sales under $10,000 in 1939; which is least efficient?

Stratification	Number of stores	
	Total	Stores under $10,000 sales
Total	1,770,355	958,972
I. Type of operation		
Chain stores	123,195	15,439
Independent stores	1,647,160	943,533
II. Kind of business		
Food	560,549	317,869
Eating and drinking, filling stations, drugs	605,147	359,768
General merchandise, apparel, furniture	210,053	88,521
Automotive, lumber-building group	139,445	41,025
Other retail	255,161	151,789
III. Geographic		
North East	534,707	269,859
North Central	562,417	302,552
South	460,204	279,696
West	213,027	106,865
IV. Number of employees		
10 or more	80,478	0
4–9	211,122	50,000
0–3	1,478,755	908,972

It is worth observing the circumstances under which there is no gain at all by stratification with proportionate sampling. This happens when σ_b^2 is approximately equal to $S_w^2/\bar{N}$. To see what this means, let us suppose that, instead of grouping the population into strata in a purposeful way, the stratification was actually accomplished by distributing the members of the population at random among the strata. Then the mean for the hth stratum would be the mean of a random sample (of size N_h) from the entire population. It turns out that with strata formed by a random grouping of elements the variance between the stratum means, σ_b^2, would be approximately equal to $S^2/\bar{N}$, which, under these circumstances, would be approximately equal to $S_w^2/\bar{N}$.* Thus, when strata are set up in such

* For proof, see Vol. II, Ch. 5, Sec. 8.

a way that they are little or no more effective in accomplishing homogeneity within strata than would be a random grouping, no gain will result from stratification (and the measure of homogeneity will be approximately zero).

From Eq. 5.3 above, it is apparent, too, that sometimes a loss can actually be taken by using stratification with proportionate sampling. This would occur when the differences between strata were even less than would be expected if the strata were made up through a random selection of the population, i.e., if there were smaller differences between strata than would be expected by a random grouping. In practice, this has very little importance, but it is worth knowing that there are circumstances where such loss can occur. The amount of possible loss is trivial if the strata are reasonably large. If, however, one is taking a sample from each of a number of very small strata, it can be shown that there is a possibility of serious loss by stratification.

Exercise 5.3. Consider a population consisting of 8 families with 4 persons in each family, the persons being the parents and 2 children, with half the families having a son and a daughter, a fourth having 2 sons, and a fourth having 2 daughters. (This assumed distribution of sons and daughters is approximately a random distribution.) Let us consider each family a stratum, and select a sample of 1 person from each family in order to estimate the proportion male. Show that the variance with stratified sampling is greater than with simple random sampling.

Remark. Note that the loss is encountered, with proportionate sampling, when the size of the stratum is small, because the factor $N_h/(N_h - 1)$ which multiplies the σ_h^2 in the hth stratum is greater than 1. The maximum possible loss occurs when $N_h = 2$, for all h; and here, when the maximum possible loss occurs, the variance for a proportionate stratified sample is about double the variance of a simple random sample of the same size.

When the estimate is a ratio of random variables, the gains due to stratification with proportionate sampling arise under essentially the same circumstances as those just described for the simple unbiased estimate. Thus, there will be substantial gains from stratification when there are large differences in the $R_h = X_h/Y_h$ between strata as compared with the variation of the $R_{hi} = X_{hi}/Y_{hi}$ within strata. However, it is no longer true that the variance within strata is necessarily less than the variance without stratification, even for large strata, if the estimate is based on the weighted sum of ratios.

The common situation with proportionate stratified sampling is a gain over simple random sampling, although frequently the gain is relatively unimportant. Sometimes significant gains can be achieved through effective stratification. Often, in such cases, still more substantial gains can be accomplished with the same size of sample if a disproportionate sample is drawn from the various strata.   It is necessary, however, that the variations from proportionate sampling be properly determined.   If disproportionate sampling is used and the variation from proportionate samples is improperly determined, one may lose considerably over either proportionate stratified sampling or even simple random sampling.   We shall turn now to a consideration of proper and improper use of disproportionate sampling.

C.   OPTIMUM ALLOCATION OF SAMPLE TO STRATA

6. Gains or losses from stratification when the sampling is disproportionate.   Formula 3.9 gives the variance for a mean estimated from a stratified sample with disproportionate sampling as well as with proportionate sampling.   We shall now examine, with a simple illustration, the kinds of gains or losses that may result with disproportionate sampling.

Suppose that we are sampling to estimate the total production of sawmills, and we have from independent sources a listing of the sawmills from which to sample, as well as information on the production of each mill at an earlier date.   One might draw a sample from such a source in order to estimate total production in a more recent period, average production per mill, or other characteristics.   Table 1 shows the distribution of the numbers of sawmills in various production size groups in the base year, 1942, and the average 1942 production for each group.   The standard deviation of the production within each group is for 1943 and would be unknown in advance of drawing the sample, but is assumed known here for purposes of illustration.

Table 1.   Lumber production in the East

Stratum (production class)	Annual production, 1942 (M bd. ft.)	Number of mills	Total production, 1942 (M bd. ft.)	Average production, 1942 (M bd. ft.)	Standard deviation, 1943 (estimated) (M bd. ft.)	Coefficient of variation, 1943 (estimated)
(1)	(2)	(3)	(4)	(5)	(6)	(7)
1	5000 and over	538	5,934,000	11,029.7	9,000	.98
2	1000–4999	4,756	8,464,000	1,779.6	1,200	.73
3	Under 1000	30,964	6,311,000	203.8	300	1.44
Total for all classes		36,258	20,709,000	571.2	1,684	3.17

With a simple random sample of 1000 mills from this population we have a coefficient of variation of the estimated total of 9.9 per cent.   By taking a proportionate sample from each of the 3 groups this coefficient of variation is reduced to 7.1 per cent.

Now let us examine what happens when we take different fractions from the various strata but still retain the same total number of sawmills in the sample, in an effort to learn when we will lose or gain with disproportionate sampling. We will explore the effect of variable sampling fractions by a systematic set of steps.

In Table 2, alternative allocations of the sample are listed for strata 1, 2, and 3, but with stratum 2 always having the same fraction as stratum 1. The table begins with stratum 3 having a substantially higher fraction than the others, and then successively lower proportions are listed for stratum 3 and higher proportions for the other two. Presented in Table 2, also, are the variances of the estimated mean based on a sample of 1000 for each set of sampling fractions shown. These results are summarized in graphic form in Fig. 3, curve I.

Table 2. Variance of estimated mean, with variable sampling fractions, such that $n_1/N_1 = n_2/N_2$, and $n_1 + n_2 + n_3 = 1000$, for sawmill data from Table 1

Stratum (production class)	Alternative sets of allocations of sample									
	n_h	$100\frac{n_h}{N_h}$	n_h	$100\frac{n_h}{N_h}$	n_h	$100\frac{n_h}{N_h}$	n_h	$100\frac{n_h}{N_h}$	n_h	$100\frac{n_h}{N_h}$
1	5	.93	15	2.8	30	5.6	61	11.3	90	16.7
2	44	.93	131	2.8	265	5.6	539	11.3	795	16.7
3	951	3.1	854	2.8	705	2.3	400	1.3	115	.37
Variance of mean (1000 bd. ft.)²	4158		1414		746		462		762	

The illustration points to two important principles. It is seen, first, that a smaller variance can be achieved by departing from proportionate sampling, and, more than that, for estimating such items as total production, a considerable gain is achieved by the departure from proportionate sampling if the right kind of departure is taken. It is seen also, however, that very much larger variances than with proportionate sampling may result for some of the allocations to strata. These increases in variance will accompany substantial departures from proportionate sampling unless the departures are in the proper direction.

7. Optimum allocation of sample to strata. From Table 2 and Fig. 3, we see that the smallest variance among the samples of 1000 mills listed in Table 2 is accomplished when the proportion included in the sample is about 11.3 per cent for strata 1 and 2 and 1.3 per cent for stratum 3.

Suppose, now, that we keep a sampling fraction of 1.3 per cent (400 mills) from stratum 3 and let the fractions differ as between strata 1 and 2, but still consider only those different sampling fractions that give us a total sample size of 1000. The results of such alternative compilations are summarized in Fig. 3, curve II. For certain of the allocations the variance is still further reduced, and for others it is increased. At this

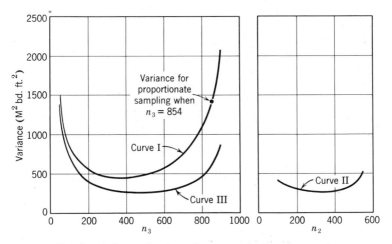

FIG. 3.   Variance of estimated mean production, for sample of 1000 sawmills, with alternative allocations of the sample to strata.

stage we find the best results if about 325 mills or 6.8 per cent are taken from the second stratum, and if about 275 or 51.1 per cent are taken from the first stratum.

This process can be extended by again varying the sampling fraction in stratum 3 and at the same time varying the fractions taken from strata 1 and 2 but in such a way that n_1 has the same ratio to n_2 as was found to be best in the preceding step; i.e.,

$$\frac{n_1}{n_2} = \frac{275}{325} \quad \text{or} \quad n_1 = \frac{275}{600}(n_1 + n_2) = \frac{275}{600}(n - n_3)$$

and

$$n_2 = \frac{325}{600}(n - n_3)$$

The results of this final step are summarized in Fig. 3, curve III. Here, again, we find that further reduction of the variance of a mean estimated from a sample of 1000 mills is accomplished when appropriate sampling fractions are used, and, also, that serious losses may result if the wrong fractions are selected.

If we now try making further adjustments in the sampling fractions, it is found that no additional gains are achieved. We say, then, that for a total sample of 1000 the "optimum" allocation of our sample among the strata is that which gives the minimum variance, which is to take $n_1 = 244$ mills from the first stratum, $n_2 = 288$ mills from the second stratum, and $n_3 = 468$ mills from the third stratum. These are the values that give the minimum point on curve III, Fig. 3, and result in a variance of 259. No other allocation of a sample of size $n = 1000$ can be found for which the estimates $\bar{x}$ or x' will have a smaller variance.

Figure 3 also shows that the variance has a broad minimum in the neighborhood of the optimum values of n_1, n_2, and n_3. For example, from curve III in Fig. 3, any value of n_3 between 350 and 600 leads to a variance not more than 10 per cent greater than the optimum variance. The fact that moderate deviations of the sample allocation from the optimum allocation do not substantially increase the variance is of real importance.

To summarize, we assumed, first, that we knew the variances of the production of mills in each of the different strata, so that we could compute the variance of a sample mean for a sample of 1000 mills allocated in various ways among the 3 strata. With this knowledge we determined the optimum allocation of the sample to each stratum, and found that the variance of the mean based on this optimum allocation was 259 compared with 1414 for proportionate stratified sampling. Thus, very substantial gains were obtained by the optimum allocation.

Let us now consider how these results can be introduced into the practical job of sample design. One problem is to recognize the circumstances when disproportionate sampling is desirable. A second problem is to reduce the amount of work involved in carrying through the operation to obtain the optimum allocation of the sample; the process of computing successive approximations followed in the illustration above would be very laborious if there were a large number of strata. A third problem is to know what to do when the variances within the strata are not known in advance of designing the sample. A fourth and particularly troublesome problem is to determine what to do when, from a single sample, a number of different characteristics are to be estimated. Another problem of considerable practical importance is to take into account differences in the cost of collecting or processing the data. We shall consider the first two of these problems together, and then the remaining three separately.

8. Ascertaining the optimum allocation and determining when to use it.
It is possible, mathematically, to show that the optimum allocation for a
given size of sample, with equal costs per unit for all strata, is accomplished by allocating the sample as follows between whatever strata have
been set up:

If n is the total size of sample that is to be drawn, then the optimum
values for the n_h will be given by:*

$$\text{opt. } n_h = \frac{N_h \tilde{S}_h}{\sum N_h \tilde{S}_h} n \tag{8.1}$$

where $\tilde{S}_h$ is defined as in (a), (b), or (c) below.

(a) For sample estimate 3.2 or 3.3,

$$\tilde{S}_h = S_h \tag{8.2}$$

P/82

with S_h defined in Eq. 1.2 (or, for a proportion, in Eq. 3.11).

(b) For sample estimate 4.1 or for an estimated total obtained by
multiplying the estimated ratio by a known total,

$$\tilde{S}_h = \frac{S_{hZ'}}{\bar{Y}} \tag{8.3}$$

with $S_{hZ'}$ given by Eq. 4.6.

(c) For sample estimate 4.10 or 4.11,

$$\tilde{S}_h = \frac{S_{hZ}}{\bar{Y}} \tag{8.4}$$

with S_{hZ} given by Eq. 4.13.

The variance, using the optimum values of n_h, is given by

$$\sigma^2 \text{ (opt.)} = \frac{1}{N^2} \left[\frac{(\sum N_h \tilde{S}_h)^2}{n} - \sum N_h \tilde{S}_h^2 \right] \tag{8.5}$$

Under certain circumstances opt. n_h (Eq. 8.1) is subject to the following
modification.   An initial computation may sometimes give a result such
that the computed optimum value of n_h is greater than the total number
of units in the stratum, N_h; i.e., the equation for the optimum seems to
say that a sample of more than 100 per cent should be taken, which, of
course, is impossible.   In this instance the procedure to follow is merely
to take n_h equal to N_h for each such stratum, and then to distribute the
remainder of the sample among the other strata in accordance with the
optimum equation.   Equation 8.5 must be modified, also, when some of

---

* For proof, see Vol. II, Ch. 5, Sec. 9.

the initial n_h are greater than the N_h. In this instance only the strata for which n_h are less than N_h are included in computing σ^2 (opt.) with Eq. 8.5, and the value for n in σ^2 (opt.) is the total number of cases in the sample from these strata.

> **Remark.** The variance with optimum allocation (Eq. 8.5) is equal to the variance given by Eq. 3.9, 4.2, or 4.5 when the optimum values for the n_h (as given by Eq. 8.1) are substituted in the appropriate variance formula. In practice, when an effort at optimum allocation has been made, it is usually desirable to compute the variance for that allocation by substitution directly in the original variance formula instead of using Eq. 8.5, especially because Eq. 8.5 is applicable only if the optimum is accurately determined, whereas usually it will be only approximated, at best.

The reader can check the results obtained from Eq. 8.1 with the sawmill data against the optimum results found experimentally above, and he will find that the formula gives exactly the results obtained by the more laborious experimental process if the successive approximation method is carried far enough. This experimental process, incidentally, would have been much more laborious had there been a larger number of strata, and we find, therefore, that our formula for the allocation of the sample, which gives us the optimum allocation directly, is very economical in terms of time spent. Thus, for the illustration above the optimum values of the n_h are computed as follows:

$$n_1 = \frac{N_1 S_1}{\Sigma N_h S_h}\, n = \frac{4,842}{19,838}\,(1,000) = 244$$

$$n_2 = \frac{N_2 S_2}{\Sigma N_h S_h}\, n = \frac{5,707}{19,838}\,(1,000) = 288$$

$$n_3 = \frac{N_3 S_3}{\Sigma N_h S_h}\, n = \frac{9,289}{19,838}\,(1,000) = 468$$

and these results agree with those obtained above.

To illustrate the procedure when the optimum n_h computed with Eq. 8.1 exceeds N_h, suppose, in the above illustration, that S_1 had been equal to 36,000, and that S_2 and the S_3 had been equal, respectively, to 1200 and 300 as before. Then the direct application of Eq. 8.1 gives as the optimum values for the respective strata:

$$n_1 = 564$$
$$n_2 = 166$$
$$n_3 = 270$$
$$\overline{\quad\quad\quad}$$
$$n = 1000$$

This tells us to take more units out of the first stratum than there are in that stratum. To deal with this we simply adjust the values obtained from Eq. 8.1, making $n_1 = N_1$, and then recompute the optimum values for the remaining strata by assigning $(n - N_1)$ units to the sample from the other strata, and distributing the remaining sample over those strata proportionately to the $N_h S_h$. Thus, in this instance we obtain the optimum by taking

$$n_1 = N_1 \qquad\qquad\qquad = 538$$

$$n_2 = \frac{N_2 S_2}{N_2 S_2 + N_3 S_3} (n - N_1) = 176$$

$$n_3 = \frac{N_3 S_3}{N_2 S_2 + N_3 S_3} (n - N_1) = 286$$

Exercises

8.1. Using the data in Table 1, Sec. 6, find the optimum allocation of a sample of 2500 mills. Notice that increasing the sample size to this extent makes the sample of mills producing over 5000 M bd. ft. larger than the total number of such mills. Compute the variance for the optimum allocation.

8.2. For a survey of pig iron scrap, the following information is available:

TONNAGE IN BASE PERIOD	NUMBER OF ESTABLISHMENTS	AVERAGE TONNAGE IN BASE YEAR	ESTIMATED STANDARD DEVIATION
0– 799	1280	311	253
800–2499	890	1369	448
2500–4999	370	3838	716
5000 and over	180	9448	4688
Totals	2720	1741	

Determine the optimum allocation of a sample of 500 establishments.

8.3. Using the data in Ex. 5.1, compute the optimum allocation for a sample of 1000 farms for the 3 sets of strata, compute the variance for the optimum allocation, and compare it with the proportionate stratified sampling variance.

Gains by using optimum allocation as compared with proportionate stratified sampling. Equations 8.1 and 8.2 tell us that for a simple unbiased estimate of a mean or total the optimum size of sample to take out of a stratum is determined jointly by the N_h, the number of units in the stratum, and the S_h, the standard deviation between those units of the characteristic being sampled. The larger the number of units in the stratum the larger the sample from the stratum, and also the greater the variability within the stratum (the greater the S_h) the larger will be the optimum sample from the stratum.   Similarly, where ratio estimates are involved, it is seen from Eq. 8.1, 8.3, and 8.4 that N_h and $S_{hZ'}$ or S_{hZ} (Eq. 4.6 and 4.13) determine the optimum allocation.

The fact that a higher sampling fraction should be taken from a stratum if the variability within the stratum is large than if it is small seems reasonable if we consider the extreme case where there is no variability within a stratum.   We would know the mean for such a stratum perfectly if a sample of only 1 were taken from the stratum, and nothing whatever would be gained by increasing the size of the sample from the stratum. The reliability of the sample estimate could be increased by taking all the rest of the sample from the strata within which the variability is large.

If the $\tilde{S}_h$ were the same for all the strata, the optimum allocation would be a proportionate sample, since Eq. 8.1 then says that the optimum value for the n_h will be to make them proportionate to the N_h.

With the simple unbiased estimate (Eq. 3.2 or 3.3), disproportionate sampling will gain when the S_h differ, and with the ratio estimate when the $S_{hZ'}$ or the S_{hZ} differ.   Worth-while gains will result only if they differ widely.   In fact, the relative gain achieved by using optimum allocation (assuming all $n_h < N_h$) is*

$$\text{Relative gain} = \frac{V^2_{\tilde{S}_h}}{(1-f)(1 + V^2_{\tilde{S}_h})} \tag{8.6}$$

$$\doteq \frac{V^2_{\tilde{S}_h}}{1 + V^2_{\tilde{S}_h}} \tag{8.7}$$

where

$$\sigma^2_{\tilde{S}_h} = \frac{1}{N}\Sigma N_h(\tilde{S}_h - \bar{S})^2 \tag{8.8}$$

is the variance between strata of the $\tilde{S}_h$, with $\bar{S} = (1/N)\Sigma N_h\tilde{S}_h$, and

$$V^2_{\tilde{S}_h} = \frac{\sigma^2_{\tilde{S}_h}}{\bar{S}^2} \tag{8.9}$$

is the rel-variance of the $\tilde{S}_h$.

Thus, the greater the coefficient of variation of the $\tilde{S}_h$ the greater will be the relative gain due to optimum allocation.   This coefficient of variation must be as large as $\frac{1}{3}$ in order to reduce the variance below that for proportionate sampling by 10 per cent; if it is equal to 1 a gain of 50 per cent will result.   In the sawmill illustration above, the coefficient of variation of the S_h was equal to 1.98, and consequently a reduction in variance of 80 per cent over proportionate sampling was achieved.

---

* See Vol. II, Ch. 5, Sec. 10.

Remark. There are many practical sampling problems from which little is to be gained in the way or reduction of sampling variance through optimum allocation of the sample to the strata. Moreover, optimum allocation may introduce some problems in tabulation and preparing estimates, since, instead of a simple aggregate of the results from the sample, the results from each stratum need to be weighted separately, which may add to the cost of tabulation.

In practice the situation usually reduces to something like this: If there are very large variations in the within-strata standard deviations, then worth-while gains will be achieved by a rough approximation to the optimum allocation, and often when the standard deviations vary widely it is possible to obtain such rough approximations. On the other hand, where the variations in the within-strata standard deviations are not large, then rough approximations to the standard deviations may lead to results no better than proportionate sampling, and perhaps worse—and at best only small gains are to be achieved if the approximations turn out to be good.*

The next sections discuss methods of approximating the standard deviation when the variability of the within-strata standard deviation is large (i.e., gains from disproportionate allocation may be large).

9. Problem created because the variances may be unknown. The third problem mentioned above (Sec. 7) in the application of optimum sampling theory to strata was that the determination of the optimum allocation of the sample depends upon knowledge of the variance of the characteristic under consideration for each stratum. The fact is that these variances will seldom be known accurately. Sometimes they can be estimated only very roughly, if at all, in advance of drawing a sample, and at best we must deal with approximations. Fortunately, rough estimates will squeeze out almost all the possible saving: exact values are not needed.

Sometimes one can derive from prior experience a fairly accurate idea of the relative sizes of the standard deviations in the different strata. If we do not know the values of $\tilde{S}_1, \tilde{S}_2, \cdots, \tilde{S}_L$, but do know some numbers proportional to them, $k\tilde{S}_1, k\tilde{S}_2, \cdots, k\tilde{S}_L$, we find that exactly the same optimum allocation of the sample to strata will result. Thus, it is sufficient to know the *relative* magnitudes of the standard deviations in the various strata, and to know them only roughly.

The reader should notice in Fig. 3 that, while the optimum values for the n_h lead to substantial reductions in the variance as compared to the use of proportionate sampling, nevertheless they do not lead to very different results from those obtained with moderate deviations from the optimum. The minimum on each of the curves is broad and not very

---

* Sukhatme (1) gives a treatment which indicates the effect of allocations based on estimates of the strata standard deviations.

sensitive to moderate departures from the optimum values for the n_h. In the lumber problem, for example, with n remaining equal to 1000, deviations of 20 per cent in the n_h increase the variance by at most 10 per cent. This means that, if one can find reasonably good approximate values for the standard deviations, or for numbers proportionate to them, from prior information or from a pretest, the approximations should lead to results nearly as good as would result if the standard deviations were known exactly.

An illustration of how one can go about obtaining rough approximate values for the variances for use in determining the optimum allocation is contained in the following discussion of the sawmill example used earlier. In the presentation of that illustration we assumed that the variances within the strata were known at the time the sample was being designed. Now let us suppose that they were not, and that we were approaching the job of designing the sample.

The information available in such a problem might be a listing of sawmills together with information on the size of each establishment at some prior date, such as total production, total employees, or total wages paid during some recent earlier period, that can be used as a rough measure of current size. With this type of information the three size groups assumed in the earlier illustration were set up. We shall assume that these same size groups are to be used, and now we want to explore how, without knowing the variances, we can approximate an optimum allocation.

There are two lines of approach that we can follow. One approach is to use a rough rule of thumb that has been found helpful in similar problems; and the other is to carry out preliminary samples or pretests, or to make a careful study of past experience with specific information that is closely related to the present problem. The rule to be given provides a useful guide for optimum allocation when the units to be sampled have a very large variability in size and at the same time have some relative stability of size over the period of time under consideration, so that the size of the unit at one period of time provides a rough prediction of its relative size at another period. For example, the total sales of a business establishment tend to have some stability through time. A store that was very large last year will ordinarily be of roughly the same relative size this year, in terms of its sales, number of employees, and related items. Similarly, a city or county large one year will be large in near-by years, and a small one will be small. Again, the farms or families with large incomes in one year will tend to have large incomes the following year, and most of those with small incomes one year will have small incomes the following year, although the stability of farm or family incomes will be considerably less than that of sales of stores in most kinds of business; and the stability of both of these will be less than that of the size of city or county. An illustration where little stability may be expected is an inventory item such as the amount of grain held on a farm, which may vary quite widely from year to year as well as from month to month within a year, or the inventory on hand of a particular type of commodity in a manufacturing establishment or retail store. The traditional methods of doing business mean that these latter types of items fluctuate much more widely than the earlier ones named, and for such inventory items one would expect relatively small correlations from year to year as compared with those for the more stable types of items mentioned.

10. Sampling fractions proportionate to average measure of size as approximation to optimum. Where there is stability in the size of the units to be sampled, a rough approximation to the optimum allocation for estimating the characteristics that are highly correlated with the measure of size may be provided by assuming that the $\tilde{S}_h$ in Eq. 8.1 are proportionate to the average measure of size of the units in that stratum.

Suppose that Y_h is the aggregate measure of size for the hth stratum, and $\bar{Y}_h = Y_h/N_h$. If we assume that the $\bar{Y}_h$ are proportionate to the S_h and substitute $\bar{Y}_h$ for $\tilde{S}_h$ in Eq. 8.1, then

$$n_h = n\,\frac{Y_h}{Y}$$

Notice, with this allocation, that

$$\frac{n_h}{N_h} = \bar{Y}_h\,\frac{n}{Y}$$

which says that the proportion of the units included in the sample from a stratum is proportionate to the average measure of size of the establishments in that stratum. With this allocation the chance of a particular unit being included in the sample is approximately proportionate to its measure of size.

In our sawmill illustration it may be reasonable to assume that there is some stability in the production of lumber from one year to the next— most large mills will continue large and most small mills will continue small. Moreover, there is a wide variation in the size of unit as measured by the production during the prior period. Also, since this measure of size was known at the time of planning the sample, it would be used as the basis for classifying establishments into size groups, and the $\bar{Y}_h$, the average sizes needed to apply the above rule, can be readily computed.

For the sawmill illustration (Table 1, Sec. 6), with $n = 1000$, our guessed optimum values are:

$$n_1 = n \frac{Y_1}{Y} = (1,000) \frac{5,934}{20,709} = 286$$

$$n_2 = n \frac{Y_2}{Y} = (1,000) \frac{8,464}{20,709} = 409$$

$$n_3 = n \frac{Y_3}{Y} = (1,000) \frac{6,311}{20,709} = 305$$

With this allocation of the sample the variance of the estimated average production is 298, as compared with 259 for the optimum allocation, and with 1414 for proportionate sampling. A substantial amount of the decrease in variance that could have been obtained with the optimum has been accomplished with this approximation to it. Table 3 shows the allocation of a sample of 1000 mills by the different methods discussed in this chapter, and the corresponding variances.

Table 3.   Allocation of a sample of 1000 mills

Stratum (production class)	Simple random sampling	Stratified sampling					
		Proportionate sampling		Optimum allocation		Proportional to 1942 total production	
		Number of mills	Per cent of stratum	Number of mills	Per cent of stratum	Number of mills	Per cent of stratum
1		15	2.8	244	45.4	286	53.2
2		131	2.8	288	6.1	409	8.6
3		854	2.8	468	1.5	305	1.0
Variance of estimated mean $(\sigma_{\bar{x}}^2)$	2758	1414		259		298	
$V_{\bar{x}}$	9.9%	7.1%		3.0%		3.3%	

The same kind of approximation to the optimum would have resulted if the characteristic to be estimated were either the total production or the total, or average, value of any of a number of items that are highly correlated with the measure of size used. Thus, total or average current employment, total or average wages paid, total or average expenses, total or average value of assets, or other similar items might have been expected to give similar results.

The basis for the rule just given is the assumption that with the simple unbiased estimate of a mean or total the coefficients of variation are about the same for all strata, in which event it follows that the S_h are roughly proportionate to the $\bar{X}_h$. We do not know the $\bar{X}_h$, of course, since it is the average value of these that we are trying to estimate from the sample; but if the X_{hi} are roughly proportionate to their measures of size, Y_{hi}, on the average, then the $\bar{Y}_h$ will be roughly proportionate to the $\bar{X}_h$, and this assumption, along with the assumption that the $S_h/\bar{X}_h$ are roughly constant, gives the rule used above. If the average measures of size differ widely between strata (for many important populations they will vary by more than a factor of 10), the coefficients of variation can be assumed to be close enough to equality if they (the coefficients of variation) vary by no more than a factor of perhaps 2 or at most 3.

The rule for approximating the optimum is applicable, also, if the characteristic being estimated is an estimate of a ratio, such as the ratio of current sales to sales during a prior period or the ratio of wages paid to total sales, whether the estimate of the ratio involves the application of Eq. 4.1 or Eq. 4.11. In fact, it is seen from Eq. 8.1 and 8.3 or 8.4 that, if the $S_{hZ}/\bar{Y}_h$ or $S_{hZ}/\bar{Y}_h$ are constant for the strata, which may be a reasonably valid assumption, the optimum sampling fractions are proportionate to the $\bar{Y}_h/\bar{Y}$.

Exercise 10.1. Consider the problem of estimating the change in sales of independent retail stores in New York City, from one month to the next, with a sample of 1000 stores. Table 4 shows stores classified by size, using as the measure of size the number of persons employed at an earlier date (in this case 1939).

The table also shows the total number of employees in 1939 for each stratum, the change in sales from one month to the next as a ratio (R_h), and the $S_{hZ}/\bar{Y}_h$ and $S_{hZ}/\bar{Y}$, where the values given are estimates that have been made separately for each stratum. The values given in the last four columns would be available only after completion of the sample, or on the basis of advance speculations.

Table 4.   Independent retail stores in New York City

Size group	Number of employees, 1939	Total employees, 1939	Number of stores N_h	Ratio of sales in present month to sales in preceding month R_h	$\frac{S_{hZ}}{\bar{Y}_h}$	$\frac{S_{hZ}}{\bar{Y}}$	$N_h \frac{S_{hZ}}{\bar{Y}}$
	(1)	(2)	(3)	(4)	(5)	(6)	(7)
1	100 and over	55,315	95	1.102	.2199	60.016	5,701.5
2	10–99	58,085	2,175	1.069	.1642	1.6274	3,539.7
3	Under 10	148,157	104,517	1.053	.4543	.25785	26,950.0
Totals		261,557	106,809	1.068			

Compute and compare the variances for the following three designs:

(*a*) Distribute the 1000 cases proportionately to the number of stores, i.e., proportionately to column 3 of Table 4.

(*b*) Distribute the 1000 cases proportionately to the total measure of size (column 2 of Table 4). We term this allocation proportionate to a measure of size. This is the allocation based on the rule of thumb given above.

(*c*) Distribute the 1000 cases proportionately to column 7. This design we term optimum allocation.

> **Remark.** In all three cases, the variance of the estimate is given by Eq. 4.12 with the substitution of the appropriate values of n_h. Note that, in the estimation of the variance for the design with allocation proportionate to a measure of size, the measures of sizes are known or estimated from past data, whereas the S_{hZ}, R_h, and perhaps the Y_h to be used in Eq. 4.12 and 4.13 are estimated from current data. The measures of size do not enter into the computations except in determining the sample allocation.

The principal thing to avoid in connection with approximating an optimum allocation is an exceedingly serious under-representation of some particular stratum. If a stratum is seriously under-represented, with perhaps only a third (or a fourth) or fewer cases from the stratum than would be provided by the optimum, then the variance of the estimate may be increased very considerably. It can be seen from Fig. 3 (p. 207), for example, that if a stratum is badly under-represented the variance may be very much larger than the minimum.

This consideration leads to a modification of the rule given at the beginning of this section which says to make the sampling fractions proportionate to average measures of size for the strata. It may be noted in the retail store illustration, Table 4 (p. 217), that $S_{hZ}/\bar{Y}_h$ is considerably larger for the stratum of small establishments than for the other two strata. Similarly, in Table 2 (p. 206) (the sawmill illustration), the stratum with the smallest size of establishments has a considerably larger coefficient of variation than the others. It is not uncommon to find this situation. It arises because the smaller establishments may be going in and out of business more frequently, and because moderate absolute changes in size make for big relative changes and consequently a large coefficient of variation.

A possible modification of the rule, therefore, is arbitrarily to over-sample the smallest size stratum, perhaps by a factor of 2 as compared with the result that would be obtained by the rule as originally given. This oversampling can be accomplished by arbitrarily doubling the measure of size for the smallest size stratum before applying the rule of allocating in proportion to measures of size.

Exercise 10.2. Recompute the approximation to the optimum, using the rule of having the sampling fractions proportionate to average measures of size, but doubling the measure of size for the smallest size group, for: (a) the retail store data in Ex. 10.1 (Table 4); (b) the tonnage of pig iron scrap data in Ex. 8.2; (c) the sawmill data in Table 1, Sec. 6; (d) the income data in Table 5, Sec. 17, as grouped into 3 strata in Ex. 17.3. Compare the variances with the variances when the original measures of size are used for the allocations, and with the optimum allocations.

> **Remark.** Sometimes a situation arises where the measure of size for a group is zero, or even negative, as in the income illustration of Sec. 17, Table 5. In this case, some families had no income in the base period. A similar situation might occur for new establishments, not in existence in a past period. In such cases, where the group is treated as a separate stratum, a straight application of measure-of-size rule would lead to no sample from the group, so the rule must be modified. In fact, especial care must be exercised not to undersample such a group because it often has a larger-than-average coefficient of variation. It is sometimes sufficient to give the group the same sampling fraction as that assigned to the next smallest size group. It is desirable, for such a group, however, to approximate in advance the optimum sampling fraction. Otherwise, the group may make a substantial contribution to the total variance.

11. Fixing number and boundaries of strata with optimum allocation. Were it not for comparatively intangible factors of cost and other difficulties that arise from the use of a great many different sampling fractions in processing the sampling returns and preparing estimates, the rule would be to have a great many strata. Little attention would need to be given to the determination of the boundaries beyond considerations of maximum homogeneity already indicated. In practice, however, costs and problems of control often make it desirable to have only a very limited number of different sampling fractions, perhaps only 2 or 3, or perhaps a half dozen or so. There may, of course, be additional strata, but without further variations in the sampling fractions. It is important, with such a limited number of sampling fractions, to give some attention to the location of the stratum boundaries for which varying sampling fractions are used, in order to achieve the maximum gains from optimum alloca-tion. A theory for determining the optimum boundaries for any fixed number of strata, where stratification is by size of establishment, is given by Dalenius and Gurney.*

An approximate rule that is often a reasonably good guide is to define the strata so that the aggregate measures of size of the respective strata are about the same. For example, in the sawmill illustration (Table 1, p. 205), in which three strata were used, the strata were roughly equal with respect to the aggregate measure of size, the total production in 1942 (column 4). This rule is often a reasonably satisfactory one to

---

* Tore Dalenius and Margaret Gurney, "The Problem of Optimum Strati-fication, II," *Skandinavisk Aktuarietidskrift*, 1951, pp. 133–148.

follow in establishing the boundaries of the major strata that distinguish sampling fractions. Some special modification of this rule may occasionally be needed, as in the case mentioned in the preceding section where the measure of size is zero for a class of establishments. Such a group, if it is of any significant size, usually should be set up as a separate stratum, whether or not it has a separate sampling fraction.

Another group that may need special consideration and modification of the above rule is the stratum of largest establishments. Whenever any establishment is large enough that it individually accounts for $1/n$th of the aggregate size of all establishments combined (where n is the total size of sample), the rules given in the preceding section for approximating the allocation will indicate that such a unit should be included in the sample with certainty. If n is the sample size and Y the total measure of size for the population of the characteristic we are measuring, then all units which are larger than Y/n will be in the sample, and the top size class should include all these units. Some units smaller than Y/n should be included with certainty also, since an optimum allocation of the remainder of the sample among the remaining members of the population will generally result in additional units being large enough to be selected with certainty. In addition, there will be other units for which the optimum would be to have a sampling fraction of perhaps .9 or .8, and if only a limited number of distinct sampling fractions is to be used it is desirable to include with certainty establishments for which the optimum fraction would be close to 1. A possible rule is that the largest size class shall consist of all units which are greater in size than $Y/2n$.

Illustration 17.1 and Ex. 17.1–17.6 illustrate the loss in precision from reducing the number of different sampling fractions and the effect of different stratification groupings.

12. Taking account of costs in optimum allocation. The discussion of optimum allocation of the sample thus far has been in terms of getting the most reliable results for a given total size of sample. The approach can be modified to take account of differences in the costs of sampling from different strata. If such differences are large, the size of the sample is not a good measure of the total cost involved. Thus, suppose that in Table 1, p. 205, we further subdivided the mills into those that are in locations more or less readily accessible to an existing field organization and those that are not. For example, it might be that the cost of obtaining the returns from those in outlying rural areas, if personal interviews were called for to get the information, would be about 4 times the cost of getting a sample from those more conveniently located. It would turn out, then, that the best allocation would involve taking account of these costs as well as of the standard deviation in the various strata.   Or, again, it might cost more to obtain a schedule from a small mill than a large one, or vice versa.   If the differences in such costs are large (say a factor of 3 or 4 or more), then it will pay to have the stratification provide, among other things, for segregating the groups that have important differences in cost levels, and to give attention to these differences in costs.

If we are to take account of cost, we must ascertain or estimate what the differences in cost are in sampling from the various strata.   In this section we shall assume that the cost per unit of including a unit in the sample from any particular stratum is the same no matter how many units are included in the sample from that stratum.*   There may be, in addition, a fixed overhead cost that does not depend upon how the sample is allocated among the strata.   The actual cost situation may be found to be more complex.   However, a simple cost relationship may provide a useful guide to what happens in more complex situations.

With these assumptions as to the cost relationship, we shall let C represent the total cost, excluding any fixed overhead costs, and let C_1 represent the cost per unit of including a unit in the sample from the first stratum, C_2 the corresponding cost for the second stratum, etc.   Then the part of the total cost of the sample which can be affected by the sample size will be

$$C = C_1 n_1 + C_2 n_2 + \cdots + C_L n_L$$

$$= \sum^{L} C_h n_h$$

With this cost function it turns out that the optimum allocation of the sample to strata that gives the most information per dollar is obtained when the number in the sample taken from the hth stratum is given by†

$$n_h = \frac{N_h \tilde{S}_h / \sqrt{C_h}}{\sum^{L} (N_h \tilde{S}_h / \sqrt{C_h})} \, n \qquad (12.1)$$

where $\tilde{S}_h$ is given by Eq. 8.2, 8.3, or 8.4, depending on the sample estimate. If the total cost of a survey is fixed, n is given by

$$n = \frac{C}{\sum^{L} N_h \tilde{S}_h \sqrt{C_h}} \sum^{L} \frac{N_h \tilde{S}_h}{\sqrt{C_h}} \qquad (12.2)$$

---

* Chapters 6, 7, and 9 cover the case where this assumption is not made, together with other aspects of more complex designs.
† For proof, see Vol. II, Ch. 5, Sec. 11.

If, however, an estimate with a specified variance, ε^2, is required, n is given by

$$n = \frac{\sum\limits^{L} N_h \tilde{S}_h \sqrt{C_h}}{N^2 \varepsilon^2 + \sum\limits^{L} N_h \tilde{S}_h^2} \sum\limits^{L} \frac{N_h \tilde{S}_h}{\sqrt{C_h}} \tag{12.3}$$

Whichever requirement is used, a fixed cost or a fixed precision, the total variance is given by

$$\sigma^2 \text{ (opt.)} = \frac{1}{nN^2} \sum\limits^{L} N_h \tilde{S}_h \sqrt{C_h} \sum\limits^{L} \frac{N_h \tilde{S}_h}{\sqrt{C_h}} - \frac{\sum\limits^{L} N_h \tilde{S}_h^2}{N^2} \tag{12.4}$$

where n is given by either Eq. 12.2 or 12.3.

Some modification is needed in Eq. 12.1, 12.2, 12.3, and 12.4 whenever the opt. $n_h > N_h$ for one or more of the strata, along the lines discussed in Sec. 8, p. 209.

If the $\tilde{S}_h$ and the cost function are not known, they must be approximated if the optimum allocation is to be attempted.

Notice that only the relative cost factors and not their absolute size affect the proportion of the sample allocated to the strata. Also, the optimum allocation formula specifies that the sample taken from a high-unit-cost stratum will be smaller and from a low-unit-cost stratum will be larger than would result by minimizing the variance for a given total size of sample without regard to cost, as was done earlier (Eq. 8.1).

Two points should be emphasized with respect to optimum allocation of the sampling to strata, in connection with differences of costs in the various strata.

(a) Since the differences in cost affect the allocation of the sample only in proportion to the square root of the relative costs per unit involved, the allocation is not very sensitive to small differences in cost. Unless the cost differences between strata are of a highly significant character, say a factor of 3 or more, little will be gained by introducing a cost function into the determination of the optimum sampling ratios.

(b) It was indicated earlier that, unless there are very substantial differences in standard deviations between strata, little is to be gained by optimum allocation to strata. However, if the differences in costs are large enough, it may be worth while to establish strata for which cost differences are substantial and to have differential allocations to them, even though the standard deviations may not differ substantially. Thus, suppose that the standard deviations in two strata are the same, but that the cost of obtaining the sample in one stratum is 10 times that in the other; then the optimum allocation will involve taking approximately 3 times as large a sampling fraction from one stratum as from the other, and fairly worth-while gains in information per unit of cost may result.

Illustration 12.1. The optimum allocation, with variable costs per stratum, was found useful in the following problem.* A population of 260,000 schedules, each a report of an accident, was at hand. Using a sample, it was desired to estimate the average, $\bar{X}$, of a certain characteristic, for example, the number of days of work lost, of the accidents reported.

As only about half the schedules were coded for punching and the processing costs would be different for coded and uncoded schedules, the population was divided into 2 groups. The first, containing $N_1 = 150,000$ coded schedules, was estimated to cost roughly .15 kr. per schedule. The second group, containing $N_2 = 110,000$ noncoded schedules, was estimated to cost .50 kr. per schedule. The standard deviations S_1 and S_2 were unknown, but there was reason to expect that they were of the same order of magnitude.

The total budget C for the survey was 5000 kr., excluding fixed costs. Using formulas 12.1 and 12.2 for the determination of optimum n_h, with the following simplifying assumptions:

$$\sqrt{C_1} = .4, \quad \sqrt{C_2} = .7, \quad S_1 = S_2 = S$$

we find

$$n_1 = \frac{(150,000)(S)}{.4} \cdot \frac{5000}{(150,000)(S)(.4) + (110,000)(S)(.7)}$$

$$= 13,700$$

$$n_2 = 5700$$

These values would result in sampling fractions in the 2 strata of approximately $\frac{1}{11}$ and $\frac{1}{19}$. However, because the optimum is broad, it was decided to modify these slightly in order to make possible a less costly weighting procedure. By changing these ratios to $\frac{1}{10}$ and $\frac{1}{20}$, respectively, i.e., taking 15,000 in the sample from the first stratum and 5500 from the second, then the punch cards for the noncoded schedules in the sample could be duplicated (an inexpensive operation) and $\bar{X}$ could be estimated directly from the enlarged deck of punch cards.

Exercises

12.1. Compute the total cost in Illustration 12.1, using sampling fractions of $\frac{1}{10}$ and $\frac{1}{20}$, respectively, in the 2 strata. Compare the relative precision in Illustration 12.1 with that for the same total cost with proportionate sampling.

12.2. In the lumber illustration in Table 1, Sec. 6, suppose that the cost of collecting each schedule is $1 for mills over 5000 M bd. ft. annual production, $4 for mills producing 1000–4999 M bd. ft., and $9 for mills under 1000 M bd. ft.

* Tore Dalenius, "Kostnadsproblemet vid Sampling," *Den Svenska Marknaden*, No. 3, 1950, pp. 1–15.

What is the total expenditure for the optimum allocation according to Table 3, Sec. 10, of a sample of 1000 mills? Using the same total expenditure, what allocation would give the smallest error, taking account of costs? What would be the sample size with this allocation? Compare the variances of the 2 allocations.

13. Problem of sampling for many characteristics with optimum allocation. Suppose that, in the illustrations we have considered thus far in connection with optimum sampling, we were sampling not for a single characteristic but for several or perhaps a great many characteristics. What effect will sampling for many characteristics have on our use of optimum allocation?

The formula for optimum allocation we have presented deals with only a single characteristic. No simple solution to an optimum design is available when more than one characteristic is to be estimated, but useful guidance can be found from the results already presented. Consider the problem of estimating the average sales of retail stores. Suppose that in addition to estimating the sales from the sample we wish also to estimate the following characteristics:

Total employment.
Total wages paid.
Total inventory.
Ratio of wages paid to sales, i.e., per cent of gross receipts spent for wages.
Ratio of inventory to sales. ,
Ratio of sales for current month to sales for prior month.
Proportion of stores that handle fresh meats.
Proportion of stores that are incorporated.
Proportion of stores operated by veterans.
Proportion of stores that were in business 10 years ago.
Proportion of stores whose proprietors have a certain opinion on a given question.

In addition, we shall consider the problem of estimating such characteristics by size groups of stores, where size is based, say, on total employees or total sales; that is to say, the problem may involve ascertaining the above characteristics separately for (a) the large establishments (perhaps 100 or more employees); (b) the medium-sized establishments (perhaps 10–99 employees); (c) the small establishments (fewer than 10 employees).

Employment, wages paid, and inventory may be expected to vary from store to store in about the same way as sales, and it may be expected that the $\tilde{S}_h$ for these items will vary roughly in direct proportion to the $\tilde{S}_h$ for sales. If this is true, the optimum allocation for estimating sales will be very close to that for wages paid, and the same should be roughly true for total inventory.*   This is a fortunate situation if we wish to estimate a number of such characteristics from a single sample because a good sample design for one such characteristic is also a reasonably good sample for the others.

Let us consider now the estimation of a characteristic like the ratio of wages to sales, or the ratio of sales this month to sales in a prior month. For such characteristics, we are dealing with a ratio estimate.   It was seen in Sec. 10 that an allocation of the sample that is reasonably good for estimating total sales and total wages will probably be reasonably good for estimating the ratio of wages to sales also and for other similar items. We are still fortunate in that each of the items thus far examined calls for roughly the same allocation of the sample.

Now let us examine the problem of estimating attributes, such as the per cent of stores that handle fresh meats, the per cent incorporated, or the per cent of establishments in which the proprietor has a certain opinion on a particular subject.   Notice that in this latter class of estimates the characteristic of the small establishment has the same importance in determining the over-all percentage as does the characteristic of a very large establishment.   This was not true in the earlier illustrations, where large establishments individually had a vastly greater influence on the total, average, or ratio that was being estimated, and where giving an establishment a chance of being included that was proportionate to its size was found to be roughly the optimum design.

If one were to pick one of these percentages and design the sample to estimate that particular percentage with the smallest possible variance, there is the possibility that substantial gains could be achieved by the best allocation for that particular item—although even this would be doubtful. It will be illustrated (Illustration 17.2 and subsequent exercises) that in sampling for attributes optimum allocation will often give only trivial gains over proportionate sampling.   When sampling for several of such percentages, the optimum allocation for one of them will ordinarily be different from that for another, and where the whole set is involved it is often true that proportionate sampling will be the best allocation.   Otherwise the effort to make an optimum allocation for one item may result in a less reliable result for another item.   Therefore, unless the sample is to be picked primarily for the purpose of estimating a single one of the attributes, it would appear desirable to use proportionate sampling.

* It was remarked above that inventories for some commodities are likely to be very unstable and not highly correlated with aggregate size, but the aggregate inventory in a retail store should ordinarily have a rough correspondence with aggregate employment or aggregate sales.

In our illustration we now have a problem because the use of optimum allocation for the items which are aggregates or ratios of aggregates is exceedingly important if they are to be estimated well, and the optimum allocation for them will be far from proportionate, whereas the sample for attributes should be proportionate. How can this apparent dilemma be resolved? There is no unique answer to this question that can be pointed to in the theory. The following approach, however, seems reasonably satisfactory.

Let us assume that it is important to estimate accurately aggregative items (such as total inventories) as well as selected attribute items (e.g., the percentage of stores having specified characteristics). Then the approach might be to allocate the sample first in what will be approximately the optimum for purposes of estimating the aggregative items. Then we can examine how good this sample will be for estimating some of the percentages. If such items are estimated well enough from the sample as allocated already, then no more need be done. If it appears that more reliable results are needed for the percentage items, we should next ascertain which stratum or strata may be expected to make the principal contribution to the variance of these latter items. Probably it will be desirable to increase the sample sufficiently in the strata that have the smaller relative representation from the original optimum allocation, to give these items the necessary reliability.

Had there been other aggregative types of items for which statistics were needed, and with which it was clear that the original allocation proportional to average sizes of the establishment in the respective strata did not deal satisfactorily, it might be essential to do some special supplementation for such items in the strata where the principal contributions to the variances for these items arise.

The suggestions above have been made on the assumption that the statistics desired are only over-all percentages of the establishments that have a particular characteristic. We suggested earlier that it might be desired to have the data separately for the large, the medium-sized, and the small establishments. One of the important aspects of the investigation may be to make such comparisons, and they may be equally or even more important than knowing the over-all characteristics for the group as a whole.

Let us see what happens in such an instance. Notice that in optimum allocation for estimating sales or change in sales a much higher sampling ratio is used in the larger size groups than in the smaller ones; and that, at the same time, the number of stores in a size group decreases sharply as the size of store increases. The optimum allocation increases the number of stores from the larger size groups while it decreases the numbers included in the sample from the smaller ones, as compared with proportionate sampling. It gives a more nearly uniform *number* of stores from the various size groups, instead of a uniform proportion in each size group. This is what is needed in order to make comparisons of certain percentages or other characteristics between size groups. Thus, if one were setting out to sample the opinions for large, medium, and small stores separately in order to compare them, he would have to take a considerably larger sampling ratio from the larger stores than from the smaller size classes, in order to achieve reasonable accuracy for each of the groups separately. We see that a good design for estimating average sales or change in sales, and related characteristics may also be a reasonably good design for making comparisons of percentages and other characteristics between the size groups.

In summary, we have seen that optimum allocation for one characteristic is often very good for a number of related characteristics, but certainly may not be for all. If comparisons are needed between the size classes, and the aggregate for all size groups combined is also needed, then optimum allocation is likely to give satisfactory results for both types of purposes. More than that, exceedingly worth-while gains in sampling efficiency may result from using stratification together with optimum allocation for many problems of this type—gains sufficient to much more than offset any additional work involved in the special weighting of the sample returns. For this type of problem optimum allocation is an exceedingly useful tool for increasing sampling efficiency.

Illustration 13.1. In allocating a sample of 1000 farms in the province of Soedermanland, Sweden, the following allocations were proposed for four acreage groups:*

Comparison of several methods for determining the sample allocation

Size class (hectares)	No. of farms	Proportionate sampling	Proportionate to average acreage	Optimum allocation, based on data for					
				Winter wheat	Winter rye	Barley	Oats	Potatoes	Hay
2–19	4101	658	268	260	293	157	311	541	322
20–49	1414	227	263	278	297	141	257	211	269
50–149	609	98	313	311	281	472	296	150	295
150 and over	112	17	156	151	129	230	136	98	114
All farms	6236	1000	1000	1000	1000	1000	1000	1000	1000

* Tore Dalenius, "Anvaendningen av Stickprovsmetodik vid 1950 Ars Arealinventering och Kreaturaraekning," *Jordbruksekonomiska Meddelanden*, February 1951, pp. 59–75.

Notice that for the four grain crops and hay the optimum allocations are similar, and much like the allocation proportionate to average acreage. We conclude that a sample good for one of these crops would provide satisfactory estimates for the others. Potatoes, however, lead to an allocation closer to proportionate sampling, since generally potatoes are grown only for home use and are not closely related to the size of farm. Also notice that the optimum allocation requires (except for potatoes) that the sample in the size class of largest farms be larger than the number of such farms. In practice we would include all 112 of the largest farms in the sample and redistribute the balance of the sample (888 farms) among the other strata.

Exercises

13.1. Using the lumber data in Table 3, Sec. 10, compare the reliability of the estimates of average production for the three strata separately, using the sample allocations of proportionate sampling, optimum allocation, and allocation proportional to a measure of size (1942 total production in this case).

13.2. How would a sample of 1000 mills be allocated if we wish to achieve the same accuracy in each stratum? Compare the variance of an estimated total, using this sample, with that for the optimum allocation.

13.3. Compare the reliability of estimates of change in sales for large, medium, and small retail stores separately, using the data for New York City in Table 4, Sec. 10, with the optimum allocation and with the samples allocated proportionately to 1939 employees.

D. OTHER CONSIDERATIONS WITH STRATIFIED SAMPLING

14. Estimation of variance from the sample.* The precision of a sample estimate is estimated from the sample itself by applying to each stratum the simple procedures already described in Ch. 4, Sec. 12. Thus,

$$s_{hX}^2 = \frac{\sum_{i}^{n_h}(x_{hi} - \bar{x}_h)^2}{n_h - 1}; \quad s_{hY}^2 = \frac{\sum_{i}^{n_h}(y_{hi} - \bar{y}_h)^2}{n_h - 1} \tag{14.1}$$

is a consistent (and unbiased) estimate of S_h^2 (see Eq. 1.2). Similarly,

$$s_{hZ'}^2 = s_{hX}^2 + r^2 s_{hY}^2 - 2r s_{hXY} \tag{14.2}$$

and

$$s_{hZ}^2 = s_{hX}^2 + r_h^2 s_{hY}^2 - 2r_h s_{hXY} \tag{14.3}$$

---

* For proofs, see Vol. II, Ch. 5, Sec. 12.

are, respectively, consistent estimates of $S_{hZ'}^2$ and S_{hZ}^2 as given by Eq. 4.6 and 4.13, where

$$r_h = \frac{x_h}{y_h} \quad \text{and} \quad r = \frac{x}{y} \tag{14.4}$$

and

$$s_{hXY} = \rho_h' s_{hX} s_{hY} = \frac{\sum\limits_{i}^{n_h}(x_{hi} - \bar{x}_h)(y_{hi} - \bar{y}_h)}{n_h - 1} \tag{14.5}$$

is the estimated covariance.

· Consequently we substitute s_h^2, $s_{hZ'}^2$, or s_{hZ}^2, respectively, for S_h^2, $S_{hZ'}^2$, or S_{hZ}^2 in the formulas given in preceding sections to obtain consistent estimates of the desired variances.

Notice that variance estimates can be computed only if two or more units have been included in the sample from each stratum. The question of how large a sample is needed in the aggregate over all strata or from the strata individually in order to obtain a reliable estimate of the variance from a sample will be considered in Chapter 10.

15. Defining the strata. It was indicated at the beginning of the chapter that, although defining the strata is one of the first steps to be taken, the explanation of the principles for setting up the strata would be deferred until after the theory was presented. A few remarks are now in order on this point.

The determination of the strata is a matter in which effective use can be made of prior knowledge, personal intuition, and judgment, as well as of objective statistical information that may be available. Whether objective information is available or not, the final determination of the strata is a subjective matter, in which the decisions must be judgments. Statistical theory does not provide a general series of procedures or steps for determining the one best set of strata. It does provide some guiding principles and gives a method for comparing and choosing among alternatives.

The most effective variable on which to stratify would be the characteristic to be measured; and, since in practice this is not feasible, stratification on the most highly correlated data available will lead to the greatest reduction in variance. However, the cost of accomplishing the stratification must be taken into account, and this may lead to simpler stratification systems.

Thus, in sampling for distribution of income among families in a city, zones or areas of the city might be delimited such that there are substantial differences in income between the areas, and as much similarity in income as feasible among families within the areas. This approach is quite often very simple and satisfactory, but there are many other and sometimes better ways.

For example, the Census of Housing provides certain information for each block in cities having 50,000 or more population. The information available for each block from the Census includes the number of dwelling units in the block, the average rental value of the dwelling units, the proportion of dwelling units occupied by white or nonwhite families, and the proportion having certain facilities. One might use such information to stratify families according to the kind of block that they live in, blocks being classified as dominantly white or nonwhite, and containing dwelling units with average rental values within specified ranges; other similar types of criteria based upon the block statistics might be used. As there is a tendency for the dwellings within a block to be within the same general economic level and to be either white or nonwhite as the case may be, such a stratification based upon the characteristics of whole blocks might be a fairly effective stratification of the individual dwellings in the block. By the use of such information, some system of classification involving both geography and block characteristics could be evolved.

On the other hand, the stratification might be carried out on the basis of a casual external inspection of each structure and of classifying the structure on the basis of its external appearance as presumably in one class or another. Another source of information for stratification might result from records of one sort or another that might be available on individual units.

The stratification of clusters would be less effective than direct stratification of elementary units on the same characteristic, if we are estimating a characteristic of the elementary unit. For example, the stratification of blocks into average rental groups as a device for selecting a sample to estimate the income of households is not as effective as stratification of individual households into rental groups would be if equally reliable information were available for the individual units.

Examples of more objective approaches to the problem of stratification are the methods for setting boundaries of strata designed by Tore Dalenius and Margaret Gurney and referred to in Sec. 11, and the use by Hagood and Bernert* of factor analysis in classifying counties into strata. However, even with a mathematical formula for assigning strata boundaries or for assigning units to strata judgment is necessary in determining

---

* Margaret Jarman Hagood and Eleanor H. Bernert, "Component Indexes as a Basis for Stratification in Sampling," *J. Amer. Stat. Assn.*, **40** (1945), 330–341.

which social and economic characteristics to use as control variables. Moreover, strictly judgment methods may yield either more or less stratification gains, depending on the quality of judgment used. Additional theoretical work may provide further guidance on this problem.

Depth of stratification. It should be pointed out that there is a practical limit, often reached very early, as to the number of strata that can be introduced, since at least one unit must be included in the sample from each stratum. Although some (and sometimes very small) reductions in variance may be expected by stratifying deeper and deeper, the first steps of stratification, if they are well chosen, are likely to be the most important, and further stratification often will yield very small gains.

From the point of view of sampling theory, if the stratification is carried to the point of including in the sample only one unit from a stratum, then there is no way of preparing a consistent estimate of the sampling variance from the sample itself. This may or may not be regarded as a serious disadvantage in any particular problem—the implications of estimating a variance under such circumstances (by a method of combining strata) are discussed in Ch. 9, Sec. 15, and in Ch. 10, Sec. 13.

It is worth emphasizing that nowhere in the theory is there anything that limits the kind of criteria of stratification that can be used. Thus, we may stratify by size of establishment, geography, age, occupation, amount of education, or any other characteristic we like. There is no assumption of "homogeneity" within strata. Whatever strata are set up and no matter how they are arrived at, the theory for measuring the precision is applicable, and unbiased or consistent estimates can be made from the sample if a method of random sampling is used for selecting two or more units from each stratum.

16. Some additional remarks.   A few other aspects of stratified sampling are mentioned in the following remarks.

  Remark 1.   Cut-off sampling.   It frequently happens that in estimating a characteristic a very small proportion of the units account for nearly the entire aggregate value of the characteristic. In such situations it may be satisfactory to make an estimate based on the larger establishments only. This is equivalent to making an estimate for the whole population from the stratum of larger elementary units, neglecting other strata made up of smaller units. Such a method is called a "cut-off method." We shall see in Ch. 11, Sec. 6, that the method can be useful and may be fairly accurate if we are estimating a ratio such as the ratio of totals in two time periods, and the larger firms account for perhaps 90–95 per cent or more of the total whose ratio is being estimated.

  Remark 2.   Stratification sometimes ineffective for subgroups.   The effect of stratification may deteriorate for detailed statistics. A rather common situation is the one in which estimates are desired for some subpopulation. In such a situation, the stratification that was introduced initially in the selection of the sample may have much or little effect. Suppose, for example, that the population has initially been stratified by income at some earlier date. This stratification may have a marked effect in reducing the variance of estimated rent for the population as a whole. However, if one now wishes to estimate average rent for a small subgroup of the population, say those in a particular occupational group, the reduction in variance by virtue of the original stratification may be extremely small, since the control on income for all classes combined has insured practically no control on the rental distribution of persons in the specified occupation. In general, one should not expect much of a gain from stratification when he estimates the characteristics of a relatively small subpopulation that was not controlled directly in the stratification.

Remark 3. Stratification after sampling. In some cases it may be difficult or impossible to set up strata, but we may still be able to achieve some of the gains of stratified sampling by means of the device of "stratification after sampling." For example, we may have a file which is in no particular order, but for which we know the totals of certain groups or subclasses. In such a case we may select a simple random sample from the whole population, classify the sample into the groups whose totals are known, and then weight the sample estimate for each group by the known totals. For this estimating procedure to be efficient it is necessary that the weights be known. The estimate of an average from the sample is given by Eq. 3.4, and the variance of the estimate is approximately*

$$\sigma_{\bar{x}}^2 = \frac{1-f}{n} S_w^2 + \frac{1-f}{n\,\bar{n}} \frac{\sum\limits^{L} S_h^* Q_h}{L} \tag{16.1}$$

where $\bar{n} = n/L$ is the average number of units in the sample per stratum used for weighting, $P_h = N_h/N$ is the proportion of the population included in the hth stratum, $Q_h = 1 - P_h$, and the other terms are as defined in Sec. 3. It is seen that, if $\bar{n}$ is large, say 25–50 or more, one might achieve nearly all the gains of initial stratification, but if the strata are made too small so that $\bar{n}$ is small, one might lose considerably by the introduction of stratification after sampling. The terms in Eq. 16.1 can be estimated from the sample, so that the precision of alternative estimates can be compared.

Remark 4. Weighting by random substitution or elimination. In Illustration 12.1 we mentioned the device of duplicating cards (or schedules) as a method for avoiding a special weighting operation. If the cards to be duplicated are all the sample cards for a given stratum, as in that illustration, the variance is not changed by the procedure. If, however, we wish to weight by a factor such as 132, we might accomplish this by selecting at random 32 per cent of the cards (or schedules) and duplicating them, and then applying the weight 100 to all the cards. Or, if we wish to weight by a factor 2.32, we might triplicate 32 per cent of the cards and duplicate the remaining 68 per cent. The effective weighting factor is then $3(.32) + 2(.68) = 2.32$. More generally, we may accomplish weighting by including the

---

* For proof of these results, see Vol. II, Ch. 5, Sec. 13.

proportion a of the cards $(w + 1)$ times, and the remaining proportion $(1 - a)$ of the cards w times. This gives the effect of weighting by $w(1 - a) + (w + 1)a = w + a$. Thus, in the illustration above, $w = 2$ and $a = .32$.

When a differs from zero for a stratum, i.e., when some cards in a stratum are included more times than others, there will be an increase in variance over the variance that we should have if the correct weight were applied to all cards. When the total number of elements in the stratum is large, the increase in variance is $a(1 - a)/(a + w)^2$ times the contribution to the variance from the stratum if the correct weight were used.* If $w = 1$ and a is less than 10 per cent, the relative increase in the variance is nearly equal to a. The maximum relative increase in the variance for any a is $12\frac{1}{2}$ per cent.

The related process of eliminating schedules may also be used; if, for example, we wish to weight by a factor 9, we may reject at random one-tenth of the schedules and then weight by 10. This obviously increases the variance, as we are throwing away the information on the schedules which are discarded. If b is the proportion of schedules discarded, the relative increase in the variance is $b/(1 - b)$.

Remark 5. Bias introduced when weighting by approximations to the appropriate strata weights, with either stratified sampling or stratification after sampling. An estimate of the form

$$\Sigma \hat{Y}_h r_h / \hat{Y} \tag{16.2}$$

is sometimes used as an estimate of X/Y where the $r_h = x_h/y_h$ are consistent estimates from a sample of the X_h/Y_h and the $\hat{Y}_h/\hat{Y}$ are known from other sources.

Equation 16.2 is a consistent estimate of X/Y if the $\hat{Y}_h/\hat{Y}$ are equal to the Y_h/Y, but otherwise is usually inconsistent. The bias of estimate 16.2 is approximately equal to†

$$\left[\Sigma \left(\frac{\hat{Y}_h}{\hat{Y}} - \frac{Y_h}{Y} \right) \frac{X_h}{Y_h} \right] \tag{16.3}$$

The mean square error of this estimate is approximately equal to

$$\Sigma \frac{\hat{Y}_h^2}{\hat{Y}^2} \sigma_{r_h}^2 + \left[\Sigma \left(\frac{\hat{Y}_h}{\hat{Y}} - \frac{Y_h}{Y} \right) \frac{X_h}{Y_h} \right]^2 \tag{16.4}$$

where

$$\sigma_{r_h}^2 = \frac{X_h^2}{Y_h^2} (V_{x_h}^2 + V_{y_h}^2 - 2\rho_h V_{x_h} V_{y_h})$$

The second term in Eq. 16.4 is approximately the square of the bias.

The loss in efficiency from the errors in the weights is primarily the square of the bias, although the variance, too, will reflect to some extent the errors in the weights. Of course, the bias, for any specified set of weights, is not reduced by increasing the size of sample. Consequently, with large enough samples, the use of such weights may result in a larger mean square error than the variance that would result from simple random sampling without such weighting.‡

---

* For proof, see Vol. II, Ch. 5, Sec. 14.
† Cochran (2), p. 102.
‡ Some additional consideration is given to this problem by F. F. Stephan (3).

Remark 6.   Comparison of estimates for two strata.   A variation in the problem of optimum allocation arises when the primary purpose of the survey design is to compare estimates for two classes of the population (i.e., for two strata).   Thus, suppose that the primary purpose of a survey is to estimate the difference between two means, for example, to compare the per cent of one class of the population, say those reading a certain magazine, with that of another.

If the total cost of the sample is given by

$$C = C_1 n_1 + C_2 n_2$$

where C_1 is the cost per unit of selecting the sample and making the estimate from the first group, and n_1 is the size of sample from that group, and C_2 and n_2 are similarly defined for the second group, then the most reliable comparison between the two groups will result when the sample from the two classes is drawn so that

$$n_1 = \frac{n \dfrac{S_1}{\sqrt{C_1}}}{\dfrac{S_1}{\sqrt{C_1}} + \dfrac{S_2}{\sqrt{C_2}}}$$

$$n_2 = \frac{n \dfrac{S_2}{\sqrt{C_2}}}{\dfrac{S_1}{\sqrt{C_1}} + \dfrac{S_2}{\sqrt{C_2}}}$$

(16.5)

where S_1 and S_2 are the standard deviations in the respective strata.

17.   Some additional illustrations and exercises.   Some illustrations and exercises will be presented now to provide a further guide as to what to expect from stratification under various circumstances and to illustrate the conditions when gains may be expected to be large or small in dealing with various types of problems.

Illustration 17.1.   Suppose that the problem is to estimate the average family income in a city during a particular year, when we have information on income in some earlier year to use as a basis for stratification.   Basic data for eleven income groups, taken from Mendershausen,* are shown in Table 5.   Actually column 5 of the table presents the average income that is to be estimated, but we shall assume that it is unknown, and consider the effect of some variations in sample design on the estimate of average income.   We shall assume also, for illustration purposes, that the standard deviations in column 6 are known.

---

* H. Mendershausen, *Changes in Income Distribution during the Great Depression*, National Bureau of Economic Research, New York, 1946.

Table 5. Income in Atlanta in 1933 by 1929 income groups

1929 income (dollars)	Group	No. of families N	Total 1929 income (1000's of dollars)	Average income $\bar{X}_h$	Standard deviation S_h	$V_h = S_h/\bar{X}_h$
(1)	(2)	(3)	(4)	(5)	(6)	(7)
0	1	340	0	486	1,202	2.473
1– 249	2	659	109	236	205	.869
250– 499	3	1,650	642	335	282	.842
500– 749	4	1,684	1,029	448	309	.690
750– 999	5	1,443	1,263	606	374	.617
1,000–1,499	6	1,975	2,419	869	549	.632
1,500–1,999	7	1,635	2,869	1,248	589	.472
2,000–2,999	8	2,251	5,515	1,753	850	.485
3,000–4,499	9	1,200	4,264	2,372	1,084	.457
4,500–7,499	10	563	3,063	3,558	1,937	.544
7,500+	11	241	3,072	6,766	4,008	.592
All families		13,641	24,245	1,223*	1,428	1.168

The column heading reads "1933 income (dollars)" spanning columns (5) and (6).

* This mean is not the same as that given in Table 7, Ch. 4. The mean in the table above is the true mean of the ungrouped data. The mean in Chapter 4 is estimated from grouped data.

Exercises

17.1. Compute the optimum allocation for a sample of 1000 families, assuming uniform costs and using the 11 income groups shown in Table 5 as separate strata, and show that the variance for this allocation is 413, as compared with a variance of 761 for a proportionate stratified sample with the same strata. Compute and compare, also, the approximations to the optimum allocation obtained by allocating the sample proportionately to the measure of size (1929 income), but using the same sampling fraction for the zero income class as for the second group. Note that rigid adherence to an allocation proportionate to a measure of size would have led to a zero allocation for the zero group and therefore an infinite variance.

17.2. Suppose that 3 groups are established from Table 5, consisting, respectively, of families having no income in 1929, income of $1–2999 in 1929, and income of $3000 and over in 1929. Compute the optimum allocation (using the variance formulas in the note below) for a sample of 1000 and compare the variance with that from Ex. 17.1. Show that the variance with optimum allocation to these strata, using simple random sampling within the groups, is 911; and show that the variance with optimum allocation to these strata, using proportionate stratified sampling within the groups, is 518.

NOTE. In computing the optimum allocation for the grouped strata one has a choice of using proportionate stratified sampling within the groups or simple random sampling within each of the 3 groups. For proportionate stratified sampling within a group the variance in the population for a group, S_g^2, is obtained from the data in Table 6 by computing

$$S_g^2 = \frac{\Sigma N_h S_h^2}{N_g}$$

where the sum is over the strata included in the group, and N_g is the number of families in the group. For simple random sampling within the group the variance for a group is obtained from the data in Table 6 by computing

$$S_g^2 \doteq \frac{\Sigma N_h S_h^2}{N_g} + \frac{\Sigma N_h \left(\bar{X}_h - \frac{\Sigma N_h \bar{X}_h}{N_g} \right)^2}{N_g} \qquad \text{(see Eq. 5.8)}$$

and the variance of $\bar{x}_g$ is approximately S_g^2/n_g.

17.3. Establish 3 groups of strata that have roughly equivalent aggregate measures of size by consolidating low, medium, and high income size groups in such a way as to equalize roughly the aggregate 1929 income for the 3 groups. Ascertain the optimum allocation of the sample to the groups where proportionate stratified sampling is used within the groups, and show that the variance for this estimate with a sample of 1000 families is 472. Show that the variance, when the allocation to groups is proportionate to the measure of size (with proportionate stratified sampling within groups), is 501. The variance when the allocation is proportionate to the measure of size, but with the measure of size arbitrarily doubled for the low income group, has already been computed in Ex. 10.2 (d) and is equal to 479.

17.4. Transfer the group with no income in 1929 from the low income stratum to the middle income stratum, and compute and compare the variance with the allocation proportionate to the aggregate size with this grouping of strata (and using proportionate stratified sampling within strata) to the results for Ex. 17.3. The variance in this case turns out to be 458. Explain why this is smaller than the variance with the optimum allocation in Ex. 17.3.

17.5. Another grouping will be obtained if we require that the 3 strata have variances so that the $N_g S_g$ are approximately equal for the 3 groups. The grouping which comes closest to meeting this condition is to combine groups 1–6, 7–9, and 10–11. Here the variance for the optimum allocation with proportionate sampling within combined groups is 478. The variance with allocation proportionate to 1929 size and proportionate sampling within strata is 528.

17.6. For the groups of strata given in Ex. 17.5, assume that the cost of obtaining a questionnaire from the low and medium income groups is $2, and from the high income groups is $4, and that a total budget of $3000 is available in addition to overhead costs. Ascertain the optimum allocation of the sample and the total sample size and show that the variance of the estimate from the sample will be 367.

Illustration 17.2. Review the illustration given in Ch. 1, Sec. 19, in which, for the population specified by Table 20 of that section, a sample estimate is to be made of the proportion of persons 25 years of age or more who have completed 2 or more years of high school.

Exercises

17.7. Compute the standard errors of the estimated proportion of the population 25 years of age or more completing 2 or more years of high school: (*a*) if a simple random sample of 1000 is drawn; (*b*) if a proportionate stratified sample of 1000 is drawn, where the strata are the age-sex-color groups shown in the table; (*c*) if a stratified sample of 1000 is drawn with optimum allocation to the strata. Note that neither proportionate stratification nor optimum allocation to strata results in very substantial gains.

Note that the gain from optimum allocation over proportionate stratified sampling is very small and in practice might not pay for the additional work involved in introducing the optimum allocation procedure. In fact, because we would not know, in advance, the standard deviations of the respective strata needed in order to introduce the optimum allocation illustrated above, the use of optimum allocation with estimated standard deviations might result in a larger variance than proportionate stratified sampling.

17.8. Compute the variance of the estimated per cent completing 2 or more years of high school for a sample of 1000 drawn from the assumed population given in the table below, where: (*a*) a simple random sample is drawn; (*b*) a proportionate stratified sample is drawn; (*c*) a sample is drawn with optimum allocation of the sample to strata.

AGE GROUP	NUMBER OF PERSONS OVER 25 YEARS OF AGE	PER CENT COMPLETING 2 OR MORE YEARS OF HIGH SCHOOL
25–34	19,110	50.0
35–49	36,333	25.0
50 and over	19,333	1.0

REFERENCES

(1) P. V. Sukhatme, "Contributions to the Theory of the Representative Method," *J. Roy. Stat. Soc. Supplement*, 1935, pp. 253–268.

(2) W. G. Cochran, *Sampling Techniques*, John Wiley & Sons, New York, 1953, Chapter 5.

(3) F. F. Stephan, "Stratification in Representative Sampling," *J. Marketing*, 6 (1945), 38–46.

(4) W. E. Deming, *Some Theory of Sampling*, John Wiley & Sons, New York, 1950, Chapter 6.

(5) L. R. Frankel and J. S. Stock, "The Allocation of Samplings among Several Strata," *Annals Math. Stat.*, 10 (1939), 288–293.

(6) J. Neyman, "On the Two Different Aspects of the Representative Method: The Method of Stratified Sampling and the Method of Purposive Selection," *J. Roy. Stat. Soc.*, 109 (1934), 558–606.

(7) A. A. Tschuprow, "On the Mathematical Expectation of the Moments of Frequency Distributions in the Case of Correlated Observations," *Metron*, 2 (1923), 646–680 (see p. 672 in particular).

(8) F. Yates, *Sampling Methods for Censuses and Surveys*, Charles Griffin and Company, London, 1949.

CHAPTER 6

Simple One- or Two-Stage Cluster Sampling

A. NOTATION, AND EXPLANATION OF CLUSTER SAMPLING

1. Some terminology and notation. The term *elementary unit* is used to denote an individual member of the particular population on which measurements are desired and for which the analyses are to be made from the survey results. When averages or percentages are being computed, the unit on which the average or percentage is based is the elementary unit. When frequency distributions are made, it is the elementary unit that is placed into class intervals on the basis of the value of one of its characteristics; it is the elementary unit for which measures such as the median are computed. Thus, if the purpose of the survey is to estimate the mean or average income, or the median income, or the distribution of income for individual persons, then the person is the elementary unit. If one is estimating the average family income, the median family income, or the distribution of family incomes, the family is the elementary unit. The elementary unit thus depends on the analysis being made and is determined by the purposes of the survey and not by the sampling design. In some instances the purpose of the survey does not involve the specification of an elementary unit, as when only aggregates are to be measured. More than one elementary unit may be involved in a single survey, as when both family characteristics and individual characteristics are measured in one survey.

Cluster sampling involves division of the population of elementary units under consideration into groups or clusters that serve as primary sampling units. In some instances, a sample of such primary units is selected and all members of the population associated with the selected units are included in the sample: this is called single-stage sampling. In other instances, the selected primary units are divided into secondary units, and there are one or more additional stages of sampling.

The initial units defined and selected will be referred to as *primary sampling units* or *first-stage units* (or simply as primary units or psu's).

By *simple one-stage sampling* we mean that there is only one stage of sampling (i.e., no subsampling is involved) and that a simple random selection method is used in selecting the units. By *simple two-stage sampling* we shall refer to a design in which:

(*a*) Two-stage sampling is used;
(*b*) The primary units are selected by simple random sampling;
(*c*) The second-stage units are selected from each of the selected primary units by simple random sampling; and
(*d*) The second-stage sampling fractions are uniform for all selected primary sampling units.

In this chapter we shall be concerned with simple sampling in one or two stages.   Some of the notation and additional terminology to be used are as follows:

M is the total number of primary units into which the population has been divided.   Thus, if the survey is taken to measure the characteristics of dwelling units in a city, we may identify each dwelling unit with a city block and then use the city block as the primary sampling unit. M is then the number of such blocks in the city.

m is the number of primary units included in the sample.

N_i is the number of listing units included in the ith primary unit.

The listing unit is the unit that is selected at the last stage of sampling: it is called a "listing unit" because we frequently make a list of these units within the primary unit and then select a sample from this listing.   With two-stage sampling, the listing unit can also be referred to as the second-stage sampling unit or as the subsampling unit.   For example, in drawing a sample of dwelling units, or of people, or of families, it is often convenient to use the individual structure as the listing unit for small structures involving one or a few families per structure, and to use the individual dwelling unit as the listing unit within larger structures such as apartment houses.

The listing unit and the elementary unit need to be distinguished.   In some instances the elementary unit and the listing unit will be identical, but they may and often will be different.

$N = \sum_{i}^{M} N_i$ is the number of listing units in the population.

$\bar{N} = N/M$ is the average number of listing units per psu in the population.

n_i is the number of listing units in the sample from the ith primary unit.

$n = \sum_i^m n_i$ is the total number of listing units in the sample unless other-wise specified.   In certain specified cases n will designate the *expected value* of the total number of listing units in the sample.

$\bar{n} = n/m$ is the average number of listing units in the sample per psu included in the sample unless otherwise specified.   In certain specified cases $\bar{n}$ will designate the *expected value* of the number of listing units in the sample per psu in the sample.

$f_1 = m/M$ is the first-stage sampling fraction.

In this chapter we shall assume that when two stages of sampling are used a uniform fraction of listing units will be included in the sample from each selected primary unit.   That is,

$f_2 = \bar{n}/\bar{N} = n_i/N_i$ is the sampling fraction at the second stage (here $\bar{n}$ is the expected value of $\bar{n}$ as defined above).

$f = n/N = f_1 f_2$ is the over-all sampling fraction (here n is the expected value of n as defined above).

X_{ij} refers to the jth listing unit within the ith primary unit in the population.

For example, if the listing unit is the individual structure, and rental value of dwelling units is being measured, and if there are two dwelling units in the ijth listing unit, then X_{ij} is the aggregate of the rental values of the two dwelling units.   If the rental value of owner-occupied units is being measured and if one of the units in the listing unit is occupied by the owner and the other is occupied by a tenant, then the X_{ij} is the rental value of only the owner-occupied unit.   Similarly, if the characteristic being measured is the number of owner-occupied units, for example, and the value 0 is assigned to a tenant-occupied unit and the value 1 to an owner-occupied unit, then if both units in the structure are owner-occupied X_{ij} will be 2, if both are tenant-occupied X_{ij} will be 0, and if one is owner-occupied and the other is vacant or tenant-occupied X_{ij} will be 1. To extend the illustration a little further, suppose that the purpose is to measure the characteristics of only those dwelling units that are occupied by families in a particular income class, say families with incomes over $5000, and the characteristic to be measured is the number of such units that are owner-occupied.   In this event, the value 1 is assigned to a unit occupied by a family that is in the specified income class and that owns its home, and the value 0 is assigned to all other units.   Then X_{ij} is the sum of these values for all dwelling units in the listing unit.

$X_i = \sum\limits^{N_i} X_{ij}$ is the aggregate value for the ith primary unit; for example, if the block is the psu, then X_i may be the total number of rooms in all dwelling units in the ith block or the total number of tenant-occupied dwelling units in the ith block.

$X = \sum\limits_{i}^{M} X_i$ is the aggregate value for all psu's in the population.

Thus, as in earlier chapters, the dropping of a subscript denotes the summation over that subscript.

$\bar{X} = X/M$ is the average value per primary unit in the population. This average value per primary unit is seldom the average in which one is interested as an aim of a survey. It nevertheless does appear in the formulas for the sampling variance.

$\bar{\bar{X}} = X/N = \bar{X}/\bar{N}$ is the average value per listing unit in the population.

Thus, $\bar{\bar{X}}$ could be the average number of dwelling units per listing unit, or the average rental value per listing unit, or the average number of tenant-occupied dwelling units per listing unit, or the average number of persons or stores per listing unit. Similarly,

$\bar{\bar{X}}_i = X_i/N_i$ is the corresponding average value per listing unit for the ith psu.

$R = X/Y$. When Y is the number of elementary units in the population, then R is an average value per elementary unit. The purposes of the survey often are to estimate the value of R for various characteristics.

x_{ij} is the value for the jth listing unit *in the sample*, from the ith primary unit *in the sample*.

$x_i = \sum\limits_{j}^{n_i} x_{ij}$ is the sum for all listing units in the sample for the ith psu in the sample.

$x = \sum\limits_{i}^{m} x_i$ is the sample total for all listing units in the sample.

The single bar and double bar have the same significance for sample averages as for population averages. Thus,

$\bar{\bar{x}} = x/n$, and $\bar{\bar{x}}_i = x_i/n_i$; $\bar{x} = x/m$.

x' and x_i' are simple unbiased estimates from the sample of, respectively, X and X_i.

$r = x/y = x'/y'$ is a sample estimate of R.

The term *ultimate cluster* is used to denote the aggregate of units included in the sample from a primary unit. The aggregate value of a characteristic for the ith ultimate cluster is x_i, the size of the ith ultimate cluster is n_i, and the average size of the m ultimate clusters in the sample is $\bar{n}$. This definition of an ultimate cluster holds for any number of stages of sampling. Thus, suppose that a county is sampled as a primary unit, a set of 5 small areas containing 20 households each is selected from the county as second-stage units, and 2 households are selected from each of the 5 small areas. The ultimate cluster consists of the total sample of 10 households selected from the county. Other notation will be introduced and defined as needed.

One additional remark here on a principle followed may help. Whenever a capital letter (X or Y) is used as a subscript to a variance, an estimated variance, or a covariance, it will designate that the symbol to which it is attached refers to a population value that does not depend on size of sample, as, for example, the population variance or covariance. The appropriate small letters will be used in the subscript to indicate the variances or covariances of sample estimates. Thus,

$$S_{2X}^2 = \frac{1}{N} \sum_i^M \frac{N_i}{N_i - 1} \sum_j^{N_i} (X_{ij} - \bar{\bar{X}}_i)^2$$

is a population variance between second-stage units within primary units, and

$$s_{2X}^2 = \frac{1}{n} \sum_i^m \frac{n_i}{n_i - 1} \sum_j^{n_i} (x_{ij} - \bar{\bar{x}}_i)^2$$

is a sample estimate of S_{2X}^2. Both these have X (a capital letter) in the subscript. They are to be carefully distinguished from

σ_x^2, which denotes the variance of the sample total, x;

or

$\sigma_{\bar{x}}^2$, which denotes the variance of the sample mean, $\bar{x}$;

or

$\sigma_{x'}^2$, which denotes the variance of the estimated total, x';

or

s_x^2, $s_{\bar{x}}^2$, and $s_{x'}^2$, which are sample estimates of σ_x^2, $\sigma_{\bar{x}}^2$, and $\sigma_{x'}^2$, respectively.

2. How cluster sampling works—illustrated with area sampling. Cluster sampling often provides a convenient and low-cost device for fixing, in advance of the survey, the probability of including each member of the population in the sample. Thus, it often makes possible the use of an efficient probability sample design in situations where the simple random sampling of individual members of the population might be very costly. For example, it would not, in most cases, be feasible to draw a simple random sample of persons from the population of the United States or from any other large group for which no complete, up-to-date, and accessible listing of individual members of the population is available. However, complete listings of "clusters" (e.g., a list of counties or of smaller areas in the United States) are frequently available or can be prepared at small effort, and from such a list clusters can be readily sampled with known probabilities. Moreover, as will be seen, the use of clustering may have a significant effect on other costs.

As an illustration of cluster sampling, suppose that we are interested in sampling for certain characteristics of the dwelling units of a city. For example, we may wish to know the total number of dwelling units, the proportion vacant, the proportions having other characteristics, and perhaps the average rentals of various types of units.

A probability sample of dwelling units in a city can be obtained by making a list of all such dwelling units and then taking a simple random sample from this listing, or a stratified simple random sample. Such approaches may yield a very efficient sample so far as sample size alone is concerned. For most practical purposes, other designs with the same size of sample can hardly yield the same precision. Why then should one consider other designs? The fact is that the cost of drawing the sample may not be at all closely related to the size of the sample. Suppose, for example, that a list for the city (such as might be in a city directory) is unavailable. Then, to select a random sample of households by one of the methods mentioned, one might have to go past and identify every dwelling unit to make up a list from which to select the sample. In a city of 10,000 households, at, say, 10 cents a household, this cost would amount to $1000 regardless of the size of the sample. The corresponding cost in a city with 300,000 dwelling units would be $30,000. Many important surveys must be conducted at a total cost of a fraction of $30,000. Thus, one would rarely consider a simple or a stratified simple random sample of dwelling units as a reasonable alternative when sampling from a large population, unless a usable listing already existed.

Moreover, if one is collecting information by direct interviewing throughout a large area, it may be uneconomical to interview a widely scattered sample even in cases where a complete listing is available beforehand. A method of reducing the cost, as compared with preparing a complete listing of elementary units and sampling from it, is to use sample units consisting of clusters of elements. "Area sampling" often provides a convenient way of identifying the population into clusters that are suitable as sampling units.

In "area sampling," the entire area in which the population is located is subdivided into smaller areas, and each elementary unit (each dwelling unit in the above illustration) is associated with one and only one such area, for example, the particular small area in which the dwelling unit is located.   Neither the identity of the individual dwelling units nor the number of dwelling units in the areas need be known in advance.   A sample of these areas is drawn, and all or a subsample of the dwelling units located in the selected areas are covered in the survey.

It can be shown that, if a list of areas is available and if a simple random selection of a sample of areas is made, and if the population associated with these sample areas is completely enumerated, then the probability of being included is the same for each member of the population,* as is illustrated below.

Illustration 2.1.   Suppose that we wish to estimate total employment in retail stores in a universe of only 5 blocks and that we proceed to do this by drawing a simple random sample of 2 *blocks* (not stores) and by obtaining the employment figures from all stores in the selected blocks. We shall assume certain values for the illustration, as is shown below, although the conclusions would be the same for any values that were assumed and for any type of population.

BLOCK NO.	TOTAL RETAIL EMPLOYEES
1	4
2	6
3	2
4	6
5	1
Total	19
Average per block	3.8

Each of the possible samples from a simple random sample of two blocks is listed in Table 1, together with the estimated total employment from each sample.   With simple random sampling of blocks, each of these samples will have the same probability of being selected.   The estimated totals shown are obtained by computing the total employment in blocks in the sample, and multiplying this sample total by the reciprocal of the sampling fraction; in this case $1/f$ equals $\frac{5}{2}$.   The results for each possible sample are as shown in Table 1.

---

* Thus, sampling of clusters does not affect the probability of including a single element, as compared with simple random sampling of elements.   However, the probability that any specified pair of elements will be in the sample is affected, and this affects the variance of the sample result.

Table 1. Samples of 2 blocks from a hypothetical population of 5 blocks

Sample consisting of blocks	Total employment for blocks in sample	Estimated total employment
1 and 2	10	25.0
1 and 3	6	15.0
1 and 4	10	25.0
1 and 5	5	12.5
2 and 3	8	20.0
2 and 4	12	30.0
2 and 5	7	17.5
3 and 4	8	20.0
3 and 5	3	7.5
4 and 5	7	17.5
Total		190.0
Average of sample estimates		19.0
Standard deviation of sample estimates		6.25

Each block appears in 4 out of the 10 possible samples of 2 that can be drawn. Therefore, the probability that a store in block 1 will be included in the sample is .4, and the same probability exists for a store in any one of the other blocks even though the number of stores in each block is different.

Earlier theory applicable. When the clusters are enumerated completely, i.e., when there is no subsampling, the theory in the previous chapters is immediately applicable. The average of the sample estimates agrees exactly with the actual number being estimated. Similarly, in the illustration above, the standard deviation of all possible estimates from the sample is equal to 6.25. This is exactly what is given by the formula for the standard error of a sample of 2 blocks, based on simple random sampling, where block characteristics are substituted in Eq. 3.9 and 9.3, Ch. 4, instead of characteristics of individual stores. Thus,

$$\sigma_{x'} = M \sqrt{\frac{M-m}{Mm} \cdot \frac{\sum_{}^{M}(X_i - \bar{X})^2}{M-1}}$$

$$= 5 \sqrt{\frac{5-2}{5(2)} \cdot \frac{(4-3.8)^2+(6-3.8)^2+(2-3.8)^2+(6-3.8)^2+(1-3.8)^2}{4}}$$

$$= 6.25$$

Of course, in any real problem the number of blocks will be much larger, subsampling or other variations in design may be introduced, more efficient methods of estimation may be practicable, and the formula for the sampling variance may be more complicated. However, the example illustrates that, when all the elements of a selected cluster are included in the sample, the probability of an individual being included in the sample is the same as that of the cluster.   Similarly, it may be shown that, if a subsampling design is used, the probability of an individual being included in the sample is equal to the product of the sampling fractions at each stage of sampling.

The example illustrates, further, that with simple random sampling of clusters the variance for simple random sampling given in Chapter 4 is applicable, but with the cluster as the sampling unit and not the individual members of the population on which measurements are desired.

Ratio estimate with variable denominator.   The use of estimates involving ratios of random variables (referred to as "ratio estimates") takes on greater importance with cluster sampling than with simple random sampling of elements, for with cluster sampling one is seldom interested in the average value per primary sampling unit.   Thus, if one has drawn a sample of blocks to estimate the characteristics of retail stores, he will rarely have an interest in the average sales per city block, but may often have an interest in the average sales per store.   Or, in sampling people, the interest will seldom be in the average number of workers or of unemployed persons per block, but rather in the percentage of the workers unemployed, or the percentage of the population having a particular characteristic, etc.   With cluster sampling, the estimates of such averages or percentages are ratios of two random variables.   The precision of such ratios must be evaluated from the variance formula for the ratio of random variables.   Estimates of such percentages or averages and their corresponding coefficients of variation were discussed in Ch. 4, Sec. 16–18.   Thus, if a simple random sample of clusters is used, the preparation of estimates from a sample of clusters and the evaluation of the precision of such estimates involve nothing very new.

Importance of uniquely associating elementary units with clusters.   An important point to note in the cluster sampling illustration (2.1) given above is that each elementary unit was uniquely associated with one and only one cluster.   Often a convenient way of associating each element with a cluster is through the use of areas.   Stores, farms, or other units, for example, can be associated with the areas in which they are located, or people can be associated with the area in which they live or in which they are located at a particular point in time.

This association of the members of a population with areas is not always easy.   Sometimes, for example, a single business establishment has two addresses or operates in two or more locations, or a person's place of residence may not be well defined; in fact, he may not have a usual place of residence at all.   When there are problems of this sort,

careful attention must be given to the establishment of workable rules for
resolving difficult cases to provide a unique association of each member
of the population with one of the areas.   Although a unique association
of each member of the population with a single cluster is not essential to
cluster sampling, special attention and theory may be needed to deal with
the situation where such unique association is not accomplished.

   3. Alternative cluster sampling designs.   There are a number of alternative ways of obtaining a cluster sample, varying in complexity from
drawing a simple random sample of city blocks and taking a census of the
sample blocks, to more complex systems involving multi-stage sampling.
For example, the design may call for starting with an initial sample of
large areas such as counties, then selecting a sample of small areas from
the selected large areas, and finally drawing a sample of farms, stores, or
households from the subsampled small areas, with varying probabilities
of inclusion for different units in the sample; it may involve also special
procedures for sampling large stores, farms, institutions, hotels, or other
special groups of the population.

   In presenting the principal types of alternative designs, it will be convenient to consider first the problem of estimating totals, percentages, or
averages with a simple random sample of clusters, and with or without a
second stage of sampling.   For the present, except as otherwise indicated,
we shall regard systematic samples obtained by methods such as described
in Procedures 1, 2, and 3 below as equivalent to simple random samples.
Where it is desired to insure a simple random sampling, a process such as
described in Sec. 5, Ch. 4, can be substituted for systematic selection.   In
later chapters we shall discuss stratification with cluster sampling, as well
as the use of variable sampling fractions, varying probabilities in selecting
a sample, and some special considerations that need to be taken into
account if an essential part of the problem is to estimate totals.

B. SOME SIMPLE PROCEDURES FOR SELECTION OF CLUSTER SAMPLES

   4. Three simple procedures for drawing an area sample.   As an illustration, let us suppose that the problem is to estimate from a sample the
characteristics of the dwelling units in a county, including, in particular,
the average rental value of dwelling units.   We shall illustrate three
alternative methods of drawing the sample.   Let us assume, for illustration, that a 1 per cent sample is to be drawn.

   Procedure 1—*A simple random or systematic sample of areas to be
enumerated completely.*   The sampling unit is the city block, or a small
area (which we shall also call a "block") in those parts of the county not

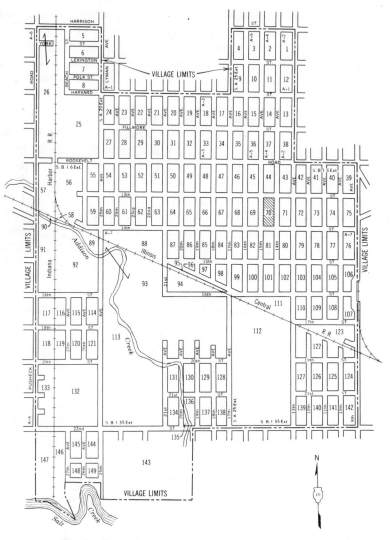

FIG. 1.   Serpentine numbering of blocks in a small town.

divided into regular blocks.   All the dwelling units in the selected blocks are to be covered.

STEP 1.   Procure a reasonably accurate block or road map of the area, and, to the extent feasible, take steps through local inquiry to bring it up to date.   Then identify the blocks in some order and number them serially.   (If systematic or stratified sampling is used, there may be some advantage if the arrangement of the blocks is such that blocks with similar characteristics are close together in the serial numbering, as described in Sec. 10 below. A serpentine number system on a map such as in Fig. 1 may accomplish this reasonably well.)

STEP 2. (*a*) To obtain a simple random sample of blocks, follow the procedure described in Sec. 5, Ch. 4.

(*b*) To obtain a systematic sample follow the procedure described in Ch. 3, Sec. 3 (p. 94). Thus, for a 1 per cent systematic sample, take a random number between 1 and 100. If this number is 70, for example, select the block numbered 70 and every hundredth block thereafter: 70, 170, 270, etc. If the starting number had been 15, the sample blocks would have been 15, 115, 215, etc. If the numbering for the county starts in the small town of Fig. 1, then the shaded block (block 70) of Fig. 1 shows the selected sample area in that town.

STEP 3. Collect desired information from all the dwelling units in the selected blocks.

In this very simple procedure, the minimum possible number of blocks is included in the sample, as compared with any alternative procedure that uses blocks as the primary units and that would yield an expected 1 per cent sample of households. The fact that so few blocks need be included in the sample for any given number of households accounts for the main advantages of the procedure as well as its main disadvantages. The advantages and disadvantages of this procedure can best be discussed in comparison with the following alternatives, which also involve obtaining a 1 per cent sample of households, but which differ in that more blocks are included in the sample and subsampling is used.

Procedure 2—A sample of areas with subsampling of smaller areas. The 1 per cent sample of households can also be obtained by drawing, say, a sample of 1 in 25 of the blocks and then a subsample of one-fourth of the dwelling units in the selected blocks. To illustrate:

STEP 1. Obtain the maps, identify the blocks, and number them serially, as in Procedure 1 above.

STEP 2. Draw a sample of blocks following one of the alternatives given in Step 2 of Procedure 1, but applied to yield a 1 in 25 sample.

STEP 3. Divide each of the sampled blocks into 4 compact segments, as illustrated in Fig. 2. The 4 segments do not need to be of the same size, although it is usually desirable to equalize roughly their size in terms of elementary units. An illustration of a block divided into segments is given in Fig. 2; a block map is used that shows individual structures and other detail. (This is a part of a page from a Sanborn map*.) Such mapping materials are often useful for sample designation.

---

* Published by the Sanborn Map Company, New York, N.Y.

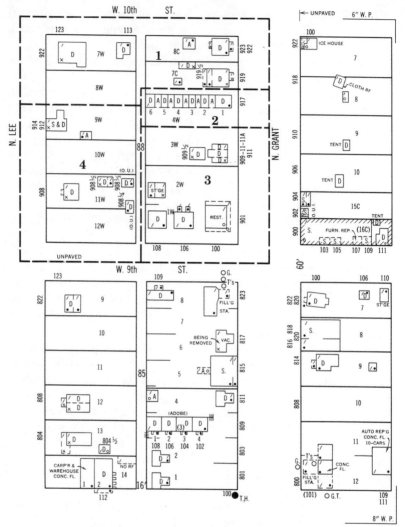

FIG. 2. Part of a Sanborn map, with a block divided
into 4 compact segments.

STEP 4. Number the segments in each sampled block from 1 to 4, as
indicated in Fig. 2. Take a random number between 1 and 4 for each
block. The serial number corresponding to the selected random number
is the selected segment. For example, if the random number is 3 for a
particular block, segment No. 3 is the sample segment for that block.

This process, if carried through for all of an area containing a fairly
large number of blocks, will yield approximately 1 per cent of the

households, since the block sampling fraction ($\frac{1}{25}$) multiplied by the within-block sampling fraction ($\frac{1}{4}$) is 1/100.

Note that, although a 1 per cent sample is obtained in both procedures, Procedure 2 includes in the sample more blocks and fewer households per sampled block.   Usually it will cost more to obtain the same percentage sample by Procedure 2, since more sample blocks need to be identified and subsampled, and travel will be increased in order to visit a greater number of blocks.

This subsampling procedure is substantially equivalent to dividing every block in the county into 4 parts or segments and taking 1 in 100 of these segments, but actually involves subdividing into segments only those blocks included in the sample.   Hence, the use of subsampling can be regarded as essentially equivalent to the sampling of full clusters, but with two-stage sampling as a device for reducing the work in drawing a sample of small clusters.   (See also the discussion of "chunking" in Sec. 29 of this chapter.)

Procedure 3—A sample of areas with listing and subsampling.   To carry out Procedure 2 it is necessary to have detailed maps (which, in practice, may not be available) or prepare field sketches in order to make possible segmenting the blocks for subsampling.   Procedure 3 described below accomplishes a somewhat similar result and is applicable in a large variety of problems.   Let us assume, again, that we wish to draw a sample of 1 in 25 blocks, and a sample of 1 in 4 from within the selected blocks.

STEPS 1 AND 2.   Same as for Procedure 2.

STEP 3.   Identify the units to be listed and subsampled within the selected blocks.   Let us suppose that the listing unit is the "dwelling place," which is defined as the entire structure where there *appear* to be fewer than 4 dwelling units, and is defined as the individual dwelling unit where the structure contains 4 or more dwelling units.   (Section 25 gives various considerations in the definition of listing units.)

STEP 4.   Visit each sample block and make a list of all the listing units, starting at, say, the northwest corner of a sampled block, and going around the block, through all alleys, courts, etc.   Number the listing units serially, either separately beginning with 1 for each block, or using a single sequence of serial numbers throughout all 'or various groups of blocks in the sample.

STEP 5.   Subsample listing units from the selected blocks at a rate of 1 in 4.   This is accomplished by:

(*a*) Choosing a 1-in-4 simple random sample from each of the selected blocks; or

(*b*) Choosing a 1-in-4 systematic sample from the selected blocks.

The dwelling units so selected will again be approximately a 1 per cent sample of all dwelling units.

The three procedures just indicated for sample selection can be used within strata to select a stratified sample of clusters, and can be combined in various ways in the same sample design.

5. Other procedures for selecting a sample.   Section 4 gives a description of several ways in which one can go about drawing an area sample.   The procedures would be similar if one were drawing a sample of farms, or of stores, or of people, or of other units.   If the sample were of people, one would have to decide whether the listing within the selected blocks would be of people, or of dwelling units, dwelling places, or something else.   If it were of dwelling units, all the people in the selected dwelling units might be included in the sample, or further sampling of people from these dwelling units might be used.   The procedures are applicable either if people are listed and subsampled, or if larger listing units are chosen and all people in the selected listing units are included in the sample.

A number of questions must be answered before one can make efficient use of procedures like those described above.   The investigator must determine how many blocks are to be drawn into the sample and how large the subsample is to be from the selected blocks.   If a compact segment is the sampling unit, as in Procedure 2, he must know how large the segments should be.   He should, in so far as feasible, determine the optimum design, i.e., that design which yields the required accuracy at a minimum cost, or that design which yields the greatest accuracy with the funds and resources at his disposal.   To meet these requirements we need to examine the estimate, the sampling error, and the relative costs and then see how to arrive at the optimum design.   We shall proceed to do this for simple random sampling of primary units in the remainder of this chapter, and for stratified sampling in succeeding chapters.

C. SAMPLE ESTIMATES, VARIANCES, AND VARIANCE ESTIMATES

6. The estimate and its variance.   For simple one- or two-stage sampling an estimate from the sample of the total of some characteristic, as, for example, the total value of dwelling units in the area, the total production of a farm product, or the total number of persons having some characteristic, is given by

$$x' = \frac{1}{f} x \qquad (6.1)$$

where x is the aggregate value of a characteristic for the listing units included in the sample, and f is the over-all sampling fraction. The estimate given by Eq. 6.1 is an unbiased estimate; and this estimate, obtained by multiplying the sample aggregate by the reciprocal of the sampling ratio, is referred to as the *simple unbiased estimate*.

The estimate of the average value per elementary unit of a characteristic, as, for example, the average rental value of dwelling units in an area or the per cent tenant-occupied, is given by the ratio

$$r = \frac{x}{y} = \frac{x'}{y'} \tag{6.2}$$

where x and x' are, respectively, the sample total and the estimated population total for the characteristic, and y and y' are, respectively, the number of elementary units in the sample and the estimated total number (given by Eq. 6.1) in the population.

Equation 6.2 also is used to obtain an estimate of the ratio of the aggregate value for one characteristic to that for a second characteristic, as the ratio of rent to income, or average yield per acre.

Estimates 6.1 and 6.2 hold whether one- or two-stage sampling is used. Estimate 6.2 is a ratio of random variables and, as discussed in preceding chapters, is subject to a bias that becomes trivial as the number of psu's in the sample increases and can be ignored for moderately large samples.

The variance of the simple unbiased estimate of a total (Eq. 6.1) is*

$$\sigma_{x'}^2 = M^2 \frac{M-m}{M} \frac{S_{1X}^2}{m} + N^2 \frac{\bar{N}-\bar{n}}{\bar{N}} \frac{S_{2X}^2}{m\bar{n}} \tag{6.3}$$

and the rel-variance of x' is

$$V_{x'}^2 = \frac{M-m}{M} \frac{B_X^2}{m} + \frac{\bar{N}-\bar{n}}{\bar{N}} \frac{W_X^2}{m\bar{n}} \tag{6.4}$$

where

$$\left.\begin{aligned} S_{1X}^2 &= \frac{\sum\limits_{i}^{M}(X_i - \bar{X})^2}{M-1} \\[2mm] B_X^2 &= \frac{S_{1X}^2}{\bar{X}^2} \end{aligned}\right\} \tag{6.5}$$

and S_{1X}^2 is the variance and B_X^2 is the rel-variance between primary unit totals.

---

* For proof, see Vol. II, Ch. 6, Sec. 1.

$$\left.\begin{aligned} S_{2X}^2 &= \frac{1}{N} \sum_i^M \frac{N_i}{N_i - 1} \sum_j^{N_i} (X_{ij} - \bar{\bar{X}}_i)^2 \\ W_X^2 &= \frac{S_{2X}^2}{\bar{\bar{X}}^2} \end{aligned}\right\}$$

(6.6)

and S_{2X}^2 is the average variance and W_X^2 is the average rel-variance between listing units within psu's, and where in Eq. 6.3 and 6.4 $\bar{n} = f_2 \bar{N}$ and is the expected value of the number of listing units in the sample per psu in the sample. The other symbols are defined in Sec. 1.

The variance of x' (Eq. 6.3) is expressed in terms of the contributions to the variance from each stage of sampling. The first term represents the contribution to the variance of x' from the first stage of sampling and is spoken of as the between-psu component of the variance. It is the variance of x' based on a sample of m first-stage units with no subsampling, and hence the variation within first-stage units does not contribute to this term. This can be seen by letting $\bar{n} = \bar{N}$ in Eq. 6.3 or 6.4, which would be appropriate if all the N_i elementary units in the ith sampled cluster are included in the sample.

The second term represents the contribution to the variance of x' from sampling second-stage units (or simply subsampling) and is spoken of as the within-psu component of the variance. It is approximately (exactly except for the finite multiplier) the variance of x' for a proportionate stratified simple random sample of n cases with the primary units serving as strata. The variation between primary units does not contribute to this term. This can be seen by letting $m = M$ in the first term of Eq. 6.3 or 6.4, which would be appropriate if a sample were selected from all primary units.

We emphasized earlier that cluster sampling is ordinarily not the method of sampling to employ when the only limitation imposed on the design is the size of sample. From Eq. 6.4 it can be seen that, when the expected sample size is fixed, i.e., with $m\bar{n}$ fixed, the way to minimize the total variance is to make m as large as possible (and consequently $\bar{n}$ as small as possible); in other words, to get as far away as possible from sampling the elementary units in clusters.

The rel-variance of the ratio estimate (Eq. 6.2) is given by*

$$V_r^2 \doteq V_{x'}^2 + V_{y'}^2 - 2V_{x'y'}$$

(6.7)

where $V_{x'}^2$ and $V_{y'}^2$ are given by Eq. 6.4, and $V_{x'y'}$ is also given by Eq. 6.4

---

* For proof, see Vol. II, Ch. 6, Sec. 1.

but with B_{XY} substituted for B_X^2, and W_{XY} substituted for W_X^2, and where

$$\left.\begin{array}{c} S_{1XY} = \dfrac{\overset{M}{\sum}(X_i - \bar{X})(Y_i - \bar{Y})}{M - 1} \\[2em] B_{XY} = \dfrac{S_{1XY}}{\bar{X}\bar{Y}} \end{array}\right\} \tag{6.8}$$

and

$$\left.\begin{array}{c} S_{2XY} = \dfrac{1}{N}\overset{M}{\sum}\dfrac{N_i}{N_i - 1}\overset{N_i}{\sum}(X_{ij} - \bar{\bar{X}}_i)(Y_{ij} - \bar{\bar{Y}}_i) \\[2em] W_{XY} = \dfrac{S_{2XY}}{\bar{\bar{X}}\bar{\bar{Y}}} \end{array}\right\} \tag{6.9}$$

Also, $V_{x'y'} = \rho V_{x'} V_{y'}$, where ρ is the coefficient of correlation between x' and y'.

The rel-variance of the ratio estimate can be restated to separate the contributions of the primary unit sampling and the sampling within psu's as follows:

$$\left.\begin{array}{c} V_r^2 \doteq \dfrac{M - m}{M}\dfrac{B^2}{m} + \dfrac{\bar{N} - \bar{n}}{\bar{N}}\dfrac{W^2}{m\bar{n}} \\[2em] \doteq \dfrac{M - m}{M}\dfrac{S_1^2}{m\bar{X}^2} + \dfrac{\bar{N} - \bar{n}}{\bar{N}}\dfrac{S_2^2}{m\bar{n}\bar{X}^2} \end{array}\right\} \tag{6.10}$$

where

$$\left.\begin{array}{c} B^2 = B_X^2 + B_Y^2 - 2B_{XY} \\[1em] S_1^2 = S_{1X}^2 + R^2 S_{1Y}^2 - 2R S_{1XY} \end{array}\right\} \tag{6.11}$$

and

$$\left.\begin{array}{c} W^2 = W_X^2 + W_Y^2 - 2W_{XY} \\[1em] S_2^2 = S_{2X}^2 + R^2 S_{2Y}^2 - 2R S_{2XY} \end{array}\right\} \tag{6.12}$$

The terms in Eq. 6.11 and 6.12 are defined in Eq. 6.3–6.9. In Eq. 6.10 $\bar{n} = f_2\bar{N}$ is the expected value of the number of listing units in the sample per psu in the sample.

The approximations to the rel-variance given by Eq. 6.10 and 6.7 are identical, but merely stated in different forms. The approximations to the rel-variance of the ratio are good with samples large enough that $V_{y'}$ is less than .05 to .15, as discussed in Sec. 18, Ch. 4.

The rel-variance for the simple unbiased estimate is a special case of that for the ratio estimate, whenever $V_{y'}^2 = 0$, and then $B^2 = B_X^2$ and $W^2 = W_X^2$.

Illustration 6.1. Assume a population of 12 stores, with the stores assigned to blocks, and employees and payrolls for each store as shown in Table 2.

Table 2. Data for individual stores in hypothetical population of 6 blocks

Block No. i	No. of stores N_i	Total retail employees Y_i	Store No. j	No. of employees in each store Y_{ij}	Payroll X_{ij}
1	2	4			
			1	3	100
			2	1	50
2	2	6			
			1	2	100
			2	4	150
3	2	3			
			1	2	80
			2	1	60
4	4	6			
			1	3	150
			2	1	40
			3	2	100
			4	0	0
5	2	2			
			1	1	50
			2	1	80
6	0	0			
			(No stores)	0	0
Total all blocks	12	21	..	21	960

Exercises

6.1. Determine the rel-variance and variance of a simple unbiased estimate of the total payroll if (a) we draw a sample of 4 stores at random, (b) we draw a sample of 4 blocks, then select one-half the stores at random from each selected block, (c) we select a simple random sample of 2 blocks and include all the stores from the selected blocks.

6.2. Compute the rel-variances of estimates of total payroll for samples selected in (a), (b), and (c) above, using the product of total employment (assumed known) and the estimated ratio of payrolls to employees (Eq. 6.2).

Remark. We include the ratio estimate in these exercises purely for the sake of practice in using the materials developed to this point. Actually the sample size is too small to insure that the approximation to the variance of a ratio is "good." As a supplemental exercise the student may wish to list all possible samples for Ex. 6.2 above and compare the results with those of the approximate formula for the variance.

7. The estimate of the variance from the sample. Two estimates of the variance from the sample will be given. One form of estimate, which will be referred to as the "ultimate cluster variance estimate," is very simple to use but does not supply separate estimates of the contributions to the variance of the first-stage sampling and the second-stage sampling (i.e., the variance contribution of the primary units and the variance contribution from sampling within psu's). For estimating the precision of results the components of the variance are not needed. For guidance in optimum design, however, the estimates of the variance components are necessary.

The ultimate cluster variance estimate. An *ultimate cluster* consists of all the listing units in the sample from a particular primary unit; i.e., the ultimate cluster consists of the entire sample from the psu, whether obtained by 1, 2, or more stages of sampling. For example, in sampling a city, the psu might be a block and the listing unit a household or address. The ultimate cluster here is the sample, 100 per cent or less, and however drawn, from the block. Thus, m is the number of blocks and also the number of ultimate clusters drawn into the sample. When the sample is self-weighting (i.e., all households have the same probability of being in the sample), the *ultimate cluster estimate** of the rel-variance of x' is

$$v_{x'}^2 = \frac{s_{x'}^2}{(x')^2} = (1-f)\frac{s_{cX}^2}{m\bar{x}^2} \tag{7.1}$$

where

$$s_{cX}^2 = \frac{\sum\limits^{m}(x_i - \bar{x})^2}{m-1} \tag{7.2}$$

Similarly, the ultimate cluster estimate of the rel-variance of the ratio estimate r is

$$v_r^2 = v_{x'}^2 + v_{y'}^2 - 2v_{x'y'} \tag{7.3}$$

where

$$v_{x'y'} = \frac{s_{x'y'}}{x'y'} = \frac{(1-f)s_{cXY}}{m\bar{x}\bar{y}} \tag{7.4}$$

and

$$s_{cXY} = \frac{\sum\limits^{m}(x_i - \bar{x})(y_i - \bar{y})}{m-1} \tag{7.5}$$

The terms in Eq. 7.3 are consistent estimates of the corresponding terms in Eq. 6.7.

---

* For proof, see Vol. II, Ch. 6, Sec. 3.

Remark. The idea of the ultimate cluster makes it possible to consider two- or more stage sampling theory as a special case of the sampling of whole clusters. For estimating a variance, it might appear reasonable to assume that a separate estimate would have to be made of the contributions to the variance for each stage of sampling. This would require at least two elements at each stage of sampling, or, if stratification were used within the first-stage units, at least two elements within each substratum. Actually the ultimate cluster approach yields a consistent estimate of the variance as long as there are two or more first-stage units in the sample,* no matter how the subsampling is done, provided the subsample is a probability sample, and provided the subsample taken in one psu does not depend on the subsample taken in another psu.

The estimate of components† of the variance. When it is desired to estimate separately the components of the rel-variance, B^2 and W^2, the following estimates may be used. An estimate of W^2 (Eq. 6.12) is

$$w^2 = w_X^2 + w_Y^2 - 2w_{XY} \tag{7.6}$$

where

$$w_X^2 = \frac{s_{2X}^2}{\bar{\bar{x}}^2} \tag{7.7}$$

$$s_{2X}^2 = \frac{1}{n} \sum_i^m \frac{n_i}{n_i - 1} \sum_j^{n_i} (x_{ij} - \bar{\bar{x}}_i)^2 \tag{7.8}$$

which is an unbiased estimate of S_{2X}^2 (Eq. 6.6);

$$w_{XY} = \frac{s_{2XY}}{\bar{\bar{x}}\bar{\bar{y}}} \tag{7.9}$$

and

$$s_{2XY} = \frac{1}{n} \sum_i^m \frac{n_i}{n_i - 1} \sum_j^{n_i} (x_{ij} - \bar{\bar{x}}_i)(y_{ij} - \bar{\bar{y}}_i) \tag{7.10}$$

which is an unbiased estimate of S_{2XY} (Eq. 6.9). Other terms are defined in Sec. 1. An estimate of B^2 (Eq. 6.11) is

$$b^2 = b_X^2 + b_Y^2 - 2b_{XY} \tag{7.11}$$

where

$$b_X^2 = \frac{1}{\bar{x}^2} [s_{cX}^2 - \bar{n}(1 - f_2)s_{2X}^2] \tag{7.12}$$

and

$$b_{XY} = \frac{1}{\bar{x}\bar{y}} [s_{cXY} - \bar{n}(1 - f_2)s_{2XY}] \tag{7.13}$$

---

* For proof, see Vol. II, Ch. 6, Sec. 2.
† For proof, see Vol. II, Ch. 6, Sec. 4.

where s_{cX}^2 and s_{cXY} are given by Eq. 7.2 and 7.5, respectively, and s_{2X}^2 and s_{2XY} are given by Eq. 7.8 and 7.10.

The individual terms in Eq. 7.6 and 7.11 are consistent estimates of the corresponding terms in Eq. 6.12 and 6.11.

8. Comparison of cluster sampling with simple random sampling. Although simple random sampling of either listing units or of elementary units may not be a useful alternative in many practical problems, simple random sampling provides a standard of comparison for guiding one in the selection of reasonable alternatives and for speculating on the variance of alternative designs. For this reason it will sometimes be convenient to express the variance of cluster sampling in terms of the variance of simple random samples of either listing units or elements, multiplied by a factor which reflects the effect of cluster sampling on the variance.

A simple case: Simple random sampling of psu's, where the psu's are equal in size, and the elementary unit is the listing unit. Assume for simplicity that the estimate to be made is an average value per elementary unit, that the listing unit is the elementary unit, and that the primary units are equal in size, i.e., N_i equals $\bar{N}$ for all i (so that, for illustration, each primary unit contains $\bar{N}$ dwelling units); then formulas 6.4 and 6.7 or 6.10 will be identical and will be very nearly equivalent to*

$$V_{\bar{x}}^2 \doteq \frac{1-f}{m\bar{n}} \, V^2[1 + \delta(\bar{n} - 1)] \tag{8.1}$$

where δ, which will be defined more fully below, is the intraclass correlation between elementary units within primary units, $f = n/N$ is the over-all sampling fraction, and

$$V^2 = \frac{\sum\limits_{i}^{M} \sum\limits_{j}^{\bar{N}} (X_{ij} - \bar{\bar{X}})^2}{(N-1)\bar{\bar{X}}^2} = \frac{S^2}{\bar{\bar{X}}^2} \tag{8.2}$$

is the rel-variance between elementary units of the characteristic being measured; X_{ij} is the value of the jth elementary unit in the ith psu, $\bar{\bar{X}}$ is the average value per elementary unit of the characteristic, and $\bar{n}$ is the average number of elementary units per ultimate cluster. The value of δ is†

$$\delta = \frac{\sigma_b^2 - \sigma^2/\bar{N}}{(\bar{N} - 1)\sigma^2/\bar{N}} \tag{8.3}$$

---

* For proof, see Vol. II, Ch. 6, Sec. 5.
† For proof, see Vol. II, Ch. 6, Sec. 6.

where

$$\sigma_b^2 = \frac{\sum\limits_{i}^{M}(\bar{\bar{X}}_i - \bar{\bar{X}})^2}{M} = \frac{M-1}{M\bar{N}^2}S_{1X}^2 \qquad (8.4)$$

$$\sigma^2 = \frac{\sum\limits_{i}^{M}\sum\limits_{j}^{\bar{N}}(X_{ij} - \bar{\bar{X}})^2}{N} = \frac{N-1}{N}S^2 \qquad (8.5)$$

and where S_{1X}^2 is defined by Eq. 6.5.

Thus, from Eq. 8.3, δ depends on σ_b^2 and σ^2. Moreover, since $\sigma_b^2 + \sigma_w^2 = \sigma^2$, where

$$\sigma_w^2 = \frac{\sum\limits_{i}^{M}\sum\limits_{j}^{\bar{N}}(X_{ij} - \bar{\bar{X}}_i)^2}{N}$$

it follows that δ depends on σ_b^2 and σ_w^2. If $\sigma_w^2 = 0$, i.e., if all elements within any cluster are alike with respect to the characteristic being measured and consequently there is no variation between elementary units within clusters, then $\sigma_b^2 = \sigma^2$. In this case,

$$\delta = \frac{\sigma^2 - \sigma^2/\bar{N}}{(\bar{N}-1)\sigma^2/\bar{N}} = 1$$

Similarly, if the means of all the clusters are exactly alike, $\sigma_b^2 = 0$, and therefore $\sigma_w^2 = \sigma^2$. In this latter case, from Eq. 8.3,

$$\delta = \frac{-1}{\bar{N}-1}$$

It is seen that the intraclass correlation will be close to $+1$ if the between-cluster variance accounts for a large part of the total variance, and will be small positive or possibly negative if the between-cluster variance accounts for a small part of the total variance. Thus, the intraclass correlation is a measure of the degree of homogeneity (or heterogeneity) within clusters. When the elementary units within clusters are relatively homogeneous, i.e., when they are very similar in respect to some characteristic, the intraclass correlation between elementary units within clusters for that characteristic will be high. Conversely, if the elementary units within clusters are relatively heterogeneous in respect to the characteristic, the intraclass correlation will be low positive or, in very unusual situations, even negative.

Clusters of moderately large size may be efficient sampling units when the intraclass correlation between elements within clusters is low positive (or negative) and will be less efficient when the correlation is positive and high.   Some simple illustrations may help to clarify how the intraclass correlation measures homogeneity, and how it affects the variance for sampling units of varying size.

High positive intraclass correlation: an example.   Suppose that most of the persons in certain blocks are white, and that most of the persons in others are nonwhite.   In this case the variance between blocks of the proportion nonwhite will be relatively large, and the correlation between persons within a block is relatively high positive.   We can look at this situation in another way that may be useful.   If we observe one person in a block to be nonwhite, then it is more likely that the next person observed will be nonwhite if he comes from the same block than if he comes from any other block.

In this case of high positive correlation, a simple random sample of blocks consisting of all the persons in one block will provide very little information concerning the color composition of the total population. It is necessary to include in the sample a great many blocks in order to get a reasonably accurate estimate of the proportion of the total population that is nonwhite.

Negative intraclass correlation: an example.   Now suppose, on the other hand, the extreme case in which the proportion nonwhite is exactly the same in every block.   In this situation, the variance between blocks of the proportion nonwhite will be zero and the correlation between persons within a block is negative.   In this instance, if we observe one person in a block to be nonwhite, then it is more likely that the next person observed will be *white* if he comes from the same block than if he comes from any other block.

In this extreme case of negative correlation a sample consisting of all the persons in one block will provide complete information concerning the color composition of the total population.   We have only to sample a single block to measure exactly the proportion of the population that is nonwhite.

Zero intraclass correlation: an example.   Finally, suppose that the proportion of the population nonwhite differs from block to block in the manner that would be expected if the clusters were made up by grouping individuals from the total population, *at random*, into clusters the size of blocks.   In this instance σ_b^2 is approximately the variance between sample means based on simple random samples of size $\bar{N}$.   Therefore, σ_b^2 will be approximately equal to $\sigma^2/\bar{N}$, and the correlation between persons within a block is approximately zero.   In this instance, if we observe one person in a block to be nonwhite, then it is just as likely that the next person observed will be nonwhite whether he comes from the same block or from any other block.

In this case of zero correlation, a sample consisting of all the persons in one block will provide as much information concerning the color composition of the total population as a sample of the same size consisting of persons drawn entirely at random without regard to blocks. The use of blocks as sampling units in this case results in the same variance of the sample estimate as does the use of individuals as sampling units.

Intraclass correlations usually positive and decrease with increasing size of compact cluster. A common situation in cluster sampling is to use clusters that consist of more or less geographically contiguous families, farms, business establishments, or other units, and with these there will ordinarily be a positive intraclass correlation. Sometimes the correlation will be relatively low, and other times moderately large. If the units included in a cluster are few and are immediately contiguous, there will ordinarily be a higher correlation, i.e., higher homogeneity among the units within a cluster, than when the clusters are larger and there is greater geographic scatter of the units.

Thus, the homogeneity of units in a segment will ordinarily be greater for a compact part of a block than for an entire block; and it will usually be greater for a single block than for a group of adjacent blocks, etc. This is well illustrated by Table 3. Some of the δ's in this table were computed by the more general formula given by Eq. 8.11, which is applicable when the units vary in size. The table also illustrates the fact that, although the measure of homogeneity ordinarily decreases as the size of compact cluster increases, in practice it usually decreases at a much slower rate than the rate of increase in cluster size.

The δ for ultimate clusters is the same as the δ for initial psu's. If ultimate clusters are made up of units scattered at random over a larger area, then the homogeneity of units within the ultimate cluster will be approximately the same as the homogeneity for the larger area. Thus, the intraclass correlation among units in a set of ultimate clusters sub-sampled from psu's will be approximately the same (exactly the same if the subsampling is simple random sampling) as that for the psu's from which the subsample was drawn.* For example, if the primary units consist of sets of 62 neighboring households and a subsample of 3 households is taken with simple random sampling from each of a set of sampled primary units, the δ for the ultimate clusters so drawn will be that of the primary units.

Effect on the variance of using a cluster sample. The total number of

---

* For proof, see Vol. II, Ch. 6, Sec. 7.

elementary units in the sample is $m\bar{n}$, and $\dfrac{1-f}{m\bar{n}} V^2$ is the rel-variance of the estimate in a simple random sample of $m\bar{n}$ elementary units. It follows that $1 + \delta(\bar{n} - 1)$ in Eq. 8.1 represents the factor by which the variance of simple random sampling must be multiplied to obtain the variance for cluster sampling when the clusters are equal in size. It follows, also, that if $\bar{n} = 1$, i.e., if 1 elementary unit is subsampled per sample psu, the factor $1 + \delta(\bar{n} - 1)$ is equal to 1, and the variance will be the same as for simple random sampling of elementary units. Moreover, any increase in the size of $\bar{n}$ (the number to be subsampled from each psu) can only increase the variance for any fixed over-all size of sample, so long as δ is positive. If the sample size, $m\bar{n}$, is fixed and if δ is greater than zero, the value of Eq. 8.1 will evidently be largest when $\bar{n} = \bar{N}$, i.e., when the whole psu is included in the sample. Thus, we see again that if cost were determined entirely by the number of elementary units in the sample, the design which would give the most reliable results for a fixed size of sample would involve no clustering of the sample at all.

To illustrate the effect of the intraclass correlation on the variance with cluster sampling, consider the problem of sampling dwelling units to estimate average rental value in a city. Thus, assume that whole city blocks are sampled and that the size of block, $\bar{N}$, is 24, and that $\delta = .25$. Then $1 + \delta(\bar{N} - 1)$ would be equal to 6.75. This means that, if a sample of blocks were drawn and *all* households in the selected blocks were included in the sample, the total number of households to be included in the sample would have to be 575 per cent larger than the number required for a simple random sample of dwelling units, to obtain the same accuracy. The loss would not be so great if the blocks were subsampled, as was the case in Procedure 3, Sec. 4. There the subsampling ratio was 1/4, and hence the average size of the ultimate cluster, $\bar{n}$, would be $\bar{n} = 6$ for this special case, and the ratio of the variance to that for simple random sampling would then be $1 + (6 - 1).25 = 2.25$, or an increase of 125 per cent. If the subsampling rate were 1 in 8, the average size of ultimate cluster would be 3, and the increase in variance would be 50 per cent. An item such as rental value has a larger δ than is to be expected for many characteristics, although some other items may have considerably larger δ's. Ordinarily, the increase in variance for cluster sampling in estimating, say, the age distribution or employment status of persons would be very much less, as is seen in the illustrative values of δ in Table 3.

Some additional observed values of δ are given in Case Study D, Ch. 12. Also in Table 4 values of δ are listed for some characteristics that have been observed to have unusually high values of δ (most of these values were computed with variable sized clusters, using Eq. 8.11).

Table 3. Measure of homogeneity, δ, between households, for several characteristics*

(Based on a sample from selected cities over 100,000 population in the United States)

Characteristic	Measure of homogeneity for clusters of			
	3 hh.	9 hh.	27 hh.	62 hh.
Proportion of households reporting				
Home owned	.170	.171	.166	.096
Rent of $10–14	.235	.169	.107	.062
Rent of $40–49	.430	.349	.243	.112
Average size of household	.230	.186	.142	.066
Proportion of persons who are				
Native white males	.100	.088	.077	.058
Males unemployed	.060	.070	.045	.034
Males 25–34	.045	.026	.018	.008

* The clusters were made up by taking a sample of successive groups of 3, 9, 27 households and blocks having an average of 62 households in order of enumeration from the 1940 Population Census and computing the variances for these clusters within strata made up of geographic areas within each of the cities. These data are based on the analysis in Case Study D, Ch. 12, where a fuller explanation is given.

A more general case for clusters that vary in size. Equation 8.1 holds for the special case when the number of listing units is the same for all psu's, and the estimate is a simple unbiased estimate of an average or total. Now we shall consider the more general case when the psu's vary in size and the estimate may be either a ratio of random variables or an unbiased estimate of a total.

As in the simple case (Eq. 8.1), we shall indicate how the variance of an estimate with cluster sampling of listing units is related to the variance of the same estimate with simple random sampling of listing units.

For simple one- or two-stage cluster sampling Eq. 6.10 is very nearly equal to*

$$\left.\begin{array}{l} V_r^2 \doteq \dfrac{1-f}{m\bar{n}}\,\hat{V}^2[1 + \delta(\bar{n}-1)] \\[2mm] \doteq \left(\dfrac{1-f}{m\bar{n}}\,V^2\right)\dfrac{\hat{V}^2}{V^2}\,[1 + \delta(\bar{n}-1)] \end{array}\right\} \tag{8.6}$$

* For proof, see Vol. II, Ch. 6, Sec. 5.

Table 4.   Some illlustrative characteristics with relatively high values of δ

Characteristic*	Average size of cluster $\bar{N}$	δ
Proportion of households reporting rent of $40–49	3 hh.	.43
Average farm population per cluster in the West	3 hh.	.40
Proportion of farms in the North reporting	3.88 farms	
Woodland		.44
Dairy products		.43
Proportions of farms having commercial orchards		
in North Carolina†	5 farms	.38
Proportion of farms in the South reporting	5.72 farms	
"All other" land		.63
Irish potatoes		.40
Sows		.39
Proportion of farms in the West reporting		
Barley	4.26 farms	.49

* Selected characteristics from a Bureau of the Census publication, *Analysis of Sampling Errors in Farm Sampling* (*April–June 1947*), *Preliminary Report*, and from other (unpublished) studies made in the Bureau of the Census.

† Based on data from F. E. McVay, "Sampling Methods Applied to Estimating Numbers of Commercial Orchards in a Commercial Peach Area," *J. Amer. Stat. Assn.*, **42** (1947), 533–540.

where in Eq. 8.6 $\bar{n} = f_2\bar{N}$ is the expected value of the number of listing units in the sample per psu in the sample, and where

$$V^2 = V_X^2 + V_Y^2 - 2V_{XY} \tag{8.7}$$

$$V_X^2 = \frac{\sum\limits_{i}^{M} \sum\limits_{j}^{N_i} (X_{ij} - \bar{\bar{X}})^2}{(N-1)\bar{\bar{X}}^2} \tag{8.8}$$

is the rel-variance between listing units in the population; V_Y^2 is defined analogously;

$$V_{XY} = \frac{\sum\limits_{i}^{M} \sum\limits_{j}^{N_i} (X_{ij} - \bar{\bar{X}})(Y_{ij} - \bar{\bar{Y}})}{(N-1)\bar{\bar{X}}\bar{\bar{Y}}} \tag{8.9}$$

$$\hat{V}^2 = \frac{M-1}{M} B^2 + \frac{\bar{N}-1}{\bar{N}} W^2 \tag{8.10}$$

with B^2 and W^2 defined, respectively, by Eq. 6.11 and 6.12, and

$$\delta = \frac{\dfrac{M-1}{M}B^2 - \dfrac{\hat{V}^2}{\bar{N}}}{(\bar{N}-1)\hat{V}^2/\bar{N}} \tag{8.11}$$

is the measure of homogeneity. Other symbols are defined in Sec. 1.

Remark· 1.   Equation 8.11 for δ can also be written in other forms that may be convenient, such as

$$\delta = \frac{\dfrac{M-1}{M}S_1^2 - \bar{N}S_2^2}{\dfrac{M-1}{M}S_1^2 + \bar{N}(\bar{N}-1)S_2^2} = \frac{\dfrac{M-1}{M}B^2 - W^2/\bar{N}}{\dfrac{M-1}{M}B^2 + (\bar{N}-1)W^2/\bar{N}} \tag{8.12}$$

where S_1^2 and S_2^2 are given, respectively, by Eq. 6.11 and 6.12. For large M it is approximately equal to

$$\delta \doteq \frac{S_1^2 - \bar{N}S_2^2}{S_1^2 + \bar{N}(\bar{N}-1)S_2^2} \tag{8.13}$$

A simple estimate of δ from the sample, made in terms of the corresponding variances between and within ultimate clusters, is*

$$\delta' = \frac{s_c^2 - \bar{n}s_2^2}{s_c^2 + \bar{n}(\bar{n}-1)s_2^2} \tag{8.14}$$

where $s_c^2 = s_{cX}^2 + r^2 s_{cY}^2 - 2r s_{cXY}$, with s_{cX}^2 and s_{cY}^2 given by Eq. 7.2 and s_{cXY} given by Eq. 7.5, and

$$s_2^2 = s_{2X}^2 + r^2 s_{2Y}^2 - 2r s_{2XY} \tag{8.15}$$

with s_{2X}^2 and s_{2Y}^2 given by Eq. 7.8 and s_{2XY} given by Eq. 7.10.

    With some qualifications Eq. 8.6 can be interpreted the same way as Eq. 8.1.   As in 8.1, for example, δ in Eq. 8.6 is a measure of homogeneity, and the larger the factor $1 + \delta(\bar{n} - 1)$, the greater the increase in variance due to cluster sampling.   Here, too, the cluster sampling variance increases with an increase in either δ, the measure of homogeneity, or $\bar{n}$, the average size of ultimate cluster.   There are some points of difference between Eq. 8.1 and 8.6, however, and it will be informative to compare these two equations.

    Equation 8.6 can be considered as being made up of three factors:

$$\frac{1-f}{m\bar{n}}V^2, \quad \frac{\hat{V}^2}{V^2}, \quad \text{and} \quad [1 + \delta(\bar{n}-1)]$$

---

* For proof, see Vol. II, Ch. 6, Sec. 5.

The first of these factors is comparable to the same factor in Eq. 8.1. In both equations, the factor $\dfrac{1-f}{m\bar{n}} V^2$ is the rel-variance for a simple random sample. However, in Eq. 8.6, it can represent the rel-variance of a ratio of random variables, whereas, in Eq. 8.1, it can only represent the rel-variance of an average per listing unit where the denominator is not a random variable.

The second factor in Eq. 8.6, $\hat{V}^2/V^2$, does not appear in Eq. 8.1. This factor is present only when the number of listing units per psu varies from psu to psu. In the special case when $N_i = \bar{N}$ for all i, $\hat{V}^2/V^2 = 1$. Usually* $\hat{V}^2$ will be larger than V^2, although if the cluster totals X_i and Y_i tend to be roughly proportionate to the N_i, then the variation of size of psu will not increase $\hat{V}^2$ substantially over V^2. Thus, $\hat{V}^2$ and V^2 may not differ materially in a great many situations in which the ratio, $R = X/Y$, is being estimated. But if, say, X_i varies roughly proportionately to N_i, but Y_i does not, then $\hat{V}^2/V^2$ may be considerably greater than 1, and consequently there may be a fairly substantial loss arising from the use of such first-stage units (psu's) in selecting the sample no matter what the average size of the ultimate clusters. In making a simple unbiased estimate of a total with variable-sized psu's $\hat{V}^2/V^2$ may be considerably greater than 1 (for example, see Sec. 1, Ch. 8).

The third factor, $1 + \delta(\bar{n} - 1)$, in Eq. 8.6 is comparable to the same term in Eq. 8.1. However, in Eq. 8.1, δ is the intraclass correlation among listing units in a psu. In Eq. 8.6 it is not necessarily an intraclass correlation, though it is a measure of homogeneity and its effect on the variance is similar to that in Eq. 8.1. Both Eq. 8.11, the equation for δ in Eq. 8.6, and Eq. 8.3, the equation for δ in Eq. 8.1, are equal to $+1$ when there is perfect homogeneity within psu's, and both have a minimum value of $-\dfrac{1}{\bar{N}-1}$. Equation 8.11 reduces to 8.3 when all psu's have the same number of listing units and the estimate is a simple unbiased estimate.

Remark 2.   The relationship between δ for listing units and δ for elementary units.   When the listing units used in subsampling are not the elementary units, it will sometimes be helpful in speculating on variances to know how the measure of homogeneity for listing units within primary units is related to the measure of homogeneity for elementary units within primary units and for elementary units within listing units. This relationship is given approximately by†

$$\delta_L \doteq \frac{[1 + \delta_1(\bar{K} - 1)] - [1 + \delta_2(\bar{\bar{K}} - 1)]}{(\bar{N} - 1)[1 + \delta_2(\bar{\bar{K}} - 1)]} \tag{8.16}$$

---

* For relationship between $\hat{V}^2$ and V^2 see Vol. II, Ch. 8, Sec. 4.
† For proof, see Vol. II, Ch. 6, Sec. 9.

where δ_L is the measure of homogeneity for listing units within primary units.

δ_1 is the measure of homogeneity for elements within primary units.

δ_2 is the measure of homogeneity for elements within listing units.

(Each of these values of δ is given by Eq. 8.11, in which the quantities M, $\bar{N}$, B^2, and $\hat{V}^2$ refer to the units appropriate to δ_L, δ_1, and δ_2.)

$\bar{N}$ is the average number of listing units per primary unit.

$\bar{K}$ is the average number of elements per primary unit.

$\bar{\bar{K}}$ is the average number of elements per listing unit.

Remark 3.   Estimate of S^2 from the sample.   An estimate of the variance between listing units, S^2 (defined by Eq. 3.10 in Ch. 4 or by Eq. 8.2 of this chapter), is given approximately by

$$s^2 = \frac{\sum\limits_{i}^{m} \sum\limits_{j}^{n_i} (x_{ij} - \bar{\bar{x}})^2}{n-1} \tag{8.17}$$

provided that δ is small, or, no matter what the value of δ, provided that the number of psu's in the sample is large.*

9. Some comments and illustrations.   The authors have found the δ-formulation of the variance discussed in the preceding section helpful in speculating on the optimum design and size of sample needed in a number of practical problems in advance of drawing a sample.   The use of δ in speculating on variances arises primarily from the feeling that, in similar situations that arise in different problems, ratios of variances may be more stable than the absolute magnitudes of the variances.   The particular ratio of variances involved in δ is convenient because it is independent of ultimate cluster size and because it is involved directly in the formula for optimum size of ultimate cluster, as will be seen later (Sec. 16 and following).

Equation 8.6 is often useful for advance speculation on variances when the elementary units are the listing units and the population variance between elementary units is known approximately in advance, as may often be the case.   For example, when sampling attributes, with a (0, 1) variate, V^2 is merely Q/P and can be obtained immediately.   Also, when a size distribution is available for a variate that takes on a number of values, the V^2 can be approximated.

For many ratio estimate problems we are willing to assume $\hat{V}^2 = V^2$ since often the ratio estimate is not seriously affected by the variability in size of the primary unit.   With a speculated value of δ (or of δ_1 and δ_2

* For proof, and for the correction to the bias when the conditions are not met for the bias being small, see Vol. II, Ch. 6, Sec. 3.

with Eq. 8.16 if listing units other than elements are subsampled), one has the basis for estimating the variance needed for sample design.

Table D–4 in Case Study D, Ch. 12, gives rel-variances for a number of types of characteristics and for the levels of primary units specified. These rel-variances, together with similar results from other experiences, may be found helpful in arriving at estimated variances. They are drawn on in the succeeding illustrations of the use of δ in the advance speculation of variances.

Illustration 9.1. Suppose that it is desired to speculate on the rel-variance to be expected for estimating the proportion of families in various income groups in a city. Because of the high correlation which we expect between income and rental value, and because we have data on rental value and not on income in Table D–4 of Case Study D, we speculate first on the value of δ involved in estimating the proportion of dwelling units in various rental groups. Assume that blocks (perhaps after subdividing some of the very large blocks) have an average of about 30 dwelling units (or families) and that dwelling units are the listing units. It is well known that there is a marked tendency for dwelling units in the same block to have similar rental values, which implies a relatively high value of δ. From Table 3, p. 264, .20 approximates the level of δ when the characteristic to be estimated is the proportion of dwelling units in a rental group and when blocks average about 30 dwelling units. We shall assume that this level of δ holds roughly also for income groups that are likely to be associated with these rental levels.

Let us assume that the proportion of the total families in the income group in which we are particularly interested will be about $P = .1$, so that $V^2 = Q/P = 9$, and we shall assume that the value of $\hat{V}^2$ is about the same. Since the elementary unit is assumed to be the listing unit in this illustration, the speculated rel-variance of the estimated proportion in the selected income group, from the sample design described, will be (using Eq. 8.6 without the finite multiplier and substituting the assumed values)

$$V_r^2 = \frac{\hat{V}^2}{m\bar{n}}[1 + \delta(\bar{n} - 1)] = \frac{9}{m\bar{n}}[1 + .20(\bar{n} - 1)]$$

and if we assume $\bar{n} = 5$ and $m = 200$, we have

$$V_r^2 = .009(1.8) = .0162$$

or $\sigma_r \doteq PV_r \doteq 1.3$ percentage points. The value of δ would be similarly speculated for other items that would be expected to have a measure of homogeneity similar to rental values within blocks.

Illustration 9.2. Suppose that it is desired to estimate the income distribution of households that rent their living quarters in the same city.

Here the income groups are to be estimated only for the tenant-occupied households instead of for all households, as was the case above.

To illustrate how the variance is affected and how one can guess at the value of δ and the consequent effect on the variance in this illustration, we shall make a simplifying assumption. We shall assume that throughout the city most blocks contain about an equal proportion of both tenant-occupied and owner-occupied households. If the ultimate cluster size is 5 dwelling units and if tenant-occupied units constitute half the total dwelling units, then $\bar{n}$ for rented units will be 2.5. If $\hat{V}^2$ and δ are assumed to have the same values for tenant-occupied units only as for all dwelling units in Illustration 9.1, then the rel-variance for the proportion of tenant-occupied units in the desired rental value group, and consequently for the proportion of households in the corresponding income group, considering only households which rent, would be

$$V_r^2 = \frac{9}{500}\,[1 + .20(2.5 - 1)] = .023$$

Notice that the effective size of sample has been reduced to 500 from the total sample size of 1000 simply because the tenant-occupied units account for half the units. However, the rel-variance is only about 40 per cent larger than that found in Illustration 9.1, which had twice as large a sample on which to base the percentage. This is explained by the fact that the average size of cluster has been reduced from 5 to 2.5 households.

If we had assumed that the homogeneity of tenancy within blocks was very high, so that for the most part all dwelling units in a block were tenant-occupied, or all were owner-occupied, then the estimated variance for tenants would have been different. Under this assumption, the number of blocks with tenant-occupied units would be half the blocks in the sample, the $\bar{n}$ for those blocks would still be 5, and the estimated variance would be twice that obtained in Illustration 9.1.

The types of speculation illustrated are very rough, but still may be helpful when only limited data are available.

D. HOW COSTS ARISE WITH CLUSTER SAMPLING— THE CONSTRUCTION OF COST FUNCTIONS

10. A simple cost function. In examining how costs enter into a survey involving the use of cluster sampling, it is necessary to identify the various phases of the survey and to determine approximately (a) overhead costs, i.e., those costs that are fixed regardless of the manner in which the sample is selected or the size of the sample; (b) the costs that depend primarily on the *number of primary units* included in the sample, and the way in which such costs vary as the number of primary units in the sample varies; and (c) the costs that depend primarily on the *number of listing units* included in the sample, and the way in which such costs vary as the number of listing units in the sample varies.

Let us assume as an illustration that a total of $5000 is available for a survey of dwelling unit tenure and rent in a county, that small areas will be the primary units and dwelling units will be the listing units, and that costs arise in the very simple way outlined below.

Total cost and fixed costs. The total cost, C, that enters into the cost function will relate only to the total of the variable costs, excluding any fixed overhead costs. The cost of the central administrative and technical work on the survey, and the costs of space and certain equipment, may be approximately the same even with rather marked variations in the size and design of the sample. We shall assume that for the particular illustrative survey under consideration it is estimated that the fixed overhead costs amount to approximately $1500. This reduces the funds available for the variable costs to $5000 − $1500 = $3500, so that we will have $C = \$3500$.

Costs that vary in proportion to the number of primary units in the sample. Certain other costs may vary directly with the number of primary units included in the sample. These costs may include the cost of selecting, traveling to, and locating each sample psu and of preparing a list of the dwellings in the psu, and the cost of designating the subsample of dwellings to be included in the sample. Let us say that the cost of such operations is C_1 per psu included in the sample, and that on the basis of prior experience and advance investigation we have been able to estimate approximately that for the illustrative dwelling unit survey $C_1 = \$2$. This means that we estimate that the cost of adding a psu to the sample is $2, not including the direct cost of interviewing and tabulating the data for the households that may be included in the sample from that psu.

Costs that vary in proportion to the number of listing units in the sample. Still other costs may vary directly with the total number of listing units included in the sample. Included in these costs, in our illustration, may be the direct cost of interviewing one sampled household and the cost of reviewing the sample return and its share in the tabulations. We shall let C_2 represent the cost per listing unit of such operations that varies directly with the number of listing units included in the sample. We shall assume, for the particular illustrative sample survey under consideration, that on the basis of prior experience and experimental work we have estimated that $C_2 = \$1$.

Total cost function. If we have a simple situation in which all the costs of the survey can be represented approximately by the types of cost just described, then C, the total expected cost of the survey (exclusive of fixed overhead), is given by the cost function

$$C = C_1 m + C_2 m \bar{n} \qquad (10.1)$$

where, as before, m is the number of primary units in the sample, and $\bar{n}$ is the expected value of the number of listing units in the sample per primary unit in the sample.

In the illustrative example with $C = 3500$, $C_1 = 2$, and $C_2 = 1$, the cost function becomes

$$3500 = 2m + m\bar{n} \qquad (10.2)$$

We shall use this simple cost function later in arriving at an optimum sample design. In practice, unit costs depend on many things; they vary widely from survey to survey and may, for example, be several times as much as assumed for this illustration.

11. A more general cost function. Although the cost function given above was arrived at without any careful examination of the elements of the cost or of the way they might enter into the total cost of a survey, nevertheless this simple approach may provide a satisfactory guide in many cases. However, in order to obtain a cost function that will more nearly approximate the costs of carrying out a survey, we need to examine some of the important elements of cost and to determine how they vary with changes in sample design.

First, let us give some attention to the travel costs which arise in taking a field survey, and the way in which they may influence total costs. Travel costs, in particular, may not be well reflected in the simple cost function introduced above.

It seems clear that costs of traveling between primary sampling units will be higher the more widespread the sample, and they will be lower the more concentrated the sample. Thus, if a sample of 400 dwelling units were drawn in a city by taking, say, 4 compact sample areas, each sample area containing about 100 dwelling units, then it appears reasonable to assume that there would be less travel to visit all the units than if the sample were scattered widely over the area into, say, 400 different spots, 1 dwelling unit to a spot. We shall attempt to give some idea of how travel costs may vary between these and other possible distributions of the sample, from an oversimplified illustration.

The travel costs will be considered in three parts: first, travel costs between primary sample units; second, travel costs within primary units; and third, travel costs from home or office to and from the psu's. With small primary units the travel costs within psu's will ordinarily be relatively small and will have an effect approximately the same as increasing the cost per unit of listing within the block, or of enumerating within the block, and can be reflected approximately in these costs rather than

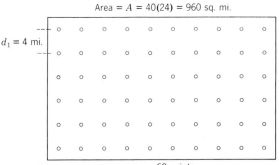

Area $= A = 40(24) = 960$ sq. mi.

$d_1 = 4$ mi.

$m_1 = 60$ points

$d_1 = \sqrt{A/m_1} = 4$ mi.

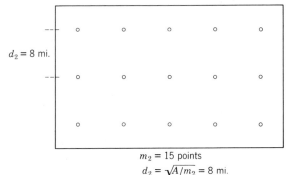

$d_2 = 8$ mi.

$m_2 = 15$ points

$d_2 = \sqrt{A/m_2} = 8$ mi.

FIG. 3.   Distances between sample points of different densities in a rectangular area of 960 square miles.

involving any separate analysis.*   The travel costs between primary units and the travel to home or office (or other central point) deserve some special consideration.

12. Illustration of travel costs between primary units.   The total cost of travel between psu's depends on the area to be covered by the survey, the way the psu's are distributed over this area, the number of psu's in the sample, the number, extent, and character of the roads, the modes of transportation available, and other factors.

* A separate analysis of such travel costs is given in Chapter 9, which deals with large psu's.

The investigator has no control over some of these factors, such as the character of the roads and perhaps also modes of transportation available. But he can specify that the most efficient modes of transportation be used in a particular area and can distribute the sample so as to attain results of the maximum reliability per unit of cost, considering travel problems and other pertinent factors.

To illustrate how travel costs may vary, depending on the number of psu's in the sample, let us examine the distance involved in beginning at one corner and traveling by the shortest possible route from one point to another, when the points are distributed at equally spaced intervals throughout an area such as that indicated in Fig. 3. Suppose that the area in this particular case is 40 miles long and 24 miles wide, and thus contains a total of $A = 960$ square miles. Now let us assume that 60 points (or small areas) to be visited are distributed at equally spaced intervals over the entire area, as shown in the first part of the figure. The vertical or horizontal distance between any consecutive pair of points, if there are m equally spaced points in the area, will be equal to

$$d = \sqrt{\frac{A}{m}} \qquad (12.1)$$

or, with $m_1 = 60$ points in an area of 960 square miles,

$$d_1 = \sqrt{\frac{A}{m_1}} = \sqrt{\frac{960}{60}} = 4 \text{ miles between any consecutive pair of points}$$

Now, let us assume that the number of points is reduced to 15 (i.e., $m_2 = 15$), and, again, these 15 points are distributed at equally spaced intervals as shown in the lower diagram. The vertical or horizontal distance between any contiguous pair of these spots will again be given by the formula $d = \sqrt{A/m}$, so that the average vertical or horizontal distance between any consecutive pair of the 15 points will be

$$d_2 = \sqrt{\frac{A}{m_2}} = \sqrt{\frac{960}{15}} = 8 \text{ miles}$$

It is seen that the average distance between points depends on the number of spots to be visited, and the distance is inversely proportional to the *square root* of the number of points to be visited.

The total distance to travel if one visits the points by the shortest possible route is approximately equal to the number of points to be visited multiplied by the average distance between them. That is, with m points to be visited and an average distance between them of d, the total distance between points in visiting them by the shortest possible route will be

$(m - 1)d$, or approximately md, and since $d = \sqrt{A/m}$, this total distance will be approximately equal to $\sqrt{mA}$.

If roads were available for travel by this shortest route in each instance, the total cost of travel might be computed approximately by finding the average cost of traveling a mile, and multiplying this by the total distance to be traveled. Thus, if an interviewer travels in his own car and is reimbursed at a rate of 5 cents per mile, and if he travels at an average rate of 20 miles per hour and is paid for his services at a rate of $1.50 per hour, then the cost per mile for his travel will be 5 cents for his car plus $7\frac{1}{2}$ cents for his time, or a total of $12\frac{1}{2}$ cents per mile. In the above illustration, then, the total travel cost between psu's would be approximately

$$\sqrt{mA}\,(.125) = \sqrt{m960}\,(.125) \doteq 4\sqrt{m} \text{ dollars}$$

or an average cost per psu of $4\sqrt{m}/m$ or $4/\sqrt{m}$ dollars.

This computation of the total or average between psu travel cost for a sample of m psu's was based on the assumption that only one visit to each was required, and, in fact, that all interviews were completed on a single visit. Suppose that one completed all first visits before making any call-backs, and completed the interviewing at 60 per cent of the psu's on the first visit; he would then have to travel back to $.4m$ psu's for a second visit. Then, roughly, the cost of travel for the second visit would be that involved in visiting $.4m$ psu's, or a travel cost of $4\sqrt{.4m}$. Suppose that 50 per cent of these remaining psu's need still a third visit in order to complete the interview. For the third visit the total travel cost would be roughly equal to $4\sqrt{.2m}$, and so on for any further visits required. The total travel cost between segments would be the total for all visits; or, if 3 call-backs were made where necessary, it would be

$$4(\sqrt{m} + \sqrt{.4m} + \sqrt{.2m}) = 8.3\sqrt{m}$$

If the interviewer were away from home overnight, or for other reasons were paid living expenses in addition to transportation and salary while traveling, this item too would have to be added into the cost function.

This approach to evaluating the cost of travel between psu's is a very rough approximation. Primary sampling units to be visited will not be uniformly distributed over an area, rates of travel will vary with roads and other conditions, and the travel in practice will not be done by visiting all sample segments successively. Whenever the work at a sample unit is completed at the end of one day and a new unit started the next day, it will not be necessary to travel *between* such pairs of psu's, and this may mean that the number of trips between psu's is reduced. Nevertheless, the indicated approach to evaluating travel costs between primary sampling units may provide a useful, although rough, guide. Where necessary it may be improved by dividing the job into separate analyses if strikingly different types of areas are involved in a survey—strikingly different with respect to density, road conditions, etc.

If we accept this approach to measuring the cost of travel between segments as a reasonably satisfactory approximation, this aspect of the total cost of a sample survey might be reflected by adding a term $C_0\sqrt{m}$ to the simple cost function given earlier (Eq. 10.1), so that the cost function (excluding fixed costs) would now be of the form

$$C = C_0\sqrt{m} + C_1 m + C_2 m\bar{n} \qquad (12.2)$$

where C_0, the coefficient of $\sqrt{m}$, is arrived at by methods such as illustrated above, plus some additional allowances that will be indicated below. The other terms in Eq. 12.2 are defined as for Eq. 10.1 (p. 272).

13. Travel from home, office, or other central point, to and from sample psu's. If the sample psu's and work assignments were such that one could travel directly from his home (or office) to a psu at the beginning of the day's work, complete the work on the psu that day, and return to home (or office) at the end of the day, then, on the average, the daily travel of such an interviewer would be simply twice the average distance between his home (or office) and all the psu's in the area. In this special situation, there would be no travel *between* psu's, and the expected total travel would be the number of psu's included in the sample, multiplied by twice the average distance from home to a segment. In practice, one may not have such a simple situation, so that there will be travel between sample psu's and travel back when the work is completed or at the end of each day.

Once the average amount of the beginning and ending travel per trip has been estimated (a trip is the travel from a central point to one or more psu's and back to the central point), the cost of beginning and ending travel can be introduced into the cost function. It should be clear that only the part of such travel which is paid for will be involved. The particular way in which such travel gets introduced into the cost function will, of course, depend upon the survey specifications.

For illustration, we shall suppose that an area being covered is large enough, and the distances for the beginning and ending travel are great enough, that the interviewer is paid for his time and his car for such travel, but small enough that it is more economical to pay for the beginning and ending travel for a trip each day than to pay for living expenses on an extended trip away from home. Such travel might be reflected in the cost function by computations like the following.

The number of beginning and ending trips is directly proportionate to the total number of days the interviewer works at interviewing. It appears reasonable, then, to regard such travel as a directly proportionate increase on the payments to interviewers for their time spent in the field. It will, then, have the effect of increasing proportionately those parts of C_0, C_1, and C_2 which arise because of direct payments to interviewers for their time spent carrying out field sampling and interviewing, as distinguished from time which is spent in the office for training or other purposes, and for which such trips are not involved.

The determination of the average distance per trip of the beginning and ending travel can be based on experimental work for any particular type of survey. If C_t represents the estimated average cost for such beginning and ending travel for a trip (including payments for travel and other expenses as well as salary), C_d represents the average rate of payment per day to interviewers for time other than that spent in beginning and ending travel, and C_0', C_1', and C_2' represent the parts of the coefficients in the cost function that are for payments to interviewers for time spent on work in the field other than for beginning and ending trips, the coefficients of the cost function can be increased in the following way to allow for the beginning and ending trip costs:

(a) Include $\dfrac{C_0' C_t}{C_d}$ as a part of C_0, so that

$$C_0 = C_0' + \frac{C_0' C_t}{C_d} + \text{other costs.}$$

(b) Include $\dfrac{C_1' C_t}{C_d}$ as a part of C_1.

(c) Include $\dfrac{C_2' C_t}{C_d}$ as a part of C_2.

These increases will make rough allowances for beginning and ending of trip time for the type of situation assumed here. For some survey designs there may be variations that need to be adapted to the particular design.

14. A more careful examination of other costs and how they may enter into the cost function. A more careful examination of the computation of values for C_0, C_1, and C_2 will necessarily be rough, but a listing of some of the elements of cost and an indication of how they may affect the costs of taking a survey may guide the user in making an analysis of his sources of cost in a particular survey.

A first step in arriving at approximate values for the various terms in the cost function is to write down the principal operations involved in taking the survey. This will be done well only if the steps and operations in the survey are carefully charted and planned. It should be recognized that the importance and effect of different operations may be very different, depending on the type of survey. The costs of a one-time survey will differ from those of a repetitive survey. Many of the costs of a survey will depend in an important measure on the time schedule established for carrying through the project. The quality of the work, for example, may be considerably more difficult to control on a short time schedule than on a longer one, and hence costs may be increased. In arriving at a plan for a survey, then, it may be desirable to budget and plan it on two or three alternative time schedules that may be acceptable, before making final decisions on the time schedule and method of approach. This will make possible comparison of the increased cost of a more rapid time schedule with the cost of a less rapid schedule, and evaluation of the relationship of the increased cost to the value of timeliness.

If we pursue further the illustration in Sec. 10 of estimating the average rental value of dwelling units in a county, and proceed on the assumption that it is a one-time survey, we might identify the following operations and assign them to the separate terms in the cost function as follows:

a. *Planning and broad direction of the survey* in both the office and the field work. These costs will presumably not vary substantially with changes in sample design and will contribute to the fixed overhead cost. This will include overhead salaries, consultation, rent, certain of the supplies, and related items that do not vary with variations in design of the survey. Let us assume that these costs are estimated to contribute $1000 towards the total overhead costs.

b. *Immediate field supervision of interviewers*, including recruiting and instructing interviewers, and assigning and reviewing their work in order to make sure that the specified procedures have been understood and followed. This may also include the cost of field reports on progress and the cost of maintaining various field checks, reports and controls, supervisor's travel, etc. These costs may reasonably call for a proportionate increase in the direct variable field costs. Thus, it may be reasonable to assume that 1 man hour of supervision is required for, say, each 10 man hours of interviewers' time required. Let us, suppose, also, that an hour of supervisory time costs 1.5 times as much as an hour of interviewer time. Then the immediate supervision of field work can be reflected in the cost function by simply increasing the cost of interviewers by a factor of 15 per cent at whatever points payment for the time of interviewers enters into the cost function. If the direct field work is broken down into different operations that require different amounts of supervision or rates of pay, an appropriate factor can be separately applied for each such operation. In our illustration, we shall assume a straight 15 per cent increase due to supervision in the direct payments for interviewer time.

c. *Selecting the sample of psu's*, and preparing maps or other materials to be used in assigning work to the interviewers. Some of the costs of planning the sample design and selecting the sample will be a part of the fixed overhead cost. Suppose that we estimate approximately a $200 contribution to overhead costs from this source. The remaining and principal costs of selecting the sample and preparing maps and other materials indicating the sample areas which can be used in assigning the work to interviewers, and in controlling the work to insure that areas are appropriately assigned and covered, may vary directly in proportion to the number of psu's included in the sample. These latter costs would contribute to C_1 in the above cost function (Eq. 12.2). Let us assume that the estimated contribution to C_1 from this source is $.75 in our particular illustrative survey.

d. *Direct payments to interviewers*, as follows:

(i) Interviewer time spent in training. Let us assume that it has been determined that interviewer training time is a specified number of hours per interviewer, say 15 hours. Suppose also that the survey schedule has been set up so that each interviewer will work for a period of 3 weeks at 50 hours per week, or a total of 150 hours, on the average, in addition to the training time. The training time can be thought of as an overhead or burden on the rest of the time spent by the interviewer; and, if training time is paid for at the same rate as the remaining time, would have the effect of a 10 per cent increase in the rate of pay of interviewers for the time spent in field work. This cost can be reflected in the cost function by a proportionate increase in direct payments for interviewers' time at whatever points such time enters into the cost function. This proportionate increase might be made before the addition for direct supervision mentioned in item *b* above, but after the allowance for beginning and ending trip travel described in item *e* below. We shall add in this training cost after ascertaining the base cost to which the 10 per cent addition is applicable.

(ii) Travel between sampled psu's. The analysis given earlier indicates how these costs can be reflected roughly in the cost function. It remains to analyze the costs of travel between sampled psu's for the particular survey under consideration. Let us suppose, in this survey, that the total area being surveyed is 1000 square miles, i.e., $A = 1000$. Suppose, also, that the survey procedure specified involves one visit to each sample psu to prepare a prelisting of the dwelling units in the psu, at which time the sample households are designated and an effort is made to complete the interview in the sample households. Then a second and third or more calls are to be made to the psu's to pick up the interviews that could not be completed on the first visit because no one was at home or for other reasons. Suppose, in addition, that it is estimated that the interviewing process, in order to complete the interviews, will involve 2 separate trips to approximately 50 per cent of the sample psu's, 3 separate trips to approximately 25 per cent, and 4 trips to 10 per cent. Then the total distance to be traveled in listing and interviewing for a sample of m psu's might be roughly equal to

$$\sqrt{A}(\sqrt{m} + \sqrt{.5m} + \sqrt{.25m} + \sqrt{.10m})$$

and with $A = 1000$, this would be

$$32(\sqrt{m} + .7\sqrt{m} + .5\sqrt{m} + .3\sqrt{m}) \doteq 80\sqrt{m} \text{ miles}$$

The cost of interviewer travel between psu's is then estimated by multiplying this result by the estimated cost of an interviewer traveling a mile.

In determining C_0, this direct cost of enumerator travel must be increased to account for indirect costs that vary with the travel costs, such as those indicated in items b, d (i), and d (iv) of this section.

If the total miles traveled in our particular survey illustration is $80\sqrt{m}$, as was estimated above, and if we compute that the cost of transportation is 6 cents per mile and the cost of personal time spent in traveling is 8 cents per mile (which, of course, depends on the average speed of travel), then we have a direct travel cost (before adding indirect costs) of $\$11.20\sqrt{m}$, of which $\$4.80\sqrt{m}$ is payment for transportation and $\$6.40\sqrt{m}$ is payment for the time the interviewer spent in travel.

Such a way of measuring travel costs does not take account of the time that might be involved in looking for a parking place and parking, if the work is being carried out in a city. Or if one travels by bus in a city, it does not take account of the fact that, while the salary of the interviewer depends on the time of travel, the bus fare is often the same regardless of distance, or for the fact that often an important part of the cost is simply waiting for the next bus or train. These latter types of costs will not vary in proportion to the square root of the number of psu's included in the sample, but directly with the number of psu's in the sample, and therefore such costs will serve to increase C_1 in the cost function, rather than C_0. In our particular illustrative problem we shall assume that these additional costs for the time involved in parking or waiting amount to 15 cents per psu, and C_1 will be increased by this amount.

(iii) Identification of the psu's that are designated for inclusion in the sample. Once the enumerator travels to a sample psu, he may require time to compare the map or description of the psu with the physical features found and to identify the boundaries of the particular area to be canvassed. The effect of this will be to increase somewhat the term C_1. This particular cost may not be significant with good maps, and may be merged with the cost outlined in (v) below. We shall assume that it is included in the cost outlined by (v) for the particular county in which we are sampling. In many rural areas, as well as in cities in which the map material is poor, the cost is likely to be large enough to have considerable importance.

(iv) Travel between home or office and sample psu's. Suppose that, in the particular illustration that we are considering, interviewers are paid for any necessary beginning and ending trip travel in excess of a total of 3 miles per day, and that it has been estimated that an average interviewer will travel a total distance of 7 miles per day for beginning and ending travel. The 4 miles per day excess is to be paid for at the rate of 6 cents per mile for the car and an estimated average of about 8 cents per mile for the interviewer's time, or a total trip cost of 4×14 cents $= 56$ cents per trip. The daily earnings assumed for interviewers are, say, $9.50 per day for the time spent, other than beginning and ending travel, so that $C_d = \$9.50$ and $C_t \doteq \$.56$, and the ratio

$$\frac{C_t}{C_d} = \frac{.56}{9.50} = .06$$

is the factor of increase on the direct cost of time spent by interviewers in the field. (The C_t and C_d are defined in Sec. 13.) This factor will be used subsequently, in assembling the costs into the cost function.

(v) Listing the listing units and designating the subsample. The cost of preparing a list of the listing units in the sampled psu's and of designating the subsample, again, will increase C_1, the fixed cost per psu in the sample. Thus, if there is an average of $\bar{N}$ dwelling places per psu to be listed, and if it costs an average of 4 cents per dwelling place to make the listing, including the travel from house to house within sample psu's, then this particular contribution to the C_1 term will be $.04\bar{N}$. If $\bar{N}$ is approximately equal to 30 in the county we are surveying, the addition to C_1 because of listing costs will be $1.20. The designation of the subsample of dwelling places in which interviews are to be made can be an automatic process as a part of the listing and need require no additional cost estimate.

(vi) The interviewing. The cost of carrying out the interviewing at the designated sample of dwelling places will vary directly with the number of interviews taken and will contribute substantially to the term C_2 in the cost function. Let us suppose that the interview time required for actually making contact with the household and interviewing is 20 minutes on the average; with interviewers paid at the rate of $1.20 per hour, this would be a cost of 40 cents for the direct interview time for a family that is home on the first visit. This will have to be increased to allow for additional interview time on call-backs, the time involved in trying to make contact with a member of the household once the enumerator has reached the dwelling, or in learning when someone will be at home from a neighbor or another member of the household, etc.

Interview time also has to be increased to cover the travel within primary units. Since travel within small psu's is limited, we shall assume that if we increase or decrease $\bar{n}$, the size of ultimate cluster subsampled from a psu, the cost per listing unit of travel between listing units within the psu is unaffected. Then the total travel cost within psu's is proportionate to the number of households (or other units) included in the sample. We shall estimate that these travel costs have the effect of increasing the interview time to an average of 50 cents per household in our particular illustration.

e. Editing, coding, and tabulating, including direct supervision of these operations. These costs will often vary roughly in proportion to the number of questionnaires taken and therefore will have an effect principally on C_2. We shall assume that for our particular survey an analysis shows that the costs of these operations are 50 cents per household.

Certain tabulation costs will be fixed, independent of the variations in sample size and design, including much of the planning work and some of the work of reviewing the tabulations. We shall assume that this phase of tabulation cost amounts to $200 for the survey, as an addition to fixed overhead costs.

f. Review of the tabulations and preparation of the report. These are assumed to be included in either item *a* or item *e* above, as fixed costs.

g. The cost of printing schedules, training materials, and supplies for use in the various aspects of the work. These must be estimated also and assigned to the various costs. In our particular survey we shall assume that these costs have the effect of increasing fixed overhead by $100, C_1 by 10 cents, and C_2 by 5 cents.

h. Other remarks on costs. Probably other operations and costs might be appropriately identified in many surveys. The analysis of costs is important for whatever survey is to be undertaken, not only for good sample design but also for study of efficiency of work methods and setting

up performance standards, a budget, and controls.   It should be emphasized that to estimate costs we depend on data and experience from
previous surveys, or special experiments, and cannot readily "pull them
out of a hat."   The reader should recognize that, because of the rough
nature of the cost estimates, it is not worth while to spend time on minor
details in cost and variation in cost, so far as determination of the optimum
sample design is concerned; it may be worth while, however, for purposes
of controlling costs.   We shall assume that the items identified above will
represent the principal cost components in the illustrative survey under
consideration.   Case Study B, Ch. 12, gives some data on survey costs
that may be useful in designing other surveys.

**15. Assembling into the cost function the estimates of costs of various
operations.**   We can now assemble our cost function from the above
materials as follows:

Computation of fixed overhead costs.   Fixed overhead has contributions
of $1000, $200, $200, and $100, respectively, from items *a*, *c*, *e*, and *g*
above, and the estimated total fixed overhead cost is therefore $1500.

Computation of C_0. C_0 has a direct contribution of $11.20 from item
d (ii) above, of which $4.80 is for transportation and $6.40 for payments
on the time of the interviewer while traveling between psu's.   We had an
increase in the direct payment to interviewers for travel of 6 per cent from
item *d* (iv), an additional increase of 10 per cent on the new total from
item *d* (i), and then an additional increase of 15 per cent from item *b*, so
that we compute an estimate of C_0 as follows:

$$C_0 = 4.80 + 6.40(1.06)(1.10)(1.15) = \$13.40$$

Computation of C_1. C_1 has contributions of 75 cents from item *c* above
and of 10 cents from item *g* that involve no interviewer time; there are,
in addition, a contribution of 15 cents and $1.20 for payment of inter-
viewer time from items *d* (ii) and *d* (v), respectively.   Therefore, if we add
the successive increases of 6 per cent, 10 per cent, and 15 per cent from
items *d* (iv), *d* (i), and *b* to the direct interviewer contributions, we have as
the estimate for fixed costs per block:

$$C_1 = .85 + 1.35(1.06)(1.10)(1.15) = \$2.70$$

Computation of C_2. C_2 has a contribution of 50 cents from item *d* (vi),
all of which is payment for interviewer time, and contributions of 50 and
5 cents, respectively, from items *e* and *g*, none of which is payment of
interviewer time.   Thus, we have, allowing for the increases in interviewer
time from items *b*, *d* (i), and *d* (iv),

$$C_2 = .50(1.06)(1.10)(1.15) + .50 + .05 = \$1.20$$

The total cost function. We now assemble as our total cost function, using Eq. 12.2,

$$\text{Total cost} = \text{Overhead} + C_0 \sqrt{m} + C_1 m + C_2 m\bar{n}$$

or, substituting $C = \$3500$ for total cost of $5000 less fixed overhead of $1500, we have

$$3500 = 13.4\sqrt{m} + 2.7m + 1.2m\bar{n} \tag{15.1}$$

It needs to be emphasized that this can be regarded only as a rough approximation to reflect the costs of the various aspects of the work. Fortunately, because moderate departures from the optimum survey design usually increase only slightly the rel-variance of the estimate, it is sufficient to have only rough cost approximations in order to achieve results reasonably near the optimum.

Other terms may be needed in cost functions for some particular problems, and some of these will be introduced later. For the problem as here stated, we shall regard the above as a reasonable indication of the way costs will arise in our housing survey, and shall proceed to determination of the optimum sampling of blocks and within blocks on the basis of this cost function.

E. OPTIMUM DESIGN WITH SIMPLE TWO-STAGE CLUSTER SAMPLING

16. Finding the optimum values of m and $\bar{n}$ with a simple cost function. Once the primary units in the population are specified, we are in a position to approximate the optimum second-stage sampling fraction, f_2, and the optimum number of psu's to include in the sample for the estimation of some particular characteristic. To approximate the optimum value of f_2 we shall first approximate the optimum $\bar{n}$, i.e., the optimum of the expected value of the average number of listing units to include in the sample per psu in the sample. The optimum value of f_2 is then simply given by the ratio of the optimum $\bar{n}$ to $\bar{N}$. To determine the actual number of cases that fall in the sample for any particular sample, the constant sampling fraction, f_2, is applied to the psu's that come into the sample. Thus, the actual take from any psu will vary from psu to psu, but the sampling fraction will be constant.

Let us consider again the problem of estimating the average rental value of dwelling units, with the rel-variance of the estimates given by either Eq. 6.10 or 8.6. We shall assume, first, the simple cost function given by Eq. 10.1 instead of the more complex cost function just discussed. We can then ascertain the different values of m and $\bar{n}$ that will involve a given total cost, and from among these the particular values that will yield a sample estimate with the smallest variance. We shall use the variance as given by Eq. 8.6 in this illustration, neglecting the finite multiplier $(1 - f)$. Let us assume that with blocks as the psu's in the area under consideration, $\delta = .25$, and $\hat{V}^2 = V^2 = 1$, where δ, $\hat{V}^2$, and V^2 are defined by Eq. 8.11, 8.10, and 8.7, respectively. Then

$$V_r^2 \doteq \frac{\hat{V}^2}{m\bar{n}}[1 + \delta(\bar{n} - 1)] = \frac{1}{m\bar{n}}[1 + .25(\bar{n} - 1)] \qquad (16.1)$$

Optimum obtained by substitution of successive values. For $C \doteq 3500$, $C_2 = 2$, and $C_1 = 1$, from Eq. 10.2 we have $m = 3500/(2 + \bar{n})$, and we can readily find the values of m for different values of $\bar{n}$ that satisfy the cost equation. Such values of m and $\bar{n}$ are entered in columns 1 and 2 of Table 5.

Table 5. Values of m and $\bar{n}$ that satisfy cost equation: $3500 = 2m + m\bar{n}$

m	$\bar{n}$	V_r^2
(1)	(2)	(3)
1167	1	.000857
875	2	.000714
700	3	.000714
583	4	.000750
500	5	.000800
350	8	.000982
292	10	.001113

Now, if we substitute successively the pairs of values of m and $\bar{n}$ that were obtained from the cost function into Eq. 16.1 with the values given above, we obtain the values of V_r^2 shown in column 3 of Table 5. With these we can perceive the approximate values of m and $\bar{n}$ that give the maximum precision of the sample estimates, i.e., for which V_r^2 is a minimum, subject to the assumed fixed total cost. Figure 4, showing V_r^2 plotted against the average number of dwellings included in the sample per psu, is an aid in perceiving the values of $\bar{n}$ that will approximate the optimum. In this particular instance, it is seen that any value of $\bar{n}$ between 2 and 4 will give values of V_r^2 that will be reasonably close to the minimum.

If we choose $\bar{n} = 3$, then we shall include $m = 700$ blocks in the sample, obtained by substituting $\bar{n} = 3$ in the cost function (Eq. 10.2) and solving for m.   With such a sample, we see from Table 5 and Fig. 4 that the rel-variance of the estimated rental value will be approximately

$$V_r^2 = \frac{1 + .25(3 - 1)}{2100} = .000714$$

or

$$V_r = .0267 \text{ or } 2.7 \text{ per cent}$$

Serious losses in reliability of results per unit of cost may be found if one departs widely from the optimum values of m and $\bar{n}$.   For example,

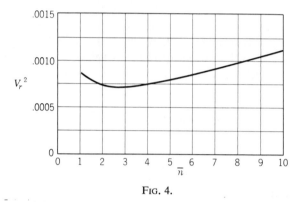

Fig. 4.

if instead of taking about 3 dwelling units per psu, we increased this to take whole psu's enumerated completely, we would have, say, $\bar{n} = \bar{N} = 30$. Then we could afford to have only $m = 110$ psu's in the sample, and the same expenditure would give results with a rel-variance that would be more than 3 times as large.

Explicit formula for optimum $\bar{n}$ with simple cost function (Eq. 10.1). The optimum values of m and $\bar{n}$ could have been obtained mathematically instead of going through the process of successive substitution followed above.   In fact, it can be shown that, when the cost function is of the form given by Eq. 10.1 and the variance of the form given by Eq. 6.10 (p. 255) or 8.6, then the optimum average size of ultimate cluster* is

$$\text{opt. } \bar{n} = \sqrt{\frac{C_1}{C_2} \frac{W^2}{B^2 - W^2/\bar{N}}} = \bar{N}\sqrt{\frac{C_1}{C_2} \frac{S_2^2}{S_1^2 - \bar{N}S_2^2}} \doteq \sqrt{\frac{C_1}{C_2} \frac{1 - \delta}{\delta}} \qquad (16.2)$$

Once $\bar{n}$ has been determined, the optimum second-stage sampling fraction is given by dividing this value by $\bar{N}$, the average size of psu in

---

* For proof, see Vol. II, Ch. 6, Sec. 10.

the population. For the illustration, we have, with $\delta = .25$, $1 - \delta = .75$, $C_1 = 2$, and $C_2 = 1$,

$$\text{opt. } \bar{n} = \sqrt{\frac{2}{1} \times \frac{.75}{.25}} = 2.4, \quad \text{opt. } f_2 = \frac{\text{opt. } \bar{n}}{\bar{N}} = \frac{2.4}{30} = .08$$

The appropriate value for m is obtained by substituting the optimum $\bar{n}$ in the cost function, Eq. 10.2, i.e., opt. $m = 3500/(C_1 + C_2\bar{n}) = 3500/4.4 \doteq 800$. This result is consistent with Table 5.

It is not always feasible to obtain explicit mathematical solutions of this sort for more complicated cost functions or variance functions. The advantage of the mathematical solution is not primarily that it saves the computing involved in the successive approximation process—the computation is ordinarily so trivial in relation to the work on the project that it can be ignored. The advantage of obtaining an explicit mathematical statement of the optimum is that it aids in thinking about good sample design, since it points out which factors are effective in determining the amount of information obtained per dollar. Thus, we see from Eq. 16.2 that the optimum size of ultimate cluster increases as C_1 increases relative to C_2. We see, also, that the optimum size is not highly sensitive to changes in the ratio of C_1 to C_2, because, instead of varying in direct proportion to this ratio, it varies in direct proportion to the square root of the ratio. We see, also, that the optimum size of cluster varies directly with $\sqrt{(1 - \delta)/\delta}$ and thus *increases* as δ decreases, and conversely; or that the optimum $\bar{n}$ increases as W^2 increases, and decreases as B^2 increases. Again, since opt. $\bar{n}$ varies directly with the square root of $(1 - \delta)/\delta$, opt. $\bar{n}$ is not sensitive to small relative changes in the value of δ but is to large relative changes.

These results support what one can readily understand intuitively, at least with respect to the directions in which the cost factors and the measure of homogeneity within clusters influence the optimum values of m and $\bar{n}$. Thus, the greater the additional cost of adding a psu as compared with the cost of obtaining an additional interview, the fewer psu's one should include in the sample and the more interviews he should take per psu, and vice versa. Also, it seems reasonable that, if δ is small, there is very little loss in including more interviews per psu, and the optimum size of cluster will be larger than when δ is large.

An interesting additional point to note is that with this cost function the optimum size of ultimate cluster is not affected at all by the total funds available or the total size of sample. We will have the same optimum size of ultimate cluster, for this simple cost function, whether we can afford a large sample or a small one. The effect of different total sizes of samples, different requirements in accuracy of results, or different total funds available is simply to change the optimum m, the number of psu's included in the sample. The fact that the optimum $\bar{n}$ is independent of m, or of the precision required or the total funds available, is not a general quality of optima but holds for this comparatively simple cost function. It follows that we would have obtained exactly the same optimum size of ultimate cluster if we had started out by specifying a certain precision of results wanted, and found the value of $\bar{n}$ that would give a minimum cost instead of starting with fixed funds and minimizing the variance for that total expenditure.

Although the mathematical formulation of the optimum is highly useful as a way of pointing up the influence of cost differences and of the measure of homogeneity or the between-psu and within-psu contributions to the variance on the optimum size of ultimate cluster, one should not be satisfied just to compute the optimum this way instead of obtaining some of the results in Table 5 giving alternative values of m and $\bar{n}$. The table has the advantage of showing the breadth of the minimum and the region in which about the same precision of results per dollar will be achieved. Thus, for $\bar{n} = 1.5$ and also for $\bar{n} = 4.6$, the variance is only about 10 per cent above the variance at the optimum. In other words, for this particular problem, use of an average size of ultimate cluster ranging anywhere from 1.5 to 4.6 would not increase the variance of the sample design by more than 10 per cent over the variance at the optimum. When the range of values of $\bar{n}$ near the minimum is large, the investigator has considerable leeway in permitting administrative considerations and other factors to influence his decision as to size of ultimate cluster.

The successive approximation process involves very little computing, and does not place an emphasis on achieving the exact optimum, but rather seeks the region of the optimum. This is sufficient because we never know our costs exactly, or the variances or other measures of homogeneity exactly, in advance of drawing the sample. If we are in roughly the right neighborhood in our advance estimates of these values, then we shall achieve results reasonably close to the optimum and will lose very little efficiency by moderate departures from the optimum.

17. Ascertaining the optimum with a more general cost function. We shall now ascertain the optimum with Eq. 12.2 as the cost function and with either Eq. 6.10 or 8.6 for the rel-variance.

We can proceed in the same manner as in the simpler determination in Sec. 16. Suppose that we are given a specified reliability of results to achieve, and want to do this at the least possible cost. For example, for the illustration followed through in Sec. 16, we might want to estimate the average rental value with a coefficient of variation of 2 per cent instead of assuming a fixed total cost. What, then, is the optimum design? One way to proceed is to set up a table such as Table 6; in this table the cost function is

$$C = 13.4\sqrt{m} + 2.7m + 1.2m\bar{n} \qquad (17.1)$$

as obtained in Sec. 15 (Eq. 15.1).

Table 6. Cost of various sample allocations with fixed precision, when

$$V_r^2 = .0004 = \frac{1}{m\bar{n}} [1 + .25(\bar{n} - 1)] \text{ and } C = 13.4\sqrt{m} + 2.7m + 1.2m\bar{n}$$

$\bar{n}$ (1)	m (2)	$C_0\sqrt{m}$ (3)	$C_1 m$ (4)	$C_2 m\bar{n}$ (5)	$C = C_0\sqrt{m} + C_1 m + C_2 m\bar{n}$ (6)
1	2,500	670	6,750	3,000	10,420
2	1,563	530	4,220	3,751	8,501
3	1,250	474	3,375	4,500	8,349
4	1,094	443	2,954	5,251	8,648
5	1,000	424	2,700	6,000	9,124
7	893	400	2,411	7,501	10,312
8	859	393	2,319	8,246	10,958

The first two columns of the table are obtained from variance Eq. 8.6 with $\delta = .25$, $\bar{V}^2 = 1$, and by setting $V_r^2 = (.02)^2 = .0004$ and solving for various values of m and $\bar{n}$ that will yield the specified coefficient of variation of 2 per cent. These paired values appear in columns 1 and 2. Columns 3, 4, and 5 are included for convenience in computing the total cost for the various values of m and $\bar{n}$, and column 6 gives the total cost. From this column we find the minimum value; then optimum values for m and $\bar{n}$ are those that give this minimum cost. The chart of C plotted against $\bar{n}$ (Fig. 5) helps in establishing the minimum. Again, we see a moderately broad minimum, as in earlier cases, which is quite fortunate since we have only rough approximations for the cost function, and the advance estimate of the contributions to the variance must also necessarily be rough. The optimum in this particular case is in the neighborhood of $\bar{n} = 3$, although values anywhere between 2 and 5 will give reasonably good results, not more than 10 per cent away from the variance at the optimum.

If it is desired to obtain a minimum variance for a fixed cost, the same type of table is set up with values of m and $\bar{n}$ that satisfy the cost function, and the variance is then computed for these. In obtaining the values from the cost function (Eq. 12.2), it will be found easier, since the equation involves both m and $\sqrt{m}$, to assume values for m and solve for $\bar{n}$ than to assume values for $\bar{n}$ and solve for m.

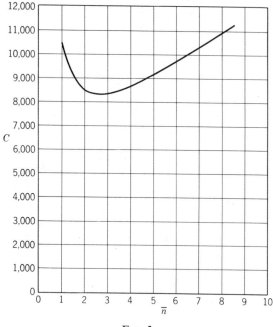

FIG. 5

18. Formulas for optimum $\bar{n}$ with general cost function. The above procedure has the advantage of indicating the breadth of the minimum, and makes clear what is accomplished by the use of optimum values of m and $\bar{n}$. In the results presented earlier with the simpler cost function not involving the term in $\sqrt{m}$, we indicated how we could solve explicitly for the optimum values of m and $\bar{n}$. This is more difficult with the present function, but there is a simple procedure for computing the optimum in a few steps by using successive approximations. A short method of computing optimum values of m and $\bar{n}$ subject to a fixed total cost with the cost function given by Eq. 12.2 and with the variance given by either 6.10 or 8.6 is by means of the following equations:*

$$\text{opt. } \bar{n} = \sqrt{\frac{W^2}{B^2 - W^2/\bar{N}} \frac{C_1 + C_0/a}{C_2}} \doteq \sqrt{\frac{1 - \delta}{\delta} \frac{C_1 + C_0/a}{C_2}} \quad (18.1)$$

---

* For proof, due to B. J. Tepping and Blanche Skalak, see Vol. II, Ch. 6, Sec. 11.

$$a = \frac{\sqrt{1 + 4\dfrac{C}{C_0}\dfrac{C_1 + C_2\bar{n}}{C_0}} - 1}{\dfrac{C_1 + C_2\bar{n}}{C_0}} \qquad (18.2)$$

$$\text{opt. } m = \tfrac{1}{4}a^2 \qquad (18.3)$$

where a in Eq. 18.3 is determined by substituting the optimum value of $\bar{n}$ in Eq. 18.2.

The two alternative forms of opt. $\bar{n}$ given in Eq. 18.1 are interchangeable. The first form is stated in terms of the rel-variances between primary sampling units, and between subsampling units within primary units, as defined for Eq. 6.10; whereas the second is stated in terms of the measure of homogeneity as defined for Eq. 8.6.

The optimum values for m and $\bar{n}$ are computed, for a specified total cost, by the following steps:

(a) Obtain the necessary values for the terms of the variance and cost function. Get approximate values for V^2, δ, or $\dfrac{W^2}{B^2 - (W^2/\bar{N})}$, and C_0, C_1, and C_2, from prior experience and advance testing. This may involve fairly extensive studies if a costly large-scale survey is contemplated or perhaps rough guesses if the study is a relatively small-scale operation. Errors in these initial numbers affect only the *economy* of the survey and can in no way bias the results. An initial total budget must be given or assumed, also, to carry through the computations.

(b) Substitute these values in Eq. 18.1 and 18.2 so that the only unknowns in these equations are $\bar{n}$ and a.

(c) Solve Eq. 18.1 for a first approximation to opt. $\bar{n}$, which we will call $\bar{n}_1$. Solve for $\bar{n}_1$ by assuming an initial value of a, which we call a_0; for convenience we will assume $a_0 = 10$. This first assumed value of $a_0 = 10$ can be adopted as a rule for all problems—it really is not important what initial value is assumed; the final answer would come out the same if a_0 were assumed equal to, say, 1 or 1000 or some other number. Fewer computations may be required if the initial assumed value is close to the final value, but the computational work is small enough that this is not important.

(d) Substitute $\bar{n}_1$ into Eq. 18.2 and solve for a. We will call the value obtained a_1.

(e) Substitute a_1 into Eq. 18.1 to obtain a second approximation to opt. $\bar{n}$, which we will call $\bar{n}_2$, and substitute $\bar{n}_2$ into Eq. 18.2 to obtain a_2.

(f) Compare $\bar{n}_2$ with $\bar{n}_1$, and a_2 with a_1. If either differs by more than, say, 2 per cent, repeat step e, using $\bar{n}_2$ and a_2 to compute new values $\bar{n}_3$

and a_3. If either of these differs from $\bar{n}_2$ and a_2, respectively, by more than a trivial amount, say 2 per cent, repeat step e, and continue repeating this step until two successive sets of values are substantially the same; then proceed to step g.

(g) The optimum $\bar{n}$ is the final value computed in step f. Substitute the final value of a_1 in Eq. 18.3 to obtain the optimum m.

(h) These optimum values $\bar{n}$ and m are now substituted into the variance formulas (Eq. 6.10 or 8.6) to ascertain the precision that will be achieved. The investigator then examines the purposes and objectives of the survey to see if this result is economically consistent with the cost of the survey, and may after this examination *change* the budget up or down, depending upon the determined value of the result in relation to the cost, and the utility of a greater or lesser precision.

Illustration 18.1. For the illustrative dwelling unit sample considered in the preceding section we have values estimated in advance of drawing the sample as follows:

$$\text{Step } a: \begin{cases} C = 3500 \\ C_0 = 13.4 \\ C_1 = 2.7 \\ C_2 = 1.2 \\ \delta = .25 \end{cases}$$

We then substitute these in Eq. 18.1 and 18.2 to obtain

$$\text{Step } b: \begin{cases} \bar{n} = 1.732 \sqrt{\dfrac{11.2}{a} + 2.25} & \text{from Eq. 18.1} \\[3mm] a = \dfrac{\sqrt{211 + 94.0\bar{n}} - 1}{.201 + .090\bar{n}} & \text{from Eq. 18.2} \end{cases}$$

and from Eq. 18.1 we compute (assuming $a = 10$)

Step c: $\bar{n}_1 = 1.732 \sqrt{1.12 + 2.25} = 3.18$

and, using this value of $\bar{n}_1$ in Eq. 18.2,

$$\text{Step } d: \quad a_1 = \frac{\sqrt{211 + 289} - 1}{.201 + .286} = 43.9$$

$$\text{Step } e: \begin{cases} \bar{n}_2 = 2.74 \\ a_2 = 46.0 \end{cases}$$

Step f: At least one of these differs by more than 2 per cent from the preceding values (in this case both do), so we repeat steps e and f.

Step e $\begin{cases} \bar{n}_3 = 2.73 \\ a_3 = 46.0 \end{cases}$
repeated:

Step f: Both these are within 2 per cent of the two preceding values, so we proceed to step g.

Step g: opt. $\bar{n} = 2.7$

$$\text{opt. } m = \frac{(46.0)^2}{4} = 529$$

That is, the optimum design in this problem calls for a sample of about 530 psu's (assumed to have an average size of about 30 households each), with a subsample of an average of about $2\frac{1}{2}$–3 households in each selected psu.

19. Steps to obtain optimum when the precision is fixed.   In the treatment above it was assumed initially that a certain budget was available for a survey, and the problem was to find the values of $\bar{n}$ and m that would bring about the smallest sampling variance for this fixed cost.   After an initial solution there was a re-evaluation of the precision of results obtained in relation to the purposes to be served and the cost, and then perhaps new specifications of cost were arrived at.   When this approach is involved, it actually makes little difference whether one begins by specifying a certain budget or a degree of precision to be achieved.   In some instances, however, the situation may be specifically to minimize cost for some specified precision, or it may be more convenient to start with a specified precision.

The approach with fixed precision* is essentially the same as that given above.   Assume that the fixed precision is specified by letting $\sqrt{\varepsilon}$ represent the coefficient of variation desired.   Then

$$\left. \begin{aligned} \varepsilon = V_r^2 &\doteq (1 - f_1)\frac{B^2}{m} + (1 - f_2)\frac{W^2}{m\bar{n}} \\ &\doteq \frac{\hat{V}^2[1 + \delta(\bar{n} - 1)]}{m\bar{n}} \end{aligned} \right\} \tag{19.1}$$

and

$$a = \sqrt{4 \frac{B^2 - \dfrac{W^2}{N} + \dfrac{W^2}{\bar{n}}}{\varepsilon + \dfrac{B^2}{M}}} \doteq \sqrt{4 \frac{\hat{V}^2\delta}{\varepsilon}\left[1 + \frac{1 - \delta}{\delta}\frac{1}{\bar{n}}\right]} \tag{19.2}$$

---

* For proof, see Vol. II, Ch. 6, Sec. 11.

The steps to obtain optimum values for m and $\bar{n}$ are the same as those described and illustrated in Sec. 18, but using Eq. 19.2 in place of Eq. 18.2.

20. Use of table to ascertain optimum and values near optimum with fixed cost and general cost function. A summary tabulation for ascertaining the optimum value of $\bar{n}$ and the breadth of the minimum is presented in Table 7. It is sufficient for determining the optimum $\bar{n}$, subject to a fixed total cost, to know only $W^2/(B^2 - W^2/\bar{N}) \doteq \delta$ from the variance (Eq. 6.10 or 8.6) and the ratios C_0^2/CC_2 and C_1/C_2 from the cost function (Eq. 12.2). Consequently, the table for optimum $\bar{n}$ shows separate entries only for δ and for these two ratios of costs. There are, however, three entries in each cell of the table. The middle entry is the optimum value of $\bar{n}$ to the nearest integer, and the first and last entries indicate to the nearest integer the range of values for $\bar{n}$ that will not increase the variance by more than 10 per cent. Thus, the table not only gives the optimum value, but also provides information on the breadth of the minimum and the region within which results will be close to the optimum. Once a value of $\bar{n}$ is chosen from the table for a specified cost situation, the corresponding value of m is obtained from Eq. 18.2 and 18.3, or directly from Eq. 12.2.

Let us carry through the simple illustration presented in Sec. 18 and see how the table can be used to obtain a value of $\bar{n}$ that will approximate the optimum in any particular problem. In that illustration we wished to minimize the variance for a fixed cost. We compute from the cost function

$$\frac{C_0^2}{CC_2} = \frac{(13.4)^2}{3500(1.2)} = .043$$

$$\frac{C_1}{C_2} = \frac{2.7}{1.2} = 2.25$$

We assumed that with primary units of size $\bar{N} \doteq 30$ the value of δ for rental value was approximately .25. With this information we look in Table 7 for values that correspond approximately to those we have. The nearest values found in the table to those for our illustration are

$$\delta = .25; \quad \frac{C_0^2}{CC_2} = .06; \quad \text{and} \quad \frac{C_1}{C_2} = 2$$

For these we find the entry 2–3–4, which says that the optimum value of $\bar{n}$ is approximately 3, and that any value of $\bar{n}$ between 2 and 4 inclusive will be close enough that a choice anywhere in this range will not increase the variance by more than about 10 per cent above what it would be for the optimum value of $\bar{n}$. The table does not give the exact cost and δ values we were trying to look up, but rough mental interpolation should be satisfactory if the values given differ substantially from those desired.

Actually, in the more precise computation of the optimum in Sec. 18 we found for this particular illustration that the optimum value of $\bar{n}$ was 2.7, and that 3 was near the optimum.   The table has given us the same result very simply.   It will sometimes lead to a less close result, but should be adequate in most instances.

Once one has determined the value to use for $\bar{n}$, then the corresponding value of m is obtained from Eq. 18.2 and 18.3; with $\bar{n} = 3$ in this illustration we have:

$$a = 45, \quad m = 506$$

which is about the same as obtained earlier in Sec. 18.

We now estimate the reliability of results to be expected from our sample by substituting $\delta = .25$, $\bar{n} = 3$, $m = 506$, and $\hat{V}^2 = 1$ in the rel-variance formula Eq. 8.6 (the value of $\hat{V}^2$ is that which was assumed earlier, Sec. 16, to be applicable in this illustration). By substituting these values in the variance function (again neglecting the finite multiplier), we obtain

$$V_r^2 = \frac{1}{1518} [1 + (.25)(2)] = .00099$$

or

$$V_r = .031 \text{ or 3 per cent}$$

The investigator then reviews his purposes and objectives, and weighs the effect of errors in the results on inferences to be made to see if this variance is economically consistent with the cost of the survey; he may then change the budget up or down, depending upon his requirements.

From Table 7 we can ascertain the effect of changes in the cost function or of δ in the variance function on the optimum design.   Table 8 indicates more clearly how $\bar{n}$ varies with changes in various cost factors.   Table 8 is made up from Table 7, with a few extensions.

21. The effect of travel and other factors on the optimum value of $\bar{n}$. The optimum $\bar{n}$ is given by Eq. 18.1, and if we substitute for a the relationship given by Eq. 18.3, we have

$$\left. \begin{aligned} \text{opt. } \bar{n} &= \sqrt{\frac{C_1 + C_0/2\sqrt{m^\star}}{C_2} \frac{W^2}{B^2 - W^2/\bar{N}}} \\ &\doteq \sqrt{\frac{C_1 + C_0/2\sqrt{m^\star}}{C_2} \frac{1-\delta}{\delta}} \end{aligned} \right\} \qquad (21.1)$$

Table 7. Size of ultimate cluster ($\bar{n}$) which yields minimum variance subject to fixed total cost with alternative variance and cost conditions

(See Eq. 6.10 or 8.6 for variance function and Eq. 12.2 for cost function)

Costs		Optimum $\bar{n}$, and range of $\bar{n}$ for a 10 per cent increase in the variance, when δ is				
$\dfrac{C_0^2}{CC_2}$	$\dfrac{C_1}{C_2}$	.02	.04	.10	.25	.50
0	.0	1–1–6	1–1–3	1–1–2	1–1–1	1–1–1
	.1	1–2–9	1–2–5	1–1–2	1–1–1	1–1–1
	.4	2–4–13	2–3–8	1–2–4	1–1–2	1–1–1
	1.0	3–7–17	3–5–11	2–3–6	1–2–3	1–1–1
	2.0	5–10–22	4–7–14	3–4–8	2–2–4	1–1–2
	4.0	7–14–29	5–10–19	4–6–11	2–3–6	2–2–3
	8.0	10–20–39	8–14–26	5–9–15	3–5–9	2–3–5
	16.0	15–28–53	11–20–36	7–12–22	4–7–13	2–4–8
.02	.0	1–2–10	1–2–5	1–1–2	1–1–1	1–1–1
	.1	1–3–11	1–2–6	1–1–3	1–1–1	1–1–1
	.4	2–5–15	2–4–9	1–2–4	1–1–2	1–1–1
	1.0	4–8–19	3–5–12	2–3–6	1–2–3	1–1–1
	2.0	5–10–23	4–7–15	3–4–8	2–3–4	1–2–2
	4.0	7–15–30	6–10–20	4–6–11	2–4–6	2–2–3
	8.0	11–20–40	8–14–26	5–9–16	3–5–9	2–3–5
	16.0	15–28–54	11–20–37	7–12–22	4–7–13	2–4–8
.06	.0	1–4–12	1–2–6	1–1–3	1–1–1	1–1–1
	.1	2–4–13	1–3–6	1–2–4	1–1–1	1–1–1
	.4	3–6–16	2–4–9	2–2–5	1–1–2	1–1–1
	1.0	4–8–20	3–6–12	2–3–6	2–2–3	1–1–2
	2.0	5–11–24	4–8–15	3–5–8	2–3–4	1–2–3
	4.0	8–15–31	6–10–20	4–6–11	2–4–6	2–2–4
	8.0	11–21–40	8–14–27	5–9–16	3–5–9	2–3–5
	16.0	16–29–54	11–20–37	7–12–23	4–7–13	2–4–8
.2	.0	2–5–15	2–3–9	1–2–4	1–1–2	1–1–1
	.1	2–6–16	2–4–9	1–2–4	1–1–2	1–1–1
	.4	3–7–18	2–5–11	2–3–5	1–2–3	1–1–1
	1.0	4–9–22	3–6–13	2–4–7	2–2–4	1–1–2
	2.0	6–12–26	4–8–16	3–5–9	2–3–5	1–2–3
	4.0	8–16–32	6–11–21	4–7–12	2–4–7	2–2–4
	8.0	11–21–42	8–15–28	5–9–16	3–5–9	2–3–6
	16.0	16–29–56	11–20–38	7–12–23	4–7–14	2–4–9
.5	.0	3–7–19	2–5–11	2–3–5	1–1–2	1–1–1
	.1	3–8–20	2–5–11	2–3–6	1–2–3	1–1–1
	.4	4–9–21	3–6–13	2–3–7	1–2–3	1–1–1
	1.0	5–11–24	4–7–15	3–4–8	2–2–4	1–1–2
	2.0	6–13–28	5–9–18	3–5–10	2–3–5	1–2–3
	4.0	9–17–34	6–12–22	4–7–13	3–4–7	2–2–4
	8.0	12–22–43	9–15–29	5–9–17	3–5–10	2–3–6
	16.0	16–30–57	12–21–39	7–13–24	4–7–14	2–4–9

Table 7—(*continued*)

Costs		Optimum $\bar{n}$, and range of $\bar{n}$ for a 10 per cent increase in the variance, when δ is				
$\dfrac{C_0^2}{CC_2}$	$\dfrac{C_1}{C_2}$	.02	.04	.10	.25	.50
1.0	.0	4–9–23	3–6–13	2–3–7	1–2–3	1–1–1
	.1	4–10–23	3–6–14	2–3–7	1–2–3	1–1–1
	.4	5–11–25	4–7–15	2–4–8	2–2–4	1–1–2
	1.0	6–13–27	4–8–17	3–5–9	2–3–5	1–2–3
	2.0	7–15–31	5–10–19	3–6–11	2–3–6	1–2–3
	4.0	9–18–37	7–12–24	4–7–13	3–4–7	2–2–4
	8.0	12–23–45	9–16–30	6–10–18	3–6–10	2–3–6
	16.0	17–31–59	12–22–40	7–13–24	4–8–14	2–4–9
2.0	.0	6–12–28	4–8–17	3–4–8	2–2–4	1–1–2
	.1	6–13–28	4–8–17	3–4–9	2–2–4	1–1–2
	.4	6–13–29	4–9–18	3–5–9	2–3–5	1–1–2
	1.0	7–15–31	5–10–20	3–6–10	2–3–5	1–2–3
	2.0	8–17–35	6–11–22	4–6–12	2–4–6	2–2–3
	4.0	10–20–40	7–13–26	5–8–15	3–4–8	2–3–5
	8.0	13–25–48	9–17–32	6–10–19	3–6–11	2–3–6
	16.0	17–32–61	12–22–42	8–14–25	4–8–15	2–4–9
4.0	.0	7–16–34	5–10–21	3–6–11	2–3–5	1–2–3
	.1	8–16–34	5–10–21	3–6–11	2–3–5	1–2–3
	.4	8–17–35	6–11–22	4–6–12	2–3–6	1–2–3
	1.0	9–18–37	6–12–23	4–7–13	2–4–7	2–2–3
	2.0	10–19–40	7–13–25	4–8–14	3–4–7	2–2–4
	4.0	12–22–45	8–15–29	5–9–16	3–5–9	2–3–5
	8.0	14–27–53	10–18–35	6–11–20	4–6–12	2–4–7
	16.0	19–34–66	13–24–44	8–14–27	5–8–16	3–5–10
8.0	.0	10–20–42	7–13–27	4–8–14	3–4–7	2–2–4
	.1	10–21–43	7–13–27	4–8–15	3–4–8	2–2–4
	.4	11–21–44	7–14–28	5–8–15	3–4–8	2–2–4
	1.0	11–22–45	8–15–29	5–8–16	3–5–8	2–3–5
	2.0	12–24–48	8–16–30	5–9–17	3–5–9	2–3–5
	4.0	14–26–52	10–18–34	6–10–19	3–6–11	2–3–6
	8.0	16–31–59	11–21–39	7–12–23	4–7–13	2–4–8
	16.0	20–37–71	14–26–48	8–15–29	5–9–17	3–5–11
16.0	.0	14–28–55	10–18–35	6–10–19	3–6–11	2–3–6
	.1	14–28–55	10–18–35	6–10–20	3–6–11	2–3–6
	.4	14–28–55	10–18–35	6–11–20	3–6–11	2–3–6
	1.0	15–29–57	10–19–36	6–11–20	3–6–11	2–3–7
	2.0	15–30–59	11–20–38	6–11–22	4–6–12	2–4–7
	4.0	17–32–62	12–21–41	7–12–24	4–7–13	2–4–8
	8.0	19–36–69	13–24–40	8–14–27	4–8–16	2–5–10
	16.0	22–42–80	16–29–54	9–17–33	5–10–20	3–6–13

NOTE. The middle value of each group of three numbers is the $\bar{n}$ which produces the lowest variance under the stated conditions. The first and last numbers define the range of values of $\bar{n}$ which yield a variance within 10 per cent of the minimum variance.

Table 8. Summary table—size of ultimate cluster ($\bar{n}$) which yields minimum variance subject to fixed total cost with alternative variance and cost conditions

(See Eq. 6.10 or 8.6 for variance function and Eq. 12.2 for cost function)

Costs				Optimum $\bar{n}$, and range of $\bar{n}$ for a 10 per cent increase in the variance, when δ is			
$\dfrac{C_0^2}{CC_2}$	$\dfrac{C}{C_2}$	$\dfrac{C_0}{C_2}$	$\dfrac{C_1}{C_2}$	.02	.10	.25	.50
0	1,000	0	0	1–1–6	1–1–2	1–1–1	1–1–1
			2	5–10–22	3–4–8	2–2–4	1–1–2
			8	10–20–39	5–9–15	3–5–9	2–3–5
.4		20	0	3–7–18	2–3–5	1–1–2	1–1–1
			2	6–13–26	3–5–10	2–3–5	1–2–3
			8	12–22–43	5–9–17	3–5–10	2–3–6
16.0		400	0	38–70–135	14–28–60	8–16–38	4–10–27
			2	38–70–140	15–29–62	8–16–38	4–10–27
			8	40–75–150	16–30–65	9–17–40	5–12–30
0	10,000	0	0	1–1–6	1–1–2	1–1–1	1–1–1
			2	5–10–22	3–4–8	2–2–4	1–1–2
			8	10–20–39	5–9–15	3–5–9	2–3–5
.04		20	0	1–3–11	1–1–3	1–1–1	1–1–1
			2	5–11–24	3–4–8	2–3–4	1–2–2
			8	11–20–40	5–9–16	3–5–9	2–3–5
16.0		400	0	14–28–55	6–10–19	3–6–11	2–3–6
			2	15–30–59	6–11–22	4–6–12	2–4–7
			8	19–36–69	8–14–27	4–8–16	2–5–10
0	1,000,000	0	0	1–1–6	1–1–2	1–1–1	1–1–1
			2	5–10–22	3–4–8	2–2–4	1–1–2
			8	10–20–39	5–9–15	3–5–9	2–3–5
.0004		20	0	1–1–6	1–1–2	1–1–1	1–1–1
			2	5–10–22	3–4–8	2–2–4	1–1–2
			8	11–20–39	5–9–15	3–5–9	2–3–5
.16		400	0	1–2–9	1–1–2	1–1–1	1–1–1
			2	5–10–23	3–4–8	2–3–4	1–2–2
			8	11–20–40	5–9–16	3–5–9	2–3–5

NOTE. The middle value of each group of three numbers is the $\bar{n}$ which produces the lowest variance under the stated conditions. The first and last numbers define the range of values of $\bar{n}$ which yield a variance within 10 per cent of the minimum variance. The first column is included to permit comparison of this table with Table 7.

where $m^\star$ is the optimum m.   Although this equation does not give an immediate solution because it depends on $m^\star$, nevertheless it does show the impact of δ and of the various terms of the cost function on the optimum average size of ultimate cluster.   Notice, first, that δ, C_1, and C_2 have the same effect on optimum $\bar{n}$ as they do in the simpler case where there is no $\sqrt{m}$ term in the cost function, and, in fact, with $C_0 = 0$, the optimum $\bar{n}$ is exactly that given by Eq. 16.2.

But with $C_0\sqrt{m}$ in the cost function we see in Eq. 21.1 that $C_0/2\sqrt{m}$ affects the optimum $\bar{n}$ in the same way as does C_1.   Since $C_0/\sqrt{m}$ approximates the average travel cost per psu in the sample (Sec. 12), it follows that one-half of each dollar of travel cost per psu has the same effect on the determination of the optimum as each dollar of C_1, the fixed cost per psu.   Moreover, as the size of sample increases, the relative effect of travel becomes less, since C_0 is divided by $\sqrt{m}$.   Although total travel increases with increasing number of psu's in the sample, it increases at a rate considerably slower than the increase in the size of the sample. Consequently the relative contribution to the total cost or to the average cost per psu becomes less with increasing numbers of psu's in the sample.

In the illustrative problem above, Eq. 21.1 is, as we have already seen in Sec. 18, equal to

$$\text{opt. } \bar{n} = \sqrt{\dfrac{\dfrac{13.4}{2(23.0)} + 2.7}{1.2} \dfrac{.75}{.25}} = 2.7$$

Note that the influence of the term $C_0/2\sqrt{m}$ on optimum $\bar{n}$ is small. Even if the number of psu's, m, were as small as 25, the optimum $\bar{n}$ would still be less than 4.   At the other extreme, the minimum value of $\bar{n}$ would be equal to 2.6 when $C_0 = 0$, with no travel cost between psu's.

This indicates that emphasis sometimes placed on the importance of travel between psu's in a local area sample may be misdirected, at least to the extent that such travel costs are reflected in the term $C_0\sqrt{m}$.   More important than travel cost are often the cost per psu of drawing the sample and of locating the psu's and getting oriented, and the cost of listing, which are reflected primarily by the term involving C_1, and perhaps the cost of travel between psu's that is involved in waiting for buses or in other losses of time that are fixed per psu.

We may now explore more fully the way travel influences costs and the optimum design by examining some additional illustrations.   Suppose, for example, that we refer to our earlier illustration, and that instead of drawing the sample from a county containing about 1000 square miles we were drawing it from an entire state containing a total of, say, 50,000 square miles.   Since C_0 is roughly proportionate to the square root of the total area (as is seen in Ch. 6, Sec. 12), the result would be to increase C_0 by a factor of about 7, or from 13 to approximately 95, and from this $C_0^2/CC_2 = 2.1$.   If, now, we ascertain from Table 7 the optimum $\bar{n}$ for this new cost function, and with δ, C, C_1, and C_2 as before, we find that the optimum is increased from $\bar{n} = 3$ to $\bar{n} = 4$, with a range of 2–6 in the neighborhood of the optimum.   Thus, the increase in travel even over a whole state has not had a very great effect on the optimum size of cluster. There would have been a greater effect if C_1 had been small.   Thus, with $C_1 = 0$ the optimum for the local sample would have been $\bar{n} = 1$, and 1 would have been the only acceptable value, but for the state sample the optimum $\bar{n}$ is between 2 and 4.

If we took a further step and spread the sample over the entire nation, a considerable increase in optimum $\bar{n}$ would be noticed.   In this event, under the same assumption as to administrative approach and sample design (which probably would not be desirable in practice), C_0 would be increased to approximately 730, and the optimum size of cluster would now be increased to $\bar{n} = 15$.   Even with this substantial increase in the optimum, the minimum would be broad, so that a size of cluster anywhere between 7 and 34 would be in the neighborhood of the optimum, although this whole range is above the values of $\bar{n}$ that are acceptable for a small area.   The fact is that for a national sample with such a limited budget this approach would be inefficient, and we should vary the design significantly (see Ch. 9, Sec. 1).   But the illustration indicates that the optimum number of units per ultimate cluster would be fairly large if this approach were used for a national sample.   It would have been much larger for a smaller value of δ.

Suppose, as another comparison, that we are going to do a national sample but have a total budget of \$1,000,000 instead of \$5000.   We now have a large enough budget so that a national sample can be taken of sufficient size that the spread between psu's will not be substantially different from the spread between psu's in the county sample we used as our illustration.   With $C = 1,000,000$ we find from Table 7 that the optimum $\bar{n}$ is still between 2 and 4 for a national sample, if the other aspects of the cost function and variance remain the same as before.

A study of Tables 7 and 8 will give an improved basis for understanding how broad the minima are in various circumstances, and how the appropriate ultimate cluster size ($\bar{n}$) varies with changes in cost and in the area to be covered.

Remark.   In the simpler cost function given earlier, in which no term involving $\sqrt{m}$ was used, the total size of the budget had no effect whatever on the optimum $\bar{n}$.   But where travel is involved in the cost function more directly, with the term $C_0\sqrt{m}$ included in the cost function, then, as should be expected, the total budget has an influence on the optimum design. However, the optimum $\bar{n}$ is but little affected by travel or by the size of the budget except where travel becomes a very important part of the total cost.

22. Need for caution in interpreting special cases of optimum. It might at first appear that a special case of the optimum two-stage sampling design would be single-stage (whole) cluster sampling; i.e., it might appear that when opt. $\bar{n} = \bar{N}$ one-stage cluster sampling should be used, but if opt. $\bar{n} < \bar{N}$ subsampling would be more efficient. The optimum determination cannot be used for this latter type of inference if the cost function (whether based on Eq. 10.1 or 12.2) has provided for listing the whole psu, drawing a 100 per cent subsample from the listing, and carrying through the interviewing. If the whole psu is to be covered the listing operation becomes unnecessary: the interviewing can be carried out directly for the whole psu. Consequently the cost of carrying out the operation most efficiently with whole cluster coverage is over-represented by the cost function. Thus, although it is true that opt. $\bar{n} = \bar{N}$ does imply whole cluster coverage, it might be desirable to use whole cluster coverage at a point where the optimum $\bar{n}$ computed for the two-stage sample cost function is considerably less than $\bar{N}$.

The point at which one-stage cluster sampling is more efficient than two-stage sampling for any fixed size of psu is determined by ascertaining both the optimum one-stage sampling design and the optimum two-stage design, and choosing the one that yields greater precision per unit of cost. The description of optimum design with one-stage cluster sampling is given in Sec. 27–29.

23. Optimum size of primary unit for listing and subsampling. All the material on optimum design presented until now has assumed that the primary sampling units were fixed in advance and not subject to optimum determination. In practice one may have a choice among alternative psu's. Thus in sampling dwelling units from a city one might use as psu's city blocks, pairs of adjoining blocks, or perhaps half blocks, or other sizes or types of units. However, the resources available for defining psu's often limit the reasonable choices to only a few alternatives.

The relationships presented in Sec. 6 and 8 suggest that the larger the psu the smaller will be the variance of a sample estimate for a two-stage sample for any fixed values of m and $\bar{n}$. We have seen also that the cost of subsampling may be increased by increasing the size of psu, particularly if a listing operation is involved and if the cost of listing is determined by the size of the psu, as it usually will be. To make the choice among reasonable alternatives for defining psu's, we can approximate the variance and cost functions and determine the optimum design for each alternative considered (using the methods and theory already given), and then define the psu's in the manner that leads to the minimum variance per unit of cost.

24. Sampling for several statistics. The problem of optimum design in sampling for several statistics, instead of for a single one, is always difficult; and, although methods for minimizing certain average variances could be specified, they may often lead to unsatisfactory results. We shall give only rough guides without attempting a general solution. However, the breadth of the minimum is the saving factor that often makes it possible to approximate reasonably well the optimum design for a number of different statistics from a single sample. But there will be many instances in which the minimum is not broad enough to cover the important statistics that are needed from a sample.

Suppose, first, that the different statistics that are needed are presumed to have δ's in the region from .02 to .25. Looking over Table 8 in Sec. 20, we see that for any given set of cost factors the minima are often broad enough that the smallest cluster size that will increase the variance over that at the optimum by no more than 10 per cent, with $\delta = .02$, is approximately the same as the largest cluster size that does not give a loss of more than 10 per cent with $\delta = .25$, and this is not far from the optimum cluster size when $\delta = .10$. A value of .10 for δ is the order of magnitude that is often encountered in sampling city blocks for many types of population items. Case Study D, Ch. 12, gives some illustrative values.

If the investigator is confronted with a situation where some of the statistics have very large δ's, and some have very small δ's, while the minima are not broad, so that a serious loss in efficiency will be taken from the sample for one or the other, then he will have to elect on which statistics to take the loss. Making this decision is really a question of ascertaining what the reliability of the different sample estimates will be and seeing where, in terms of the purposes of the survey, the loss will be felt the least.

F. CHOICE OF LISTING UNIT AND METHOD OF LISTING

25. Alternative listing or subsampling units. It was mentioned earlier that the units to be listed and subsampled in a block can be determined

in several ways, and the choice of unit should be determined by considerations of accuracy of definition, variance, cost, and administrative convenience. Thus, if one were drawing a sample of individual people, in
order to estimate individual characteristics, any one of the following units
(or others) might serve as the subsampling (or listing) units:

(a) The individual person.

(b) The household or dwelling unit.

(c) The group of related persons within a household.

(d) The structure.

(e) The dwelling place. The term *dwelling place* is used here to indicate
a unit that consists of an entire structure in instances where the
structure contains comparatively few families or persons, but to
indicate individual dwelling units or individual living quarters
within larger structures such as apartment houses and hotels.

For some purposes and problems one type of listing unit may have
advantages over another. We shall discuss some of these alternative
listing units more fully. The considerations mentioned in the selection
of a listing unit for population sampling may indicate the types of considerations involved in other sampling problems.

The elementary unit as the listing unit. The individual person as the
listing unit involves no problem of definition, but this may not hold for
other types of elementary units, such as the farm or business establishment. If a selected classification of elementary units is wanted in the
sample, such as veterans, persons in a particular age group, or firms of a particular type, it may be that the characteristics required can be ascertained
at the time of listing, and then the subsampling confined to a sample from
the groups having the characteristics that are to be covered by the survey.

Two principal disadvantages may arise in the use of the individual
person as the listing unit in population surveys. The first is the cost of
listing. It may cost considerably more to make initial interviews at
households and list individual names than to list dwelling places, most of
which can be listed from the street. However, the extra cost of listing
individuals may in some types of surveys be more than offset by the gains
of being able to select the desired classification of individuals to be
included in the final sample, and in some surveys may be offset also by
avoiding the use of a cluster as the second-stage unit, which is involved
when households serve as the listing unit.

A second disadvantage of the individual person as the listing unit arises in
surveys in which the listing is made for use at a later date. People moving
in and out of the area create problems of keeping the list from which to
sample up to date. Dwelling places show a great deal more stability.

The dwelling unit as the listing unit.   The dwelling unit is often found
to be a useful listing unit, with special definitions of listing units within
hotels, institutions, and similar places where dwelling units as ordinarily
defined do not exist.   The dwelling unit will ordinarily be a considerably
less expensive unit to list than the individual person; the variance with
this listing unit usually will be larger than with the individual person,
although often not much larger.

Among the disadvantages of the dwelling unit as the listing unit are that
the unit is not always clearly recognized or defined, and that it may be
more costly to list than either the dwelling place or the structure.

The investigator should realize that if he is attempting to list dwelling
units he will sometimes find in practice that what was listed as a single
dwelling unit turns out to be two or more dwelling units.   There is no
bias so long as the whole listing unit, when selected for inclusion in the
sample, is actually included in the sample, whether it turns out to be a
single dwelling unit or more than one dwelling unit.   In other instances
what appears to be two dwelling units actually is only one.   In this
instance the dwelling unit or household is in fact listed twice and has two
chances of coming into the sample.   Unless care is taken in treating such
cases a bias may be introduced into the sample results.   If this type of
situation happens exceedingly rarely, any bias would be very small.
However, it is avoided by using a method of including only half of such
cases in the sample when one or the other listing unit falls in the sample.
This type of problem is discussed more fully elsewhere (Ch. 2, Sec. 3–8).

The structure as the listing unit.   The structure usually makes a clearly
defined listing unit and one that is inexpensive to list.   It may be an ideal
listing unit in types of areas where most families are living in single-family
structures and there are no large multi-unit structures.   The unit becomes
inefficient where there are larger structures, and exceedingly inefficient
where large apartment houses and other structures containing large
numbers of families are involved.   For this reason a "dwelling place" or
"address" has sometimes been defined and used as the listing unit.

The dwelling place or address as the listing unit.   The dwelling place,
as defined in (*e*) on p. 303, has the advantage of being rapidly listed,
without the need for entering structures and locating information on the
inside to ascertain if there is more than one dwelling unit in a structure
that obviously does not contain a considerable number of dwelling units.
The important principle in defining a dwelling place or similar type of
unit as a listing unit is that the listing shall be done easily without having
to enter too many structures, but that each unit listed shall be so clearly
defined that it can be recognized and identified uniquely if it is selected
for inclusion in the sample.

In one sample survey the listing unit was defined as follows: If from the street a structure appeared to contain no more than 3 dwelling units, the structure was to serve as the listing unit; but if the structure appeared to contain more than 3 dwelling units, then the lister was to enter and list individual dwelling units or living quarters.*

There is no serious loss in such a situation if the lister calls some places under 3 when in fact they are more than 3, so long as the units are clearly identified, and so long as he does not make such gross errors on the basis of the appearance that he lists as single units some structures that contain many (say 10 or more) families.   Errors in judgment, in which the lister includes no more than 5–10 times the average number of dwelling units per listing unit, may not be serious, provided such misfortunes happen only rarely.   With a listing unit such as the dwelling place one includes in the sample either all or a subsample of the people in the selected units, or all of the dwelling units if he is interested in family or dwelling unit statistics.   Part II of Case Study D, Ch. 12 (p. 604), gives a striking illustration of possible losses in the use of the dwelling place as a listing unit when one is making a simple unbiased estimate of population totals.

26. Some further comments on listing and subsampling.   The considerations in deciding between alternative listing units are administrative convenience, accuracy of the field control (so that reliable work can be insured), cost of carrying out the operation, and sampling variability associated with the listing unit chosen.   Structures or other listing units that may contain large numbers of dwelling units or people ordinarily will be less efficient, and sometimes considerably less efficient, than will smaller listing units.   The comparative efficiency is estimated by analysis along the lines indicated in the preceding sections of this chapter.

The listing can be done simultaneously with an interviewing process or can be done in advance.   In either event, procedures for selection of the subsample need to be supplied.   There are some risks in simultaneous listing that biases may enter into the selection because of either purposive or nonpurposive violation of instructions by the interviewer.   On the other hand, there may be a cost advantage if listing and interviewing are done simultaneously, especially if the survey is a one-time survey and the listing will not be used again.

Unless fairly foolproof procedures can be provided and reasonably adequate control of the interviewer's work is insured, the listing operation

---

* For a description of the survey see *A Chapter in Population Sampling*, Sampling Staff, U.S. Bureau of the Census, U.S. Government Printing Office, Washington, D.C., 1947.

should be separated from the interviewing. This may be done by carrying out the listing first, bringing or sending the lists into an office for sub-sampling, and returning the units for interviewing after the subsample has been designated. Advance listing as a separate operation, with the selection of one or more subsamples in the office, is likely to be a particularly advantageous procedure if one listing is to serve for several different surveys.

Two methods of subsampling that have proved satisfactory when the subsampling is done in the office are as follows: (1) Choose a number at random between 1 and k, and take the listing unit with this number in the sample and every kth listing unit thereafter. (2) Use a table of random numbers to select the sample (see Ch. 4, Sec. 5, for a discussion of the use of random numbers).

Either of these methods and variations of them can be worked out to be fairly simple procedures applied by the interviewer while carrying out the field work. Thus, a common method is to assign each household a visitation number and take into the sample those having predesignated numbers, such as the 4th, 9th, 14th, 19th. A method of predesignating lines on the listing sheet (not necessarily every kth line) has also been found useful. For example, the Census of Population in 1940, and also in 1950, relied upon a predesignated line to determine which persons would be in the sample for additional data. The lines were marked on the blank schedules; wherever a name was written on a sample line, that person was in the sample. If the head of the household fell on a sample line, certain other questions were asked about the household. Each interviewer worked under detailed instructions as to the order in which persons were to be listed within the household so as to make the sample selection independent, so far as possible, of the interviewer's whims or predilections.* Illustrations 8.1 (p. 507) and 8.3 (p. 510) in Chapter 11 provide some evaluation of the use of such sample selection methods in the 1940 and 1950 Censuses of Population in the United States.

G. OPTIMUM DESIGN WITH ONE-STAGE SAMPLING OF COMPACT CLUSTERS

27. Relationship between size of compact clusters and homogeneity within clusters. One-stage cluster sampling with clusters made up of

---

* See Frederick F. Stephan, W. Edwards Deming, and Morris H. Hansen, "The Sampling Procedure of the 1940 Population Census," *J. Amer. Stat. Assn.*, **35** (1940), 615–630.

contiguous units or compact areas is referred to as sampling of compact clusters or of whole clusters. It is to be distinguished from the case where psu's are selected and a simple random subsample of listing units is selected. Both Procedures 1 and 2 for selection of cluster samples described in Sec. 4 are methods of drawing a compact cluster sample. Procedure 1 involves initial selection of compact clusters without sub-sampling, and Procedure 2 involves initial selection of psu's and sub-sampling of compact clusters from the selected psu's.

The manner in which δ tends to decrease with increase in size of compact cluster is described in Sec. 8. The estimates of averages or ratios with a compact cluster sample are the same as those given in Sec. 6 (Eq. 6.1 and 6.2); the variance or rel-variance of the estimate is given by Eq. 6.3, 6.4, 6.7, 6.10, or 8.6 with $\bar{n} = \bar{N}$; and the estimate of the variance is as given in Sec. 7 (Eq. 7.1 and 7.3).

The problem of determining the optimum size of compact clusters is more difficult than the problem of determining the optimum value of $\bar{n}$ with two-stage sampling. This follows because with two-stage sampling the size of psu was assumed fixed, and the value of δ did not change with a change in $\bar{n}$, the average size of the ultimate cluster. With compact clusters, however, the magnitude of δ does vary with the size of the com-pact cluster, and it is necessary to find or to assume a relationship between δ and the average size of cluster to arrive at an optimum value of $\bar{N}$. One can get such a relationship by constructing compact clusters of various average sizes and computing the value of δ for each of a number of these sizes. Usually, however, it is feasible to compute only relatively few such values from empirical data, and hence it is necessary to interpolate values intermediate to those for which empirical data are available.

Table 9 shows some comparisons of values of δ for differing sizes of compact clusters of listing units. Some average results are shown for clusters of dwelling units of various sizes in estimating a number of different population and housing characteristics, and for clusters of farms in estimating an agricultural characteristic. Some of the values are plotted in Fig. 6, together with a smoothed curve fitted to the points. The curve fitted in each case is of the form

$$\delta_{\text{calc.}} = a\bar{N}^b \qquad (27.1)$$

where $\delta_{\text{calc.}}$ indicates the value read from the curve for various sizes of cluster, and $\bar{N}$ indicates the average size of compact cluster. The curves do not always fit the individual points closely, but represent them satis-factorily on the average. Curves in general similar to this have been found by several different investigators to represent fairly satisfactorily the nature of the variation in δ (or of the variance between primary

Table 9. Variation in δ for different sizes of compact cluster

$$\delta_{calc.} = a\bar{N}^b$$

A. Some characteristics for selected cities over 100,000*

No. of dwelling units in cluster $\bar{N}$	Proportion of													Average rental value $a = .806$ $b = -.416$	
	Males in labor force $a = .220$ $b = -.432$		Males unemployed $a = .0875$ $b = .206$		Males 25–34 $a = .0861$ $b = -.541$		Persons per household $a = .396$ $b = -.384$		Dwelling units having rent of $10–14 $a = .407$ $b = -.433$		Home-owned dwelling units $a = .227$ $b = -.162$			
	δ	$\delta_{calc.}$	δ	$\delta_{calc.}$	δ	$\delta_{calc.}$	δ	$\delta_{calc.}$	δ	$\delta_{calc.}$	δ	$\delta_{calc.}$	δ	$\delta_{calc.}$
3	.12	.14	.060	.070	.045	.048	.23	.26	.24	.25	.17	.19	.45	.51
9	.10	.09	.070	.056	.026	.026	.19	.17	.17	.16	.17	.16	.36	.32
27	.07	.05	.045	.044	.018	.014	.14	.11	.11	.10	.17	.13	.25	.20
62	.03	.04	.034	.037	.0079	.0092	.07	.08	.06	.07	.10	.12	.12	.15

B. Proportion of farms having commercial orchards in North Carolina†

$$a = .478, \quad b = -.191$$

$\bar{N}$	δ	$\delta_{calc.}$
5	.38	.35
10	.31	.31
15	.27	.29
20	.25	.27
25	.24	.26
30	.25	.25
50	.25	.23

* Data from unpublished studies made in the Bureau of the Census.
† Based on data from F. E. McVay (*op. cit.*).

sampling units) with variation in size of clusters.   We shall assume that the values do fit satisfactorily.*

One might do as well with a curve fitted freehand, or with the initial unsmoothed values if they are estimated with sufficient precision, but it is more convenient to use a smoothed curve.   The values of a and b for the curve for $\delta_{\text{calc.}}$ for each characteristic are also shown in Table 9.

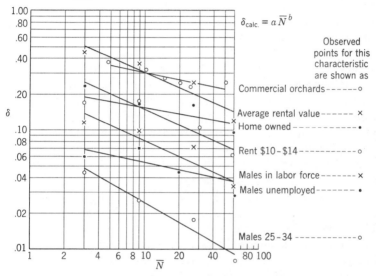

FIG. 6.   Relation of δ to size of segment.

The rate of decline in δ with increasing $\bar{N}$ is not very rapid in any of the cases illustrated and is usually very much slower than the rate of increase in the size of $\bar{N}$.   Thus, for $\bar{N} = 3$ and $\bar{N} = 9$, δ would have to be one-third as large for the larger cluster if it were to decrease at the same rate as the increase in $\bar{N}$, whereas it seldom approaches anything like such a rate of decline.

28. Optimum size of compact cluster.   With estimated values of δ for each of the values of $\bar{N}$, the cost function specified, and the variance formula, it is possible to determine the optimum values of $\bar{N}$ and m in a manner similar to that illustrated in Sec. 17.   Thus, the variance of the sample estimate of an average or total with compact clusters is approximately (from Eq. 8.6 with $\bar{n} = \bar{N}$ and f small)

$$V_r^2 \doteq \frac{\hat{V}^2}{m\bar{N}} [1 + \delta(\bar{N} - 1)] \qquad (28.1)$$

* References: H. Fairfield Smith (1), P. C. Mahalanobis (2), and R. J. Jessen (3).

and we shall assume that the cost function is of the form (from Eq. 12.2 with $\bar{n} = \bar{N}$)

$$C = C_0\sqrt{m} + C_1 m + C_2 m\bar{N} \qquad (28.2)$$

Illustrative methods for approximating C_0, C_1, and C_2 have been given in Part D (Sec. 10–15).

Now, we shall assume that the value of $\hat{V}^2$ is not very sensitive to change in $\bar{N}$, and that it can be approximated from available data. We shall assume, further, that the values of δ for various values of $\bar{N}$ can be approximated, as, for example, from charts such as Fig. 6, and that estimates are made for C_0, C_1, and C_2. With these values known we can either minimize the cost for a fixed precision or minimize the variance for a fixed cost. If we wish to do the former, we solve for different values of m from Eq. 28.1 by assuming different values of $\bar{N}$ with their corresponding values of δ. For each value of $\bar{N}$, we then have, in addition to a value of δ, a value of m. Substituting $\bar{N}$ and its corresponding value of m in the cost function (Eq. 28.2), we then have a total cost C associated with each assumed value of $\bar{N}$, and the optimum values of m and $\bar{N}$ are those which minimize the cost. The procedure for minimizing the variance for a fixed cost is similar, as is illustrated in the following example.

Illustration 28.1. Assume, now, that the problem is to find the values of m and $\bar{N}$ which minimize the variance of the estimate of average rental value, continuing the illustration given in Sec. 18 and earlier sections; and assume that for this compact cluster design the values for the coefficients in the cost function are $C = 3500$, $C_0 = 13.4$, $C_1 = 1.5$, and $C_2 = 1.2$. The use of compact clusters (rather than two-stage sampling) may not introduce any essential differences in the cost coefficients C_0 and C_2, and hence we have assumed that these have the same values as in Sec. 18. The value of C_1 is assumed different because of the substitution of the cost of delimiting compact clusters for the cost of field listing and subsampling.

We shall assume that in the variance equation $\hat{V}^2 = 1$, and further that δ is approximated by $a\bar{N}^b$ with $a = .806$ and $b = -.416$ as shown in Fig. 6 and Table 9. We proceed by substituting values for m in the cost function and solving for $\bar{N}$. Then, for these paired values of m and $\bar{N}$, we compute the rel-variance. The curves of total rel-variance for different values of $\bar{N}$ are plotted in Fig. 7 for several characteristics. The optimum in each instance is, of course, the point at which the rel-variance is a minimum. Notice that for average rental value the minimum is in the neighborhood of $\bar{N} = 1$, although the rel-variance will still be within 10 per cent of the minimum value if $\bar{N}$ is no greater than 5.

We can now compare the optimum design for estimating rental value, with one-stage sampling of compact clusters, with the optimum with two-stage sampling. We see, for the cost assumed and for the values of δ for rental value, that whole block listing and subsampling would be slightly less efficient, since the minimum variance with compact clusters is

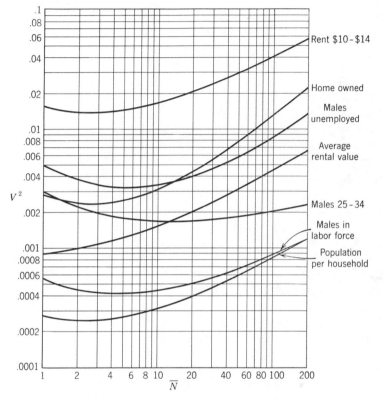

Fig. 7.   Rel-variances for varying sizes of compact cluster, with fixed cost, $3500 = 13.4\sqrt{m} + 1.5m + 1.2m\bar{N}$, and rel-variance specified by Eq. 28.1.

.00089, whereas the minimum with listing and subsampling is .00099. This would not have been the case if C_1 had been assumed considerably larger for the one-stage compact cluster cost function, or if C_1 had been considerably smaller for the two-stage cost function.

Exercises

28.1. Compute an approximate value for the optimum size of compact cluster with one-stage sampling for estimating average rental value in the illustration just given, but assume $C_1 = 3.0$ instead of 1.5.

28.2. Compute the optimum size of ultimate cluster with two-stage sampling for estimating average rental value in the illustration just given, but assume $C_1 = 4$. Compare the results with those of Ex. 28.1 and with the illustrations given above.

28.3. Using the same costs as in Ex. 28.1 for compact clusters, and δ from Table 9, what is the optimum size of compact cluster for estimating the proportion of males in the labor force? Using the same costs as in Ex. 28.2, what is the optimum size of ultimate cluster for two-stage sampling? Compare the variances of the two designs.

29. Comparison of efficiency of one-stage compact cluster sampling with two-stage sampling.

Suppose, now, that there are resources for compact cluster sampling as well as for two-stage sampling, and that it is concluded that both are administratively feasible. Which approach should one use?

The analysis of the optimum by either procedure does not cover the other one as a special case (see Sec. 22), and therefore a comparison of the efficiencies of the optimum design by each procedure should be made. If there is not a substantial difference between the two (as often will be the case), then one chooses either, letting intangible factors such as administrative convenience, feasibility, and past experience determine the choice. In some surveys it may be desirable to employ both methods.

The compact cluster approach requires the use of field sketches or maps showing physical features in sufficient detail that small segments containing approximately equal numbers of listing units can be identified clearly. Even with the best of maps it is frequently impossible to delineate segments of approximately equal numbers of listing units from the map. Thus, a single structure may contain many dwelling units or many stores, and it may not be feasible without additional field work to subdivide it into groups containing the desired small number of listing units. It is then necessary either to give the interviewer additional instructions for sub-sampling in the field, or to do some preliminary field work before assigning the segment to the interviewer.

One way of subdividing such a unit is to list it and subsample from the listing. Another way of subdividing is to "chunk" it, i.e., to divide a block or other area roughly into chunks of the desired size and to select one of these chunks in a random manner. Thus, an apartment house might be divided into chunks consisting of floors, and, if necessary, within floors into groups of apartments. This chunking procedure may be as much trouble to apply as the listing operation, and a choice between the two should be made on the basis of administrative convenience and cost.

Chunking may be a feasible technique in other situations, also, with the use of aerial photographs or sketches prepared in the field. Thus, secondary roads, property lines, and even tenuous boundaries cutting across fields may become eligible for the boundaries of segments, and therefore make possible the designation of smaller and less variable units than were possible with standard maps.

REFERENCES

(1) H. Fairfield Smith, "An Empirical Law for Heterogeneity in the Yields of Agricultural Crops," *J. Agr. Sci.*, **28** (1938), 1–23.

(2) P. C. Mahalanobis, "On Large-Scale Sample Surveys," *Phil. Trans. Roy. Soc.*, Series B, **231** (1946), 329–451.

(3) R. J. Jessen, "Statistical Investigation of a Sample Survey for Obtaining Farm Facts," *Iowa Agr. Exp. Stat. Res. Bull.* 304, 1942.

(4) W. G. Cochran, *Sampling Techniques*, John Wiley & Sons, New York, 1953, Chapters 9 and 10.

(5) W. E. Deming, *Some Theory of Sampling*, John Wiley & Sons, New York, 1950, Chapter 5.

(6) R. A. Fisher, *Statistical Methods for Research Workers*, Oliver and Boyd, Edinburgh, tenth edition, 1934, Chapter 7.

(7) A. J. King and R. J. Jessen, "The Master Sample of Agriculture," *J. Amer. Stat. Assn.*, **40** (1945), 38–56.

(8) P. C. Mahalanobis, "A Sample Survey of the Acreage under Jute in Bengal," *Sankhyā*, **4** (1940), 511–530.

(9) F. X. Schumacher and R. A. Chapman, *Sampling Methods in Forestry and Range Management*, Duke University, School of Forestry, 1942, Chapter 6.

(10) F. Yates, *Sampling Methods for Censuses and Surveys*, Charles Griffin and Company, London, 1949.

(11) F. Yates and I. Zacopanay, "The Estimation of the Efficiency of Sampling with Special Reference to Sampling for Yield in Cereal Experiments," *J. Agr. Sci.*, **25** (1935), 543–577.

CHAPTER 7

Stratified Single- or Multi-stage
Cluster Sampling

1. Use of stratification with cluster sampling. Stratification with cluster sampling may be carried out with proportionate sampling at each stage of sampling for all strata, or with variable sampling fractions. Variable sampling fractions may be used for some or all stages of sampling, either within strata or for different strata, and variable primary unit sampling fractions may be used with variable subsampling fractions in such a way that the over-all fraction is uniform for all classes of the population. This flexibility in the sampling fractions offers different kinds of advantages in different kinds of situations.

2. Notation. The notation with stratified cluster sampling is the same as that with simple cluster sampling except that a subscript h is introduced to designate the stratum. Thus, N_h is the number of second-stage units in the population in the hth stratum, and $N = \sum_h^L N_h$ is the number of second-stage units in the total population. The sample numbers n_h and n are similarly defined, and other notation of the preceding chapter is modified in this way, i.e., by simply inserting a subscript h to designate the stratum. Some additional notation required will be introduced as needed; the notation defined in the beginning of Chapter 6 will be retained but with the stratum designation added, and with additional terms for additional stages of sampling.

3. Criteria on which to stratify. With small clusters, the type of stratification that is often used is either stratification on the basis of knowledge of the characteristics of individual clusters or groups of clusters, or simply geographic stratification. Stratification on the basis of knowledge of characteristics of individual clusters may be used, for example, where data are available for blocks or other small areas from the Census or from other sources. For example, data on rental value have been published from the 1940 and 1950 Housing Censuses by blocks, and blocks can be stratified on this basis. For specific methods of stratification, in a particular case, see Ch. 12, Case Studies A and B.

Often geographic stratification alone is as effective as efforts to stratify on other characteristics, although this is by no means always so. Where geographic stratification is used, it is often convenient, instead of making a simple random sampling of clusters within strata, to choose a systematic sample by taking every kth segment in a geographic sequence that allows blocks which are more or less similar to be near each other on the list (see Fig. 1, Ch. 6, p. 248). The systematic sampling can often, for purposes of estimating the variance, be regarded as roughly equivalent to random sampling within strata such that one or a few blocks are regarded as taken from each stratum (see Ch. 11, Sec. 8).

One type of stratification that is often particularly desirable is to make separate strata of unusual types of blocks and of especially large blocks, which are often unusual as to type also (see Ch. 8, Sec. 7 and 9, for a fuller treatment of this problem).

4. Gains from stratification of clusters.   The gains due to proportionate stratified sampling of clusters may be measured in the same way, but in terms of cluster characteristics, as in Chapter 5, where we dealt with ratios estimated from a stratified sample of individual elements.   Equation 5.5, Ch. 5, computed in terms of psu totals, indicates the reduction in the psu contribution to the variance due to proportionate stratification in the selection of the psu's.   As in Chapter 5, gains will be achieved when the stratification is effective in grouping together clusters which are homogeneous in the characteristics being measured.   However, for a given set of strata, the reduction in variance from stratification often can be expected to be relatively greater with cluster sampling than with simple random sampling of listing units.

As a simple illustration, assume that psu's of equal numbers of listing units ($N_i = \bar{N}$) are classified into strata of equal size. Assume further that a sample of m psu's is selected from each stratum. Then the reduction in the variance between psu's relative to the variance for simple random sampling of the psu's is given approximately by

$$\frac{\sum\limits_{}^{L}(\bar{\bar{X}}_h - \bar{\bar{X}})^2\bar{N}}{L\sigma^2[1 + \delta(\bar{N} - 1)]} \tag{4.1}$$

where $\bar{\bar{X}}_h$ is the average per listing unit in the hth stratum.

$\bar{\bar{X}}$ is the average per listing unit over all strata.

σ^2 is the population variance between listing units with no stratification.

δ is the intraclass correlation among listing units within psu's given by Eq. 8.3, Ch. 6.

The reduction in variance for a proportionate stratified sample of listing units drawn from the same strata as above relative to that for a simple random sample selected without stratification is

$$\frac{\sum\limits_{}^{L}(\bar{\bar{X}}_h - \bar{\bar{X}})^2}{L\sigma^2} \tag{4.2}$$

The ratio of Eq. 4.1 to Eq. 4.2 is

$$\frac{\bar{N}}{1 + \delta(\bar{N} - 1)} \tag{4.3}$$

Thus, the relative gain from stratification with cluster sampling is approximately $\bar{N}$ times as large as the relative gain from the same stratification with simple random sampling, when δ is very small. However, the relative gains are about the same when δ is close to 1.

When subsampling is used, relationship 4.3 holds approximately, if we substitute $\bar{n}$, the expected value of the size of subsample per cluster, for $\bar{N}$. Then, as $\bar{n}$ approaches 1, and we have almost the equivalent of simple random sampling, the relative gains are about the same, as is to be expected.

Similar types of gains will occur when the clusters vary in size. For proofs of statements above see Sec. 5, Ch. 7, Vol. II.

5. The estimate and its variance with stratified two-stage sampling. The sample design we shall now consider is one involving stratified two-stage sampling in which, within a stratum, the first-stage units are selected with equal probability, and, within a psu, the second-stage units are selected with equal probability. The first-stage sampling fraction is $f_{1h} = m_h/M_h$, where M_h is the number of first-stage units in the hth stratum and m_h is the number in the sample. The second-stage sampling fraction is $f_{2hi} = n_{hi}/N_{hi}$, where N_{hi} is the number of second-stage units in the hith first-stage unit, and n_{hi} is the number in the sample.

A consistent estimate of $R = X/Y$ from such a sample is

$$r = \frac{x'}{y'} \tag{5.1}$$

where

$$x' = \sum_h^L x_h' = \sum_h^L \frac{M_h}{m_h} \sum_i^{m_h} x_{hi}' = \sum_h^L \frac{M_h}{m_h} \sum_i^{m_h} \frac{N_{hi}}{n_{hi}} x_{hi} \tag{5.2}$$

x_{hi} is the aggregate for the n_{hi} units in the sample from the hith psu,

$(N_{hi}/n_{hi})x_{hi} = x'_{hi}$ is an unbiased estimate of X_{hi}, the hith psu total, and

$$x'_h = \frac{M_h}{m_h} \sum_i^{m_h} \frac{N_{hi}}{n_{hi}} x_{hi}$$

is an unbiased estimate of X_h, the hth stratum total. Similarly, y' is given by Eq. 5.2 with Y's substituted for the X's. The rel-variance of Eq. 5.1 is*

$$V_r^2 \doteq \frac{1}{X^2} \sum_h^L \frac{M_h^2}{m_h} \frac{M_h - m_h}{M_h} S_{1h}^2 + \frac{1}{X^2} \sum_h^L \frac{M_h}{m_h} \sum_i^{M_h} \frac{N_{hi}^2}{n_{hi}} \frac{N_{hi} - n_{hi}}{N_{hi}} S_{2hi}^2 \quad (5.3)$$

where

$$S_{1h}^2 = S_{1hX}^2 + R^2 S_{1hY}^2 - 2R S_{1hXY} \quad (5.4)$$

$$S_{1hX}^2 = \frac{\sum^{M_h}(X_{hi} - \bar{X}_h)^2}{M_h - 1} \quad (5.5)$$

S_{1hY}^2 is similarly defined for the Y's;

$$S_{1hXY} = \frac{\sum^{M_h}(X_{hi} - \bar{X}_h)(Y_{hi} - \bar{Y}_h)}{M_h - 1} \quad (5.6)$$

$$R = X/Y \quad (5.7)$$

and where

$$\bar{X}_h = \frac{X_h}{M_h} \quad \text{and} \quad \bar{Y}_h = \frac{Y_h}{M_h} \quad (5.8)$$

are average values per primary unit for the hth stratum.
Similarly,

$$S_{2hi}^2 = S_{2hiX}^2 + R^2 S_{2hiY}^2 - 2R S_{2hiXY} \quad (5.9)$$

$$S_{2hiX}^2 = \frac{\sum^{N_{hi}}(X_{hij} - \bar{\bar{X}}_{hi})^2}{N_{hi} - 1} \quad (5.10)$$

S_{2hiY}^2 is similarly defined for the Y's;

$$S_{2hiXY} = \frac{\sum^{N_{hi}}(X_{hij} - \bar{\bar{X}}_{hi})(Y_{hij} - \bar{\bar{Y}}_{hi})}{N_{hi} - 1} \quad (5.11)$$

and where

$$\bar{\bar{X}}_{hi} = \frac{X_{hi}}{N_{hi}} \quad \text{and} \quad \bar{\bar{Y}}_{hi} = \frac{Y_{hi}}{N_{hi}} \quad (5.12)$$

are average values per listing unit for the ith psu in the hth stratum.

---

* For proof, see Vol. II, Ch. 7, Sec. 1.

The rel-variance, instead of the variance, of the ratio is given in Eq. 5.3 so that it will be general for the ratio and for totals or averages obtained by multiplying the ratio by a constant. It is readily converted to a variance by multiplying by R^2 or by the appropriate constant squared.

The rel-variance of x', the simple unbiased estimate, is a special case of Eq. 5.3 obtained by setting the terms involving Y in Eq. 5.4 and 5.9 equal to zero, i.e., by setting S^2_{1hY}, S_{1hXY}, S^2_{2hiY}, and S_{2hiXY} equal to zero.

Note that the first term in Eq. 5.3 is the contribution to the rel-variance from sampling first-stage units and the second term is the contribution to the rel-variance from sampling second-stage units. The first term in Eq. 5.3 would be the rel-variance if there were no subsampling. This is identical with σ_r^2/R^2, where σ_r^2 is given by Eq. 4.5 of Ch. 5 with M_h representing the number of psu's in the hth stratum. Equation 5.3 reduces to Eq. 6.10 of Ch. 6 when $L = 1$ and the second-stage sampling fractions are uniform.

Remark 1. A special case often occurring in practice is that where the second-stage sampling fractions n_{hi}/N_{hi} are kept uniform within a stratum, i.e., $n_{hi}/N_{hi} = f_{2h}$. In this special case the estimate of R is

$$ r = \frac{\sum\limits_{}^{L} \dfrac{1}{f_h} x_h}{\sum\limits_{}^{L} \dfrac{1}{f_h} y_h} \tag{5.13} $$

where

$$ f_h = f_{1h} f_{2h} = \frac{m_h}{M_h} \frac{\bar{n}_h}{\bar{N}_h} $$

and $\bar{N}_h$ is the average number of second-stage units per first-stage unit in the hth stratum, and $\bar{n}_h$ is the expected value of the number of second-stage units in the sample per first-stage unit in the sample. Then the rel-variance of r is given by Eq. 5.3 with the substitution of $\bar{n}_h/\bar{N}_h$ for n_{hi}/N_{hi}. With this substitution, the first term of Eq. 5.3 remains unchanged, and the second term of Eq. 5.3 is as shown in Eq. 5.14.

$$ V_r^2 \doteq \frac{1}{X^2} \sum_h^L M_h^2 \frac{M_h - m_h}{M_h m_h} S_{1h}^2 + \frac{1}{X^2} \sum^L N_h^2 \frac{\bar{N}_h - \bar{n}_h}{\bar{N}_h m_h \bar{n}_h} S_{2h}^2 \tag{5.14} $$

where

$$ S_{2h}^2 = \frac{\sum\limits_i^{M_h} N_{hi} S_{2hi}^2}{M_h \bar{N}_h} \tag{5.15} $$

and S_{2hi}^2 is given by Eq. 5.9.

Another form of the rel-variance of r when $n_{hi}/N_{hi} = f_{2h}$ which is often useful is

$$ V_r^2 \doteq \frac{1}{X^2} \sum_h^L X_h^2 \frac{M_h - m_h}{M_h} \frac{B_h^2}{m_h} + \frac{1}{X^2} \sum_h^L X_h^2 \frac{\bar{N}_h - \bar{n}_h}{\bar{N}_h} \frac{W_h^2}{m_h \bar{n}_h} \tag{5.16} $$

where $B_h^2 = S_{1h}^2/\bar{X}_h^2$, $W_h^2 = S_{2h}^2/\bar{\bar{X}}_h^2$, $\bar{X}_h = X_h/M_h$, $\bar{\bar{X}}_h = X_h/N_h$, and $\bar{n}_h = f_{2h}\bar{N}_h$.

Remark 2.   In the special case when both the first-stage and the second-stage sampling fractions are uniform in all strata, i.e., when $m_h/M_h = f_1$ and $n_{hi}/N_{hi} = f_2$, the estimate is given by

$$r = \frac{x}{y} \tag{5.17}$$

and the variance reduces to the form given by either Eq. 6.10 or 8.6 of Ch. 6 but with

$$S_1^2 = \frac{\sum_h^L M_h S_{1h}^2}{M} \tag{5.18}$$

where S_{1h}^2 is given by Eq. 5.4;

$$S_2^2 = \frac{\sum_h^L N_h S_{2h}^2}{N} \tag{5.19}$$

where S_{2h}^2 is given by Eq. 5.15; and where $m = \sum_h^L m_h$ is the number of psu's in the sample and $n = \sum_h^L n_h$ is the expected value of the number of listing units in the sample over all strata.

Note that, if the sampling fractions are uniform at each stage of sampling for all strata, then the rel-variance of r can be expressed in the same form as given by Eq. 8.6 of Ch. 6, and the terms can be interpreted in the same manner as discussed in Sec. 8 of Ch. 6.   Thus, for this case,

$$V_r^2 \doteq (1-f)\frac{\hat{V}^2}{m\bar{n}}[1 + \delta(\bar{n} - 1)] \tag{5.20}$$

where

$$\hat{V}^2 = \frac{\hat{M}-1}{\hat{M}}B^2 + \frac{\bar{N}-1}{\bar{N}}W^2 \tag{5.21}$$

$$\delta = \frac{\dfrac{\hat{M}-1}{\hat{M}}B^2 - \dfrac{\hat{V}^2}{\bar{N}}}{(\bar{N}-1)\hat{V}^2/\bar{N}} \tag{5.22}$$

and

$$f = f_1 f_2, \qquad \hat{M} = \frac{M}{L}$$

$$B^2 = \frac{S_1^2}{\bar{X}^2}, \qquad W^2 = \frac{S_2^2}{\bar{\bar{X}}^2}$$

$$\bar{X} = \frac{X}{M}, \qquad \bar{\bar{X}} = \frac{X}{N}$$

and $\bar{n}$ is the expected value of the number of listing units in the sample per psu in the sample.

6. The ultimate cluster estimate of the rel-variance of r.   Assume that a subsample of psu's is selected from each stratum, and let m'_h equal the number selected in the hth stratum.   If all the psu's in the original sample are used to estimate the variance, m'_h is equal to m_h.

A simple estimate* of the rel-variance of r is

$$v_r^2 = \frac{1}{x'^2} \sum_h^L \frac{M_h^2}{m_h} s_{c'h}^2 \tag{6.1}$$

where

$$s_{c'h}^2 = s_{c'hX}^2 + r^2 s_{c'hY}^2 - 2r s_{c'hXY} \tag{6.2}$$

with

$$s_{c'hX}^2 = \frac{\sum_i^{m'_h} \left(x'_{hi} - \frac{\sum_i^{m'_h} x'_{hi}}{m'_h} \right)^2}{m'_h - 1} \tag{6.3}$$

and

$$x'_{hi} = \frac{N_{hi}}{n_{hi}} x_{hi} = N_{hi}\bar{x}_{hi} \tag{6.4}$$

is an unbiased estimate of the hith psu total.

$s_{c'hY}^2$ is similarly defined, and

$$s_{c'hXY} = \frac{\sum_i^{m'_h} \left(x'_{hi} - \frac{\sum_i^{m'_h} x'_{hi}}{m'_h} \right) \left(y'_{hi} - \frac{\sum_i^{m'_h} y'_{hi}}{m'_h} \right)}{m'_h - 1} \tag{6.5}$$

This estimate is applicable when the first-stage sampling fraction is relatively small, i.e., m_h is small relative to M_h.   When m_h is large relative to M_h, a more appropriate estimate is given in Sec. 7.

Remark.   In the special case when $n_{hi}/N_{hi} = f_{2h}$ a more accurate estimate of the total rel-variance is given by

$$v_r^2 = \frac{1}{x'^2} \sum_h^L (1 - f_h) \frac{m_h}{f_h^2} s_{ch}^2 \tag{6.6}$$

where

$$s_{ch}^2 = s_{chX}^2 + r^2 s_{chY}^2 - 2r s_{chXY} \tag{6.7}$$

$$s_{chX}^2 = \frac{\sum_i^{m'_h} (x_{hi} - \bar{x}_h)^2}{m'_h - 1} = f_{2h}^2 s_{c'hX}^2 \tag{6.8}$$

---

* For derivation, see Vol. II, Ch. 7, Sec. 2.

where $s_{c'hX}^2$ is given by Eq. 6.3; s_{chY}^2 is similarly defined, and

$$s_{chXY} = \frac{\sum_i^{m'_h}(x_{hi} - \bar{x}_h)(y_{hi} - \bar{y}_h)}{m'_h - 1} = f_{2h}^2 s_{c'hXY} \qquad (6.9)$$

where $s_{c'hXY}$ is given by Eq. 6.5, $f_h = f_{1h}f_{2h}$, x_{hi} and y_{hi} are the sample aggregates for the hith psu in the sample, and

$$\bar{x}_h = \frac{\sum_i^{m'_h} x_{hi}}{m'_h} \quad \text{and} \quad \bar{y}_h = \frac{\sum_i^{m'_h} y_{hi}}{m'_h}$$

Note that, if $f_{1h}f_{2h} = f$, i.e., the sample is self-weighting, and also $m'_h = m_h$,

$$v_r^2 \doteq (1 - f)\frac{\sum_h^L m_h s_{ch}^2}{x^2} \qquad (6.10)$$

where s_{ch}^2 is defined by Eq. 6.7 with $m'_h = m_h$.

7. Estimate of the components of the variance.*

To estimate the contributions to the variance from each stage of sampling, it is convenient to estimate first S_{2hi}^2 given by Eq. 5.9 and then estimate S_{1h}^2 given by Eq. 5.4.

We might take a subsample for estimating variances or a sample different from the sample used for estimating averages or other characteristics.

Assume that we selected a sample of psu's from each stratum and a sample of second-stage units from each of the selected psu's for the purpose of estimating the components. Let m'_h be the number of psu's selected from the hth stratum, and let n'_{hi} be the number of second-stage units selected from the ith selected psu in the hth stratum.

Estimate of S_{2hi}^2. An estimate of S_{2hi}^2 is

$$s_{2hi}^2 = s_{2hiX}^2 + r^2 s_{2hiY}^2 - 2r s_{2hiXY} \qquad (7.1)$$

with $r = x'/y'$,

$$s_{2hiXY} = \frac{\sum_j^{n'_{hi}}(x_{hij} - \bar{\bar{x}}_{hi})(y_{hij} - \bar{\bar{y}}_{hi})}{n'_{hi} - 1} \qquad (7.2)$$

$$s_{2hiX}^2 = s_{2hiXX} = \frac{\sum_j^{n'_{hi}}(x_{hij} - \bar{\bar{x}}_{hi})^2}{n'_{hi} - 1} \qquad (7.3)$$

and

$$s_{2hiY}^2 = s_{2hiYY} \qquad (7.4)$$

---

* For derivations, see Vol. II, Ch. 7, Sec. 3.

and where $\bar{\bar{x}}_{hi} = \sum\limits_{j}^{n'_{hi}} x_{hij}/n'_{hi}$ and $\bar{\bar{y}}_{hi}$ is similarly defined.

Estimate of S_{1h}^2.   An estimate of S_{1h}^2 is

$$s_{1h}^2 = s_{c'h}^2 - \hat{s}_h^2 \tag{7.5}$$

where

$$s_{c'h}^2 = s_{c'hX}^2 + r^2 s_{c'hY}^2 - 2r s_{c'hXY} \tag{7.6}$$

and

$$s_{c'hXY} = \frac{\sum\limits_{i}^{m'_h}\left(x'_{hi} - \dfrac{\sum\limits_{i}^{m'_h} x'_{hi}}{m'_h}\right)\left(y'_{hi} - \dfrac{\sum\limits_{i}^{m'_h} y'_{hi}}{m_h}\right)}{m'_h - 1} \tag{7.7}$$

with

$$x'_{hi} = \frac{N_{hi}}{n'_{hi}} x_{hi}, \quad y'_{hi} = \frac{N_{hi}}{n'_{hi}} y_{hi} \tag{7.8}$$

and

$$s_{c'hX}^2 = s_{c'hXX}, \qquad s_{c'hY}^2 = s_{c'hYY} \tag{7.9}$$

Note that $s_{c'h}^2$ and $s_{c'hXY}$ are also given by Eq. 6.2 and 6.5, respectively, if it is recognized that x'_{hi} and y'_{hi} are defined by Eq. 7.8 instead of by Eq. 6.4. The estimated total, x_{hi} in Eq. 6.4, is based on the originally selected n_{hi} units, while Eq. 7.8 is based on the n'_{hi} subsampled units. Finally, $\hat{s}_h^2$ in Eq. 7.5

$$\hat{s}_h^2 = \frac{\sum\limits_{i}^{m'_h} \dfrac{N_{hi}^2}{n'_{hi}} \dfrac{N_{hi} - n'_{hi}}{N_{hi}} s_{2hi}^2}{m'_h} \tag{7.10}$$

An estimate of the first-stage contribution to the rel-variance with varying sampling fractions is obtained simply by substituting estimates of S_{1h}^2 and X^2 in the first term of Eq. 5.3. An estimate of X^2 is x'^2 (Eq. 5.2), and an estimate of S_{1h}^2 is s_{1h}^2 (Eq. 7.5).

An estimate of the second-stage contribution to the rel-variance is

$$\frac{1}{x'^2} \sum\limits_{h}^{L} \frac{M_h^2}{m_h} \hat{s}_h^2 \tag{7.11}$$

where here

$$\hat{s}_h^2 = \frac{\sum\limits_{i}^{m'_h} \dfrac{N_{hi}^2}{n_{hi}} \dfrac{N_{hi} - n_{hi}}{N_{hi}} s_{2hi}^2}{m'_h} \tag{7.12}$$

with s_{2hi}^2 given by Eq. 7.1. Note that $\hat{s}_h^2$ in Eq. 7.12 is equal to $\hat{s}_h^2$ in Eq. 7.10 with $n'_{hi} = n_{hi}$.

The estimate of the components of Eq. 5.14. With the simplification that $n_{hi}/N_{hi} = f_{2h}$, a simple estimate of the second-stage contribution to the rel-variance is possible. The second-stage contribution to the rel-variance is given by the second term in the right-hand member of Eq. 5.14. An estimate of the second-stage contribution is obtained by substituting in that term s_{2h}^2 for S_{2h}^2 and x' for X, where

$$s_{2h}^2 = \frac{\sum_{i}^{m'_h} n'_{hi} s_{2hi}^2}{m'_h \bar{n}'_h} \tag{7.13}$$

and where s_{2hi}^2 is given by Eq. 7.2 provided also that the n'_{hi} are proportionate to the $\bar{n}'_h$, i.e., that $n'_{hi}/\bar{n}'_h = n_{hi}/\bar{n}_h$. An estimate of the between-psu component of the rel-variance is, as before, given by substituting x'^2 for X^2 and s_{1h}^2 from Eq. 7.5 for S_{1h}^2 in Eq. 5.14.

8. Optimum design with two-stage sampling, a simple cost function, and a uniform over-all sampling fraction. It is sometimes desirable to depart from uniform sampling fractions for selecting first-stage units, but still maintain uniform over-all sampling fractions. The optimum values for the sampling fractions under these circumstances are given in Ch. 8, Sec. 12, and probably the usual application of this theory will be for the special case discussed in Chapter 8.

The equations for optimum design given there are more generally applicable to any case of two-stage sampling where the first-stage sampling fractions vary between strata, and also the second-stage sampling fractions, but such that the over-all fraction is uniform for all strata.

For this more general application, assume that the cost equation is

$$C = \sum_{h}^{L} C_{1h} m_h + C_2 \sum_{h}^{L} m_h \bar{n}_h$$

where C_{1h} is the fixed cost per primary unit in the hth stratum, and C_2 is the cost associated with each listing unit in the sample. Then the optimum value of the sampling fractions are given by the equations in Sec. 12, Ch. 8, by the substitution of $C_{1h} = C'_1 + C''_1 \bar{N}_h$.

The conditions under which a uniform over-all sampling fraction will be optimum are given in Ch. 9, Sec. 6.

9. Optimum design with two-stage sampling, a simple cost function, and variable over-all sampling fractions. Sometimes substantial gains can be achieved by appropriate division of the population into strata and by using over-all sampling fractions that vary between the strata.

As an illustration of a problem where this procedure would be desirable, suppose that it is desired to obtain an estimate of the number and

Table 1. Advance estimate for the Jewish population in a city

Stratum	No. of blocks M_h	No. of families N_h	No. of Jewish families Y_h	No. of Jewish families having specified characteristic X_h	B_{hX}^2	B_{hY}^2	B_{hXY}	B_h^2	W_{hX}^2	W_{hY}^2	W_{hXY}	W_h^2	C_{1h}	C_{2h}
1	600	30,000	10,000	2,000	1	.2	.1	1	14	1.8	2.4	11	4.5	.8
2	2,000	80,000	3,000	800	7	5	4	4	95	22	13	91	4.0	.25
3	5,000	200,000	2,000	500	40	33	32	9	350	80	78	274	4.0	.2
Totals	7,600	310,000	15,000	3,300										

characteristics of the Jewish population (assuming that a workable definition of members of the Jewish population is available), or of some other
ethnic or nationality group, in a city.   The problem may be to estimate the
proportion of Jewish population in a particular age group, the proportion
working, the average income of Jewish families, or some other characteristic, as well, perhaps, as the total Jewish population and the total number
of Jewish persons having various characteristics.   Let us suppose, for
example, that we have been able to identify the blocks of the area on a
city-block map into strata that represent rough groupings of individual
blocks according to the speculated proportions of the population that are
Jewish.   Suppose, for illustration, the results of this stratification are as
indicated in Table 1.

With such a high proportion of the Jewish families in areas of the city
that can be identified approximately in advance, one should not sample
proportionately from all these strata but should draw proportionately
higher sampling fractions in the strata where Jews constitute a higher proportion and, therefore, can be identified and included in the sample at a
lower cost.   Let us now proceed to obtain a guide to optimum design
for such a sampling problem.

We shall for the present assume that travel costs are not large relative
to other costs, and that we can approximate well enough the total cost of
carrying out the survey by a simple cost function of the following form
(where C represents the total cost, excluding fixed overhead costs):

$$C = \sum_h^L C_{1h} m_h + \sum_h^L C_{2h} m_h \bar{n}_h \qquad (9.1)$$

The advance speculated unit costs are also included in Table 1.   The
values for C_{1h} were computed by taking $1 + (1 + .05\bar{N}_h)$, where 1 is in
this instance assumed to be the fixed cost per block other than listing
costs, and $1 + .05\bar{N}_h$ represents the listing cost for a block of size $\bar{N}_h$ in
the hth stratum.   The advance speculated values of C_{2h} were obtained by
assuming that the cost per listing unit for non-Jewish households is 20
cents, and the cost for Jewish households is $2.00, including both inter-
viewing and tabulating costs.   A form of sample estimate to be used
ordinarily in such a problem is given by Eq. 5.13, and the rel-variance of
this estimate is given by Eq. 5.14.

With the variance and cost functions just specified the optimum values
of the $\bar{n}_h$ and m_h are given by*

$$\text{opt. } \bar{n}_h = \bar{N}_h \sqrt{\frac{C_{1h} S_{2h}^2}{C_{2h}(S_{1h}^2 - \bar{N}_h S_{2h}^2)}} = \sqrt{\frac{W_h^2}{B_h^2 - W_h^2/\bar{N}_h} \frac{C_{1h}}{C_{2h}}} \qquad (9.2)$$

---

* For proof, see Vol. II, Ch. 7, Sec. 6.

and

$$\text{opt. } m_h = \frac{CX_h W_h / \bar{n}_h \sqrt{C_{2h}}}{\sum_h^L (C_{1h} + C_{2h}\bar{n}_h) X_h W_h / \bar{n}_h \sqrt{C_{2h}}}$$

$$= \frac{CN_h S_{2h} / \bar{n}_h \sqrt{C_{2h}}}{\sum_h^L (C_{1h} + C_{2h}\bar{n}_h) N_h S_{2h} / \bar{n}_h \sqrt{C_{2h}}} \tag{9.3}$$

where S_{1h}^2 is given by Eq. 5.4, S_{2h}^2 is given by Eq. 5.15, and the additional terms needed are defined for Eq. 5.14. An estimate of S_{1h}^2 is given by Eq. 7.5 and of S_{2h}^2 by Eq. 7.13.

Exercise 9.1. (*a*) Compute the optimum allocation for the illustration, Table 1 above, in order to estimate X/Y; (*b*) compute the variance for the optimum allocation; (*c*) also compute the variance for proportionate stratified sampling; (*d*) ascertain the relative gain by optimum allocation. Assume a fixed total budget of $20,000.

10. Optimum design with joint use of one- and two-stage sampling, a simple cost function, and variable sampling fractions. It was indicated in Sec. 22, Ch. 6, that one-stage sampling is not a special case of two-stage sampling so far as the optimum is concerned, i.e., the fact that the optimum with a cost function for two-stage sampling yields opt. $m_h < M_h$, or opt. $\bar{n}_h < \bar{N}_h$ is not sufficient to indicate that a single-stage sample design would necessarily be less efficient. In instances where opt. m_h is a substantial proportion of M_h, or opt. $\bar{n}_h$ is a substantial proportion of $\bar{N}_h$ (say approaching a third or a half in either case), one should examine the cost function and decide whether the modifications that would be involved if one-stage sampling were used (with whole clusters as the sampling units when opt. $\bar{n}_h$ is a substantial part of $\bar{N}_h$, and with listing units as the sampling units when opt. m_h is a substantial part of M_h) would be sufficient so that a single-stage sampling plan would be more efficient than the optimum two-stage sampling plan.

Such considerations may point to the use of one-stage sampling in certain strata and two-stage sampling in others. This type of design is often involved, also, when some part of the population is sampled from a list and two-stage or a combination of one- and two-stage sampling is used for the remaining strata.

A simple cost function that provides explicitly for some strata with one-stage sampling, and some with two-stage, is

$$C = \sum_h^{L_2} m_h C_{1h} + \sum_h^{L_2} m_h \bar{n}_h C_{2h} + \sum_k^{L_1} m_k C_k' \tag{10.1}$$

where C, as usual, represents the total cost, excluding fixed costs that are not affected by the sampling fraction taken from each of the strata; the first two terms in the cost function are as defined in the preceding sections and relate to the L_2 strata for which two-stage sampling is used; the final term relates to the L_1 strata for which a single-stage sample is used. The m_k is the total number of units (whether they be clusters or elementary units) in the sample from the kth stratum in which a single-stage sample is used, and C'_k is the cost per unit included in the sample from that stratum.

With the estimate given by Eq. 5.13, the cost function given by Eq. 10.1, and the rel-variance given by Eq. 5.14 [but with $1 - (\bar{n}_h/\bar{N}_h) = 0$ for the strata for which a single-stage sample is used], the optimum values are:*

$$\text{opt. } m_k = \frac{M_k S_k}{\sqrt{C'_k}} a \tag{10.2}$$

$$\text{opt. } m_h = M_h \frac{\sqrt{S_{1h}^2 - \bar{N}_h S_{2h}^2}}{\sqrt{C_{1h}}} a \tag{10.3}$$

$$\text{opt. } \bar{n}_h = \bar{N}_h \sqrt{\frac{S_{2h}^2}{S_{1h}^2 - \bar{N}_h S_{2h}^2} \frac{C_{1h}}{C_{2h}}} \tag{10.4}$$

$$a = \frac{C}{\sum\limits_{h}^{L_2} M_h \sqrt{C_{1h}} \sqrt{S_{1h}^2 - \bar{N}_h S_{2h}^2} + \sum\limits_{h}^{L_2} N_h S_{2h} \sqrt{C_{2h}} + \sum\limits_{k}^{L_1} M_k S_k \sqrt{C'_k}} \tag{10.5}$$

where S_{1h}^2 and S_k^2 are given by Eq. 5.4, and S_{2h}^2 is given by Eq. 5.15.

Joint sampling from a list and one- or two-stage area sampling. An interesting and useful case for the application of the theory presented in this section is the situation where one is drawing a sample from a population that is a subgroup of a larger population, and has a partial list of addresses of members of the subpopulation. An illustration is the problem of sampling the Jewish population discussed in the preceding section, or some other subgroup of a larger population. Thus, one might find that local Jewish organizations have a partial list of Jewish families in the area, and that the list includes the addresses at which Jews are presumed to live. Such a list need not be completely up to date; it still will provide a guide to the location of a substantial proportion of Jews in the community.

One might then proceed to sample by drawing from the list a sample of addresses where Jews are presumed to live, and collect the desired information from any Jews living at those addresses. The list constitutes a stratum. In addition, a sample of areas is drawn to pick up a sample

---

* For proof, see Vol. II, Ch. 7, Sec. 8.

of Jews in the stratum of those not residing at addresses on the list.   One-
or more stage sampling may be used for this latter stratum.

The general theory in this section is immediately applicable.

The value of a list in such a situation is illustrated in a simple case by
Table 2, which shows the reduction in variance for a given total cost
where:

(a) A list is available covering the indicated proportion, P_1, of the
subpopulation.

(b) The subpopulation is the indicated proportion, P_2, of the total
population.

(c) The sample is drawn by:
(i) Identifying two strata: the list population and the remaining
population.
(ii) Making optimum allocation of the sample to the two strata.

(d) It costs 4 times as much to include a member of the subpopulation
in the sample as to include other cases, whether selected from the
list stratum or from the stratum of the remaining population.

(e) The rel-variance of a member of the subpopulation is $V^2 = 1$, and
the mean of the subpopulation is the same, whether from the list
stratum or from the remaining population.

Note that for the simplified case represented by Table 2 all the sampling
is one-stage, and cluster sampling is not involved.   The table is indicative,
however, of possible gains in more complex problems.   The reader may
wish to verify some of the numbers in Table 2 as an exercise.

Table 2.   Values of σ_l^2/σ^2

(Where σ^2 is the variance of the estimated total number of members
of the subpopulation when simple random sampling from the total
population is used; σ_l^2 is the variance of the same estimate when the
available list is used and optimum allocation of the sample is made to
the list sample and to the remaining population; and where the cost
is $C = C_1 n_1 + C_2 n_2$, where C_1 is the per unit cost of those on the list
and C_2 is the per unit cost of those not on the list.)

Proportion of subpopulation to total cases (P_2)	Proportion of subpopulation on the list (P_1)			
	.3	.5	.8	.98
.01	.76	.59	.31	.076
.10	.85	.74	.52	.27
.20	.88	.79	.61	.39
.50	.94	.89	.78	.63
.90	.996	.99	.97	.92

11. Optimum design with two-stage sampling, more complicated cost functions, and variable sampling fractions. With more complicated cost functions, it is difficult to get explicit solutions, but we can with several successive steps obtain a satisfactory approximation to the optimum design. It is sometimes desirable to recognize only 2–4 different classes of strata in which there are different over-all sampling fractions.

The usual additional complication is to introduce into the cost function terms involving $\sqrt{m}$ or $\sqrt{m_h}$. Where such terms are involved the steps below can be followed to obtain the optimum.*

Case I. Suppose that the cost function is of the form

$$C = C_0\sqrt{m} + \sum_h^L C_{1h}m_h + \sum_h^L C_{2h}m_h\bar{n}_h \tag{11.1}$$

The rel-variance is given, again, by Eq. 5.14.

The optimum values for the $\bar{n}_h$ and m_h are computed by use of the following equations:

$$a_h = \frac{\dfrac{M_h}{X}\sqrt{S_{1h}^2 - \bar{N}_h S_{2h}^2}}{\sqrt{d + C_{1h}}} = \frac{\dfrac{X_h}{X}\sqrt{B_h^2 - \dfrac{W_h^2}{\bar{N}_h}}}{\sqrt{d + C_{1h}}} \tag{11.2}$$

$$b = \frac{\displaystyle\sum_h^L C_{1h}a_h + \sum_h^L \frac{N_h S_{2h}}{X}\sqrt{C_{2h}}}{\displaystyle\sum_h^L a_h} = \frac{\displaystyle\sum_h^L C_{1h}a_h + \sum_h^L \frac{X_h}{X}W_h\sqrt{C_{2h}}}{\displaystyle\sum_h^L a_h} \tag{11.3}$$

$$d = \frac{C_0}{2\sqrt{m}} = \frac{b}{\sqrt{1 + \dfrac{4C}{C_0^2}b} - 1} \tag{11.4}$$

$$\text{opt. } \bar{n}_h = \frac{N_h S_{2h}}{Xa_h\sqrt{C_{2h}}} = \frac{X_h W_h}{Xa_h\sqrt{C_{2h}}} \tag{11.5}$$

$$\text{opt. } m_h = \frac{C_0^2 a_h}{4d^2\displaystyle\sum_h^L a_h} \tag{11.6}$$

where the terms are as defined in connection with Eq. 5.14 and the above cost function, Eq. 11.1.

The steps to follow are similar to those described in arriving at the optimum values by successive approximations in Sec. 18, Ch. 6 (where uniform sampling fractions were involved). The first step is to obtain

---

* For development of these formulas, see Vol. II, Ch. 7, Sec. 7.

approximate values for all the terms in Eq. 11.2, 11.3, and 11.4, except, of course, for a_h, b, and d. We assume, next, an initial guessed value for d; and, although it is not important what initial value is assumed, let us, as a simple starting point, assume that d (guessed) $= 1$. This is substituted into Eq. 11.2, to obtain initial values for the a_h. Then successive values of the a_h, b, and d are computed until two successive sets agree, say within 2 per cent, for each of the three values. After this process of successive approximation is completed and two successive sets of these values agree, we substitute the last set of a_h and the d computed in Eq. 11.5 and 11.6 to obtain optimum values of $\bar{n}_h$ and m_h. It should be noted that Eq. 11.5 can be restated in another way that appears more familiar in relation to earlier results as follows:

$$
\begin{aligned}
\text{opt. } \bar{n}_h &= \bar{N}_h \sqrt{\frac{S_{2h}^2}{S_{1h}^2 - \bar{N}_h S_{2h}^2} \frac{(C_0/2\sqrt{m}) + C_{1h}}{C_{2h}}} \\
&= \sqrt{\frac{W_h^2}{B_h^2 - W_h^2/\bar{N}_h} \frac{(C_0/2\sqrt{m}) + C_{1h}}{C_{2h}}}
\end{aligned}
\tag{11.7}
$$

Case II.   Suppose, now, that the cost function is of the form:

$$
C = \sum^L C_{0h}\sqrt{m_h} + \sum^L C_{1h}m_h + \sum^L C_{2h}m_h\bar{n}_h
$$

The variance is given, again, by Eq. 5.14, and the optimum values for the $\bar{n}_h$ and m_h are now computed by the use of the following equations:

$$
a_h = \frac{\dfrac{M_h}{X}\sqrt{S_{1h}^2 - \bar{N}_h S_{2h}^2}}{\sqrt{d_h + C_{1h}}} = \frac{\dfrac{X_h}{X}\sqrt{B_h^2 - W_h^2/\bar{N}_h}}{\sqrt{d_h + C_{1h}}}
\tag{11.8}
$$

$$
d_h = \frac{\cdot C_{0h}}{2\sqrt{m_h}}
$$

$$
= \frac{\left(\sum^L C_{1h}a_h + \sum^L \dfrac{N_h S_{2h}}{X}\sqrt{C_{2h}}\right)C_{0h}/\sqrt{a_h}}{\sqrt{\left(\sum^L C_{0h}\sqrt{a_h}\right)^2 + 4C\left(\sum^L C_{1h}a_h + \sum^L \dfrac{N_h S_{2h}}{X}\sqrt{C_{2h}}\right)} - \sum^L C_{0h}\sqrt{a_h}}
\tag{11.9}
$$

$$
= \frac{\left(\sum^L C_{1h}a_h + \sum^L \dfrac{X_h}{X}W_h\sqrt{C_{2h}}\right)C_{0h}/\sqrt{a_h}}{\sqrt{\left(\sum^L C_{0h}\sqrt{a_h}\right)^2 + 4C\left(\sum^L C_{1h}a_h + \sum^L \dfrac{X_h}{X}W_h\sqrt{C_{2h}}\right)} - \sum^L C_{0h}\sqrt{a_h}}
$$

$$\text{opt. } m_h = \frac{C_{0h}^2}{4d_h^2} \tag{11.10}$$

$$\text{opt. } \bar{n}_h = \frac{N_h S_{2h}}{X a_h \sqrt{C_{2h}}} = \bar{N}_h \sqrt{\frac{S_{2h}^2}{S_{1h}^2 - \bar{N}_h S_{2h}^2} \cdot \frac{(C_{0h}/2\sqrt{m_h}) + C_{1h}}{C_{2h}}}$$

$$\tag{11.11}$$

$$= \frac{X_h W_h}{X a_h \sqrt{C_{2h}}} = \sqrt{\frac{W_h^2}{B_h^2 - W_h^2/\bar{N}_h} \cdot \frac{(C_{0h}/2\sqrt{m_h}) + C_{1h}}{C_{2h}}}$$

The optimum is computed in the same manner as for Case I, by successive approximations, but beginning with a set of assumed values for the d_h. It will be convenient to assume $d_h = 1$, for each of the d_h's, as the first step in the solution, and to solve for the a_h's and then proceed with successive values of a_h and d_h until two successive sets of values are essentially the same (say within 2 per cent of each other for the corresponding items in the two sets). When the successive approximations have been completed and final values for the a_h and d_h obtained, the last step is to compute the opt. m_h and opt. $\bar{n}_h$ by substituting the final values from the preceding steps into Eq. 11.10 and 11.11.

Exercises

11.1. Suppose that we assume the following values for a very simple problem with only two strata, and with the M_h large:

Stratum h	$\dfrac{X_h}{X}$	B_h^2	W_h^2	$\bar{N}_h$	C_{0h}	C_{1h}	C_{2h}
1	.1	.30	1	100	1	7	1
2	.9	.06	1	20	2	3	1

Set up the computations systematically and compute the optimum allocation and the rel-variance for the optimum, assuming a fixed total budget of $10,000.

11.2. Show how Eq. 5.3 and 5.14 can be simplified when Y_{hi} is the number of elementary units having a characteristic, X_{hi} is the number of these that have a second characteristic, and the elementary unit is the listing unit.

11.3. For the population defined in Table 3 compute the optimum sample design to estimate X/Y from a sample, and compute the variance for the optimum and compare it with proportional stratified sampling.

Table 3.   Hypothetical values of N_{hi}, X_{hi}, and Y_{hi}

h	i	N_{hi}	X_{hi}	Y_{hi}
1	1	50	3	20
	2	20	0	12
	3	80	0	25
	4	40	4	10
	5	100	10	25
	6	10	3	8
2	1	50	4	10
	2	70	0	10
	3	20	1	5
	4	60	3	5
	5–20	600	0	0
3	1	40	0	5
	2	90	4	20
	3	20	1	5
	4	50	5	10
	5–100	3800	0	0

Assume that the cost function is the same as for Ex. 9.1 (see Table 1 of Sec. 9) above, that a total budget of $20,000 is available, that the elementary unit is the listing unit, that Y_{hi} is the number of elementary units that have a characteristic, and that X_{hi} is the number of these that have a second characteristic.

12. Three- or more stage sampling.   For a large number of problems involving small clusters, the theory given earlier on two-stage sampling is all that is needed.   There are some practical problems, such as in marketing or opinion surveys, where there may be need for theory involving more than two stages of sampling, even with small psu's.   A general treatment of multi-stage sampling is given in Chapter 9.   Although the treatment in that chapter, as in this section, is equally applicable to both large-psu problems or small-psu problems, the major emphasis in Chapter 9 is on the large-psu problem, with variable probabilities of selecting psu's within strata.   The emphasis in this section will be on the theory involved in multi-stage sampling with small psu's with equal probabilities of selection within strata.

Let us assume that the psu's are classified into L strata, with M_h psu's (first-stage units) in the hth stratum and m_h psu's in the sample from the hth stratum.   Let N_{hi} and n_{hi} be the population and sample numbers, respectively, of second-stage units in the hith psu, and Q_{hij} and q_{hij} the population and sample numbers of third-stage units in the hijth second-stage unit.

The estimate.   The estimate of $R = X/Y$ is

$$r = \frac{x'}{y'} \qquad (12.1$$

where

$$x' = \sum_h^L \frac{M_h}{m_h} x_h' = \sum_h^L \frac{M_h}{m_h} \sum_i^{m_h} \frac{N_{hi}}{n_{hi}} x_{hi}'$$

$$= \sum_h^L \frac{M_h}{m_h} \sum_i^{m_h} \frac{N_{hi}}{n_{hi}} \sum_j^{n_{hi}} \frac{Q_{hij}}{q_{hij}} x_{hij} \qquad (12.2)$$

where x_{hij} is the sample aggregate for the *hij*th second-stage unit, and y' is given by Eq. 12.2 if we substitute y for x in that equation.

The rel-variance of r.   The rel-variance of r is*

$$V_r^2 = \text{Eq. 5.3} + \frac{1}{X^2} \sum_h^L \frac{M_h}{m_h} \sum_i^{M_h} \frac{N_{hi}}{n_{hi}} \sum_j^{N_{hi}} \frac{Q_{hij}^2}{q_{hij}} \frac{Q_{hij} - q_{hij}}{Q_{hij}} S_{3hij}^2 \qquad (12.3)$$

where

$$S_{3hij}^2 = S_{3hijX}^2 + R^2 S_{3hijY}^2 - 2RS_{3hijXY} \qquad (12.4)$$

and

$$S_{3hijX}^2 = \frac{\sum_k^{Q_{hij}} (X_{hijk} - \bar{\bar{X}}_{hij})^2}{Q_{hij} - 1} \qquad (12.5)$$

with $\bar{\bar{X}}_{hij} = X_{hij}/Q_{hij}$.

S_{3hijY}^2 is similarly defined for the Y's, and

$$S_{3hijXY} = \frac{\sum_k^{Q_{hij}} (X_{hijk} - \bar{\bar{X}}_{hij})(Y_{hijk} - \bar{\bar{Y}}_{hij})}{Q_{hij} - 1} \qquad (12.6)$$

Extension to more than three stages of sampling.   The extension to any number of stages of sampling for both the estimate and the rel-variance can be inferred from Eq. 12.2 and 12.3.   Note that V_r^2 for, say, a four-stage sampling design will simply be Eq. 12.3 plus a term representing the contribution to the variance from the fourth stage of sampling.

Estimates of the total variance.   The estimate of the total variance for a three- or more stage sampling design is given by Eq. 6.1, where x_{hi}' is, again, an unbiased estimate of the *hi*th psu total.   Thus, for a three-stage design

$$x_{hi}' = \frac{N_{hi}}{n_{hi}} \sum_j^{n_{hi}} \frac{Q_{hij}}{q_{hij}} x_{hij} \qquad (12.7)$$

---

* For proof, see Vol. II, Ch. 7, Sec. 4.

when the sample is self-weighting within strata, i.e.,

$$\frac{n_{hi}}{N_{hi}} \frac{q_{hij}}{Q_{hij}} = f_{2h} \qquad (12.8)$$

then

$$x'_{hi} = \frac{1}{f_{2h}} x_{hi} \qquad (12.9)$$

Application to a marketing or opinion poll problem. In problems in marketing or opinion research, it is sometimes important to enumerate only one person per household. This restriction is often imposed because of the possibility that conditioning might bias the results of the survey, if more than one member of the household were interviewed. It is sometimes imposed because of a belief that more information may be obtained by spreading the sample to as many different households as possible.

In such designs, usually, one stratifies the psu's (e.g., blocks of a city), draws a sample of blocks from each stratum with equal probability (perhaps varying the first-stage sampling fractions as between strata), lists the blocks, selects a sample of households from the selected blocks, and draws one person per household from the selected households. As was pointed out earlier, recognition of the varying probabilities of selection must be taken into account in making estimates from the sample. Equation 12.1 provides the appropriate weights.

The estimate of any proportion or ratio from this system of sampling is given by Eq. 12.1, where q_{hij} is 1 for all households. The sample is often selected so that $n_{hi}/N_{hi} \doteq f_{2h}$, i.e., the second-stage sampling fractions are the same for all psu's within a stratum. Moreover, the selection frequently is so made that the product of the first- and second-stage sampling fractions for a stratum is the same for all strata. In this special case, the estimating procedure can be simplified over what is implied in Eq. 12.1. The households to be sampled can be classified by size (determined in terms of persons eligible for the survey). For any class, the estimate of X_c for the cth size class is given by $x_c(N_c/f)$, where f is the product of the first- and second-stage sampling fractions and N_c is the size of household. The value x_c is the aggregate value in the sample of the X characteristic for the cth size class of household. Such estimates are computed for each size class and summed to determine x'. A similar technique can be employed for calculating an estimate of another variable y', and $x'/y' = r$ would then be the estimate of R. The rel-variance of r is given by Eq. 12.3.

REFERENCES

(1) W. G. Cochran, "The Use of Analysis of Variance in Enumeration by Sampling," *J. Amer. Stat. Assn.*, **34** (1939), 492–510.

(2) R. J. Jessen, "Statistical Investigation of a Sample Survey for Obtaining Farm Facts," *Iowa Agr. Exp. Stat. Res. Bull.* 304, 1942.

(3) F. Yates, *Sampling Methods for Censuses and Surveys*, Charles Griffin and Company, London, 1949.

CHAPTER 8

Control of Variation in Size of Cluster in Estimating Totals, Averages, or Ratios

1. When control of variation in size of cluster is important. The variation in size of clusters may have a serious effect on the variance of the estimates of totals. On the other hand, moderate variation in size usually has a relatively small effect on the variance of estimates of averages or ratios.

The contribution of variation in size of psu to the sampling variance (Eq. 8.6, Ch. 6) is reflected in the term $\hat{V}^2/V^2$ and also in the value of δ. An increase in the variance resulting from the variation in size of psu occurs whenever $\hat{V}^2/V^2$ is greater than 1. This term ordinarily will be greater than 1,* but often will be not much greater than 1 in estimating ratios or averages. On the other hand $\hat{V}^2/V^2$ may be substantially greater than 1 for estimating totals unless special precautions are taken. The controls and precautions to be taken for estimating totals are dealt with in Part A (Sec. 2–10). In addition to indicating how the controls can be relaxed for estimating ratios, Part B (Sec. 11–14) describes how optimum allocation of the sample to strata based on size of psu can be approximated, and compares this procedure with selecting psu's with varying probabilities.

A. CONTROL OF VARIATION IN SIZE OF CLUSTER FOR ESTIMATING TOTALS

2. Control of variation in size of cluster important in estimating totals. If we want to estimate an aggregate of some characteristic from a sample, such as the total quantity or value of an agricultural product, the total sales or total inventory of retail stores, the total number of people or total dwelling units in an area, the total family income, and similar population aggregates, the control of variation in the size of cluster (in addition to special sampling of unusually large elementary units when

---

* For proof, see Vol. II, Ch. 8, Sec. 4.

the characteristic is highly skewed) may take on a much more important role than when estimating an average, percentage, or other ratio from a sample. For estimating an aggregate we shall often need a sample especially designed to control the variation in size of the psu. Such a sample designed for estimating totals will also be good for estimating averages, although perhaps less efficient in that, if only the averages or ratios were to be estimated, a lower cost sample could be designed that would yield results of the same precision.

We shall illustrate how variability in size of sampling unit affects the sampling variance of a simple unbiased estimate of a total and then investigate various methods of reducing the effect of variation in size of psu on the variance.

3. Earlier theory applicable. A simple unbiased estimate of a total is given by

$$x' = \sum^{L} \frac{1}{f_h} x_h \qquad (3.1)$$

and with a uniform over-all sampling fraction this becomes

$$x' = \frac{1}{f} x \qquad (3.2)$$

where f_h is the over-all sampling fraction in the hth stratum, and x_h is the sample aggregate of the characteristic for the hth stratum. With a uniform over-all sampling fraction, f and x are similarly defined for the total population.

The rel-variance of x' is given by Eq. 5.3, Ch. 7, but with terms involving the Y characteristic dropped out so that

$$S_{1h}^2 = S_{1hX}^2 \qquad (3.3)$$

and

$$S_{2hi}^2 = S_{2hiX}^2 \qquad (3.4)$$

Similarly, the estimate of the rel-variance is given by $s_{x'}^2/x'^2$, from Eq. 6.1, Ch. 7, with terms involving Y dropped out. Corresponding formulas in Chapter 6 are applicable when there is no stratification.

Thus it is seen that the estimation of totals is covered by the theory already given. There are some special considerations that need attention. We shall discuss the special aspects of estimating totals from a simple one- or two-stage cluster sample or from a stratified sample with a uniform over-all sampling fraction. The same type of considerations will be involved when the over-all sampling fractions are variable.

4. Contribution of variation in size of cluster to sampling variance.* Let us consider for simplicity a two-stage sampling design without stratification. The rel-variance of an estimated total with a uniform over-all sampling fraction is given by Eq. 6.4, Ch. 6, and this equation can be stated in the following form, which may be useful in arriving at an efficient sample design:

$$V_{x'}^2 \doteq V_r^2 + V_n^2 + 2\rho_{rn}V_rV_n \tag{4.1}$$

where n is the total number of listing units in the sample, x is the total of the characteristic for the units in the sample, $r = x/n$, and ρ_{rn} is the coefficient of correlation between r and n. If we ignore the finite multiplier, then from Eq. 8.6, Ch. 6,

$$V_r^2 \doteq \frac{1}{m}\frac{\hat{V}^2}{\bar{n}}[1 + \delta(\bar{n} - 1)] \tag{4.2}$$

is the approximate rel-variance of r.

$$V_n^2 = \frac{1}{m}B_N^2 \tag{4.3}$$

is the direct contribution of the variation in size of the primary units to the rel-variance of x', over and above what would be involved in the rel-variance of r; and

$$\rho_{rn}V_rV_n = V_{rn} \doteq \frac{1}{m}(B_{XN} - B_N^2) \tag{4.4}$$

is the rel-covariance of r and n and may make an additional contribution, arising from the variation in size of the primary units, to the rel-variance of x'.

The $B_N^2 = \overset{M}{\Sigma}(N_i - \bar{N})^2/(M-1)\bar{N}^2$ is defined by Eq. 6.5, Ch. 6, with N_i substituted for X_i, and B_{XN} is defined by Eq. 6.8, Ch. 6, with N_i substituted for Y_i. The δ in Eq. 4.2 is the measure of homogeneity within psu's involved in the variance of r and is given by Eq. 8.11, Ch. 6, but with N_i substituted for Y_i and $N_{ij} = 1$ substituted for Y_{ij}.

It is often, although not necessarily, true that r will be uncorrelated†

---

† One need not assume that n and r are uncorrelated. The value of the rel-covariance from Eq. 4.4 should be added to Eq. 4.5, in making this type of analysis, unless enough work is done to establish the fact that the correlation is small. The correlation will be small when the regression line of X_i on N_i is approximately through the origin, i.e., when $(B_N^2 - B_{XN})$ is small in relation to B_N^2 and B_X^2. For a great many problems this term will be small.

or have a comparatively low correlation with n, so that ρ_{rn} will be close to 0, in which event Eq. 4.1 becomes

$$V_{x'}^2 \doteq \frac{1}{m} \left\{ \frac{\hat{V}^2}{\bar{n}} [1 + \delta(\bar{n} - 1)] + B_N^2 \right\} \tag{4.5}$$

which shows how the variation in size of psu may substantially increase the rel-variance of x' as compared to the rel-variance of the ratio r. The rel-variance will be more than doubled, because of the variation in size of psu, when B_N^2 is larger than $(\hat{V}^2/\bar{n}) [1 + \delta(\bar{n} - 1)]$.

Illustration 4.1.   Assume that we are estimating total persons in an area with $\bar{n} = 3$ and $\bar{N} = 25$.   Here δ is the measure of homogeneity among listing units within blocks of the number of persons per listing unit.   Assume also that the value of δ for the listing units used is approximately equal to .15 (see Table D–2 in Case Study D, Ch. 12) and $\hat{V}$ is approximately equal to .9.   Assume, also, that B_N^2 is approximately equal to 1.   These assumptions correspond reasonably well with the actual facts for this particular characteristic in some surveys that have been carried through.   Then the terms in braces in Eq. 4.5 become

$$[.27(1.3) + 1] = .35 + 1 = 1.35$$

In this instance the coefficient of variation of the ratio of population to dwelling places contributes less than one-third to the total variance, whereas the variation in size of cluster contributes more than two-thirds. These relative contributions will vary from problem to problem, but it is not unusual to find important contributions to the variance from the variation in size of cluster.

Illustration 4.2.   There are important instances in which one would not expect much contribution to the variance due to the variation in size of cluster in making a simple unbiased estimate of a total, even though there is considerable variation in cluster size.   These instances often arise when the aggregate that is being estimated is only a small part of the population. For example, suppose that we were estimating the total number of unemployed in the population, instead of the total population of the area, and suppose that the number of unemployed constituted about, say, 2 per cent of the total population.   Suppose, also, that, with $\bar{N} = 25$, δ for the per cent of the population unemployed is approximately equal to .05 (see Table D–2, Case Study D, Ch. 12) and that $\bar{n} = 3$.   Then the terms in the braces of Eq. 4.5 would be $(\hat{V}^2/3)[1 + .05(2)] + 1$.   We need yet to obtain an approximate value of $\hat{V}^2$.   Now (from the relationships discussed in Sec. 8 of Ch. 6), $\hat{V}^2$ will be at least as large as or larger than $Q/\bar{\bar{N}}P$, where P is the proportion of the population unemployed, $Q = 1 - P$, and $\bar{\bar{N}}$ is the average number of persons per listing unit in the population so that, if $\bar{\bar{N}} = 3.2$, $\hat{V}^2$ is equal to or greater than 15.   If we assume that it is equal to 15, we have $5.5 + 1$ for the terms in the braces of Eq. 4.5, and we see in this instance that the variation in size of cluster has made a comparatively small additional contribution to the variance of the estimate of the total number of unemployed.   (It is still the same absolute contribution.)   The small relative increase due to variation in size of cluster has arisen in this instance because the characteristic being estimated is a very small part of the total population and consequently $\hat{V}^2$ is large.

There are many situations such as that of Illustration 4.1, where the variation in the size of cluster makes an important contribution to the total variance, so important as to require several times as large a sample, in order to achieve a specified coefficient of variation of the estimated total, as is required to achieve the same coefficient of variation for the ratio r.   Consequently, the variance of the estimated total may need to be reduced by some method of controlling the variation in the size of psu. The method of control may involve the definition of a different kind of sampling unit, or perhaps appropriate use of stratification, a change in the method of estimation or in the method of selecting the sample, or some other device.   Some of these will now be examined.

5. Definition of initial sampling units with low variability in size.   An obvious method of reducing the contribution of the variation in size of psu to the variance of a simple unbiased estimate of a total with cluster sampling is to define psu's that have a small amount of variation in size. It should be noted that, if the psu's are about equal in size, B_N^2 is small and consequently will make no significant contribution to the variance. One may have a city directory from which to sample, very detailed maps showing individual residences and addresses, or aerial photographs or other resources such that this procedure may be feasible.   With adequate resources of this type, in fact, one might even avoid cluster sampling of households, and sample individual dwelling places or other similar units at random.   With such resources one might be able at low cost to define psu's of approximately equal size, sample these and subsample, and so achieve a comparatively small increase in the variance due to variation in size of psu.

It is fairly obvious that one should not spend resources in reducing the variation in size below the point where B_N^2 is comparatively small relative to $(\hat{V}^2/\bar{n})[1 + \delta(\bar{n} - 1)]$ for the important totals to be estimated, because then the variation in size of cluster is no longer contributing heavily to the variance and resources can better be spent in other ways.

Primary sampling units of approximately equal size can be defined without detailed maps if one has reasonably satisfactory rough approximations to the measure of size of small areas such as city blocks. One can group small blocks together, or small blocks with large ones, and split large blocks, to form primary sampling units of roughly equal total size before the selection of primary units is made.

Information on size of blocks is often available. In the cities of 50,000 or more population in the United States, for example, the Bureau of the Census has published information on the numbers of dwelling units by blocks. If such information is old, it can be brought up to date by local inquiry about areas of heavy new construction or demolition.

In some cases where data are not available for blocks, it may be worth while to make a special survey to determine approximate measures of size of blocks. Such a "block size survey" is particularly useful in outlying parts of a rapidly growing metropolitan area where the available maps are often not up to date and where, even if blocks are well indicated, no measures of size are available. A survey to determine rough measures of size may be relatively inexpensive and may provide valuable information for the sample selection.

Alternative procedures may be available that will sometimes prove to be simpler and less expensive than those described above. The alternatives should be considered and the best one chosen for the particular problem.

6. Sampling with probability proportionate to size, listing, and subsampling.* Another procedure for controlling variation in size of psu when making a simple unbiased estimate of a total is to sample with probability proportionate to a measure of size (referred to as sampling with probability proportionate to size, or pps). Selection with pps means that, on the average, a psu which is, for example, 5 times as large as another will be in the sample 5 times as frequently as the other psu. It might appear, at first, that this would introduce a bias in the sample result with some psu's over-represented and others under-represented— and it would, in fact, if no special attention were given to the varying probabilities in the estimating or subsampling procedure. To avoid a bias, the estimate of a total, if no subsample is taken, is†

$$x' = \frac{A}{m} \sum_i^m \frac{X_i'}{A_i} \qquad (6.1)$$

---

* Some additional considerations and illustrations of selection with probability proportionate to size are given in Sec. 14 of this chapter and in Chapter 9, including variances and estimates of variances.

† For proof, see Vol. II, Ch. 8, Sec. 1.

where X_i' is the total, A_i is the measure of size of the ith psu in the sample, A is the aggregate measure of size for the population, and the A_i is less than A/m for all i. mA_i/A is in fact the probability of selection of the ith unit in a sample of m, for all units with measures of size A_i less than A/m when sampling without replacement. Thus, an unbiased estimate of X is obtained by multiplying each sample number by the reciprocal of its probability of selection, and adding the results for the units in the sample.

> **Remark.** If some of the psu's have a size greater than A/m, these will come in the sample with certainty when sampling without replacement (such as in the procedure described later in this section). A selection method is sometimes used such that units with somewhat smaller measures of size than A/m may be included with certainty. In any event, whenever the selection method is such that some units are included in the sample with certainty, and the operation of selection with pps is carried out for the remaining units, then Eq. 6.1 is modified so that A is the aggregate measure of size of the units not included with certainty, and m is the number of such units included in the sample. Then the estimate given by Eq. 6.1 (for units not selected with certainty) is added to the aggregate for those units included with certainty.
> Another method of treating units selected with certainty when subsampling is used is indicated later in this section.

Ordinarily, considerations of optimum sampling suggest that it would be inefficient to include all the listing units of a selected psu in the sample and that instead, one should subsample the selected psu's. After selection of primary units with pps the subsampling can be done in such a way that the sample will be self-weighting, i.e., the over-all probability of including a member of the population in the sample is the same for all members of the population. With this type of sampling, instead of having to multiply the sample value for each psu by a different weight as is implied by estimate 6.1, one would be able to use Eq. 3.2 as the estimate. The procedure for doing this is merely to make the subsampling fraction for the ith selected psu equal to fA/mA_i. The expected total sample size by this procedure would be equal to fN, where N is the number of listing units in the population. To illustrate this procedure, let us suppose that we have divided a city into blocks—10 blocks in this case to keep the problem small—as listed in Table 1. In addition to the measure of size for each block, the table shows cumulative totals of the measures of size in column 3.

Steps for choosing sample with pps. A procedure for obtaining a sample of psu's with pps (without replacement) and then subsampling ultimate clusters of about equal size (i.e., equal $\bar{n}$) is as follows:

(a) Specify the primary sampling units to be used. We shall assume, for illustration, that city blocks will be the psu's.

Table 1. **Hypothetical city of 10 blocks, to illustrate selection with probability proportionate to size (pps)**

Block no. (1)	Measure of size (2)	Cumulative measure of size (3)	Sample designation (4)
1	50	50	13.7
2	12	62	
3	20	82	
4	31	113	101.2
5	10	123	
6	100	223	188.7
7	15	238	
8	13	251	
			276.2
9	240	491	363.7
			451.2
10	17	508	

(b) Determine the desired size of ultimate cluster, $\bar{n}$, and the desired over-all sampling fraction, f. (Optimum values for these with a simple cost function can be obtained from Eq. 14.11–14.14 with Y_{hij} set equal to 1. Section 20 of Ch. 6 also provides an approximate guide that may be sufficient for practical purposes.) Let us assume that we have decided for our particular problem that $\bar{n} = 3.5$ is in the neighborhood of the optimum design. Let us call $F = 1/f$ so that f is equal to 1 in F. Suppose that $F = 25$; i.e., a 4 per cent sample is desired.

(c) Compute $I = \bar{n}F$. We will refer to I as the "spacing interval." In this illustration $I = 3.5(25) = 87.5$.

(d) Prepare a table listing each psu in the population, its measure of size, and the cumulative totals of the measures of size (as illustrated in columns 1, 2, and 3 of Table 1).

(e) Choose a random number (using a table of random numbers) between 00.1 and 87.5 (use 3-digit random numbers, with the last digit regarded as after the decimal point). Let us suppose that 13.7 is the random number.

(f) Take this random number as the starting number, and place it in column 4 of the table beside the first cumulative frequency that is as large as or larger than the random number chosen. In this instance, the first number in column 3 is larger than 13.7 and so 13.7 is placed opposite that number, as shown. If the random number chosen had been between 50.1 and 62.0, inclusive, it would have been placed on the same line with the 62.

(g) Add 87.5 to 13.7, and place the resulting sum opposite the first cumulative total in column 3 that is as large as or larger than the result obtained. Thus, $87.5 + 13.7 = 101.2$, and 113 is the first number in column 3 that is as large as or larger than 101.2, so we place the 101.2 in the fourth column on the same line on which the 113 appears.

(h) We repeat this operation successively until the last figure obtained exceeds the last figure in column 3. The results are illustrated in column 4 of Table 1.

(i) The blocks with numbers included beside them in column 4 are in the sample, so that, in the illustration, blocks 1, 4, 6, and 9 are included in the sample. But block 9 has 3 such numbers beside it, and so will, in effect, be in the sample 3 times. This means, as will be seen below, that 3 times as large a subsample will be taken from this block as would have been taken if the block had fallen in the sample only once.

(j) This method of selection is such that each block with a measure of size of less than 87.5 had a chance of being selected proportionate to its "measure of size." Those blocks with measures of size of 87.5 or more were certain of being included in the sample. It should be noted that a measure of size of zero would give a block no chance of being selected. Blocks with zero size must be given a chance of inclusion to avoid bias. There would be no bias if their actual size were zero, but often their actual size is not known. This bias can be avoided by using a method for small blocks such as that indicated later in this section.

(k) Designate the subsampling fraction to be taken from each block. We want to do this in such a way that the sample is self-weighting, i.e., the over-all probability of an element of the population being included in the sample is the same no matter what the size of the block with which it is associated. Consequently, a block that had a large chance of being selected will have a corresponding small subsampling fraction. Thus, if the measure of size of the ith block is designated by A_i, the chance that block had of being in the sample, by the procedure used for selecting blocks, is A_i/I [provided $A_i < (A/m)$]. In instances where A_i/I exceeds 1 but is less than 2, the block is certain of being designated for inclusion in the sample once, and $(A_i/I) - 1$ is the chance that it will be designated twice. Each additional whole integer in the ratio A_i/I adds one more time the psu is certain to be designated for inclusion in the sample. Thus, if $A_i/I = 3.6$, that particular block is certain of being designated 3 times, and has a probability of .6 of being designated a fourth time.

For blocks designated only once, the subsampling fraction will be $\bar{n}/A_i$. For those selected twice, it will be $2\bar{n}/A_i$; and for those selected 6 times, it will be $6\bar{n}/A_i$. Thus, for block 1 the subsampling fraction will be 3.5/50 or 1 in 14.3. For block 9, which is in the sample 3 times, the subsampling fraction will be $(3 \times 3.5)/240 = .044$ or 1 in 22.9.

Where one block falls in the sample more than once, it is convenient, for purposes of computing the variance of the sample estimates, to identify the subsample into random subgroups and treat these as separate segments. Thus, block 9 above fell in the sample 3 times, and we took a subsampling fraction 3 times as large as would have been taken had the block fallen in the sample only once.　Now, once the subsample is obtained by choosing every kth listing from the primary unit, it will be desirable for purposes of estimating variances from the sample to divide the subsample into 3 separate random subsamples to be treated as separate ultimate clusters in estimating the variance of sample estimates.

(l) The appropriate subsampling rates are applied to each psu by listing all the listing units in the designated blocks and subsampling with the designated fraction, beginning with a random start each time.　Thus, to take 1 in 10.8 from a block one chooses a number at random between 00.1 and 10.8 (using 3-digit random numbers), adds 10.8 successively to the selected starting number, and takes the listing units assigned the serial numbers equal to or immediately above these numbers.　For example, if the random number selected is 1.4, then the units with serial numbers 2, 13, 23, etc., are included in the sample.

Exercises

6.1. Suppose that the 10 blocks in the illustration above are found to have the following characteristics:

BLOCK	No. OF HOUSEHOLDS	No. OF PERSONS	MALES IN LABOR FORCE
1	55	165	60
2	15	40	10
3.	20	75	30
4	40	100	35
5	10	50	15
6	120	250	120
7	30	50	20
8	20	60	15
9	250	500	200
10	15	70	15

Using a table of random numbers to determine the starting number, select a sample of blocks with pps in accordance with the procedure of this section, on the assumption that a sample of households is to be drawn with an over-all sampling fraction of 1 in 30, and an ultimate cluster size of 4 households. Estimate the total number of (*a*) households, (*b*) persons, and (*c*) males in the labor force from the sample psu totals.　(See Eq. 6.1 for estimating totals.)

6.2. Using a different random number, select another sample in the same way as in Ex. 6.1.　Estimate the same totals, and compare the results.

Measure of size may vary from actual size. The reader should note that, if the measure of size of a psu is equal to the actual number of listing units in the psu, then the number subsampled (with an average expected number of 3.5) will be either 3 or 4 from the psu. But if the number of listing units actually found in each block, when the block is listed, varies widely from the measure of size of the block, the number obtained in the subsample will vary widely between blocks. Thus, suppose that the measure of size of a block is 40 dwelling units, but the block turns out actually to have 300. The subsampling fraction of 3.5/40 from the block will yield either 26 or 27 units instead of 3.5. Or, on the other hand, if the block is totally vacant then no units will be found. This variation in actual size from the advance measure of size will in no way bias the sample. Once the measure of size has been assigned, the chance of selection of an element within a block remains fixed, no matter how wide the variation of the actual size from the measure of size. Of course, the variation will increase the sampling variance, especially of estimated totals, because the ultimate clusters, instead of all having 3 or 4 units, will vary widely in number of units. As was indicated earlier, the amount of the increase will depend upon the amount of variation in the size of the ultimate clusters.

Exercise 6.3. To see that a poor measure of size will not bias the results, consider the following situation, in which all blocks have the same measure of size.

BLOCK NO.	MEASURE OF SIZE	ACTUAL NO. OF HOUSEHOLDS	ACTUAL NO. OF PERSONS
1	30	10	40
2	30	50	160
3	30	100	350
4	30	20	50

Using an expected cluster of 3 households and a sampling fraction of 1 in 20:
(a) Determine all possible samples of 2 blocks, using the selection method described above and with the blocks in the order listed.
(b) Estimate the number of households and number of persons from the block totals in each sample.
(c) Show that the estimated totals are unbiased estimates of the actual totals.

There is no reason for concern over minor variations in the actual size from the measure of size in estimating totals, but large variations will call for a larger sample to achieve the same precision of results if one is making simple unbiased estimates of totals. Often a coefficient of variation of ultimate cluster sizes of .1–.4 will be about as small as can be achieved. With a much larger variation the increase in size of sample required for a specified accuracy in estimating aggregates may be considerable. One has to achieve a balance between spending more money for increasing the size of sample and spending more money to cut down the variation in size. It may pay to exert considerable effort to increase the accuracy of the measures of size in order to decrease the variation in ultimate cluster size when one must make a simple unbiased estimate of totals; on the other hand, this will often not be worth while in estimating averages, percentages, or ratios.

Treatment of "zero" blocks or blocks of size smaller than $\bar{n}$. A problem that has been ignored so far arises when A_i is less than $\bar{n}$. When the measure of size, A_i, is greater than zero but smaller than $\bar{n}$, the procedure indicated above must be modified. Thus, if the measure of size for a particular psu is 1, then $A_i = 1$, and the subsampling rate would be $\bar{n}/A_i = 3.5/1$ or 350 per cent. This is, of course, impossible. One unbiased method of dealing with this particular problem would be to include the whole psu in the sample and weight the result by $\bar{n}/A_i$, but this is ordinarily inefficient, and one of the procedures described below may be followed.

If the psu had a measure of size of zero, it would have no chance of being included in the sample by the procedure mentioned above. No problems would be involved if the actual size were zero, but usually this will not be the case, and important parts of the population may be present in psu's of measure zero.

One quite satisfactory procedure for dealing with psu's where $A_i = 0$, as well as where A_i is greater than 0 but less than $\bar{n}$, is to combine such psu's with adjoining ones, in advance of the sample selection, so that all psu's have measures of size equal to or greater than $\bar{n}$. This approach may be particularly useful in sampling for something like retail trade, where the great majority of blocks have no stores. It is also applicable for population or agriculture surveys when psu's are likely to be completely vacant or have no units with the desired types of characteristics.

Another method, often desirable in cases where the measure of size is less than the $\bar{n}$, is to segregate such psu's into a separate stratum and sample them with equal probability. Thus, it may pay to spend some resources in a quick review of such blocks in order to separate those with high growth rates from the others, assign appropriate measures of size to them, and include them in the regular list of blocks.

Sampling with pps and subsampling compact clusters. This section until now has dealt with sampling with pps, listing, and subsampling. If the listing and subsampling can be done at very low cost with the resources available, such a procedure will be efficient. However, the method for sampling with pps and listing and subsampling described above might be varied to one of subsampling whole compact segments. This latter procedure is practicable only when fairly detailed maps or other records which identify individual listing units are available or when field visits are made to prepare sketches.

In this procedure, one first decides on the average size of segment to be used. The measure of size of each psu is then stated in terms of the number of segments into which the psu will be divided. The size of the segment will be designated by $\bar{N}$. If $\bar{N} = 3.5$ and a particular block has an estimate of 40 dwelling units, then we would divide this block into $40/3.5 = 11$ segments, always assigning a whole number of segments into which the cluster will be divided, rather than a number involving a fraction. The numbers of segments into which the psu's will be divided will then become the measures of size which serve as the basis for the sample selection. Once the sample blocks are selected, they are subdivided into the designated numbers of segments, and one of these is chosen at random (more than one segment is included in the sample from a block if the block is designated more than once for inclusion in the sample).

7. Stratification to control variation in size. Another method of using measures of size for psu's to reduce the contribution of variation in size to the variance, particularly for simple unbiased estimates of totals, is to stratify the psu's into a number of size groups before the sample is selected. Then varying sampling fractions can be used in the various size groups to select psu's and to subsample them, perhaps with a uniform over-all sampling fraction. However, if a primary purpose of the sample is to estimate totals, and if stratification is the device relied upon to control the effect of variation in size, a number of size groups should be used with some attention to having reasonably good measures of size. This particular procedure is illustrated in *A Chapter in Population Sampling* (1). The optimum theory for this approach is given in Ch. 7, Sec. 8–11, and in Sec. 10 and 12 of this chapter.

8. Use of ratio estimates to control effect of variation in size of psu. Another procedure and frequently one to be preferred, assuming other aspects of optimum design for estimating ratios have been approximated, is a method that depends upon a ratio or regression estimate. This use of ratio estimates has been presented in earlier chapters and also in Chapter 9. Regression estimates, which may be particularly useful in estimating totals, are discussed in Ch. 11, Sec. 2. Some additional remarks on the application of ratio estimates will be given here. Two different methods of ratio estimation of totals need to be distinguished; either may be used and may be desirable, depending upon the circumstances.

Estimates of totals based on ratio of sample estimate to estimate from sample with known psu totals. We have already seen that, in estimating totals, the use of psu's that vary widely in size may lead to a large variance if primary units are selected with equal probability and the estimate is the simple unbiased estimate, as given by Eq. 3.1. But if one makes a second estimate, also based on Eq. 3.1, for some independent characteristic such as the measures of size of the psu's, computes the ratio of the two estimates, and applies this ratio to the known total for the independent characteristic used as the measure of size, the effect of variation in size of the psu's may be substantially eliminated.

The estimate of a total, using this procedure, is given by

$$x'' = \frac{x'}{y'} Y \qquad (8.1)$$

where x' and y' are given by Eq. 3.1. Note that, if y' is estimated from the measures of size for the psu's or other known psu totals, the sampling fraction for computing y' is the first-stage sampling fraction (the proportion of psu's included in the sample). The rel-variance of an estimated total (Eq. 8.1) in this case is given approximately by Eq. 5.3 of Ch. 7, with terms involving the Y characteristic dropped out of the *within*-psu contribution to the variance (since there is no sampling within psu's) so that $S_{2hi}^2 = S_{2hi.X}^2$. Of course, the terms in Y are retained in the *between*-psu contribution to the variance.

In order to make the fullest gain with the ratio estimate (when the selection of psu's is carried out with equal probability within strata and the denominator of the ratio is estimated from psu totals) one should ordinarily avoid subsampling each primary unit independently. Instead, a systematic selection procedure should be used, and the systematic selection should be carried over from one psu to another. For example, if one has a stratum in which the subsampling rate is to be, say, 1 in 5.5 from the selected primary units, then subsampling from listings for the primary units should be carried through from one psu to another (for the present purpose it makes no difference what order the psu's are in). Subsampling independently within each psu will involve a "tail-end" variance that will increase the variance of estimated totals and reduce the effect of the correlation between the measure of size and the actual size.

Exercise 8.1. Suppose that the following 4 blocks are in the sample:

BLOCK NO.	NO. OF HOUSEHOLDS
17	6
56	21
65	10
83	15

If the subsampling fraction is 1 in 4, and systematic selection with a random start is used, compare the estimated total number of households when the sampling is carried over from block to block with the estimated total derived from independent sampling in each block.   Use random numbers to select two samples by each procedure.   What are the highest and lowest estimates possible with independent sampling from each block?

It may be found desirable to use different measures of size or different independent data for estimating different aggregates for different characteristics from the sample.   The requirement for a ratio estimate of the form $(x'/y')Y$ to be a consistent estimate of X is that x' be a consistent estimate of X and y' be a consistent estimate of Y.

Estimates of totals based on sample ratios applied to independent totals. We are often in the position of having a ratio from the sample, with the denominator of the ratio relating to a characteristic that is known for the total population from other sources.   For example, we may know the number of farms in an area from a census or a recent estimate based on information other than the particular sample under consideration, and the sample may provide a sample estimate of farms as well as of various characteristics of the farms, as, for example, acres in various crops or farm facilities.

One method of estimating from the sample would be to take the average value of some characteristic per farm from the sample and multiply this by the independent total number of farms.   For estimates of characteristics of human populations it is often true that the sample provides information on the total population, the total population in a particular age-sex group, or some other class of the population, which total is also known independently from other sources for the total population.   The sample also provides information on some characteristic of this group, as, for example, the number who have a particular opinion, the number who are unemployed, or the number who have some other characteristic. From the sample one computes the average value of the characteristic (or the percentage), and this average is applied to the independent total for the group, to provide an estimate of the total.

This method of estimation is to be distinguished from that in the preceding subsection.   It may often have a smaller mean square error than would a ratio estimate of the same characteristic based on measures of size for the characteristic available for each psu and built up to the total for the area, but no longer is it necessarily a consistent estimate of the total.   If the denominators of the sample ratios are not consistent estimates of the independent figures to which the sample ratios are applied, the estimate may be more or less seriously biased.   The rel-variance of this second type of estimate, $(x'/z')Y$, is given by the usual equation for the rel-variance of x'/z', for it is simply a ratio multiplied by the constant Y, provided Y is a constant and is known from independent sources. For some further consideration of this type of estimate, see Ch. 5, Sec. 16, Remarks 3, 4, and 5, and also Ch. 9, Sec. 23.

9. Precautions against a few extremely unusual psu's. Precautions should be taken against a relatively few psu's existing in the population which might contribute significantly to the sampling variance. Such a situation could arise when there are a few psu's of very extreme size as compared with the others. It is not sufficient to examine whether the unusual psu's are so extreme as to have a large effect on the *average* size of psu. A relatively few psu's may have a large effect on the sampling variance even though they have only a small effect on the average size of psu. Suppose, for example, that one is selecting a sample to estimate the total earnings of farm workers and is attempting to sample in such a way as to have an average of 4 farm workers per psu. Suppose, further, that his material for sampling is such that he finds in his sample 499 psu's each containing from 0 to 10 farm workers, with an average for these of 3.5 farm workers per psu in the sample, and then one remaining psu containing, say, 400 farm workers. The average size of psu for all 500 psu's is close to the 4 farm workers desired, but the one psu containing 400 farm workers may have an exceedingly important impact on the sampling variance. Any moderate difference between the earnings of the workers in this large psu and the incomes of the other workers in the population would serve to increase the sampling variance tremendously.

Thus, suppose that the extremely large psu contained a prison farm with 400 prisoners working for pay, but at a very low rate of pay as compared with other farm workers in the area. What would be the effect on the precision of a sample estimate of having this one psu in the sample? It is obvious that with it in the sample one will have a substantial underestimate of the average earnings of farm workers. On the other hand, if it is not in the sample and if this is the only such unusual psu in the population, the result will be a small overestimate of the average income per worker. With a large enough sample the impact on the sample estimate of such an unusual psu will not be noticeable, but it can be very great on a small or even moderate-sized sample. In any event one or a few such psu's in a population, sampled with the same probability as the others, or with probabilities proportionate to measures grossly understating the actual size of the psu, can have a serious effect on the sample estimate and its variance. It is often worth while taking precautions such as those given below to minimize the effect of unusual psu's on the variance.

An appropriate type of precaution is to deal with large institutional populations, such as prisons, hospitals, hotels, or other similar large and special types of aggregations, as a special class in sampling, if such populations are to be included in the population that is being sampled. Ordinarily, one can identify such large institutions in an area and provide for separate sampling within them. Similarly, if one is sampling dwelling units or stores, one may have to take precautions to identify special areas where extensive new construction has taken place, with perhaps hundreds of units in an area that on the basis of earlier information might be expected to have comparatively few units, or none.

Precautions may be taken by a check with locally informed groups as to the existence and location of new construction areas. Once such areas with large population growths are identified, they should be broken into small units of a size about the same as other primary units being sampled. Or they might be listed and subsampled with the desired over-all sampling fraction, without any use of primary units as an intermediate device in sample selection. Such advance precautions avoid or reduce the risk of having a relatively few psu's contributing significantly to the variance. Such steps ordinarily can be taken at relatively small cost in connection with an area sample design, but considerable care and attention are needed to insure identifying essentially all such unusual psu's in the population.

It may be possible to reduce the variance if the sample contains an extremely unusual psu. Suppose that one has taken what he has assumed to be reasonable precautions against unusual primary units but finds himself with a sample containing one or two unusual units, whose inclusion has a significant effect on the estimates made from the sample. The estimate from the sample with one or two unusual units included is substantially different from the estimate when these units are excluded. How does one proceed?

The sample estimate in this circumstance is still consistent, no matter what the variation in size of cluster, and with a large enough sample will be as close as one pleases to the characteristic being estimated. But the variance of a sample estimate is obviously very large when the inclusion or exclusion of one or two units has an important effect on the estimate. One of the following procedures may be used, although only great care in eliminating all such units from the population is satisfactory.

The best thing to do is to try to discover not only the one or two units in the sample, but also any others of similar character in the population that are not in the sample. We must discover all such possible cases and proceed to resample from them, perhaps by subdividing them into smaller units and selecting a sample with the proper sampling fraction or by assigning their appropriate measures of size. This should be done for both those in the sample and those not in the sample.

However, suppose that one finds such a psu in the sample, and, although further checking has revealed no more in the population, he is not sure that no more exist in the population. What does he do then? If he leaves this extreme observation in the sample, it has a serious effect on the sample estimate and makes for a very large coefficient of variation in the estimate. If he subsamples it at a rate such that it represents only itself, a bias of unknown magnitude is introduced. This is not a very satisfactory set of alternatives to have to choose between. Some speculation on the probable number of such unusual units in the population will guide in a decision between these alternatives. If the unusual unit is presumed to be the only one, or one of a very few unusual units, and is allowed to represent only itself, the bias of such a procedure may be smaller than the increase in the coefficient of variation that will result from retaining the full impact of such an extreme and unusual observation. If it is suspected that there may be a number of such unusual units, then the proper course will be to leave the unusual unit in the sample, with the weight appropriate to an unbiased estimate.

If an effort is made to identify all unusual units other than the ones in the sample, and if there are other such units in the population that are not discovered by this further work, one will still be better off for having made the effort, in that failure to find additional ones lends some assurance that they are relatively infrequent. Whenever additional extreme units *are* identified, the bias of the procedure just suggested will be smaller to that extent.

For example, in the Current Business Survey of the Bureau of the Census (Ch. 12, Case Study A) it was found, during the late 1940's, that the measures of size for automotive dealers were very poor, having been based on activity during the war years, when no new cars were being produced. The few in the cluster sample contributed heavily to the estimate and its variance. Consequently, a new listing of very large automotive dealers in the areas of the current survey was prepared, and these firms were removed from the cluster sample and put on the "large-store list," where they were certain to be included in the sample.

10. Use of theory presented earlier for optimum design in estimating totals. It should be clearly understood that we do not have any complete theory on the optimum *way* of selecting a sample or the *way* to define the primary and subsampling units. The investigator, by an understanding of how variances, costs, and administrative problems arise, and by experimental studies and comparison of alternatives, must make a decision as to the general approach. The procedures described above for fairly close control on the variation in size of psu will sometimes be expensive. But where the estimates of totals are important enough to be the determining factor in the sample design, then the procedures of Sec. 2–9 and variations of them are useful. They can be introduced into many different sample designs. Thus, the investigator who knows the general principles involved can bring ingenuity and a knowledge of available or potential resources to the design of a particular sample survey.

Once one has decided on the general approach to defining sample units and to the whole problem of sample design, all the theory presented earlier and in subsequent chapters is applicable for determining optimum design, whether estimating totals or ratios, or both. The optimum sampling theory given in other sections may be applied by using the appropriate estimates and variances which have been specifically given or referred to for alternative approaches.

Two case studies in which the estimation of a total was important are summarized in Case Studies A and B, Ch. 12.

Exercise 10.1.   Using the data given in Ex. 11.3, Ch. 7, and the costs for the 3 strata given in Table 1, Ch. 7 (p. 324), and assuming a total budget of $20,000: (*a*) compute the variances needed for making the optimum allocation to estimate the total X; (*b*) compute optimum values for the f_{1h} and f_{2h}; (*c*) compute the rel-variance of x'; (*d*) make the same computations for estimating the total Y; (*e*) compare these results with those in Ex. 11.3, Ch. 7.

B.   EFFECT OF VARIATION IN SIZE OF PSU ON THE VARIANCE OF RATIOS OR AVERAGES

11. Moderate variation in psu size often has little effect on percentages, averages, or ratios.   The reduction in variance resulting from reducing the variability in psu size is ordinarily small for estimating percentages, averages, or ratios, and it may not be worth incurring any considerable cost to achieve it. Often this is true if the coefficient of variation in size of psu is moderate, say less than .5 or 1. Steps to reduce variation in the size of psu will ordinarily not be worth while unless they can be accomplished with very little difficulty or cost, unless there is very wide variation in psu size, or unless the ratio or average being estimated, when computed for individual psu's, is highly correlated with size of psu.

The use of ratio estimates is one of the procedures recommended for controlling the variation in size for estimating totals. In effect, a measure of size is obtained for every sampling unit in the population in order to reduce the problem of estimating totals to one of estimating ratios. When the purpose of the survey is to estimate a ratio, the investigator is in the fortunate position of having all the information that he needs for constructing the ratio from the psu's in the sample. There is, then, no impelling need for obtaining relatively accurate measures of size for each unit in the population, as there is when the ratio estimate is used for controlling variation in size of cluster for estimating a total. Hence, with a few exceptions the steps indicated in Sec. 2–10 can accomplish only relatively small reductions in the variance for estimating ratios. A notable exception, however, is the treatment of unusual segments, and the precautions given in Sec. 9 should be taken.

There may be some advantages in using the other devices indicated in Sec. 2–9, but any reductions in variance must be considered in relation to the increase in costs which is involved. Thus, the use of probability proportionate to size will ordinarily tend to decrease the variance for a fixed number of psu's in the sample and a fixed over-all sampling fraction, as compared with uniform first- and second-stage sampling fractions. This is true whenever N_i and $N_i(X_i/N_i - X/N)^2$ (as defined in Sec. 1, Ch. 6) are positively correlated, which tends to be the case for the types of populations that we meet in practice.*   On the other hand, the average size of psu in the sample, when sampling with probability proportionate to size, increases by a factor of $(1 + B_N^2)$ over the average size of psu when the sampling is made with equal probability, where $B_N^2 = \overset{M}{\sum}(N_i - \bar{N})^2/(M - 1)\bar{N}^2$ is the rel-variance of size of psu. This factor usually reflects the additional cost of listing, and pps should not be employed unless the gain in precision offsets the increase in cost. Section 14 gives specific conditions for when it will pay, with the simple cost function assumed, to use pps in sampling to estimate ratios.

12. Stratification by size of psu in estimating averages or ratios, with a uniform over-all sampling fraction.   Moderate reductions in variance per unit of cost can often be obtained in estimating averages or ratios with the introduction of a few size strata. If the psu's vary widely in size, it may be desirable to classify them into a limited number of size strata and use variable first- and second-stage sampling fractions, but retaining a uniform over-all fraction. In many instances two strata will suffice for the purpose. More specifically, assume that the sample estimate is the ratio of sample aggregates, $r = x/y$, and that the total cost of the survey can be expressed as

$$C = C_1'm + C_1'' \overset{L}{\sum} m_h \bar{N}_h + C_2 fN \qquad (12.1)$$

_____

* For proof, see Vol. II, Ch. 8, Sec. 4.

where C_1' is the fixed cost per primary unit included in the sample, excluding listing costs.

C_1'' is the cost of listing per listing unit listed.

C_2 is the direct cost per listing unit included in the sample.

m_h is the number of psu's in the sample from the hth stratum.

$\bar{n}_h = f_{2h}\bar{N}_h$ is the expected value of the average number of listing units in the sample per psu in the sample from the hth stratum, and also $\bar{n}_h = n_h/m_h$, where n_h is the expected value of the number of listing units in the sample from the hth stratum.

$\bar{N}_h = N_h/M_h$ is the total number of listing units per psu in the hth stratum.

N is the total number of listing units in the population.

f is the over-all sampling fraction.

fN is the expected number of listing units in the sample.

L is the number of size strata.

The rel-variance of the sample estimate is given by Eq. 5.3 of Ch. 7. The optimum sampling fraction for second-stage units in the hth size stratum is*

$$f_{2h} = \frac{\bar{n}_h}{\bar{N}_h} = \frac{S_2\sqrt{C_1' + C_1''\bar{N}_h}}{\sqrt{C_2}\sqrt{S_{1h}^2 - \bar{N}_h S_{2h}^2}} \qquad (12.2)$$

where S_{1h}^2 and S_{2h}^2 are defined by Eq. 5.4 and 5.15 of Ch. 7, and

$$S_2^2 = \frac{\sum\limits_{}^{L} N_h S_{2h}^2}{N} \qquad (12.3)$$

Since the sample is self-weighting, $f_{1h}f_{2h} = f$, where $f_{1h} = m_h/M_h$ is the first-stage sampling fraction, or the probability of selecting a psu in a sample of m. The optimum sampling fractions for first-stage units are proportionate to

$$\frac{\sqrt{S_{1h}^2 - \bar{N}_h S_{2h}^2}}{\sqrt{C_1' + C_1''\bar{N}_h}} \qquad (12.4)$$

More specifically the optimum first-stage sampling fractions are given by

$$\frac{m_h}{M_h} = f \star \frac{\bar{N}_h}{\bar{n}_h} = \frac{\sqrt{S_{1h}^2 - \bar{N}_h S_{2h}^2}}{\sqrt{C_1' + C_1''\bar{N}_h}} \frac{f \star \sqrt{C_2}}{S_2} \qquad (12.5)$$

---

* For proof, see Vol. II, Ch. 8, Sec. 3.

where $f^\star$, the optimum value of f, is

$$f^\star = \frac{CS_2}{\sqrt{C_2}\left(\sum_{h}^{L}\sqrt{C_1' + C_1''\bar{N}_h}\ M_h\sqrt{S_{1h}^2 - \bar{N}_h S_{2h}^2} + \sqrt{C_2}NS_2\right)} \quad (12.6)$$

Note that

$$\frac{S_{1h}^2}{\bar{N}_h^2} - \frac{S_{2h}^2}{\bar{N}_h} \doteq \delta_h \hat{S}_h^2 \quad (12.7)$$

where δ_h is a measure of homogeneity among listing units per first-stage unit in the hth stratum and is defined by Eq. 8.11, Ch. 6, and $\hat{S}_h^2 = \hat{V}_h^2 \bar{X}_h^2$, where $\hat{V}_h^2$ is given by adding the appropriate subscript h to the terms in Eq. 8.10 of Ch. 6, and is approximately equal to the variance of a ratio for a simple random sample of listing units within the hth stratum.   It is then possible to formulate some rules for approximating the optimum first-stage sampling fractions m_h/M_h. Approximate rules are needed because often the variances required for the optimum equations are not available.

Remark.   Whenever the cost equation is of the form

$$C = \sum_{h}^{L} C_{1h} m_h + C_2 \sum_{h}^{L} m_h \bar{n}_h$$

and the over-all sampling fractions are uniform, even though the first-stage sampling fractions and second-stage fractions vary from stratum to stratum, the formulas for the optimum sampling fractions are given by Eq. 12.2, 12.3, and 12.4, with $C_{1h} = C_1' + C_1''\bar{N}_h$. These optimum values will hold whether the estimates are for averages, percentages, or totals.

13. Some rules for approximating the optimum first- and second-stage sampling fractions with stratification by size of psu and a uniform over-all sampling fraction.   We have seen before that for many of the populations with which we deal δ tends to decrease with increasing size of unit, but seldom as fast as the size of unit increases.   The rate of decrease is often small relative to the increase in $\bar{N}_h$, and empirical data for a number of problems indicate that even the assumption of δ_h being fairly constant with increasing size of unit may not lead one far astray from the optimum sampling fractions.   Under this assumption ($\delta_h = \delta$ for all h) the sampling fractions depend only on $\bar{N}_h$, C_1', and C_1'', and lead to the following results:

(a) When $C_1' > 0$ and $C_1'' = 0$, the first-stage sampling fraction should be proportionate to average size of psu.
(b) When $C_1' = 0$ and $C_1'' > 0$, the first-stage sampling fraction should be proportionate to the square root of average size.

If we go to the other extreme (extreme not in terms of mathematically possible values but in terms of most practical populations), and assume that δ_h decreases at the same rate that $\bar{N}_h$ increases, the results would be:

(a) When $C_1' > 0$ and $C_1'' = 0$, the first-stage sampling fraction should be proportionate to the square root of the average size of psu.

(b) When $C_1' = 0$ and $C_1'' > 0$, the first-stage sampling fraction should be the same for all strata.

The minimum is broad in the neighborhood of the optimum, as indicated elsewhere, and the results for either of these extremes and the values in between often will be reasonably close to the minimum.

To illustrate the application of these rules in the special case where there are only two size strata, let us say that M_L is the number of psu's from the stratum with large psu's, and M_S the number from the stratum with small psu's. Let m_L and m_S be the corresponding numbers for the sample. Now assume that the situation is one that could call for having a uniform over-all sampling fraction, and first-stage sampling fractions proportionate to the square root of the average sizes on the basis of the rules just given. Then

$$f = \frac{m_L}{M_L}\frac{\bar{n}_L}{\bar{N}_L} = \frac{m_S}{M_S}\frac{\bar{n}_S}{\bar{N}_S} \tag{13.1}$$

i.e., the product of the sampling fractions would be the same for both strata; and

$$\bar{n}_L = \bar{n}_S \sqrt{\frac{\bar{N}_L}{\bar{N}_S}} \tag{13.2}$$

Here $\bar{n}_L$ and $\bar{n}_S$ are the expected values of the numbers of listing units in the sample per psu in the sample for the two size strata. The appropriate values for the over-all sampling fraction f may be given in advance or determined by joint considerations of available resources and desired precision. With f specified, we have from Eq. 13.1

$$\frac{m_S}{M_S} = f\frac{\bar{N}_S}{\bar{n}_S} \quad \text{and} \quad \frac{m_L}{M_L} = f\frac{\bar{N}_L}{\bar{n}_L} \tag{13.3}$$

Thus, all the necessary sampling fractions can be determined if $\bar{n}_S$ is determined. From Eq. 12.2

$$\bar{n}_S = \bar{N}_S \frac{S_2\sqrt{C_1' + C_1''\bar{N}_S}}{\sqrt{C_2}\sqrt{S_{1S}^2 - \bar{N}_S S_{2S}^2}} \doteq \sqrt{\frac{C_1' + C_1''\bar{N}_S}{C_2}}\sqrt{\frac{1-\delta_S}{\delta_S}} \tag{13.4}$$

where, for the "small-block" stratum, S_{1S}^2 is given by Eq. 5.4 of Ch. 7, S_{2S}^2 is given by Eq. 5.15 of Ch. 7, and δ_S is the measure of homogeneity given by Eq. 8.11, Ch. 6.   As was seen in Ch. 6, Sec. 16–20, the $\bar{n}_S$ needs to be only roughly determined, because the optimum is broad.   Consequently, only rough values are needed for the terms of the cost function and for δ_S.   For many problems $\bar{n}_S$ will be in the neighborhood of 2–6, as is seen in Table 7, Sec. 20, Ch. 6, p. 296.

Illustration 13.1.   Assume that a sample of 5 per cent of the households of a city is to be taken, and that the average number of families per block in the "small-block" stratum is approximately 25, and in the "large-block" stratum is approximately 100.   Assume that the appropriate value for $\bar{n}_S$ is 5 families.   Therefore, the appropriate value for $\bar{n}_L$, from Eq. 13.2, is

$$\bar{n}_S \sqrt{\frac{\overline{N}_L}{\overline{N}_S}} = 5 \sqrt{\frac{100}{25}} = 10$$

The within-sampling fraction for small blocks is

$$\frac{\bar{n}_S}{\overline{N}_S} = \frac{5}{25} = .20 \quad \text{or 20 per cent}$$

and for large blocks is

$$\frac{\bar{n}_L}{\overline{N}_L} = \frac{10}{100} = .10 \quad \text{or 10 per cent}$$

Since the over-all sampling fraction f is to be the same for both strata, and in this illustration is equal to .05, the proportion of blocks to be selected from the "small-block" stratum is, from Eq. 13.3,

$$.05 \left(\frac{1}{.25}\right) = 25 \text{ per cent}$$

Similarly the proportion of blocks to be selected from the "large-block" stratum is

$$.05 \left(\frac{1}{.10}\right) = 50 \text{ per cent}$$

Some indication of the gains from the use of the rules just given for determining first- and second-stage sampling fractions, with a uniform over-all sampling fraction, as compared with uniform sampling fractions at each stage in all strata, is given in Table 2 (p. 364).

14. Use of varying probabilities to control variation in size.   Instead of classifying the primary units into size strata, one could accomplish almost the same control on variation in size by assigning differing probabilities of selection to the units in the population.   A method of selection with varying probabilities is described in Sec. 6.

An estimate of R with varying probabilities.*   An estimate of $R = X/Y$ with varying probabilities is

$$r = \frac{x'}{y'} = \frac{\sum\limits^{m} \frac{x_i'}{P_i}/m}{\sum\limits^{m} \frac{y_i'}{P_i}/m} \tag{14.1}$$

where x_i' and y_i' are simple unbiased estimates of the psu totals, X_i and Y_i, respectively; P_i is the probability of selecting the ith first-stage unit on a single draw; and m and M are the numbers of first-stage units in the sample and in the population, respectively.   Specifically, for a two-stage design

$$x_i' = N_i \frac{x_i}{n_i}, \quad \text{and} \quad y_i' = N_i \frac{y_i}{n_i}$$

where, for the ith psu in the sample, N_i and n_i are respectively the total number of elementary units and the number in the sample.   When the sample is self-weighting [i.e., $P_i(n_i/N_i)$ is a constant] the estimate of R is simply

$$r = \frac{x}{y} \tag{14.2}$$

The rel-variance of r.†   The rel-variance of r is approximately

$$V_r^2 \doteq V_{x'}^2 + V_{y'}^2 - 2V_{x'y'} \tag{14.3}$$

where

$$V_{x'}^2 \doteq \frac{\sum\limits_{i}^{M} P_i \left(\frac{X_i}{P_i} - X\right)^2}{mX^2} + \frac{\sum\limits_{i}^{M} \frac{N_i^2}{P_i} \frac{N_i - n_i}{N_i n_i} S_{iX}^2}{mX^2} \tag{14.4}$$

where

$$S_{iX}^2 = \frac{\sum\limits_{j}^{N_i} (X_{ij} - \bar{\bar{X}}_i)^2}{N_i - 1} \tag{14.5}$$

and is simply the variance within the ith cluster of a sample of one elementary unit. $V_{y'}^2$ is similarly defined, and

$$V_{x'y'} = \frac{\sum\limits_{i}^{M} P_i \left(\frac{X_i}{P_i} - X\right)\left(\frac{Y_i}{P_i} - Y\right)}{mXY} + \frac{\sum\limits_{i}^{M} \frac{N_i^2}{P_i} \frac{N_i - n_i}{N_i n_i} S_{iXY}}{mXY} \tag{14.6}$$

---

* For proof, see Vol. II, Ch. 8, Sec. 1.
† For proof, see Vol. II, Ch. 8, Sec. 1.

where

$$S_{iXY} = \frac{\sum\limits_{j}^{N_i}(X_{ij} - \bar{\bar{X}}_i)(Y_{ij} - \bar{\bar{Y}}_i)}{N_i - 1} \tag{14.7}$$

A sample estimate of the rel-variance of r is given by Eq. 7.1, Ch. 6.

   Remark. The rel-variance of x' (Eq. 14.4) is exact with pps sampling if the primary units are selected with replacement, and is an approximation if they are selected without replacement (following procedures such as those described in Sec. 6).

*Optimum probabilities and comparison of optimum probabilities with stratification as a control of variation in size.** Assume that, instead of sampling from each size stratum as was done in Sec. 12, we assign the probability P_h to each psu in the hth size class, i.e., the probability of a psu being selected in the hth size class is the same for all units in the hth size class, but varies from one size class to another. The selection of units without stratification but with varying probabilities differs from the selection of units from strata with varying sampling fractions described in Sec. 12. In the former case, the number of units included in the sample from the hth class is a random variable, whereas with stratification the number included from the hth stratum is fixed in advance of drawing the sample. With varying probabilities a particular sample may not include any units from some of the size classes, whereas with stratification by size the sample is certain to have some units from every size class.

   Assume that the total expected cost for the survey is represented by the simple cost function

$$C = C_1'm + C_1''m\sum^{L}P_h M_h \bar{N}_h + C_2 fN \tag{14.8}$$

where P_h is the probability of selecting a psu from the hth class on a single draw, i.e., with a sample of one psu; M_h is the total number of psu's in the hth size class; and $\Sigma P_h M_h \bar{N}_h$ in the cost function is the expected average size of psu included in the sample. Since the sample is self-weighting,

$$f = mP_h f_{2h}$$

where f_{2h} is the second-stage sampling fraction from a unit included in the sample from the hth size class. Hence mP_h here is comparable to m_h/M_h, the first-stage sampling fraction when stratification by size is used, and is equal to the probability of selecting a psu from the hth size class in a sample of m when the sampling is without replacement.

---

   * For proof, see Vol. II, Ch. 8, Sec. 2.

Each of the three terms in Eq. 14.8 represents the same type of costs as the comparable term in Eq. 12.1. The optimum value of P_h is proportionate to

$$\sqrt{\frac{\Delta_h^2 - \bar{N}_h S_{2h}^2}{C_1' + C_1'' \bar{N}_h}} \tag{14.9}$$

where S_{2h}^2 is given by Eq. 5.15 of Ch. 7, and

$$\Delta_h^2 = \frac{\sum_j^{M_h} Y_{hj}^2 \left(\dfrac{X_{hj}}{Y_{hj}} - \dfrac{X}{Y} \right)^2}{M_h} \tag{14.10}$$

where X_{hj} and Y_{hj} are values of the jth first-stage units in the hth size class. Note that the optimum probabilities and optimum sampling fractions are proportionate to the same numbers except that Δ_h^2 in Eq. 14.9 replaces S_{1h}^2 in Eq. 12.4. When the X_h/Y_h do not vary a great deal from stratum to stratum, the two expressions are approximately the same.*

If we assume that $\Delta_h^2/\bar{N}_h^2 - S_{2h}^2/\bar{N}_h$ is approximately equal to $\delta_h \hat{S}_h^2$ (see Eq. 12.7), we then have the same rules for approximating the optimum probabilities as those given for approximating the optimum first-stage sampling fractions. Summarizing these rules, we have, in terms of probabilities:

(a) When $C_1'' \sum_h^L P_h M_h \bar{N}_h$, the expected cost per primary unit of listing and related operations, is small in relation to C_1', the fixed cost per primary unit, the optimum probabilities will be between proportionate to size and proportionate to the square root of size, and either of these will be reasonably close to the optimum.

(b) When C_1' is small compared to $C_1'' \sum_h^L P_h M_h \bar{N}_h$, the optimum probability will be between equal probability and probability proportionate to the square root of size, and either of these will be reasonably close to the optimum.

(c) When both C_1' and $C_1'' \sum_h^L P_h M_h \bar{N}_h$ are of significant size, i.e., when the costs vary substantially with both the number of primary units in the sample and the size of the units, then probability proportionate to the square root of the size will be a reasonably good approximation to the optimum.

(d) When units of small size are used and all the subunits in the selected primary units are included in the sample (i.e., there is no subsampling), equal probability is close to the optimum. It should be

---

* For proof, see Vol. II, Ch. 8, Sec. 3.

noted that this rule does not follow directly from the above analysis based on subsampling, but from a separate analysis in which no subsampling is involved.

If the rules of thumb given above are followed (and note that they are the same rules as given in Sec. 12), we should still find the optimum over-all sampling fraction f and the optimum values for m for the given cost equation. If, in Eq. 14.8, we let

$$f = mk \qquad (14.11)$$

the optimum value of k for whatever system of probabilities is used is

$$k = \sqrt{\dfrac{S_2^2(C_1' + C_1'' \sum\limits^{L} P_h M_h \bar{N}_h)}{C_2 \sum\limits_{h}^{L} \dfrac{M_h(\Delta_h^2 - \bar{N}_h S_{2h}^2)}{P_h}}} \qquad (14.12)$$

where S_2^2 is given by Eq. 12.3 and S_{2h}^2 is given by Eq. 5.15 of Ch. 7. The optimum value of k can be approximated from prior experience or preliminary studies. The value of m is then equal to

$$m = \dfrac{C}{C_1' + C_1'' \sum\limits^{L} M_h P_h \bar{N}_h + C_2 kn} \qquad (14.13)$$

When the appropriate value of P_h is determined, i.e., the system of probabilities is selected, Eq. 14.11, 14.12, and 14.13 give the optimum values of f and m for the cost equation 14.8. The second-stage sampling fraction f_{2h} is given by

$$\dfrac{f}{m P_h} \qquad (14.14)$$

Illustration 14.1.   A characteristic published for city blocks in the 1940 Census of Housing is the number of dwelling units that are in need of major repairs or that lack a private bath.   Suppose that we were sampling to estimate the proportion of the dwelling units having this characteristic for the Bronx in New York City, at the time of the 1940 Census.   Let us assume that once we selected a system of probabilities we used the optimum numbers of blocks and the optimum sampling fractions appropriate to these probabilities, i.e., the optimum values of k and m.   For specified values of the unit costs, Table 2 shows the sampling variances of each system relative to the variance of sampling with equal probability. It also shows values of $C_1'' \sum\limits^{L} P_h M_h \bar{N}_h$ for comparison with C_1'.

Table 2.   Variances for different probability systems relative to the variance for an equal probability system for specified unit costs in the cost function

$$C = C_1'm + C_1''m\sum_{}^{L}P_hM_h\bar{N}_h + C_2fN$$

Unit costs			Average cost per primary unit of listing and related operations $C_1''\sum^{L}P_hM_h\bar{N}_h$			Variances relative to equal probability		
C_1'	C_1''	C_2	Equal proba-bility	Proba-bility propor-tionate to square root of size	Proba-bility propor-tionate to size	Equal proba-bility	Proba-bility propor-tionate to square root of size	Proba-bility propor-tionate to size
5	.10	1	13.49	21.15	27.63	100	92	104
5	.05	1	6.75	10.58	13.82	100	88	97
5	.02	1	2.70	4.23	5.53	100	83	87
5	0	1	0	0	0	100	75	73
2	.10	1	13.49	21.15	27.63	100	96	111
2	.05	1	6.75	10.58	13.82	100	93	106
2	.02	1	2.70	4.23	5.53	100	90	97
2	0	1	0	0	0	100	79	77
1	.10	1	13.49	21.15	27.63	100	97	114
1	.05	1	6.75	10.58	13.82	100	96	110
1	.02	1	2.70	4.23	5.53	100	93	103
1	0	1	0	0	0	100	82	81
0	.10	1	13.49	21.15	27.63	100	99	117
0	.05	1	6.75	10.58	13.82	100	99	115
0	.02	1	2.70	4.23	5.53	100	99	113

Some of the costs given in the table do not have unreasonable relationships in terms of the situations encountered in practice in various types of jobs. The comparisons are not affected by the absolute magnitudes of the costs but only by their relative magnitudes. The results are consistent with the rough rules of thumb given above. The use of varying probabilities in selecting large psu's offers some opportunities for larger gains. This topic is discussed in Chapter 9.

REFERENCES

(1) U.S. Bureau of the Census, Sampling Staff, *A Chapter in Population Sampling*, U.S. Government Printing Office, Washington, D.C., 1947.
(2) W. G. Cochran, "Sampling Theory When the Sampling Units Are of Unequal Size," *J. Amer. Stat. Assn.*, **37** (1942), 199–212.
(3) M. H. Hansen and W. N. Hurwitz, "On the Determination of Optimum Probabilities in Sampling," *Annals Math. Stat.*, **20** (1949), 426–432.

CHAPTER 9

Multi-stage Sampling with Large Primary Sampling Units

A. SOME PRELIMINARY CONSIDERATION OF THE USE OF LARGE PRIMARY SAMPLING UNITS

1. Problems where large primary sampling units are preferred to small ones. The preceding chapters have dealt with general methods, but in the applications discussed, emphasis was placed primarily on problems involving the initial sampling of small first-stage units. Small psu's are used primarily in surveys where travel between psu's is not a major cost factor, as when the entire survey is confined to a small geographic area such as a city or county, or when a sample taken throughout a large area such as the entire United States, is large enough that a number of segments are drawn from every or nearly every county in the country. However, if a very small sample is to cover a large area, the appropriate method of sampling may be to select a first-stage sample of large units and proceed within each of these as though sampling from a local area. Consequently, in designing a small sample for making, say, a national opinion survey, or a national estimate of retail sales in the United States, total crop land in farms, or total employment, or for many types of special- or general-purpose samples, the efficient primary sampling unit is likely to be large, such as a county. Thus, the methods given in this chapter are particularly useful when a survey is to cover a widespread area, and information is to be collected from a small sample through field visitation or by a process that involves field visitation as an important phase. As an illustration, we shall compare alternative methods for obtaining a small national population sample with a uniform over-all sampling fraction for estimating an average or percentage.

2. A small sample from a large area with small primary units. Illustration 2.1. With a sample of small psu's drawn throughout the United States, the sample selection might be accomplished by (1) drawing a sample of, say, Census enumeration districts (ED's);* (2) dividing each selected ED into an equal number of smaller areas (referred to as blocks); (3) subsampling one such block from each selected ED; and (4) listing and subsampling dwelling units, persons, or other listing units from the selected blocks.

Since only one block is drawn from an ED by this approach, the selection of enumeration districts is simply a convenient intermediate device for stratifying and selecting the sample blocks. The variance of an estimate from this design is approximately the same as the variance for a design in which the blocks serve as psu's and are sampled directly from within whatever strata the ED's are selected.

We shall regard this case as such a two-stage sample design, and shall determine the number of blocks and the average size of the ultimate clusters included in the sample by optimum sampling principles. The estimate from the sample and its variance are given in Remark 2, Sec. 5, Ch. 7. For purposes of arriving at the optimum design we shall use the form of the rel-variance given by Eq. 5.20, Ch. 7, i.e.,

$$V_r^2 \doteq (1-f)\frac{\hat{V}^2}{m\bar{n}}[1 + \delta(\bar{n} - 1)]$$

and shall assume that from prior work or pretesting we have approximate values for $\hat{V}^2$ and δ for the principal characteristic we are interested in estimating, and that for this characteristic

$$\hat{V}^2 = 2, \quad \delta = .10$$

It is assumed, also, that the blocks contain approximately 30 dwelling units on the average, and that dwelling units are the listing units. These assumed values, as well as those given in the illustration that follows, are hypothetical.

Illustrative values for the kinds of costs that might arise, and the optimum design within this framework of sampling, are given below. We shall suppose, for purpose of illustration, that a total budget of $15,000 is available for the survey under consideration, in addition to overhead costs, and that the survey work will be done by interviewers traveling from psu to psu within their respective assigned areas. Then the values of the terms in the cost function

$$C = C_0\sqrt{m} + C_1 m + C_2 m\bar{n} \qquad (2.1)$$

* Areas with approximately 500–1000 persons into which the United States was divided to provide a reasonable workload for an enumerator during the Decennial Census. Such areas are carefully mapped and are sometimes useful for drawing samples.

given in Sec. 12, Ch. 6, might be roughly as follows (the assumed values would, of course, depend on more specific conditions than have been explicitly stated here):

$$C = 15,000, \quad C_0 = 500,^* \quad C_1 = 20, \quad C_2 = 2$$

Given these facts, the optimum values of $\bar{n}$ and m can be obtained through the use of Eq. 18.1–18.3, Ch. 6. The optimum values obtained by substituting in these equations are found to be $\bar{n} = 13$ and $m = 180$. The rel-variance of the estimate of the characteristic from the sample, ignoring the factor $(1 - f)$, is

$$V_r^2 = \frac{2}{(180)(13)} [1 + (.1)(12)] = .0019$$

Notice that in this case the term $C_0\sqrt{m}$ contributes nearly \$7000 to the total cost of the survey, so that the estimated travel between psu's amounts to nearly half the total cost and is an exceedingly important factor in the total cost.

> **Remark.** The operations of selecting enumeration districts, subdividing the selected ED's into "blocks," and drawing a sample of blocks result in the same widespread sample of the small areas as the procedures described in Chapter 6. With this approach the size of the initial units (ED's in the illustration) should be so determined as to minimize the cost of selecting the sample. Such considerations as convenience, availability of information on which to stratify, availability of appropriate mapping materials, and work involved in subdividing into smaller areas should be the primary bases for making the decision whether to use such intermediate units in the selection of sample psu's.
>
> For example, a city with, say, 50,000 people would have about 60 ED's. A simple random sample of, say, 200 blocks would almost surely require drawing a sample in nearly every ED. Since nearly every ED must be subdivided, it is obvious that a procedure involving the sampling of smaller areas directly would be appropriate. However, with a sample of 200 blocks in a state having 3,000,000 people one may go into 5 or 10 per cent of the 4000 ED's, and therefore only a fraction of the ED's would need to be subdivided. This might mean a considerable reduction in sample selection work. The relative savings in clerical work would increase greatly for large areas such as regions or the United States.

---

* In this particular case the total area is 3,000,000 square miles, and the value of C_0 is assumed to be $.2\sqrt{3,000,000 \times 2} \doteq 500$. The factor of 2 under the radical is to provide for call-back costs, as illustrated in Ch. 6, Sec. 12. The .2 for cost per mile of travel is larger than the .14 direct cost assumed in the illustration in Chapter 6 because it is here assumed that living expenses are paid as well as salary, thus increasing the cost per hour of work.

The following illustration of large-psu sampling differs from the one just described in that the psu is much larger and several "blocks" are included in the sample from each psu.

3. A small sample from a large area with large primary units.   Illustration 3.1.

Suppose, now, that instead of the above procedure we apply the method summarized later in this chapter and use counties as the psu's, group them into strata, and select counties with probabilities proportionate to the estimated populations.   We then subsample from each primary unit a number of second-stage units of approximately the same average size as the blocks in Illustration 2.1, list the dwelling units or other listing units in these, and subsample them.   The over-all sampling fraction will be made the same for all strata.

Let us denote by m the number of primary units (counties) in the sample, by $\bar{n}$ the average number of second-stage units to be subsampled per psu in the sample, by $\bar{\bar{Q}}$ the average number of listing units per second-stage unit in the population, and by $\bar{\bar{q}}$ the average number of listing units in the sample per second-stage unit in the sample.   Let us suppose that the number of interviewers used is considerably less than the number of psu's in the sample, so that travel between psu's is still necessary in order to carry out the field interviewing.   The approximate cost function for the design will be represented by

$$C = C_0\sqrt{m} + C_1 m + C_2 m\bar{n} + C_3 m\sqrt{\bar{n}} + C_4 m\bar{n}\bar{\bar{q}}$$

where $C = 15,000$ (as before C is the total amount available in addition to overhead costs); and where:

$C_0 = 500$: This reflects the cost of travel between psu's and of telephone calls between psu's, and other costs that are proportionate to the distance between psu's.   As in small-cluster sampling, this value covers only communication between psu's, and not from one or more central points to and from the psu's.   This latter is spread over various contributions to the cost.

$C_1 = 20$.   This is the fixed cost associated with a psu in the sample. It will include, among other things, the cost of identifying the psu in the sample and of assembling the materials with which to draw the sample within the psu.

$C_2 = 3$.   This is the average cost per second-stage unit included in the sample, and includes the cost of selection of the second-stage units, designating the sample on maps, field identification, and listing.

$C_3 = 7$. This figure, when multiplied by $\sqrt{\bar{n}}$ may approximate roughly the cost of travel between blocks (second-stage units) within a psu. Since the average county in the sample will contain, say, 650 square miles, this might be $.2\sqrt{(650)(2)} = 7$, in line with the reasoning in Chapter 6 for small-cluster sampling.

$C_4 = 2$. This is the cost per listing unit included in the sample and is the same as in the small-cluster sampling design of Sec. 2.

For this sample design the rel-variance of an estimated mean or percentage will be approximately

$$V_r^2 \doteq \frac{V^2}{m\bar{n}\bar{\bar{q}}} [\delta_1 \bar{n}\bar{\bar{q}} + 1 + \delta_2(\bar{\bar{q}} - 1)] \qquad (3.1)$$

where δ_1 is the average within-strata measure of homogeneity between listing units within primary units, and δ_2 is the average measure of homogeneity between listing units within second-stage units (the average value computed within primary sampling units). These are specifically defined later in Sec. 17, where the nature of the approximation in Eq. 3.1 is also given along with a more accurate formula for the rel-variance.

For primary units as large as counties, the measure of homogencity ordinarily will be much smaller than for small clusters such as city blocks. In fact, with δ for blocks equal to .10, it would not be unusual for the value of δ_1 for counties to be as small as .01, or even considerably smaller. We shall assume in this illustration that the value of δ_1 is .01. If the actual value turned out to be smaller, the reduction in variance of the large-cluster approach over the small-cluster approach would be greater than will result from this illustration.

The value of δ_2, the average within-county measure of homogeneity between listing units within second-stage units, would be expected to be slightly less in this illustration than the value of δ of the preceding illustration. There δ is the same measure of homogeneity as δ_2 but within strata instead of within psu's (see remark below). For this illustration it is assumed that δ_2 is approximately equal to .09.

We now have the information necessary to obtain the optimum values of $\bar{n}$, $\bar{\bar{q}}$, and m. We can obtain these values by following through the steps given in Sec. 19, and they turn out to be $\bar{n} = 12$, $\bar{\bar{q}} = 5$, and $m = 56$ (the steps for this particular problem will be carried through as an illustration in Sec. 19).

By substituting these values in Eq. 3.1, we find that the rel-variance is .0012. We recall that the rel-variance for the illustration on the small-psu design was .0019. In these illustrations therefore, the variance of the small-psu design, for the same total cost, is 50 per cent larger than the variance of the "large-cluster" approach. There may be some additional advantages in the large-cluster approach which are not reflected in this computed increase in sampling efficiency. Some important advantages to be considered are summarized in the next section.

> **Remark.** We have assumed that the second- and third-stage units used in Illustration 3.1 are of the same type and size as the first- and second-stage units in Illustration 2.1. If the strata in Illustration 2.1 were the same as the primary strata in Illustration 3.1, and if all clusters had equal numbers of listing units, then the relationship between δ_2 and δ would be very nearly $\delta_2 = \delta - \delta_1$. In this illustration $\delta_1 = .01$, and $\delta = .10$. Therefore δ_2 would be approximately equal to .09. This does not differ enough from δ to be worth drawing any practical distinction, and we will not know the value of δ_2 this accurately, in any event. But in this instance we used .09 in order to have results consistent with those of the preceding illustration.

4. Some possible advantages of large-primary-unit sampling. The first advantage of large psu's to be mentioned is, of course, the point already illustrated in the preceding example: that, under appropriate circumstances, there will be a smaller variance of the sample estimates per unit of cost. This gain in precision per unit of cost depends on a considerable reduction in some of the unit costs.

Another advantage of large primary units over small primary units is the greater possibilities offered for control of nonsampling errors. As was indicated earlier (Introduction and Chapters 1 and 2), the control of nonsampling errors may be equal in importance to the control of sampling errors, and in many surveys will be of more importance. There is often a greater tendency to cut corners in making the call-backs necessary to obtain a response from a well-informed respondent if the better answer can be obtained only by traveling long distances or making long-distance telephone calls. When the distance between observations is large, such makeshift devices as talking to the neighbors, accepting answers from an uninformed respondent, or imputing the information from observation or by substitution may be resorted to more frequently.

In the large-cluster approach, call-backs can be completed more conveniently with more limited travel, particularly if the interviewer lives in the area where he works. The greater facility in making call-backs, and the tendency toward more nearly completing them when the sample is concentrated in a smaller area, are real advantages that cannot be fully reflected in the cost function.

The same type of argument holds for administrative controls to insure compliance with the survey design. It is easier to arrange for review and inspection of the work, and it may be easier to speed up operations and insure quality with the large-cluster method.

Factors such as these may sometimes make it desirable to cluster the sample into primary units to a greater extent than the available formulas for the optimum would indicate.

5. Some background considerations for large-primary-unit sample design. There are a number of variations in the nature of the problem, or in the type of resources to be used in taking a survey, that have an important bearing on the costs and on the design that is optimum for a particular problem. Such factors as type of survey organization, frequency of survey, and need for multiple statistics will affect the design of the sample. Some of these factors will now be considered.

Types of survey organization with small samples from large areas. Many different approaches to organizing a staff for carrying out field interviewing or other field work need to be considered in arriving at any particular survey design. Thus, at one extreme, all interviewers could be recruited centrally, trained, and sent out over the area to carry out the canvass. In this case, they would be in travel status, with additional costs for living expenses over and above the costs of travel, for all phases of the work. Such a central staff might be organized into groups and each group assigned a territory, or the members of the staff might be given individual assignments in various parts of the country. Under either arrangement the interviewers would not have established residences in the psu's to which they were assigned, and there would be the expense involved in maintaining them in travel status. Such a method might have the advantage of making it possible to use highly trained staff members and might be worth the extra costs involved, particularly if the work in the field were of a highly specialized character and if a one-time survey were being conducted, so that selecting and training a new field staff would be expensive. In addition, if such a staff knew of the need for, and were strongly interested in, the survey results, this knowledge and interest might serve as incentives to do the job more carefully and with higher production rates than would be expected from a temporary staff recruited in the field.

This central-staff method is relatively expensive per man-hour, because of the necessity of travel status and the cost of travel from a central point for the entire field organization, and should be used only if the advantages clearly outweigh the extra costs. The appropriate costs can be reflected in the cost function. The elements of cost arising from basic salaries may be increased to reflect the cost of living expenses whenever persons are doing work while in travel status overnight or longer. In addition, there is travel from the central point out to the assigned territory. Such travel, as we saw earlier (Ch. 6, Sec. 13), does not directly affect the average travel between psu's (reflected by the term involving the square root of m in the cost function) but is increased approximately in proportion to the number of different interviewers being sent out (assuming one trip from the central point per interviewer), which in turn will be determined by the total magnitude of the job.   The investigator planning the survey needs, in each particular case, to approximate the effect on the several terms of the cost function for the particular field organization, system of costs, and survey design being considered.

With this kind of field staff, perhaps the most important advantage in clustering the sample into primary units is that of call-backs, discussed earlier.   Consequently, the approach should lead to the minimum of clustering of the sample that is consistent with making call-backs convenient.   Some other considerations affecting the optimum amount of clustering of the sample are very difficult to reflect in the cost function, but need attention.   Thus, if the workload, in terms of completed interviews, in a psu is such that an eight-hour day is just enough to complete the work in that psu, and if the interviewers are willing to do their traveling in the evening or at night, then one psu can be done per day without loss of interviewers' time for travel.   If this is not even approximately the situation, then a real cut in performance rate can be expected to the extent that the day is used for travel.   Such factors are hard to foresee and reflect accurately in the cost function.

Another approach very similar to that of picking interviewers at a central point is to select interviewers residing in some of the selected psu's and willing to travel to other psu's.   The form of the cost function will be essentially the same in this case, but some of the elements of costs will be decreased to reflect the proportion of time that a person works in his own community at lower cost.

Another quite different system is to recruit interviewers locally, one or more within each of the selected psu's.   In this system, there is no payment for living expenses while away from home, and no travel between psu's, with considerable reductions in cost of the survey from this factor. This system puts a requirement on the design that there be sufficient clustering within psu's to justify the work of one or more interviewers in an area.   Training might be done in many ways, as, for example, by bringing the interviewers into one or several central points for training, by sending a limited number of supervisors or trainers to the psu's, or possibly simply by mailing the instructions to the interviewers.   The last method is likely to result in less control of the interviewer unless there are frequent field visits by supervisors to insure reasonable understanding of the instructions and performance.   Under this plan the cost of the supervisors' visits should be reflected in the appropriate terms of the cost

function.   If the clustering is sufficient, a supervisor might be assigned to
each psu or to a small group of psu's.   In the extreme, with a supervisor
for each separate psu, the fixed cost per psu would be increased considerably, and the optimum would call for considerably more clustering of the
sample within the selected psu's, and consequently for fewer and larger
psu's.

There are many other variations in design and approach of the survey
organization, each of which has its own impact on the survey design.

*Relationship of frequency and timing of the survey to large-psu sample
design.*   The most efficient choice of the type of field organization and the
most efficient choice of the sample design will depend upon how often
the survey is to be taken and on the time allowed for completing the work.
Thus, for a one-time survey, it may be uneconomical to use a relatively
costly method of sample selection and designation.   But for a repetitive
survey in which most of the basic work on design contributes to a considerable number of surveys, the initial cost of sample selection and of
interviewer selection and training may be trivial in relationship to the
aggregate of the survey costs.

The field organization's ability to train, direct, review, and control the
work also will be much affected by the frequency of the survey.   The
Current Population Survey and the Retail Trade Survey, referred to in
Case Studies B and A, Ch. 12, are illustrations of repetitive surveys.   A
common experience with repeated surveys is that the initial surveys in the
series are both more expensive per interview and less satisfactorily carried
out than subsequent ones.   This points to the need for great care in
one-time surveys to insure satisfactory work.

*Effect on survey design of the need for multiple statistics or of multiple
broad purposes to be served.*   For many types of multi-purpose surveys,
the large-primary-unit approach is advantageous, particularly if the
surveys are repetitive and a trained staff is available in individual psu's to
carry out different surveys.   Thus, in a sample of counties, population
samples can be readily drawn, as well as samples for other characteristics
that are closely associated with population, such as those of dwelling units
or families.   In addition, the same sample of counties will constitute
relatively heterogeneous units with respect to retail trade and many
services, and therefore may be good sampling units for estimating retail
sales, kinds of business, etc.   This may also be true for many other types
of business activities.   One may be able to use a single set of primary
units for many different types of surveys, with greater efficiency than would
result if each survey were carried out separately in its own set of sample
areas, selected to be best for the particular survey, because of the cost
advantages that come with joint operations and with overhead costs

spread over a number of surveys.   Such multi-purpose survey designs may be particularly convenient for survey or marketing organizations with broad types of activities or for government organizations.   Thus, the Bureau of the Census operates surveys of population, housing, family and individual income, and retail trade, and also numerous special investigations within the same sample of primary units.   Different subsampling methods are used within the psu's for different purposes, where this is desirable.   This plan results usually in variances that are not much larger for the size of sample than those for the best design for the particular types of surveys, and a considerable gain in efficiency for each type may be achieved because of the reduction through joint costs and the use of a trained field staff.

Summary.   The investigator needs to consider factors of the types mentioned above in connection with optimum survey design.   These factors affect the conditions under which the work will be carried out, the accuracy of the work, the speed, and many other aspects.   The decisions made on some of these points will partly determine the sample design and are partly consequences of considerations of the efficiency of alternative sample designs.   The broad implications of the various alternatives should be compared before arriving at a general decision on the problem of determining the specific survey design.

Remark 1.   Importance of psu contribution to variance and need for efficient psu sample.   One general remark is appropriate before introducing a step-by-step discussion of the sample design.   When the survey design is such that C_1, the fixed cost per psu, is large, it follows that the psu's are large, are relatively few in number, and include a fairly large subsample. Under these circumstances the between-psu contribution to the variance is often a substantial part of the total variance of a sample estimate.   It then becomes important to take advantage of techniques available to reduce this between-psu contribution to the variance.   Thus, not only is the definition of psu's of the appropriate size and type desirable, but also stratification of the primary units becomes more important than with small-cluster sampling for the same characteristics.   In addition, it may pay to exercise more care in the choice of estimation procedures and in the systems of probabilities used in selecting the primary units.   These and other principles will be discussed more fully below.

Remark 2.   Most accurate results for fixed size of sample if there is no clustering into psu's.   A point made in connection with small-cluster sampling needs particular emphasis in large-psu sampling.   When only a few psu's are included in the sample, it is particularly important to bear in mind that a large sample in terms of listing units does not necessarily mean a small sampling error.   An estimate based on a much smaller sample dispersed widely over a geographic area may have a considerably smaller sampling error.

Only consideration of nonsampling errors and large costs associated with a widely dispersed sample may dictate the clustering of the listing units into a relatively few psu's; without such considerations the design would call for no clustering.

Let us compare a design with no clustering of listing units but with the same size of sample as in Illustration 3.1. In that illustration, the optimum design with the cost conditions imposed called for a clustering of an average of 60 listing units per psu ($\bar{n}\bar{q} = 60$) and a total of 3360 listing units in the sample. Now assume that we retained the over-all sample size of 3360 but made $\bar{n}\bar{q} = 1$. In that case, from Eq. 3.1,

$$V_r^2 = \frac{2}{3306}\,[.01 + 1 + .09(0)] = .0006$$

This represents a reduction of about 50 per cent, as compared with the optimum large-cluster design. Had the measures of homogeneity been higher at either level, as is not infrequent, the reduction would have been still greater.

B. LARGE-PRIMARY-UNIT SAMPLING WITH A UNIFORM OVER-ALL SAMPLING FRACTION

6. Statement of the problem. The problem now to be considered is to obtain a small sample from a large area, using large primary sampling units and one or more stages of subsampling, with a uniform over-all sampling fraction.

A uniform over-all sampling fraction is near the optimum* whenever the ratio of the variance within the final-stage sampling units to the unit cost that varies directly with the number of final-stage units in the sample is about the same for all final-stage sampling units. This does not mean that with uniform sampling fractions there will be a very large increase in sampling error if these ratios have considerable variability. In practice, the convenience in having a self-weighting sample may be considerable. When there is doubt whether the variation in the costs or variances is large enough to justify variable over-all sampling fractions, an optimum design using variable rates based on estimated variances and costs can be compared with the optimum using a fixed over-all fraction. Usually, of course, the variances and costs required for this decision can be known in advance only very roughly, and as a consequence one uses fixed over-all sampling fractions, unless the advance knowledge clearly indicates a need for differential rates.

The important principles to consider in the design of a sample survey will be emphasized in the following discussion of the main steps in

---

* The proof is given in Vol. II, Ch. 9, Sec. 11.

designing and selecting the sample, preparing estimates, and evaluating their precision. We shall consider point by point some of the more important aspects of the problem and indicate some of the implications of each on good survey design. The topics to be developed include:

Definition of primary units.
Stratification of primary units.
Selection of the sample of primary units.
Sampling within the selected psu's.
The sample estimate.
The variance of the sample estimate.
Estimation of variances from the sample.
The cost function.
The optimum allocation of the sample.

The first step in this type of sample design, as in any other, is to determine the general nature of the problem—to formulate the purposes of the survey and to arrive at certain general decisions as to approach. It is necessary first to define the characteristic or the set of important characteristics to be estimated from the sample and to form an idea of the precision needed. From this the considerations of optimum design, when carried through roughly, will indicate the size of budget required. Alternative approaches should be considered, and that general approach to data collection and sample design should be selected which will yield maximum over-all accuracy per unit of cost, considering jointly both the effect of response errors and sampling precision.

We shall now consider a design in which we select a sample of primary units, within each of the selected primary units we select a sample of second-stage units, and finally we subsample listing units. Although, for the present, we confine our discussion to a design in which the same over-all sampling fraction is used in each stratum, this does not mean that the probabilities of selection need to be the same for all stages of sampling. It merely means that the product of the probabilities of sampling for the combined stages will be the same.

7. Definition of primary units. The first step we shall consider is the definition of the primary sampling units. The first phase of this step is to consider the alternative types of primary units that are available. Several types of primary units might be considered in sampling for characteristics of the population of business establishments, of farms, or of many other types of activity. For example, in the United States, we might use counties, small groups of counties, smaller units such as major parts of counties, still smaller units such as minor civil divisions or enumeration districts, or groups of such units. In other countries the counterparts of these might be used.

Some general characteristics of primary units need to be considered. In the first place, often the sample must include from 25 to 50 primary units at the very least, even if bare minimum standards of reliability are required for the survey results. The number required to achieve the necessary precision of results may be considerably greater. The population from which the sample is drawn will need to have considerably more than this number if there is to be any significant saving through the use of large primary units as a device for clustering the sample. Thus, whole states ordinarily would be unsatisfactory as primary units in drawing a sample from the United States. They are so large that one would have to include nearly all of them in the sample to obtain reliable results for many sampling purposes, and consequently practically no benefits from clustering would arise.

A second requirement of the psu is that it be uniquely and clearly defined, with boundaries mapped well enough to be identified in the field, or that it be a well-recognized political or administrative unit such that the elements associated with each such unit can be established by local inquiry or inspection. Administrative or political units such as counties, cities, and often minor civil divisions will meet these conditions quite satisfactorily.

Another characteristic of the psu that is desirable, although not essential, is that it be a unit for which statistical and other types of information are available. Such information is useful in stratifying, in selecting the sample, in preparing estimates from the sample, and sometimes also in evaluating the precision of sample results.

This, again, suggests that often the psu should be some type of political or natural unit, as was suggested earlier. We need not, however, accept the limitations of available units without modification. Obviously, the considerations that led to the establishment of counties or other political units are not necessarily those that are most desirable from a sampling point of view. However, one will frequently find that units already defined can be effectively used either directly or as building blocks to form primary units which may be more efficient than the units initially available.

Thus, some counties may be too small in population to be efficient population sampling units, or they may be small enough in area that very little will be lost in cost of administration or travel by grouping two or more of them in order to increase the internal heterogeneity of the unit. So long as cost is not significantly increased by increasing the size of the psu, the size should be increased, because the internal heterogeneity will usually increase with increased size, and loss of information due to clustering within psu's will be reduced (as was pointed out in Sec. 8, Ch. 6).

Sometimes it may be desirable to split a natural unit into two or more psu's even though this may mean that less statistical information is available for the resulting psu's. However, when considerable statistical information is available for the psu's but not for subdivisions of them, this approach should be employed sparingly. If used indiscriminately, it might mean loss of the ability to utilize available information for setting up strata and obtaining improved methods of estimation and of selecting psu's. A type of area may be inefficient as a psu when considered without regard to information available. It may be highly efficient when such available information is taken into account.

A logical question is, Since the larger the psu the better, why not increase the size indefinitely? Ultimately, this would reach the point where large psu's would not be used at all, since they would become co-extensive with the populations or strata from which the sample was being drawn. This sometimes may be the best answer. It will be, for example, in situations where the approach in Illustration 2.1, above, yields more reliable results than that in Illustration 3.1. Often, however, the increase in size of psu will be limited by the extra cost of traveling to cover the second-stage units throughout the psu. For a fixed number of psu's in the sample and a fixed number of second- and third-stage units of specified sizes sampled from the psu's the variance will decrease with increase in size of psu's. But the cost of travel, and perhaps other costs, will increase with the increasing spread of the sample. To arrive at the optimum size, one should continue increasing the size of the psu as long as the gains in sampling efficiency outweigh the added costs.

It is possible to determine the optimum average size of primary unit mathematically. However, restricting the choice to a relatively few reasonable alternatives will usually be sufficiently close to the optimum for all practical purposes. Thus, one can usually restrict the choice to units which are conveniently defined and for which at least some limited information on size and characteristics is available, or to combinations of such units. With a relatively few alternatives, one can compare them and choose the one that yields the lowest costs or variance. For a quick survey, not involving a large investment, it will probably be sufficient to use one of the readily available types of units. For a survey with considerable investment, more intensive investigations as to the optimum size and type of units should be undertaken.

There are ways other than changing the size of the psu in which heterogeneity can be introduced into the psu at little cost. Thus, if counties are being combined to form psu's, and one has a choice of pairing a county which is dominantly agricultural with one which is also agricultural, or with another which is dominantly urban, the latter will usually be the better choice, because it will make for greater internal heterogeneity within the psu. This illustration would hold, of course, only if rural and urban populations tend to differ with respect to the characteristic being estimated, which will be the case for a great many characteristics. The principle applies in any formulation of sampling units, no matter whether they are large or small.

Illustration 7.1. In a North Carolina sample study* an analysis was made of the variance between counties and also of the variance between minor civil divisions of counties. Both analyses were based on a fixed set of 20 strata. The psu's in each case were selected with probabilities proportionate to 1940 farms, and variances were computed for several 1945 agricultural characteristics. The comparison of the variances for simple unbiased estimates and ratio estimates to 1945 number of farms is shown in Table 1.

Table 1. Rel-variances for a sample of 20 psu's selected from 20 strata, with probability proportionate to number of farms in 1940

	Rel-variance			
Item (1945)	County as psu		MCD as psu	
	Unbiased estimate	Ratio estimate*	Unbiased estimate	Ratio estimate*
Number of tobacco farms	.0048	.0047	.0098	.0085
Acres of tobacco	.0058	.0061	.0127	.0125
Value of lands and buildings	.0027	.0020	.0096	.0070
Number of cotton farms	.0075	.0080	.0151	.0146
Acres of cotton	.0182	.0184	.0324	.0263
Number of nonwhite operators	.0063	.0054	.0160	.0138
Number of tenants	.0017	.0016	.0068	.0056

* The ratio to number of farms in 1945 is used for the ratio estimate.

In this illustration there is a consistent reduction in the between-psu variance for the larger psu. This reduction is reflected also in the

* Lillian H. Madow, "On the Use of the County as the Primary Sampling Unit for State Estimates," *J. Amer. Stat. Assn.*, **45** (1950), 30–47; and Marvin A. Kastenbaum, "On Sampling for State Estimates of the Farm Population in North Carolina Using the Township as a Primary Sampling Unit" (unpublished thesis), Raleigh, N.C., 1950, p. 13.

decreased value of the measures of homogeneity shown in Table 2, but increased *efficiency* of sample estimates will result from use of the larger psu only if the increased size of psu does not add to the costs more than it reduces the variance.

Table 2.   Measure of homogeneity, δ, between farms within counties and minor civil divisions

| Item (1945) | Measure of homogeneity, δ | | | |
| | County as psu | | MCD as psu | |
	Unbiased estimate	Ratio estimate*	Unbiased estimate	Ratio estimate*
Number of tobacco farms	.18	.19	.37	.32
Number of cotton farms	.13	.14	.27	.26
Number of nonwhite operators	.05	.05	.14	.12
Number of tenants	.03	.03	.12	.10

* The ratio to number of farms in 1945 is used for the ratio estimate.

In a national sample used by the Bureau of the Census for labor force sampling, and also for estimates of characteristics of the population and of retail trade, and for a number of other general purposes, it was decided to use counties, and frequently combinations of two or three individual counties, as the psu's.   This case is discussed more fully in Ch. 12, Case Studies A and B.

8. Stratification of primary units.   The second major step in designing the sample is to group the psu's into strata.   As was pointed out earlier (Sec. 4, Ch. 7), stratification of large primary units may be effective in reducing the variance even in situations where stratification of small clusters or of elements does not have a very important effect.*   Stratification of the psu's is particularly important when large subsamples are being included in the sample from each primary unit, since the between-primary-unit contribution to the variance may then be a significant part of the total variance.

It will often pay to sample as few as one or two primary units per stratum in order to take full advantage of the possible stratification gains, or perhaps go still further and use a method of sampling that introduces restrictions in the sample selections as between strata in order to increase

* For proof, see Vol. II, Ch. 9, Sec. 9.

the effectiveness of stratification. (See Ch. 11, Sec. 4.) The only basis for taking more than one unit per stratum is to make it possible to estimate the variance from the sample itself. If, however, the gain from further stratification is sufficiently worth while, it may still pay to take only one unit per stratum and perhaps to use a restricted design (as discussed in Ch. 11, Sec. 4), at the expense of not being able to obtain an unbiased or consistent estimate of the variance directly from the sample itself. The actual variance of estimates from the sample will then be somewhat smaller than the expected value of the estimate of the variance, and it may be desirable to make variance estimates from supplemental data (see Ch. 10, Sec. 19). We shall proceed on the assumption that the decision has been made to draw either one or two psu's per stratum.

If a fixed number of psu's (whether one psu or more than one) is to be included in the sample from each stratum, and if the variances between psu's do not differ too widely among strata, it will be desirable to make the sizes of all strata approximately the same with respect to a measure of size that is highly correlated with the denominator of the ratio that is being estimated. It is desirable, also, to achieve the maximum differentiation between strata with respect to the average values of the characteristics to be estimated. It is the second of these principles that applies in general in stratification, and involves the principal work of examining and classifying the psu's in order to accomplish as much homogeneity as possible within strata with respect to the characteristics being estimated and as much heterogeneity as possible between strata.*

What we mean by saying that the sizes of strata should be equalized with respect to a characteristic is that the aggregate value of that characteristic over all psu's in a stratum should be approximately the same for all strata. The measures used in determining and equalizing the sizes of the strata will ordinarily be the same as the measures used for assigning the probabilities with which the psu's are to be selected.

Let us consider the principle of equalizing the sizes of strata first from the point of view of a single statistic to be estimated from the sample, and then consider its implications when a number of statistics are being sampled or a general-purpose sample is being drawn.

If the sample is being drawn solely to estimate an average value for the population, such as the proportion of the total families that have incomes in a particular income class, then the units on which the aggregate numbers

---

* Of course, with large psu's that are already made internally as heterogeneous as feasible, following the principles of the preceding section, there will be somewhat less opportunity for classifying such psu's effectively so as to achieve substantial differences between the strata. But the object is to go as far as is practicable with this classification after the psu's have been defined.

in the strata should be equalized are the total number of families.   If, on the other hand, the sole purpose is to measure a characteristic for a subset of all families, such as the proportion of nonwhite families that have incomes in a particular income class, then the strata should be equalized with respect to the number of nonwhite families.

This rough rule for approximating the optimum sizes of strata applies, of course, only if the costs are about the same in the different strata.   If the costs or variances are strikingly different between strata, this fact will affect the design, as indicated in a later section (Sec. 24).

One will often find himself in the dilemma of attempting to apply two opposing principles given for defining strata, i.e., to make them as internally homogeneous as possible and at the same time to make them about equal in size.   Thus, one may, for example, be able to increase the internal homogeneity of each of the strata by making some strata much larger, and some much smaller, than average.   If, in fact, enough increase in homogeneity can be achieved thereby, it will be worth while.   However, one should be cautious in proceeding far in this direction unless the gains in increased homogeneity within strata are considerable.

As an illustration, we shall consider a hypothetical population which is divided into strata, from each of which one psu is selected and sub-sampled.   Consider an estimate of the form $r = x'/y'$, and the rel-variance given by Eq. 5.14 of Ch. 7.   For this illustration the psu contribution to the variance, with one psu per stratum, would be equal to $\Sigma Y_h^2 \hat{S}_h^2 / Y^2$, where $\hat{S}_h^2 = S_{1h}^2 / \bar{Y}_h^2 R^2$, $\bar{Y}_h = Y_h/M_h$, $Y = \Sigma Y_h$, and $R = X/Y$ and where S_{1h}^2 is defined by Eq. 5.4, Ch. 7.   The $\hat{S}_h^2$ is proportionate to the approximation to the variance within the hth stratum of the ratios X_{hi}/Y_{hi}. Let us confine our comparison to a pair of strata which have been equalized in size in terms of the Y's, i.e., $Y_h/Y = \frac{1}{2}$ for both strata. Assume that the values of $\hat{S}_h^2$ are as given below:

CASE I

Stratum	$\dfrac{Y_h}{Y}$	$\hat{S}_h^2$	$\dfrac{Y_h^2}{Y^2}\hat{S}_h^2$
a	$\frac{1}{2}$	2	$.5 = (\frac{1}{2})^2(2)$
b	$\frac{1}{2}$	3	$.75 = (\frac{1}{2})^2(3)$
Total			1.25

But suppose that by making stratum a three times as big as stratum b, through the process of transferring half the psu's from b to a, it turned out that the transferred psu's were similar to those in a, and that the transfer removed much of the heterogeneity in b and reduced the variance between psu's in that stratum by one-third. This might then yield the following result:

CASE II

Stratum	$\dfrac{Y_h}{Y}$	$\hat{S}_h^2$	$\dfrac{Y_h^2}{Y^2}\hat{S}_h^2$
a'	$\tfrac{3}{4}$	2	$1.125 = (\tfrac{3}{4})^2(2)$
b'	$\tfrac{1}{4}$	2	$.125 = (\tfrac{1}{4})^2(2)$
Total			1.250

Even with the considerably smaller variance in stratum b and no increase in the variance in stratum a, there is no reduction in the total between-psu variance.

We have a most interesting and striking result in this illustration. Suppose now that this situation was repeated throughout the other strata being set up for the survey. It would then be true that *for half the strata the between-psu variances within strata would be 50 per cent larger* (and the *average* within-psu variance would be *25 per cent larger*) when the equal instead of the unequal sized strata were used. Nevertheless, the variance of the estimate would be *no smaller* with the unequal but more homogeneous strata. In this situation, the investigator might at first be led to conclude that the more homogeneous strata of unequal size would be as good a choice as the equalized strata, and that either stratification would be equally satisfactory.

However, in practice, this conclusion would not be sound. Ordinarily, one would not know the variances in the respective strata, and he would have to estimate them. Some error in estimating these variances might lead him to believe that he was getting an improved result when in fact the result was worse. Moreover, if one is speculating on the variances rather than actually computing them, it is a rather common intuitive error to speculate that more is accomplished in reducing variances through stratification than is in fact achieved. Thus, if the within-stratum variance in Case II above were estimated from a sample or represented numbers speculated from past data, the use of unequal sizes of strata might actually introduce a larger sampling error than the use of equal sizes of strata, even though the computations from the speculated numbers indicated no increase in sampling error. It is possible, too, for one to proceed laboriously to redefine a population originally defined in terms of equal sizes of strata and then discover to his dismay that, even though he has been·successful in reducing the within variance for each of the resulting strata, the total variance has been increased. Such a situation is illustrated by Ex. 8.1. If it were possible to make more substantial reductions in the variances within strata, the variance of the estimate would be reduced, as illustrated in Ex. 8.2.

Remark 1. If one is making a simple unbiased estimate of a total (Eq. 6.1, Ch. 8), the appropriate measure of size for each psu is a measure that is, as nearly as possible, proportionate with this total itself. The probabilities of selection of psu's should be proportionate to this measure, and the sizes of the strata equalized with respect to it.

Remark 2. If the *rel-variances* between psu's are more nearly alike among the primary strata than the *variances*, the measures of size on which the strata should be equalized should be as nearly as possible proportionate to the characteristic in the numerator of the ratio being estimated, instead of the denominator.

Exercises

8.1.   Consider a sample of psu's grouped into strata of equal size for which within-strata variances are:

STRATUM	RELATIVE SIZE OF STRATUM Y_h/Y	APPROXIMATE WITHIN-STRATA VARIANCE BETWEEN PSU'S $\widehat{S}_h^2 = S_{1h}^2/\bar{Y}_h^2 R^2$
a	.25	3
b	.25	5
c	.25	7
d	.25	10

Suppose that by regrouping strata the within-strata variance can be reduced so that we now have:

STRATUM	RELATIVE SIZE OF STRATUM Y_h/Y	APPROXIMATE WITHIN-STRATA VARIANCE BETWEEN PSU'S $\widehat{S}_h^2 = S_{1h}^2/\bar{Y}_h^2 R^2$
a'	.125	2
b'	.25	4
c'	.25	6
d'	.375	8

Calculate the variance of the sample estimate for the regrouped strata, when one psu is selected from each stratum. Note that although all the within-strata variances were decreased, the variance of the sample estimate was increased.

8.2. Suppose that it is possible to find a third grouping having within-strata variances as shown below:

STRATUM	RELATIVE SIZE OF STRATUM	WITHIN-STRATA VARIANCE BETWEEN PSU'S
a''	.025	2
b''	.125	4
c''	.35	4
d''	.50	3

Compare the variance for the regrouped strata with the variance in Ex. 8.1.

Of course, in making a comparison for strata, such as that illustrated above, where the investigator feels that there is some prospect for gain by making strata unequal in size, one must have an estimate of the between-psu variances within the strata. If very closely related data are available for the total population, these variances can be estimated directly from such data and used as a guide (employing the formulas to be given later).

But frequently a good reason for equalizing the sizes of strata stems from the need for estimating multiple statistics, more than one of which is important in the survey. If proportionate sampling as between the strata would be roughly satisfactory for these statistics, or if quite different allocations are optimum for the different characteristics, strata of equal size, or at least strata not varying tremendously in size, may be advantageous.

With multiple statistics, if the investigator has decided to equalize the sizes of the strata, he still has to determine the measure of size to use. If all statistics being estimated are averages or ratios based on the same total, the measures of size should be the corresponding psu totals, or estimates of these numbers, or numbers known in advance that are presumed to be highly correlated with them. But often the statistics to be estimated are percentages, averages, or ratios based on different sets of units. Those averages that are based on numbers highly correlated with the total of all classes of elementary units in the population will be treated adequately by equalizing the sizes in terms of the total number of elementary units. But for others, equalizing the strata in terms of the total number of elementary units may not be satisfactory. In such instances, as in some other multiple statistics problems, one may make a compromise choice that will yield the maximum of accuracy for the more important statistics to be estimated. One must then be prepared to accept any consequent loss in efficiency for the remaining items and perhaps to use special supplementation of the sample for certain items in order to achieve the required precision of results.

In many problems it may happen that some psu's are individually considerably larger than the average size of stratum decided upon. The handling of this problem, along with related ones, is taken up in Sec. 10.

9. Number of strata when a fixed number of psu's is included from each stratum. In Chapter 7, in determining the optimum number of psu's to be included in the sample, the steps followed were: (1) set up a fixed number of strata; (2) estimate the appropriate within-strata variances; and (3) determine opt. m, the number of psu's to be included in the sample.   There, the determination of the optimum number of psu's to be included was essentially independent of the number of strata.   On the other hand, when a fixed number of psu's is to be selected from each stratum, as is recommended here, the number of strata will not be independent of m.   For example, if it is decided that one psu is to be selected from each stratum, the number of strata (L) will be equal to m.   Suppose that the average within-strata variance between psu's is computed for some arbitrary number of strata, say L'.   Then, if the optimum m is computed on the basis of this variance, the optimum m will differ from L'.   Some additional steps are then needed to determine m and L jointly in such a way that $m = L$ if there is to be one psu per stratum, or $m = 2L$ if there are to be two psu's per stratum, etc.

The investigator may make a joint determination of the within variance and opt. m in the following way.   He may proceed by calculating the within-strata variance for an arbitrary number of strata, say 50.   He may then use this value of the variance and arrive at a first value for m, say m_1.   Setting up m_1 strata, he may recalculate the within-strata variance, and arrive at another value of m, say m_2.

Proceeding in this fashion, he will usually find that the successive values of m converge.   In fact, in two or three trials, if not in the initial one, the value of m may be close to the optimum.   Thus, the problem would present no real difficulty if the necessary data were at hand.   In practice, however, the data needed for the refined calculation indicated above usually are not readily available.   One must speculate with past data, or conduct a small-scale pilot study which is bound to give results that are not sufficiently reliable to permit refined calculations.   As a rule of thumb, one can estimate the variance between psu's within strata for, say, 80 strata, and then accept the value of m which is arrived at by the steps indicated in Sec. 19 unless this value of m is greater than 150 or less than 50.   If it is outside these values, a recomputation of the variance can be made.

10. Treatment of large psu's.   Often the initial determination of the average stratum size will need to be revised because one will find that the size of one or of a number of the individual psu's will greatly exceed this average stratum size.   Thus, in the United States, New York City (or the psu containing it) will be larger than the average stratum size in almost any sample for estimating characteristics of the population and of business establishments.   When the investigator has the situation where such psu's exceed, say, two-thirds of the average stratum size, he takes all these large psu's into the sample, i.e., each of these large psu's is defined to comprise a separate stratum.   He then subtracts the number of these large psu's from m and their aggregate size from the total population size, and ascertains the average size for the remaining strata. There may still be some individual psu's larger than two-thirds of the new average size, and if so, these are set up separately, as above. After these psu's, if any, have been taken care of, the average size is computed, and the remaining psu's are grouped into classes of roughly this average size.

The psu's that will be large enough to constitute individual strata will represent only themselves in the sample, and these particular psu's need not be defined by following the principle of heterogeneity within the psu's that was suggested in Sec. 7. For the large psu's that constitute strata in their own right and represent only themselves, and therefore come into the sample with certainty, the convenience of the area as an administrative unit for carrying on the survey should be the principal consideration in defining its boundaries and fixing its size.

> **Remark.** With large psu's, stratification of the psu's is more important than with small psu's. Considerable attention should be given to it. However, one should not spend a great deal of time in looking for the best "modes" of stratification. Many alternative modes will give equally good results. Important supplemental information that cannot be used in the stratification can sometimes be taken into account subsequently in the sample selection and in the estimation procedure. In fact, inattention to the proper application of the principles of optimum allocation (which may result in too many or too few psu's in the sample) and failure to employ the appropriate selection and estimation procedures may increase the variance more than can the arbitrary choice of methods of stratification among the many possible alternatives.

It should be clear to the investigator that the method of stratification proposed here, with equal-sized strata in terms of some aggregate characteristic, will result in strata that contain very different *numbers of psu's* in the population. The number of psu's in a stratum may vary from one to perhaps several hundred or thousand in some problems.

Illustration 10.1. The kinds of gains to be expected from different modes and levels of stratification of counties as psu's are illustrated by the data in Table 3, based on an unpublished study by H. Nisselson, R. Goodman, and F. Berger. The "Hagood strata" were established* within broad types of farming areas and regions after an analysis of principal components to establish an index as a guide for maximizing the differences between strata with respect to a set of economic and social

---

* Margaret Jarman Hagood, "The BAE General Purpose Sample of 101 Counties," U.S. Department of Agriculture, Bureau of Agricultural Economics, February 1945 (processed report); also, Margaret Jarman Hagood and Eleanor H. Bernert, "Component Indexes as a Basis for Stratification in Sampling," *J. Amer. Stat. Assn.*, **40** (1945), 330–341.

characteristics for rural areas. The data used were drawn primarily from the 1940 Censuses of Population and Agriculture. The counties in a stratum are not necessarily contiguous.

The "Jessen strata" were established on the basis of expert judgment with emphasis placed on soil type, type of farming, and geographic location, with only geographically contiguous counties within a stratum.

The sizes of both the Hagood and the Jessen strata were roughly equalized in terms of numbers of farms, and the design called for selection of one psu from each stratum with probability proportionate to the number of farms. The size of sample in each case is the same as the number of strata. Table 3 shows the estimated average rel-variances between counties within the strata for estimates of a number of agricultural characteristics with these samples.

The general principle expressed in the Remark above is brought out clearly in this table. Whereas the broad types of stratification were similar in both cases, the points of emphasis were different. Still, the magnitudes of the variances from both types of stratification for the same sample sizes are of about the same order. Some items are better estimated from the Jessen strata, others from the Hagood strata, but neither is uniformly better for all items.

To measure the gains due to greater depth of stratification in Table 3 the differing numbers of psu's must be taken into account. For example, to measure the gain from stratification going from 100 to 200 strata, one should divide the rel-variance in the 100-strata case by 2 to represent the rel-variance one would get if a sample of 2 psu's were selected from each of the 100 strata. The difference between that result and the rel-variance shown for 200 strata then would measure approximately the reduction in variance due to the additional stratification. Any apparent losses from the additional stratification probably represent only the variances of the estimated variances.

The rel-variances at the bottom of Table 3 for ratio estimates also indicate how the use of supplemental information with an appropriate method of estimation brings about further reductions in the variance. For example, the additional reductions in the rel-variance with the use of ratio estimates based on the same characteristic in the preceding census range from 50 to 90 per cent. The comparable reductions in using different modes of stratification are nowhere near that large. In fact, going from 100 to 200 strata with the use of ratio estimates by and large shows trivial gains from the additional stratification. The reductions in variance shown for the ratio estimates are about what would be expected from the increase in size of sample. The gains from additional stratification are often worth while for the simple unbiased estimate.

Table 3. Precision of estimates of specified items from 1935 Census of Agriculture for Hagood and Jessen county samples—United States totals*

Item	Estimated rel-variance of sample estimate			
	Hagood sample		Jessen sample	
	101 strata	196 strata	100 strata	200 strata
Simple unbiased estimate				
Total acres in farms	.01547	.00640	.01504	.00659
Cropland harvested (acres)	.00156	.00074	.00135	.00077
Value of land and buildings (dollars)	.00172	.00073	.00133	.00059
Number of farms of 10–29 acres	.00206	.00096	.00183	.00104
Land in farms of 140–179 acres	.00188	.00084	.00149	.00044
Cropland harvested, farms of 10–29 acres	.00273	.00124	.00327	.00149
Ratio estimate—ratio to 1940 Census data for the same characteristic				
Total acres in farms	.00098	.00041		
Cropland harvested (acres)	.00057	.00023		
Value of land and buildings (dollars)	.00075	.00030		
Number of farms of 10–29 acres	.00044	.00021	.00061	
Land in farms of 140–179 acres	.00023	.00010	.00023	
Cropland harvested, farms of 10–29 acres	.00077	.00037	.00101	

* 1945 Census data were not available at the time of this analysis. Estimation of 1935 Census characteristics was used to simulate the estimation of characteristics for years subsequent to 1940.

11. Selection of the sample of primary sampling units. After having classified the psu's into strata, the next step is to select the sample psu's, perhaps either one or two from each stratum. For the method of stratification just outlined, the number of psu's will differ from stratum to stratum, and therefore the probability of selection of a psu will not be the same in the various strata.

A frequent problem in selecting large psu's arises when there is wide variation in the sizes (in terms of the elementary units being sampled or other measures) of the psu's. A number of size strata could be set up to control the variability in size, but then a large proportion of the already limited number of strata available would be exhausted in order to control this source of variation, and there would be less opportunity for stratification on the basis of other important characteristics that may be considerably more effective in differentiating among the resulting strata.

Stratification on the basis of size may gain little and should be avoided in situations where it is economical to use probability proportionate to size in selection.* The only exception occurs when size is highly correlated with the average or percentage or ratio to be estimated, or when the measure of size is not roughly proportionate to the psu aggregate for a characteristic if a simple unbiased estimate of a total is to be made. (The relationship between probability proportionate to size and stratification by size is indicated in Ch. 8, Sec. 14.)

Selection of a single psu from a stratum with probability proportionate to a measure of size can be illustrated as follows. Suppose that we wish to estimate the number of persons that have a particular characteristic, and that we have a stratum containing 4 psu's and wish to select 1 of the units with probability proportionate to the number of inhabitants in the unit in a past census. Suppose that the population (and cumulative totals) in those units are as given in the table below.

PRIMARY SAMPLING UNIT	1940 POPULATION	CUMULATIVE TOTAL
No. 1	85,938	85,938
No. 2	60,835	146,773
No. 3	10,976	157,749
No. 4	35,127	192,876

The order in which the psu's are entered in the table is immaterial. The first step is to draw a number from a table of six-digit random numbers. If the number is greater than 192,876, draw another number. Primary sampling unit No. 1 will be selected if the number drawn is any number from 000,001 to 085,938 inclusive. Primary sampling unit No. 2 will be selected if the number drawn is any number between 085,939 to 146,773 inclusive, psu No. 3 if the number drawn is any number between 146,774 to 157,749 inclusive, and psu No. 4 if the number drawn is between 157,750 and 192,876. Note that, of the 192,876 possible numbers from 000,001 to 192,876 inclusive, psu No. 1 would be selected for 85,938 of them, psu No. 2 for 60,835 of them, psu No. 3 for 10,976 of them, and psu No. 4 for 35,127 of them. In other words, the probability of psu No. 1 being selected is 85,938/192,876. The probabilities for psu's No. 2, 3, and 4 are 60,835/192,876, 10,976/192,876, and 35,127/192,876, respectively. These probabilities are proportionate to the measures of size.

The following illustration shows how the estimating procedure avoids a bias when units are drawn with varying probabilities.

---

* For the conditions under which a gain is to be expected with pps see Vol. II, Ch. 9, Sec. 2.

Illustration 11.1. Assume that the stratum being considered is the one given on p. 391, and in addition that total employment figures are as given below.

PRIMARY SAMPLING UNIT	1940 POPULATION	1945 EMPLOYMENT
No. 1	85,938	60,632
No. 2	60,835	44,832
No. 3	10,976	6,847
No. 4	35,127	22,833

Now assume that we want to estimate the total 1945 employment, drawing one psu from this stratum, with probability proportionate to 1940 sizes. An unbiased estimating procedure is

$$x' = \sum_h^L \frac{X_{hi}}{P_{hi}} \tag{11.1}$$

where X_{hi} is the total employment for the ith unit in the hth stratum; P_{hi} is the probability with which the ith unit is selected; and L is the number of strata. It will be recalled that the expected value of an estimate is equal to its average for all possible samples. The probability of selection for each unit, along with the number of samples in which each occurs, is given on p. 391. Since we are dealing with a single stratum, the estimate for the stratum total will simply be equal to X_{hi}/P_{hi}.

Exercise 11.1. Find the expected value of x' in this illustration, and show that it is unbiased.

When the psu is sampled with probability proportionate to size, the subsampling rate can be made proportionate to the reciprocal of the size, and then the sampling fraction within the entire stratum will be the same no matter which psu is in the sample. The sampling fraction within the selected psu will of course depend on the psu that is selected. With this method of subsampling, a uniform over-all sampling fraction is obtained, and the sample is "self-weighting": no special adjustment in the estimate is required because of the varying probabilities in the selection of the primary units. Note that this is not the case when there is no subsampling, the estimating procedure then being given by Eq. 11.1.

Thus, suppose that a uniform sampling fraction f is to be taken from all strata. Suppose that within each stratum the psu is selected with probability proportionate to some measure of size, and that A_{hi} is the measure of size of the psu that happens to be selected within the hth stratum. Then $P_{hi} = (A_{hi}/A_h)$ is the probability of selecting this particular psu.

The over-all sampling rate f is the product of the probability of selecting the psu and the subsampling fraction within the psu. If we let Q_{hi} be the total number of listing units in the ith psu of the hth stratum and q_{hi} the number in the sample, then q_{hi}/Q_{hi} will be the subsampling rate from the hith psu.   By letting $f = P_{hi}(q_{hi}/Q_{hi})$, we get

$$\frac{q_{hi}}{Q_{hi}} = \frac{f}{P_{hi}} \qquad (11.2)$$

In practice the desirability of using probability proportionate to size in selecting the psu's depends primarily upon whether or not there is any significant added cost in subsampling from within a psu of large size as compared with one of small size.   As was indicated in Ch. 8, Sec. 14, probability proportionate to size usually will give higher precision of results per unit of cost than the alternatives considered only if there will be no substantial difference in cost for a psu with a large measure of size as compared with a psu with a small measure of size, for the subsampling or field work to be done in the psu.

The differences in cost are often relatively small in practice because the sampling from large psu's does not involve field listing for subsampling, but rather simply an accounting for blocks or segments on a block map, and subsampling these, or a similar process.   Also the psu with a big measure of size may be more densely populated, but not larger in area, so that field travel is not necessarily more widespread.   Even if the psu is considerably larger physically and thus may have a higher travel cost, this factor alone may not have a substantial impact on cost, particularly if the subsample is large.

Alternatives to selection with pps that should be considered are selection with equal probability and selection with probability proportionate to square root of size.   The conditions where each may have advantages are given in Ch. 8, Sec. 14.

The number of elementary units in the subsample will be the same *on the average* by each of the methods of selection if a uniform over-all sampling fraction is used.   With pps, however, the number subsampled in a stratum will be nearly the same (if the measures of size are good) no matter what psu is selected, and the same for all strata, if the strata are equal in size.   With equal probability the number subsampled will vary from psu to psu.   This points to another possible advantage of pps over equal probability in that the workload with pps will be about the same no matter which psu falls in the sample.   With equal probability there may be several times as large a workload in one psu as in another. This advantage of pps may not be particularly significant for some types of field work, but if one is operating a continuing survey, with a worker in each psu, the equalization of the workload may have significant advantages.

Another possible advantage of pps over equal probability, particularly for general-purpose sampling, is that pps places the survey organization in a higher proportion of large cities or other centers, where it is often more convenient to operate and to train personnel, as travel and other facilities usually are better than for smaller areas.

Whenever probability proportionate to the square root of size or equal probability is used, one either will be estimating averages or ratios or will use a ratio or regression type estimate in order to obtain estimates of totals; this will often be desirable with pps, also, to reduce the variance of subsampling or if the measures of size are not close to the actual sizes.

The use of probability proportionate to the square root of size will have advantages when pps results in added costs. However, in practice, with large-psu sampling, one ordinarily will not go far astray by sampling with pps, as long as the costs do not depend significantly on the size of the psu, and this is approximately the case in a large number of problems.

12. Sampling within the selected psu's. It is assumed throughout this chapter, except where otherwise specified, that only one psu is to be taken from a stratum, that it will be selected with pps, and that the sample is self-weighting. Once the psu's are chosen we must draw the subsample from each selected psu. It is at this point that the treatment of large-psu sampling is in one respect quite different from that of small-psu sampling given in Chapter 6. One of the feasible methods of drawing a sample when the psu's are small is to list every household or store or farm in the selected psu and draw a subsample from this listing. With large-psu sampling, listing the entire unit will usually be unnecessary and exceedingly wasteful of the time and money available for the survey.

Subsampling within selected psu's is effectively the same problem as that of drawing a sample from a local area by means of procedures discussed in Chapter 6. Thus, in most important respects, one may conceive of each psu as a local area, and the method of drawing that sample will follow closely the principles given in the preceding chapters. This does not mean that the sample to be drawn from each psu should or will be large enough to give a small sampling error for each psu. The precision of the estimate for the total sample depends on the aggregate of the small samples drawn from each of a number of psu's. Thus the total sample estimate may have a small variance even though the variance of the estimate for each psu taken individually is enormous. We should take full advantage of the available resources in each psu to minimize the sampling variance for the psu. Different resources may be utilized in subsampling from the different psu's or from the different substrata within a psu.   Thus, one could stratify in subsampling within the psu's, and use the most efficient types of subsampling units in the various substrata.   The sampling resources may differ, for example, between urban and rural areas.

Before one can actually carry through the subsampling within a psu, he must determine the general approach to the subsampling, the substrata into which the psu can be divided, the second- and third-stage sampling units, the fraction of the second-stage units to be included in the sample, and the fraction of listing units to be subsampled from the selected second-stage units.

Sometimes the second-stage units will be given, i.e., only one feasible or reasonable type will be available, and in this event a determination of the average size of the ultimate cluster will be sufficient to determine the second- and third-stage sampling fractions.   Thus, suppose that only a city block map is conveniently available for defining the second-stage units, and city blocks are chosen as the second-stage units.   In this event, a knowledge of the over-all within-psu sampling fraction and of $\bar{\bar{q}}$, the expected value of the average number of listing units to be included in the sample per second-stage unit included in the sample, will be sufficient to determine both the second-stage sampling fraction and the sampling fraction within second-stage units.   We shall consider only this case in the optimum sampling theory to be presented.   The comparison of the relative efficiency of the alternative types of second-stage units is made by observing the minimum variances for various alternatives.

We have already indicated, in the discussion of the selection of the psu, that the within-psu sampling fraction will be fixed by the over-all sampling fraction and by the probability of selection of the particular psu.   This subsampling fraction is given by

$$\frac{q_{hi}}{Q_{hi}} = \frac{f}{P_{hi}} \tag{12.1}$$

where f is the over-all uniform sampling rate and P_{hi} is the probability that the particular psu had of being selected.   This holds no matter whether equal probability or variable probabilities are used in the selection of the psu's within strata.   With q_{hi}/Q_{hi} as the over-all within-psu sampling rate for the hith psu, one then proceeds to carry through the sampling within the psu's in accordance with the principles already given in earlier chapters.

We shall describe how to arrive at an approximation to the optimum allocation of the sample after consideration of the types of estimates that may be made from the sample, and the variances of these estimates.

13. The sample estimate. If X is the value of a characteristic to be estimated from the sample, and x is the aggregate value of this characteristic for the sample, and if a constant over-all sampling rate of f has been used in all strata, then a simple unbiased estimate of X will be given by

$$x' = x \frac{1}{f} \tag{13.1}$$

This estimate may be satisfactory if probability proportionate to size has been used in selecting the sample, and if the measures of size are good. But often, in estimating a total, a ratio estimate of the type discussed in preceding chapters, or a regression estimate of the type discussed in Chapter 11, may be used, and there will often be significant gains by employing one of them. Perhaps most often one will be estimating averages or ratios from the sample. For such an average or ratio, or for a ratio estimate used in estimating a total, the estimate may be of the form

$$r = \frac{x'}{y'} = \frac{x}{y} \tag{13.2}$$

where y is the number of elementary units in the sample on which the average or percentage is based or is the aggregate from the sample for a second characteristic. We shall give first the variance and optimum design considerations for estimates 13.1 and 13.2 above, and then indicate later (Sec. 23) some other estimates that may sometimes be desirable.

When the sample is not self-weighting, the form of the estimate is more complicated than formula 13.1 or 13.2. For a more general estimate see Sec. 25.

14. The variance of the sample estimate. We shall assume that there are three stages of sampling and two stages of stratification, that the psu's are selected with varying probabilities, that a constant number, $\bar{m}$, of the psu's are selected from each primary stratum, and that there is a uniform over-all sampling fraction. In addition for simplicity we shall assume that the second-stage sampling fraction is small relative to 1 and the third-stage sampling fraction is constant for all second-stage units. For many practical problems, in a self-weighting sample, the results given may be satisfactory even though the last two assumptions are not met.

For the more general approach in which differential weighting is used (i.e., variable sampling fractions) the reader is referred to Sec. 26. A self-weighting sample is a special case of the general variance formula Eq. 26.1 and is arrived at by setting the product of the sampling fractions equal to a constant.

For those interested only in knowing how to estimate the precision of r from a sample, it is unnecessary to read this section. Such a reader may proceed directly to Sec. 15, which gives some simple estimating formulas that do not involve making separate estimates of each of the variance components.

The rel-variance* of r (Eq. 13.2) is approximately

$$V_r^2 \doteq \frac{B^2}{m} + \frac{W_b^2}{m\bar{n}} + \frac{\bar{\bar{Q}} - \bar{\bar{q}}}{\bar{\bar{Q}}} \frac{W_w^2}{m\bar{n}\bar{q}} \tag{14.1}$$

where the terms in each of the contributions are defined below.

The contribution of the first-stage sampling to the rel-variance, B^2/m, is the rel-variance for a sample of m primary sampling units without sub-sampling. It is assumed that the sampling is done with replacement if more than one primary unit is drawn from a stratum, and that the same number, $\bar{m}$, of primary units is drawn from each stratum. Here m is the total number of primary units in the sample, $\bar{n}$ is the expected value of the average number of second-stage units in the sample per sample primary unit, $\bar{\bar{Q}}$ is the average number of third-stage units per second-stage unit in the population, and $\bar{q}$ is the expected value of the number of third-stage units in the sample per second-stage unit in the sample. Specifically,

$$B^2 = B_X^2 + B_Y^2 - 2B_{XY} \tag{14.2}$$

where

$$B_{XY} = \frac{\displaystyle\sum_h^L \sum_i^{M_h} P_{hi} \left(\frac{X_{hi}}{P_{hi}} - X_h \right) \left(\frac{Y_{hi}}{P_{hi}} - Y_h \right)}{L\hat{X}\hat{Y}}$$

$$= \frac{\displaystyle\sum_h^L S_{hXY}}{L\hat{X}\hat{Y}} \tag{14.3}$$

where

$$S_{hXY} = \sum_i^{M_h} P_{hi} \left(\frac{X_{hi}}{P_{hi}} - X_h \right) \left(\frac{Y_{hi}}{P_{hi}} - Y_h \right) \tag{14.4}$$

and X_{hi} is the aggregate of the X characteristic for the ith primary sampling unit in the hth stratum, X_h is the corresponding stratum total, P_{hi} is the probability of selecting the ith primary unit of the hth stratum, and $\hat{X} = \Sigma X_h/L$ is the average of the stratum totals for the X characteristic; Y_{hi}, Y_h, and $\hat{Y}$ are defined similarly. The rel-variances B_X^2 and B_Y^2 are special cases of the rel-covariance, B_{XY}. Thus, if we replace Y's by X's

---

* The proof is given in Vol. II, Ch. 9, Sec. 1d.

in Eq. 14.3, or, specifically, if we replace $(Y_{hi}/P_{hi} - Y_h)/\hat{Y}$ by $(X_{hi}/P_{hi} - X_h)/\hat{X}$, we have

$$B_X^2 = B_{XX} = \frac{\sum\limits_{h}^{L} \sum\limits_{i}^{M_h} P_{hi} \left(\dfrac{X_{hi}}{P_{hi}} - X_h\right)^2}{L\hat{X}^2}$$

and similarly

$$B_Y^2 = B_{YY}$$

Note that B_X^2/m is the rel-variance of the simple unbiased estimate of a total when the psu's are completely enumerated and reduces to the psu contribution term of Eq. 14.4, Ch. 8, when there is no stratification, i.e., when $L = 1$.

The second-stage contribution to the rel-variance is $W_b^2/m\bar{n}$, where

$$W_b^2 = W_{bX}^2 + W_{bY}^2 - 2W_{bXY} \qquad (14.5)$$

$$W_{bXY} = \frac{\sum\limits_{h}^{L} \sum\limits_{i}^{M_h} \sum\limits_{a}^{D_{hi}} N_{hia} S_{hiaXY}}{N\bar{\bar{X}}\bar{\bar{Y}}} \qquad (14.6)$$

and D_{hi} is the number of substrata in the hith psu.

$$S_{hiaXY} = \frac{\sum\limits_{j}^{N_{hia}} (X_{hiaj} - \bar{\bar{X}}_{hia})(Y_{hiaj} - \bar{\bar{Y}}_{hia})}{N_{hia} - 1} \qquad (14.7)$$

where X_{hiaj} is the aggregate value of the X characteristic for the $hiaj$th second-stage unit, N_{hia} is the number of second-stage units in the ath substratum in the hith psu, and

$$\bar{\bar{X}}_{hia} = \frac{\sum\limits^{N_{hia}} X_{hiaj}}{N_{hia}}$$

The Y_{hiaj} and $\bar{\bar{Y}}_{hia}$ are defined similarly. Note that S_{hiaXY} is given by Eq. 5.11 of Ch. 7 if the subscripts hia replace hi. As before

$$W_{bX}^2 = W_{bXX} \quad \text{and} \quad W_{bY}^2 = W_{bYY} \qquad (14.8)$$

The third-stage contribution to the rel-variance is $\dfrac{\bar{\bar{Q}} - \bar{\bar{q}}}{\bar{\bar{Q}}} \dfrac{W_w^2}{m\bar{n}\bar{q}}$, where

$$W_w^2 = W_{wX}^2 + W_{wY}^2 - 2W_{wXY} \qquad (14.9)$$

with

$$W_{wXY} = \frac{\Sigma Q_{hiaj} S_{hiajXY}}{Q\bar{\bar{X}}\bar{\bar{Y}}} \qquad (14.10)$$

where the summation is over h, i, a, and j, and S_{hiajXY} is given by Eq. 12.6 of Ch. 7 if the subscripts $hiaj$ replace hij.   Specifically,

$$S_{hiajXY} = \frac{\sum\limits^{Q_{hiaj}}(X_{hiajk} - \bar{\bar{\bar{X}}}_{hiaj})(Y_{hiajk} - \bar{\bar{\bar{Y}}}_{hiaj})}{Q_{hiaj} - 1} \qquad (14.11)$$

where Q_{hiaj} is the number of third-stage units in the $hiaj$th second-stage unit, and $\bar{\bar{\bar{X}}}_{hiaj}$ and $\bar{\bar{\bar{Y}}}_{hiaj}$ are averages over these units.

$$W_{wX}^2 = W_{wXX} \quad \text{and} \quad W_{wY}^2 = W_{wYY}$$

The simple unbiased estimate of X is $x' = x/f$.   The rel-variance of x' is obtained by merely ignoring the terms involving Y in Eq. 14.1–14.11.

The variances given in this section are the population variances or approximations to them in terms of the characteristics of the total population.   A very simple estimate of the precision of the sample results from a sample, involving ultimate clusters, will be given in the next section. Methods of estimating the components of the variance will be indicated in Sec. 30–32.

15. A simple variance estimate for evaluating sample precision but not isolating the components of the variance.   The investigator may find extensive use for simple estimates of the precision of the results from samples without attempting to isolate the sources or components of the error.   For this purpose, the notion of an ultimate cluster as defined in Sec. 1 of Ch. 6 is important.   It provides a particularly simple estimate of the total variance when the sample is self-weighting and there are 2 or more psu's selected from a stratum.   Here, despite the fact that the psu's were selected with varying probabilities, that there were several stages of sampling, and that the second and subsequent stages of sampling were made within substrata of a psu (with perhaps only 1 unit selected from a psu or a substratum or from a second-stage unit), we can still regard x_{hi} as an ultimate cluster aggregate.   The reader may recall that x_{hi} is simply equal to the aggregate value of the q_{hi} listing units sampled from the ith psu and hth stratum.   Thus, the estimate of the rel-variance given by Eq. 6.10 of Ch. 7 will hold for the more complex sampling design given in this chapter.

When the sample is not self-weighting (i.e., the sampling fractions differ from stratum to stratum), the estimate of the rel-variance is given by Eq. 27.1, which reduces to Eq. 6.10 of Ch. 7 whenever the sample is self-weighting and we ignore the finite multiplier.

It may sometimes happen that the sample from each primary stratum will consist of only 1 primary unit.   In such instances one cannot apply

Eq. 6.10, Ch. 7, or Eq. 27.1; nor is it possible to obtain a consistent estimate of the variance. However, an estimate can be obtained which tends to overstate the variance and which nevertheless may give a satisfactory approximation when the number of primary strata is large. This estimate can be obtained as follows.

With only 1 psu in the sample per stratum, we first combine the original strata into groups so that each of the newly formed groups has at least 2 primary units in the sample. The strata to be combined into a group should be selected so that they are as similar as possible in respect to the characteristic being measured and are not widely different in size. Thus, if degree of urbanization were the only mode of stratification, the strata to be grouped together should be those having approximately the same degree of urbanization. In general, one should aim towards combining those strata for which the gains anticipated through the use of stratification appear to be a minimum. It is to be strongly emphasized that the groupings should be made without any reference to the psu's in the sample. One should examine all the psu's in the stratum, or look only at stratum characteristics. Looking at the psu's in the sample for leads as to which strata to group will introduce a bias, often in the direction of seriously understating the variance.

Once the grouping of strata is made, an estimate of the rel-variance of r for a self-weighting sample is*

$$v_r^2 = \frac{1}{m}(v_{cx}^2 + v_{cy}^2 - 2v_{cxy}) \tag{15.1}$$

where

$$v_{cxy} = \frac{1}{m\bar{x}\bar{y}} \sum_g^G L_g \frac{\sum_h^{L_g}\left(x_{gh} - x_g \frac{A_{gh}}{A_g}\right)\left(y_{gh} - y_g \frac{A_{gh}}{A_g}\right)}{L_g - 1} \tag{15.2}$$

$$v_{cx}^2 = v_{cxx}, \quad \text{and} \quad v_{cy}^2 = v_{cyy} \tag{15.3}$$

where x_{gh} is simply equal to the sample aggregate for the hth stratum and (with 1 psu per stratum) is equal to the sample aggregate for the psu, and

$$x_g = \sum_h^{L_g} x_{gh}, \quad y_g = \sum_h^{L_g} y_{gh}, \quad \bar{x} = \frac{\sum_g^G x_g}{m}, \quad \text{and} \quad \bar{y} = \frac{\sum_g^G y_g}{m}$$

L_g is the number of strata in the gth group and $\sum_g^G L_g = L$. The A_{gh} was employed earlier as the aggregate of the measures of size of the psu's in

---

* This estimate is developed in Vol. II, Ch. 9, Sec. 5.

the hth stratum (Sec. 8–11), and the ratio A_{gh}/A_g is used to adjust for the variability in sizes of strata.   If the total number of elementary units in the hth stratum at some past date was used as the measure of size, then A_{gh}/A_g will be approximately equal to Q_{gh}/Q_g, the proportion of elementary units in the hth stratum.

For the simple unbiased estimate, the estimate of the rel-variance is given by Eq. 15.1 if we ignore terms involving Y.

> **Remark.**   The estimates of the rel-variances above apply when the number of psu's in every stratum *in the population* is greater than 1 and thus no psu's are included in the sample with certainty (as discussed in Sec. 10).   Frequently, however, some of the strata consist of only 1 psu (e.g., see Case Studies A and B, Ch. 12), and the estimates of the variance need to be modified.   Estimate 6.10 of Ch. 7 is not applicable because it assumes at least 2 psu's in the sample from each stratum.   Estimate 15.1 is not applicable because this estimate would imply a contribution to the variance arising from sampling psu's, when in fact some psu's were selected with certainty.   The modifications required in the estimates are given in Sec. 29, Eq. 29.1 and 29.2.

16. Estimates of the components of the variance from the sample.   The formulas for estimating the rel-variances between first-, second-, and third-stage units, i.e., B^2 (Eq. 14.2), W_b^2 (Eq. 14.5), and W_w^2 (Eq. 14.9), are given in Sec. 32.   There, the equations apply whether the sample is self-weighting or not.

17. The variance of the sample estimate compared with the variance of simple random sampling.   The sampling variance for a one- or two-stage design was compared with simple random sampling of listing units in Ch. 6, Sec. 8.   Here we shall make a similar comparison for three stages of sampling, but shall confine the comparison, for simplicity, to the case where the sample is self-weighting, the sampling fraction at the second stage of sampling is small relative to 1, and the third-stage sampling fraction is constant for all second-stage sampling units.   For this case, the sampling rel-variance is given by Eq. 14.1.   This case may approximate, also, situations where such uniform probabilities are not maintained.   The rel-variance as given by Eq. 14.1 can be restated approximately as follows*

$$V_r^2 \doteq \frac{\hat{V}_1^2}{m\bar{Q}} [1 + \delta_1(\bar{Q} - 1)] + \frac{\hat{V}_2^2}{m\bar{n}q} [1 + \delta_2(\bar{\bar{q}} - 1)] \qquad (17.1)$$

$$\hat{V}_1^2 = B^2 + \frac{\bar{Q} - 1}{\bar{Q}} W^2 \qquad (17.2)$$

---

* The proof is given in Vol. II, Ch. 9, Sec. 6.

[The factor $(\bar{Q} - 1)/\bar{Q}$ will be close to 1 and need not be used; it is retained here simply for consistency.] B^2 is given by Eq. 14.2 and W^2 is

$$W^2 = W_X^2 + W_Y^2 - 2W_{XY}$$

where

$$W_{XY} = \frac{\Sigma\Sigma\Sigma \, Q_{hia}S_{3hiaXY}}{Q\bar{\bar{X}}\bar{\bar{Y}}} \tag{17.3}$$

$$Q_{hia} = \sum_{j}^{N_{hia}} Q_{hiaj}$$

$$S_{3hiaXY} = \frac{\Sigma\Sigma \left(X_{hiajk} - \dfrac{X_{hia}}{Q_{hia}}\right)\left(Y_{hiajk} - \dfrac{Y_{hia}}{Q_{hia}}\right)}{Q_{hia} - 1} \tag{17.4}$$

(the subscript 3 indicates that the variance is between third-stage units) and

$$W_X^2 = W_{XX}, \quad W_Y^2 = W_{YY} \tag{17.5}$$

$$\delta_1 = \frac{B^2 - (W^2/\bar{Q})}{\hat{V}_1^2} \tag{17.6}$$

with $\bar{Q} = Q/M$ the average number of listing units per psu.

$$\hat{V}_2^2 = W_b^2 + \frac{\bar{\bar{Q}} - 1}{\bar{\bar{Q}}} \, W_w^2 \tag{17.7}$$

where W_b^2 is 'efined by Eq. 14.5 and W_w^2 by Eq. 14.9, and

$$\delta_2 = \frac{W_b^2 - (W_w^2/\bar{\bar{Q}})}{\hat{V}_2^2} \tag{17.8}$$

We now make some further simplifying assumptions. We have indicated earlier that the measure of homogeneity usually decreases with increasing size of cluster, but at a rate considerably slower than the size of cluster increases. Consequently, for large enough psu's, we will find that the term $1 + \delta_1(\bar{Q} - 1)$ will be so dominated by $\delta_1\bar{Q}$ that it will be a satisfactory approximation to substitute $\delta_1\bar{Q}$ for it. If $\bar{Q}$ is large enough to make this approximation satisfactory, then the rel-variance of r will be given approximately by

$$V_r^2 \doteq \frac{V^2}{m\bar{n}\bar{\bar{q}}} \{k_1\delta_1\bar{n}\bar{\bar{q}} + k_2[1 + \delta_2(\bar{\bar{q}} - 1)]\} \tag{17.9}$$

where

$$k_1 = \frac{\hat{V}_1^2}{V^2}; \quad k_2 = \frac{\hat{V}_2^2}{V^2} \tag{17.10}$$

and V^2 is the rel-variance between listing units within the primary strata.

With ratio estimates or averages the values of k_1 or k_2 will often be near 1, and in that event we have

$$V_r^2 \doteq \frac{V^2}{m\bar{n}\bar{\bar{q}}} [\delta_1 \bar{n}\bar{\bar{q}} + 1 + \delta_2(\bar{\bar{q}} - 1)] \qquad (17.11 \text{ or } 3.1)$$

This form of the rel-variance may be useful when planning a survey, for speculating on sampling variances and optimum sample design. It was this form that was used in Illustration 3.1 of this chapter (Eq. 3.1).

18. The cost function. In arriving at the optimum design we must, as usual, give consideration to how the costs arise. This question was considered briefly in the first section of this chapter, and more fully in Chapter 6 and earlier chapters. We shall add only a little here, giving some remarks on some of the situations and variations that need special attention in sampling with large primary sampling units, and arrive at an average cost function for all strata combined.

The cost function is always difficult to approximate. Often, only a crude approximation can be obtained. A great deal more work and empirical studies and results are needed to improve this phase of the analysis. Fortunately, as indicated several times before, the optimum is usually rather broad, and it may therefore be sufficient to approximate the optimum only roughly.

We shall use the cost function indicated below, which was also employed in the illustration in Sec. 3.

$$C = C_0\sqrt{m} + C_1 m + C_2 m\bar{n} + C_3 m\sqrt{\bar{n}} + C_4 m\bar{n}\bar{\bar{q}} \qquad (18.1)$$

The term $C_0\sqrt{m}$ represents the cost of travel or communication between primary sampling units, and the method of approximating this term follows the approach given in Chapter 6. Thus C_0 is computed as in Sec. 12, Ch. 6, and is determined by the total area to be surveyed and certain unit costs assumed. Whenever long-distance telephone calls *between* psu's (and not to or from one or more central points) are used extensively, the average cost per mile of such costs may be added to the multiplier of $\sqrt{A}$ in arriving at C_0. It should be clear from the earlier discussion that, so far as travel is concerned, only travel between psu's affects the $C_0\sqrt{m}$ term, and travel to or from a central point may be distributed over a number of terms in the cost function, as already illustrated in Sec. 12, Ch. 6. One must, of course, study his own cost situations and arrive at approximate cost functions from these.

The term $C_3 m\sqrt{\bar{n}}$ represents the travel between second-stage units within psu's and is again the same as that described in Chapter 6, but now it relates to an average value over all the psu's in the sample. Thus, C_3 is also computed as in Sec. 12, Ch. 6, but now A is the average area per psu.

Whenever there are great differences between the cost situations in broadly different types of strata, for example, strata which are primarily urban, as compared with strata which are primarily rural, the costs may need to be determined separately, as if for separate problems. We shall assume here that this does not occur. More general cases are given in Ch. 7, Sec. 11, and in Vol. II, Ch. 9, Sec. 11.

We shall now assume that an analysis comparable to that given in Chapter 6 has led to reasonably satisfactory values for the terms in the cost function.

19. Optimum allocation of the sample.* The optimum allocation of the sample given first will be an average optimum, not differentiating among the primary strata, the psu's, or the substrata in the sampling. Often the variances and costs needed for separate optimum sampling within each individual psu and for various substrata within psu's will not be known accurately. Consequently, it may not be worth while to attempt to apply special procedures to each psu and substratum within each psu. Instead, a broad general approach may be called for. But there is nothing wrong with specialized approaches in sampling within the psu's, and particularly worth-while gains may result where large and costly subsamples are being taken. The extension of the theory to cover this type of situation is indicated later (Sec. 24–32).

We have seen how to arrive at values for the terms of the variance and the cost function. We shall now use the rel-variance given by Eq. 14.1 or 17.11 and the cost function given by Eq. 18.1 to obtain approximate optimum values for m, $\bar{n}$, and $\bar{\bar{q}}$.

The steps in computing the optimum values of m, $\bar{n}$, and $\bar{\bar{q}}$ are as follows:

(1) Divide the cost function through by C_4, the coefficient of $m\bar{n}\bar{\bar{q}}$, to obtain revised coefficients in the cost equation. The relationships in this revised equation are identical with those in the initial cost equation, but the coefficients are stated relative to C_4 and, of course, the revised C_4 is equal to 1. The result of using the revised cost function will be exactly the same as with the original, but the computational steps are simplified slightly by having it in this form.

The remaining steps are described in terms of these revised cost coefficients.

(2) Take $\bar{n} = 9$ as the first approximate value of $\bar{n}$. Any other number

---

* The derivation of the optimum allocations is given in Vol. II, Ch. 9, Sec. 7.

could be used. Substitute this value into Eq. 19.1, below, to obtain the first approximate value of $\bar{\bar{q}}$:

$$\bar{\bar{q}} = \frac{W_w}{\sqrt{W_b^2 - W_w^2/\bar{\bar{Q}}}} \sqrt{\frac{C_3}{2\sqrt{\bar{n}}} + C_2} = \sqrt{\frac{1 - \delta_2}{\delta_2}\left(\frac{C_3}{2\sqrt{\bar{n}}} + C_2\right)} \quad (19.1)$$

where W_w^2 is given by Eq. 14.9, W_b^2 by Eq. 14.5, and δ_2 by Eq. 17.8.

(3) Substitute these first approximate values of $\bar{n}$ and $\bar{\bar{q}}$ into Eq. 19.2 to obtain a first approximate value of a. The equation for a is:

$$a = \tfrac{1}{4}k + \sqrt{\tfrac{1}{4}k(C_3\sqrt{\bar{n}} + C_2\bar{n} + \bar{n}\bar{\bar{q}} + C_1 + \tfrac{1}{4}k)} \quad (19.2)$$

where $k = C_0^2/C$.

(4) Substitute these first values of $\bar{n}$, $\bar{\bar{q}}$, and a into Eq. 19.3 to obtain a second value of $\bar{n}$, and substitute this value of $\bar{n}$ into Eq. 19.1 to obtain a second value of $\bar{\bar{q}}$. The equation for $\bar{n}$ is

$$\bar{n} = \frac{1}{\bar{\bar{q}}} \frac{W_w}{B} \sqrt{\frac{C_3\sqrt{\bar{n}}}{2} + C_1 + a} \doteq \frac{1}{\bar{\bar{q}}} \sqrt{\frac{1 - \delta_2}{\delta_1}\left(\frac{C_3\sqrt{\bar{n}}}{2} + C_1 + a\right)} \quad (19.3)$$

where B is given by Eq. 14.2 and δ_1 is given by Eq. 17.6.

(5) If the second value of either $\bar{n}$ or $\bar{\bar{q}}$ differs from the first by more than 1, repeat steps 3 and 4, but now begin with the second values of $\bar{n}$ and $\bar{\bar{q}}$ and compute third values to be compared with the second. In some instances the whole process may need to be repeated several times.

(6) When the last computed values of $\bar{n}$ and $\bar{\bar{q}}$ differ from the preceding values by less than 1, the process is ended. The last values computed may be rounded to the nearest whole numbers if desired. These become the final values of $\bar{n}$ and $\bar{\bar{q}}$ to use in step 7.

(7) Substitute the values of $\bar{n}$ and $\bar{\bar{q}}$ from step 6 into Eq. 19.2 to obtain a revised value of a, and compute m by using this revised a in the equation below:

$$m = \frac{C_0^2}{4a^2} \quad (19.4)$$

m is then rounded to the nearest whole number. Then as a check substitute the values of $\bar{n}$, $\bar{\bar{q}}$, and m into either the revised or the original cost function, and it should be satisfied approximately. It would be satisfied exactly except for rounding in the computation of m. This check is, in fact, a check only on the computations of step 7. The earlier computations can be verified by repeating the earlier calculations.

Illustration 19.1. Let us now follow through the computation of the optimum values for Illustration 3.1, introduced in Sec. 3.

Step 1.   The original cost function was:

$$15,000 = 500\sqrt{m} + 20m + 3m\bar{n} + 7m\sqrt{\bar{n}} + 2m\bar{n}\bar{\bar{q}}$$

from which we obtain the revised coefficients by dividing through by 2, the coefficient of $m\bar{n}\bar{\bar{q}}$, to obtain the coefficients of the cost equation that we use in Eq. 19.1–19.4:

$$7500 = 250\sqrt{m} + 10m + 1.5m\bar{n} + 3.5m\sqrt{\bar{n}} + m\bar{n}\bar{\bar{q}}$$

and from this:

$$k = \frac{C_0^2}{C} = \frac{(250)^2}{7500} = 8.33.$$

C_1 = coefficient of m = 10.

C_3 = coefficient of $m\sqrt{\bar{n}}$ = 3.5.

C_2 = coefficient of $m\bar{n}$ = 1.5.

Step 2.   With $\delta_1 = .01$ and $\delta_2 = .09$, and the above cost coefficients, we have from Eq. 19.1

$$q = \sqrt{\frac{17.69}{\sqrt{\bar{n}}} + 15.17}$$

and we compute from this, assuming as an initial value $\bar{n}_1 = 9$:

$$\bar{\bar{q}}_1 = 4.59$$

Step 3.   Equation 19.2 with the appropriate values substituted from the variance and cost function gives

$$a = 2.08 + \sqrt{7.29\sqrt{\bar{n}} + 3.12\bar{n} + 2.08\bar{n}\bar{\bar{q}} + 25.17}$$

and, substituting the first values of $\bar{n}$ and $\bar{\bar{q}}$, we have

$$a_1 = 14.8$$

Step 4.   Equation 19.3 with the appropriate values from the variance and cost function gives:

$$\bar{n} = \frac{9.54}{\bar{\bar{q}}} \sqrt{1.75\sqrt{\bar{n}} + a + 10}$$

and, substituting the first values of $\bar{n}$, $\bar{\bar{q}}$, and a, we have

$$\bar{n}_2 = 11.4$$

and, using $\bar{n}_2$ and Eq. 19.1, we compute

$$\bar{\bar{q}}_2 = 4.52$$

Step 5.   The value of $\bar{n}_2$ differs from the preceding value by more than 1, so we use $\bar{n}_2$ and $\bar{\bar{q}}_2$, obtained in step 4, go back to steps 3 and 4 again, and compute

$$a_2 = 16.0, \quad \bar{n}_3 = 11.9, \quad \bar{\bar{q}}_3 = 4.51$$

These values of $\bar{n}$ and $\bar{\bar{q}}$ differ from the preceding values by less than 1, so we proceed to step 6.

Step 6.   The rounded values from these final computations of $\bar{n}$ and $\bar{\bar{q}}$ are:

$$\bar{n} = 12, \quad \bar{\bar{q}} = 5$$

Step 7.   We now compute from Eq. 19.2

$$a_3 = 16.7$$

and from 19.4

$$m = \frac{C_0^2}{4a^2} = \frac{(250)^2}{4(16.7)^2} = 56$$

Substituting these values in the revised cost function as a check, we have:

$$7500 = 3.5(56)\sqrt{12} + 1.5(56 \times 12) + 56 \times 60 + 560 + 250\sqrt{56}$$
$$= 7477$$

which is within $\frac{1}{3}$ per cent of the specified cost.

Remark 1.   Where multiple statistics are to be estimated from the sample, a rough guide for arriving at optimum design is to use some kind of average values for δ_1 and δ_2, and proceed with the above steps. Although the following suggestion needs more specific exploration for particular problems, suggested values to use are something like the third quartile values of the δ_1 and δ_2 computed from among the important statistics to be estimated. By the third quartile values are meant values selected for δ_1 and δ_2 such that three-fourths of the important items have a smaller value and one-fourth have a larger value. The choice of values on the high side is suggested because the lack of fullest efficiency for the items with the lower δ's may be compensated for by the fact that for these, simply because of the low δ's, comparatively high precision of results is obtained, and by the fact that the range of values around the optimum that gives results close to the optimum is usually broader for low values of δ than for high. This rule provides a beginning point for a first approximation to an optimum with multiple statistics. It must be followed by examination of the variances for each of the important statistics to be estimated to make sure that results of needed precision will be achieved. Some supplementation of the sample may be necessary in order to meet the standards of precision which have been set.

Remark 2.   The optimum sample using a simpler cost function than given by Eq. 18.1.   We have seen that the effect of travel between psu's is reflected primarily by the term $C_0\sqrt{m}$ of the cost function given by Eq. 18.1, and the effect of travel between second-stage units within psu's is reflected primarily by the term $C_3 m\sqrt{\bar{n}}$.

When these terms are not involved or are small in their effect and can be omitted from the cost function, simple explicit solutions are readily obtained for the optimum sample design. Suppose that our cost situation is well enough approximated by the cost function:

$$C = C_1 m + C_2 m\bar{n} + C_4 m\bar{n}\bar{\bar{q}} \qquad (19.5)$$

and that a uniform sampling fraction, with a constant second-stage fraction, will be used as before. The variance is still given by Eq. 14.1 or 17.11. The optimum values of $\bar{\bar{q}}$, $\bar{n}$, and m are then given by:

$$\bar{\bar{q}} = \frac{W_w}{\sqrt{W_b^2 - W_w^2/\bar{\bar{Q}}}} \sqrt{\frac{C_2}{C_4}} = \sqrt{\frac{1 - \delta_2}{\delta_2} \frac{C_2}{C_4}} \qquad (19.6)$$

$$\bar{n} = \frac{1}{\bar{\bar{q}}} \frac{W_w}{B} \sqrt{\frac{C_1}{C_4}} \doteq \frac{1}{\bar{\bar{q}}} \sqrt{\frac{1 - \delta_2}{\delta_1} \frac{C_1}{C_4}} \qquad (19.7)$$

$$m = \frac{C}{C_1 + C_2\bar{n} + C_4\bar{n}\bar{\bar{q}}} \qquad (19.8)$$

Exercises

19.1. Find the optimum values of $\bar{\bar{q}}$, $\bar{n}$, and m if $C_0 = C_3 = 0$, and the other costs are those in the illustration earlier in this section. What is the rel-variance with these costs?

NOTE. The rel-variance when we assume $C_0 = C_3 = 0$ is smaller than that found by using cost equation 18.1, since we are here neglecting two major items of cost. If we compute the cost with $\bar{n} = 8$, $\bar{\bar{q}} = 4$, $m = 139$, and using the original cost equation, we find that the total cost is not $15,000, but much more, $19,324 in fact.

19.2. Show that the same results obtained in Ex. 19.1 can also be obtained by setting $C_0 = C_3 = 0$ and applying the iterative steps indicated above.

20. Optimum values with fixed precision instead of fixed cost. If the problem is to achieve a fixed precision at minimum cost, one can proceed as above, with an initial roughly speculated $\bar{n}$ (say $\bar{n}_1 = 9$) but using Eq. 20.1 instead of Eq. 19.2.* This optimum is obtained from the rel-variance given by Eq. 14.1 or 17.11 and the cost function given by Eq. 18.1. Then

$$a = \frac{\varepsilon C_0}{2\sqrt{B^2 + \frac{1}{\bar{n}}\left(W_b^2 - \frac{W_w^2}{\bar{\bar{Q}}}\right) + \frac{1}{\bar{n}\bar{\bar{q}}}W_w^2}}$$

$$\doteq \frac{\varepsilon C_0}{V\sqrt{\delta_1 + \frac{\delta_2}{\bar{n}} + \frac{1 - \delta_2}{\bar{n}\bar{\bar{q}}}}} \qquad (20.1)$$

* The proof is given in Vol. II, Ch. 9, Sec. 7, Remark 3.

where $\varepsilon^2 = V_r^2$, $V = \sqrt{V_X^2 + V_Y^2 - 2V_{XY}}$, V_X^2 is the within-strata rel-variance for a simple random sample of listing units, and V_{XY} is the corresponding rel-covariance. In Eq. 20.1, ε is the specified precision to be achieved, expressed as the coefficient of variation of the estimate (not the rel-variance). Thus, here, Eq. 19.1, 20.1, 19.3, and 19.4 are used in the same way that Eq. 19.1, 19.2, 19.3, and 19.4 are used in Sec. 19. The total cost of the survey is then found by substituting the optimum values for $\bar{n}$, $\bar{\bar{q}}$, and m into Eq. 18.1. A final check is to substitute the computed optimum values for $\bar{n}$, $\bar{\bar{q}}$, and m into the variance equation to assure that the results yield the specified precision.

21. Optimum size of the first-stage units and of the second-stage units. An approximation to the optimum average size of the primary sampling unit is obtained simply by comparing the results for specific alternatives. Thus, as one level of primary unit for sampling in the United States, it may be convenient to define primary units consisting of individual large counties (or of groups of two or three counties where one or more of them is small in area) and to compare the variance for the optimum design with these primary units with that for a larger primary sampling unit, consisting of pairs or larger multiples of such units, or perhaps smaller units consisting of minor civil divisions or groups of minor divisions. The method of approximating the optimum for each type and size of primary sampling unit is to obtain approximate values for the B^2, W_b^2, and W_w^2 (or for δ_1 and δ_2) and for the values of the coefficients of the cost function for each, and to compute the optimum m, $\bar{n}$, and $\bar{\bar{q}}$ for such cases. Then the variance is computed for each of these, and from among those alternatives considered, the optimum is the one with the most reliable results per unit of cost. Special information which may be available for making a different type of estimate, or for stratification, or for varying the probabilities of selection can be made use of, where it is advantageous, in arriving at the optimum size and type of psu. Unless there is a substantial advantage in terms of efficiency for one particular type of unit, the choice among several types of psu's should be made on the basis of other considerations such as administrative convenience.

For the second-stage sampling the second-stage units are assumed to be specified in advance, and then the optimum size of ultimate cluster is given by the theory already presented. In choosing among second-stage units, the alternatives may be compared and the choice made on the basis of maximum precision per unit of cost.

22. Breadth of optimum. As in other sample designs the optimum is usually fairly broad, and it is essential only to be close enough to the optimum set of $\bar{n}$, $\bar{\bar{q}}$, and m that the variance or cost is near (say within 10 per cent) that of the optimum. It should be noted, however, that, whereas there may be considerable choice in two of the three values, the remaining one will be fixed by the accuracy requirement or the funds available.

Where multiple statistics are to be estimated from the sample, the breadth of the minimum is a particularly important consideration in arriving at the optimum design. No indication of the breadth of the minimum is given by the optimum values of m, $\bar{n}$, and $\bar{\bar{q}}$. However, we can find by trial and error various values of m, $\bar{n}$, and $\bar{\bar{q}}$ that satisfy the cost function and that do not give a variance that is greater than the minimum variance by more than, say, 10 per cent, and any such values ought to be regarded as equally good. The choice among them can be made on the basis of other considerations, such as choosing values that may be in the neighborhood of the optimum for several different characteristics where this is possible.

Table 4 shows the optimum m, $\bar{n}$, and $\bar{\bar{q}}$ for a fixed set of costs and for some alternative values of δ_1 and δ_2. The table shows, for the values specified, how far one may depart from the optimum without increasing the variance by more than 10 per cent. These numbers were computed so as to satisfy the cost condition Eq. 18.1, for specified values of the costs in that equation, with the variance being given by Eq. 17.11. An examination of this table will show that, for the specific choice of the cost coefficients, it is possible to select values of m, $\bar{n}$, and $\bar{\bar{q}}$ that satisfy the cost function and that are sufficiently near the optimum for several different characteristics, i.e., several different values of δ_1 and δ_2.

23. Some other useful estimates from the sample. Three other special estimates that may be found useful will be considered briefly. These will be discussed below as special estimates 1, 2, and 3, respectively.

Special estimate 1. Suppose that we have, for each primary sampling unit, auxiliary information that would have been effective but that was not fully used in stratification and in selecting the sample. For example, in estimating population characteristics it might be found that the incidence of a characteristic varies widely between farm and nonfarm residents. Suppose that, along with a number of other characteristics, one is estimating the number or proportion of the population that is agricultural workers. A stratification of the psu's by percentage of the population that is farm residents might have been very effective in reducing the variance of this particular estimate. But with only a limited number of strata, other criteria of stratification may have already been used, or may be found to be more helpful than a control on the proportions of

Table 4. Values of opt. m, opt. $\bar{n}$, and opt. $\bar{\bar{q}}$ for specified measures of homogeneity

For $C/C_4 = 50{,}000$, $C_0^2/C_4 = 50{,}000$, $C_1/C_4 = 100$, $C_2/C_4 = 4$, $C_3/C_4 = 40$, and where the rel-variance is given by Eq. 17.11 and the cost function by Eq. 18.1

		Optimum values			Range values*					
					$\bar{\bar{q}} = $ opt. $\bar{\bar{q}}$		$m = $ opt. m		$\bar{n} = $ opt. $\bar{n}$	
δ_1	δ_2	Opt. $\bar{\bar{q}}$	Opt. m	Opt. $\bar{n}$	m	$\bar{n}$	$\bar{\bar{q}}$	$\bar{n}$	$\bar{\bar{q}}$	m
(1)	(2)	(3)	(4)	(5)	(6)	(7)	(8)	(9)	(10)	(11)
.005	.01	36.0	124	4.9	81	9.3	14.1	9.0	19.6	155
					179	2.5	92.8	2.3	69.2	88
.01	.01	39.1	156	3.1	106	5.9	91.0	1.6	20.0	192
					213	1.6	14.3	5.8	72.0	117
.005	.1	8.6	84	22.5	51	46.0	4.1	31.0	4.5	99
					128	11.0	19.7	13.7	17.4	63
.01	.1	9.2	109	14.2	71	28.0	3.9	20.0	4.7	127
					158	7.0	22.0	8.5	18.5	84
.05	.1	10.9	181	4.8	132	9.2	4.1	6.8	6.0	199
					232	2.5	30.8	2.7	24.0	147
.005	.2	5.4	71	35.6	42	75.5	2.4	47.5	2.6	84
					114	16.5	12.3	23.5	11.4	55
.01	.2	5.7	94	22.4	59	46.2	2.4	29.7	2.7	109
					138	11.2	14.1	14.2	12.0	74
.05	.2	6.7	162	7.6	116	14.7	2.6	9.9	3.0	178
					212	3.9	17.6	4.8	16.0	131
.2	.2	7.8	227	3.0	171	6.3	2.4	4.0	3.0	244
					278	1.5	24.7	1.8	21.6	191
.005	.4	3.2	60	56.4	35	121.0	1.5	68.0	1.6	67
					97	26.0	7.3	40.0	6.4	49
.01	.4	3.3	80	35.5	50	72.0	1.4	43.8	1.5	90
					121	17.3	8.5	24.3	7.5	65
.05	.4	3.8	142	12.1	97	25.0	1.4	14.7	1.5	154
					192	6.0	11.0	8.0	9.2	119
.2	.4	4.4	205	4.8	152	10.0	1.3	5.9	1.5	218
					258	2.3	15.7	3.0	14.8	173

* The entries in columns 6 and 7 represent the range of values in m and $\bar{n}$ for $\bar{\bar{q}} = $ opt. $\bar{\bar{q}}$ for which the variance is within 10 per cent of the variance at the optimum. The entries in columns 8–11 are similarly interpreted.

411

farm residents. One can still make use of this information in the estimating formula by preparing an estimate as follows:

$$x'' = \frac{x'}{y'} \, Y \tag{23.1}$$

where x' is the estimate obtained by Eq. 13.1, and y' is the estimate obtained by using the auxiliary information available for the sample psu's from a prior census or other source of information, i.e.,

$$y' = \sum_h^L \sum_i^1 \frac{Y_{hi}}{P_{hi}} \tag{23.2}$$

where Y_{hi} is, for example, the number of farm residents in the psu at some earlier date, and Y is the population aggregate for this second characteristic. This estimate differs from the usual ratio estimate (Eq. 13.2), in that the denominator of the ratio is not based on information for the elementary units or for the second-stage units included in the sample, but only for the primary units.

To illustrate the use of this estimate more specifically, if the estimate to be made is of the number of agricultural workers (as one of a set of many different estimates made from the sample, other estimates being for the total population, nonagricultural workers, etc.), x' may be the unbiased estimate of agricultural workers from the sample, and y' the estimated number (and Y the actual number) of agricultural workers based on whole-psu information from the preceding census. This method is more likely to be useful in instances where multiple statistics are being estimated from the sample. Otherwise the initial sample design would have taken account of an important characteristic such as farm population in the stratification. But with multiple statistics, and the availability of the estimate given by Eq. 23.1, it might not be worth while to pay any premium to stratify on this particular characteristic of the population, if it can be used satisfactorily in the estimating procedure.

The rel-variance of x'' given by Eq. 23.1 is, as usual, equal to $V_{x'}^2 + V_{y'}^2 - 2V_{x'y'}$. The rel-variance of x', $V_{x'}^2$ is the rel-variance of Eq. 13.1 indicated earlier. However, $V_{y'}^2$ and $V_{x'y'}$ must now take into account the fact that there is no subsampling and that the psu's are selected with varying probabilities. Hence $V_{y'}^2 - 2V_{x'y'}$ is given by $(B_Y^2 - 2B_{XY})/m$, where B_Y^2 and B_{XY} are given by Eq. 14.3.

Special estimate 2. A variant of this type of estimate is to subdivide the elements included in the sample, on the basis of currently collected information, into certain major classes, say white farm residents, nonwhite farm residents, white nonfarm residents, nonwhite nonfarm residents. Suppose that we designate a class by the subscript c so that x_c is the aggregate value in the sample of some characteristic of those elements in a particular class, and Σx_c is the total value of this characteristic for the entire sample. Then the total estimate for all classes combined is

$$x'' = \sum_c \frac{x_c'}{y_c'} Y_c \tag{23.3}$$

where x_c' and y_c' are unbiased estimates of X_c and Y_c, respectively, the aggregate values for the cth class. The estimates x_c' are given by Eq. 13.1 and the estimates y_c' are given by Eq. 23.2. Thus, $(x_c'/y_c')Y_c$, where y_c' is an unbiased estimate of Y_c, is the same type of estimate for the cth class as Eq. 23.1 is for the whole population. We need merely add these estimates for all the classes to obtain the estimate given by Eq. 23.3.

The variance of the estimate given by Eq. 23.3 involves considerable computing if very many classes are used. It is given by Eq. 8.1, Ch. 9, Vol. II, as a special case of the more general estimate given there. As a practical matter the computation of the variance may involve grouping some of the classes, to reduce the amount of calculation.

Special estimate 3. A number of other extensions and variants of the type of estimate given in Eq. 23.3 are possible. For example, suppose that the total number of persons by age groups is known from independent sources, and assume that the known total population for the ath age group is Z_a. Suppose, further, a *past* census gave the total number of persons in the rural population and urban population for the United States and for each psu in the population. The question then is how all this information can be used in the estimating procedure. We can from a sample make a current estimate of some characteristic of the persons in the ath age group in rural areas, $(x_{aR}'/y_R')Y_R$, and similarly $(x_{aU}'/y_U')Y_U$, for the urban population. The sum of these numbers will yield a consistent estimate of the aggregate value of the specified characteristic for persons in the ath age group. Thus, we can construct an estimate of a characteristic for the ath age group by Eq. 23.3,

$$x_a'' = \sum_c \frac{x_{ac}'}{y_c'} Y_c$$

where x_{ac}' is an unbiased estimate of the aggregate value of the characteristic for the ath age group within the cth urban-rural class, and y_c' (given by Eq. 23.2) is an unbiased estimate of Y_c, the aggregate value of the cth class at some past date.

Similarly, we can make a ratio estimate of the total population in the ath age group

$$z_a'' = \Sigma \frac{z_{ac}'}{y_c'} Y_c$$

Finally, we make the estimate $(x_a''/z_a'')Z_a$, which is an estimate of X for the ath age group, and then sum over the age groups to obtain

$$x''' = \Sigma \frac{x_a''}{z_a''} Z_a \qquad (23.4)$$

which uses all the current and past information indicated earlier.

Remark. A special word of caution is called for in the use of Eq. 23.4, which implies that there is a current value Z_a for the ath age group known from an independent source, such that z_a'' is a consistent estimate of Z_a. If z_a'' is not a consistent estimate of Z_a, then x''' may have a serious bias. The nature of this type of bias is discussed in Ch. 5, Sec. 16.

However, where good independent information is available for Z_a, comparable to the information available in the sample, the use of the information in the manner indicated by Eq. 23.4 may be an effective method of improving the sample estimate. This estimate is the only one of the special estimates mentioned in this section which may have the effect of reducing the within-psu variance as well as the between-psu variance. Therefore, if good independent information is known currently, it may have an appreciable effect in reducing the total variance.

This type of estimate is being used currently for the Current Population Survey of the Bureau of the Census, and an illustration of its application is given in Case Study B, Ch. 12.

The calculation of the variance for this type of estimate involves a great deal of computing, and in practice many of the classes must be grouped. The variance of this estimate is given in Vol. II, Ch. 9, Sec. 8.

Such extensive use of sets of ratio estimates is not necessarily worth while and may result in increases in the variance instead of reductions. For a discussion of possible increases in variance when separate ratio estimates are made for too many subclasses in the population, see Ch. 5, Sec. 16, Remark 3.

C. LARGE-PRIMARY-UNIT SAMPLING WITH VARIABLE OVER-ALL SAMPLING FRACTIONS

24. Need for a variable sampling fraction. In all the immediately preceding discussions of sample design, it was assumed that a uniform over-all sampling fraction was used for all classes of elements in the population. As was pointed out earlier, a uniform over-all sampling fraction may be efficient in a number of problems, although it will be very inefficient in others. For example, in the illustration in Sec. 10 of Ch. 5, if total production is to be estimated, a sample in which each business establishment has the same chance of being selected needs to be about five times as large as a sample in which the larger establishments have a much higher chance of being selected than the smaller ones. A similar situation frequently obtains for the estimation of such characteristics as total land in farms, total production of a particular crop, sales of retail establishments, production of manufacturing establishments, and other situations where a relatively small number of elementary units account for a substantial part of the aggregate being measured.

Differential sampling fractions will be required also for the estimation of such ratios as the ratio of crop land to total land in farms, and inventory to sales. The situation when different sampling fractions are required for the several strata, with the elementary unit as the sampling unit, was described in Chapter 5, and it is under essentially these same circumstances that differential sampling fractions are required in multi-stage sampling.

In the estimation of such characteristics as total sales of retail establishments, total shipments for manufacturing establishments, or total land in farms, with multi-stage sampling, it may be desirable to obtain a list of exceedingly large units, to include all of them, wherever located, and to take a sample of primary units to represent the remaining elements of the population. Within the selected primary units, it may be desirable to list the units which are large locally and sample differentially according to size, and finally to select second-stage area sampling units to represent the remaining elements (those not on the list of large units) in each primary sampling unit.

The over-all sampling fraction for the very large units will be 1 if all the very large units are to be selected. The sampling fraction for the locally large units will be the product of the probability of selecting a primary unit and the sampling fraction assigned to each class (substratum) into which the list of locally large units is divided. Finally, the sampling fraction for the remaining units will be the product of the probability of selecting a primary unit, the sampling fraction for second-stage units, and the third-stage sampling fraction if the second-stage units are subsampled. More than one sampling fraction may be used, of course, for both the very large units and the remaining units not on the local large list, if optimum sampling considerations point to the need, but as a practical matter it is usually desirable to use a limited number of different over-all sampling fractions. For a detailed description of a sample design which illustrates the type of sampling described above see Ch. 12, Case Study A.

We shall assume, in summary, that the population of establishments or other units being sampled is divided into substrata on the basis of size, or of some other property, for which there are important and substantial cost differences or differences in the standard deviations (say differences by factors of at least 2 or more in costs or in standard deviations between substrata). The subsampling within psu's within substrata can be simple sampling from a list, or one- or more stage cluster sampling can be used in some or all of the substrata.

Many of the principles discussed earlier in this chapter for drawing a sample of large clusters with a uniform over-all sampling fraction are equally applicable to large-cluster sampling with variable sampling fractions. The principles for defining the primary sampling units given earlier seem to be applicable to the present situation. The principle of specifying in advance a fixed number of psu's to be included in the sample from each primary stratum, such as including 1 psu from each stratum, or perhaps 2 or 3 from each, is again an effective way to use stratification in the selection of primary units. This differs from the principle of optimum determination of the m_h (the number of psu's in the sample from the hth stratum) as was done in Chapter 7 and substitutes the principle of determining optimum sizes of strata.

If a fixed number of units is included in the sample from each primary stratum, the principle of equalizing the sizes of the strata with respect to some measure of size will still provide a rough guide to optimum design, but the measure of size to use in this instance should be more fully considered. The sizes of the strata should be roughly equalized* with respect to the X_h when the B_h^2 are presumed to be roughly the same for the different strata; or the sizes of the strata should be roughly equalized with respect to the Y_h when the $S_{1h}^2/\bar{Y}_h^2$ are presumed to be roughly the same for the different strata. Here the ratio X/Y is assumed to be the characteristic being estimated (for a simple unbiased estimate of X, the Y is simply the aggregate measure of size and should be made as nearly as possible proportionate to X); X_h and Y_h are the aggregate values for the hth stratum of the characteristics in the ratio; B_h^2 is the rel-variance between psu's within the hth stratum; and $S_{1h}^2/\bar{Y}_h^2 = \bar{X}_h^2 B_h^2/\bar{Y}_h^2$ is the approximation to the variance of the ratio X_h/Y_h for a sample of 1 in the hth stratum where $\bar{X}_h$ and $\bar{Y}_h$ are average values per psu (cf. Sec. 8).

The principle of selecting the primary units with probabilities proportionate to measures of size will also be desirable under conditions similar to those discussed in Sec. 11.

25. The sample estimate. Suppose that we want to estimate the ratio of aggregate values, X/Y, where X represents the aggregate value of one of the characteristics and Y represents the other. The estimate of X is built up by making an estimate of the aggregate value for each sample

* Section 3, Ch. 9, Vol. II, gives the basis for this statement.

psu, and multiplying each such value by the reciprocal of the probability of selecting the psu. The estimating method for Y is the same as that for X.

A general estimating equation for any number of stages of sampling is

$$r = \frac{x'}{y'} = \frac{\sum\limits_{h}^{L} \frac{1}{m_h} \sum\limits_{i}^{m_h} \frac{1}{P_{hi}} x'_{hi}}{\sum\limits_{h}^{L} \frac{1}{m_h} \sum\limits_{i}^{m_h} \frac{1}{P_{hi}} y'_{hi}} \qquad (25.1)$$

where x'_{hi} and y'_{hi} are unbiased estimates of X_{hi} and Y_{hi}. With three stages of sampling and substratification

$$x'_{hi} = \sum\limits_{a}^{D_{hi}} \frac{1}{f_{hia}} \sum\limits_{j}^{n_{hia}} \frac{1}{f_{hiaj}} x_{hiaj} \qquad (25.2)$$

where f_{hiaj} and f_{hia} represent, respectively, the sampling fractions for listing units and second-stage sampling units. As before, P_{hi} represents the probability of selecting the ith primary unit within the hth stratum and m_h the number of primary units in the sample from that stratum, and y'_{hi} is similarly defined for the Y's.

Often, in practice, instead of having a different sampling fraction for each second-stage unit within each primary sampling unit or a different sampling fraction for each stratum, a common sampling fraction will be applied to all units of a particular substratum whatever primary unit may have been selected. Thus, it may be economical to let the over-all sampling fraction for the substratum represented by the area sample be constant. Similarly, it may be efficient to assign the same over-all fraction to a particular size class of establishments. By such a procedure the number of differential weights to be applied can be kept small.

26. The rel-variance. The rel-variance of Eq. 25.1 is approximately*

$$V_r^2 \doteq V_{x'}^2 + V_{y'}^2 - 2V_{x'y'} \qquad (26.1)$$

where

$$V_{x'y'} = \frac{1}{XY} \sum\limits_{h}^{L} \frac{1}{m_h} S_{hXY} + \frac{1}{XY} \sum\limits_{h}^{L} \frac{1}{m_h} \sum\limits_{i}^{M_h} \frac{1}{P_{hi}} \sigma_{x'_{hi}y'_{hi}} \qquad (26.2)$$

S_{hXY} is given by Eq. 14.4, and $\sigma_{x'_{hi}y'_{hi}}$ is the covariance between x'_{hi} and y'_{hi}, the estimated totals for the hith psu. Hence, when x'_{hi} and y'_{hi} are given by Eq. 25.2, $\sigma_{x'_{hi}y'_{hi}}$ is the covariance of a two-stage stratified sample design within the hith psu. The variance for a two-stage stratified sample design with varying sampling fractions is given in Ch. 7, Sec. 5.

---

* For proof, see Vol. II, Ch. 9, Sec. 1.

Specifically, in a three-stage sampling design, $\sigma_{x'_{hi}y'_{hi}}$ can be expressed in terms of the contribution from the second and third stages of sampling and is equal to

$$\sigma_{x'_{hi}y'_{hi}} = \sum_a^{D_{hi}} N_{hia}^2 \left(\frac{N_{hia} - n_{hia}}{N_{hia}} \right) \frac{S_{hiaXY}}{n_{hia}}$$

$$+ \sum_a^{D_{hi}} \frac{N_{hia}}{n_{hia}} \sum_j^{N_{hia}} Q_{hiaj}^2 \frac{Q_{hiaj} - q_{hiaj}}{Q_{hiaj}} \frac{S_{hiajXY}}{q_{hiaj}} \qquad (26.3)$$

where S_{hiaXY} is given by Eq. 14.7, and S_{hiajXY} is given by Eq. 14.11. From Eq. 26.2, we have

$$V_{x'}^2 = V_{x'x'} \quad \text{and} \quad V_{y'}^2 = V_{y'y'} \qquad (26.4)$$

Note that the rel-variance, V_r^2, given in Eq. 26.1 may also be written as follows:

$$V_r^2 \doteq \frac{1}{X^2} \sum_h^L \frac{1}{m_h} S_h^2 + \frac{1}{X^2} \sum_h^L \frac{1}{m_h} \sum_i^{M_h} \frac{1}{P_{hi}} \sigma_{hi}^2 \qquad (26.5)$$

where

$$S_h^2 = S_{hX}^2 + R^2 S_{hY}^2 - 2R S_{hXY} \qquad (26.6)$$

with S_{hXY} given by Eq. 14.4,

$$S_{hX}^2 = S_{hXX} \quad \text{and} \quad S_{hY}^2 = S_{hYY}$$

$$R = \frac{X}{Y}$$

and where

$$\sigma_{hi}^2 = \sigma_{x'_{hi}}^2 + R^2 \sigma_{y'_{hi}}^2 - 2R \sigma_{x'_{hi}y'_{hi}} \qquad (26.7)$$

In the specific case of a three-stage design, $\sigma_{x'_{hi}y'_{hi}}$ and therefore also $\sigma_{x'_{hi}}^2$ and $\sigma_{y'_{hi}}^2$ are given by Eq. 26.3. The first term in Eq. 26.5 is the contribution to the rel-variance due to sampling psu's, and the second term is the contribution to the rel-variance due to sampling within psu's regardless of the number of stages of sampling within selected psu's.

The optimum values for the sampling fractions for three-stage sampling with a simple cost function are given in Vol. II.*

27. The estimate of the total rel-variance of estimate 25.1 when more than one primary sampling unit is taken from each stratum. An estimate of the rel-variance of x'/y' (given by Eq. 25.1) when more than one primary sampling unit is taken from a stratum is†

---

* See Vol. II, Ch. 9, Sec. 11.
† The proof is given in Vol. II, Ch. 9, Sec. 4.

$$v_r^2 = v_{x'}^2 + v_{y'}^2 - 2v_{x'y'} \tag{27.1}$$

where

$$v_{x'y'} = \frac{1}{x'y'} \sum_h^L \frac{\sum_i^{m_h} \left(\frac{x'_{hi}}{P_{hi}} - \frac{\sum_i^{m_h} \frac{x'_{hi}}{P_{hi}}}{m_h} \right) \left(\frac{y'_{hi}}{P_{hi}} - \frac{\sum_i^{m_h} \frac{y'_{hi}}{P_{hi}}}{m_h} \right)}{m_h(m_h - 1)} \tag{27.2}$$

and

$$v_{x'}^2 = v_{x'x'}, \quad v_{y'}^2 = v_{y'y'} \tag{27.3}$$

where x'_{hi}/P_{hi} is an unbiased estimate of the total for the hth stratum based on the ith unit in the sample. This estimate is applicable for any number of stages and any probability methods of subsampling. For three-stage sampling, x'_{hi} is given by Eq. 25.2. Equation 27.1 reduces to Eq. 6.10 of Ch. 7 when we ignore the finite multiplier, and the sample is self-weighting, as would be the case in three-stage sampling when $\bar{m} P_{hi} f_{hia} f_{hiaj} = f$.

28. The estimate of the total variance when only one primary unit is drawn per stratum. When only one primary unit is drawn per stratum, a consistent estimate of the variance is not available. An estimate* of the rel-variance (similar to Eq. 15.1 for a self-weighting sample) is made by grouping strata following the principles discussed in Sec. 15. Then

$$v_r^2 = v_{x'}^2 + v_{y'}^2 - 2v_{x'y'} \tag{28.1}$$

where

$$v_{x'y'} = \frac{1}{x'y'} \sum_g^G \frac{L_g}{L_g - 1} \sum_h^{L_g} \left(x'_{gh} - \frac{A_{gh}}{A_g} x'_g \right) \left(y'_{gh} - \frac{A_{gh}}{A_g} y'_g \right) \tag{28.2}$$

$x'_{gh} = x'_{ghi}/P_{ghi}$, $x'_g = \sum_h^{L_g} x'_{gh}$, x'_{ghi} is defined by Eq. 25.2, and y'_{gh} and y'_g are similarly defined for the Y characteristic. A_{gh} and A_g are defined in Sec. 15, and

$$v_{x'}^2 = v_{x'x'}; \quad v_{y'}^2 = v_{y'y'} \tag{28.3}$$

The subscript g in the definitions designates the gth group of strata.

29. Estimate of the variance when some of the psu's are selected with certainty, i.e., some of the strata consist of only one psu (see Sec. 10 and 24). To estimate the variance when some of the psu's are selected with certainty, i.e., when some of the strata consist of only one psu, one may consider the population as having been divided into two classes. Class I will consist of all the psu's which have been selected with certainty.

---

* The development of this estimate is given in Vol. II, Ch. 9, Sec. 5.

Class II will consist of all other strata.   Equations 27.1–27.3 or 28.1–28.3 are applicable to class II.   If sampling from the class I strata involves the use of only two stages of sampling, Eq. 6.1 of Ch. 7 is appropriate.

An estimate of the rel-variance of x'/y' is a weighted average of the rel-variances of the two classes.   Thus, if we let $v_{\mathrm{I}x'}^2$, $v_{\mathrm{I}y'}^2$, $v_{\mathrm{I}x'y'}$ be the appropriate terms in the estimate of the rel-variance for class I and $v_{\mathrm{II}x'}^2$, $v_{\mathrm{II}y'}^2$, and $v_{\mathrm{II}x'y'}$ be the appropriate terms in the estimate of the rel-variance for class II, then

$$v_{(x'/y')}^2 = \frac{x_{\mathrm{I}}'^2 v_{\mathrm{I}x'}^2 + x_{\mathrm{II}}'^2 v_{\mathrm{II}x'}^2}{x'^2} + \frac{y_{\mathrm{I}}'^2 v_{\mathrm{I}y'}^2 + y_{\mathrm{II}}'^2 v_{\mathrm{II}y'}^2}{y'^2}$$
$$- 2\frac{x_{\mathrm{I}}'y_{\mathrm{I}}' v_{\mathrm{I}x'y'} + x_{\mathrm{II}}'y_{\mathrm{II}}' v_{\mathrm{II}x'y'}}{x'y'} \tag{29.1}$$

where x_{I}' and y_{I}' are estimated aggregates for class I, x_{II}', y_{II}' are estimated aggregates for class II, and

$$x' = x_{\mathrm{I}}' + x_{\mathrm{II}}', \quad y' = y_{\mathrm{I}}' + y_{\mathrm{II}}' \tag{29.2}$$

30. Estimates of the components of the variance with more than one psu per stratum.*   In multi-stage sampling it is often important to estimate the components that enter into the variance for the determination of optimum allocation or the determination of major sources of the variance. Assume that we have a sample of m_h' psu's from the hth stratum, n_{hia}' second-stage units from the ith psu in the ath substratum in the hth stratum, and q_{hiaj}' third-stage units in the $hiaj$th second-stage unit, for estimating the components.   The components for the variance of Eq. 25.1 with three stages of sampling can be stated in terms of S_h^2, S_{hia}^2, and S_{hiaj}^2, where

$$S_h^2 = S_{hX}^2 + R^2 S_{hY}^2 - 2RS_{hXY} \tag{30.1}$$

is the variance between first-stage units, with S_{hXY} and therefore S_{hX}^2 and S_{hY}^2 defined by Eq. 14.4;

$$S_{hia}^2 = S_{hiaX}^2 + R^2 S_{hiaY}^2 - 2RS_{hiaXY} \tag{30.2}$$

is the variance between second-stage units; and

$$S_{hiaj}^2 = S_{hiajX}^2 + R^2 S_{hiajY}^2 - 2RS_{hiajXY} \tag{30.3}$$

is the variance between third-stage units.

---

* For proof, see Vol. II, Ch. 9, Sec. 10.

Estimate of S^2_{hiaj}. To estimate S^2_{hiaj} we need s_{hiajXY}, the estimate of S_{hiajXY}. Then $s^2_{hiajX} = s_{hiajXX}$ and $s^2_{hiajY} = s_{hiajYY}$. An unbiased estimate of S_{hiajXY} is

$$s_{hiajXY} = \frac{\overset{q'_{hiaj}}{\sum} (x_{hiajk} - \bar{\bar{\bar{x}}}_{hiaj})(y_{hiajk} - \bar{\bar{\bar{y}}}_{hiaj})}{q'_{hiaj} - 1} \qquad (30.4)$$

with $\bar{\bar{\bar{x}}}_{hiaj} = \overset{q'_{hiaj}}{\underset{k}{\sum}} x_{hiajk}/q'_{hiaj}$, and $\bar{\bar{\bar{y}}}_{hiaj}$ similarly defined. Since r is a consistent estimate of R, a consistent estimate of S^2_{hiaj} is

$$s^2_{hiaj} = s^2_{hiajX} + r^2 s^2_{hiajY} - 2r s_{hiajXY} \qquad (30.5)$$

Estimate of S^2_{hia}. A consistent estimate of S^2_{hia} is

$$s^2_{hia} = \hat{s}^2_{hia} - \tilde{s}^2_{hia} \qquad (30.6)$$

where

$$\hat{s}^2_{hia} = \hat{s}^2_{hiaX} + r^2 \hat{s}^2_{hiaY} - 2r \hat{s}_{hiaXY} \qquad (30.7)$$

with

$$\hat{s}_{hiaXY} = \frac{\overset{n'_{hia}}{\sum} (x'_{hiaj} - \bar{x}'_{hia})(y'_{hiaj} - \bar{y}'_{hia})}{n'_{hia} - 1} \qquad (30.8)$$

$$x'_{hiaj} = \frac{Q_{hiaj}}{q'_{hiaj}} \overset{q'_{hiaj}}{\sum} x_{hiajk} \qquad (30.9)$$

$$\bar{x}'_{hia} = \frac{1}{n'_{hia}} \overset{n'_{hia}}{\sum} x'_{hiaj} \qquad (30.10)$$

y'_{hiaj} and $\bar{y}'_{hia}$ are similarly defined;

$$\hat{s}^2_{hiaX} = \hat{s}_{hiaXX} \quad \text{and} \quad \hat{s}^2_{hiaY} = \hat{s}_{hiaYY}$$

and where

$$\tilde{s}^2_{hia} = \frac{1}{n'_{hia}} \overset{n'_{hia}}{\sum} Q^2_{hiaj} \frac{Q_{hiaj} - q'_{hiaj}}{Q_{hiaj}} \frac{s^2_{hiaj}}{q'_{hiaj}} \qquad (30.11)$$

Estimate of S^2_h. Finally, a consistent estimate of S^2_h is

$$s^2_h = \hat{s}^2_h - \tilde{s}^2_h \qquad (30.12)$$

where

$$\hat{s}^2_h = \hat{s}^2_{hX} + r^2 \hat{s}^2_{hY} - 2r \hat{s}_{hXY} \qquad (30.13)$$

with

$$\hat{s}_{hXY} = \frac{1}{m'_h - 1} \overset{m'_h}{\underset{i}{\sum}} \left(\frac{x'_{hi}}{P_{hi}} - \frac{\overset{m'_h}{\sum} \frac{x'_{hi}}{P_{hi}}}{m'_h} \right) \left(\frac{y'_{hi}}{P_{hi}} - \frac{\overset{m'_h}{\sum} \frac{y'_{hi}}{P_{hi}}}{m'_h} \right) \qquad (30.14)$$

$$x'_{hi} = \overset{D_{hi}}{\underset{a}{\sum}} \frac{N_{hia}}{n'_{hia}} \overset{n'_{hia}}{\underset{j}{\sum}} x'_{hiaj} \qquad (30.15)$$

x'_{hiaj} given by Eq. 30.9, and y'_{hi} similarly defined;

$$\hat{s}^2_{hX} = \hat{s}_{hXX} \quad \text{and} \quad \hat{s}^2_{hY} = \hat{s}_{hYY}$$

and

$$\tilde{s}^2_h = \frac{1}{m'_h} \sum_i^{m'_h} \frac{1}{P^2_{hi}} \sum_a^{D_{hi}} \frac{N^2_{hia}}{n'_{hia}} \left(\frac{N_{hia} - n'_{hia}}{N_{hia}} \hat{s}^2_{hia} + \frac{n'_{hia}}{N_{hia}} \tilde{s}^2_{hia} \right) \quad (30.16)$$

31. Estimate of the total rel-variance in terms of estimates of the contributions to the rel-variance from each stage of sampling.

A consistent estimate of the total rel-variance (Eq. 26.1) in terms of estimates of the contribution to the rel-variance from each stage of sampling is given by

$$v^2_r = \frac{1}{x'^2} \sum_h^L \frac{1}{m_h} s^2_h + \frac{1}{x'^2} \sum_h^L \frac{1}{m_h} \frac{1}{m'_h} \sum_i^{m'_h} \frac{1}{P^2_{hi}} \sum_a^{D_{hi}} N^2_{hia} \frac{N_{hia} - n_{hia}}{N_{hia}} \frac{s^2_{hia}}{n_{hia}}$$

$$+ \frac{1}{x'^2} \sum_h^L \frac{1}{m_h} \frac{1}{m'_h} \sum_i^{m'_h} \frac{1}{P^2_{hi}} \sum_a^{D_{hi}} \frac{N_{hia}}{n_{hia}} \frac{N_{hia}}{n'_{hia}} \sum_j^{n'_{hia}} Q^2_{hiaj} \frac{Q_{hiaj} - q_{hiaj}}{Q_{hiaj}} \frac{s^2_{hiaj}}{q_{hiaj}} \quad (31.1)$$

where the terms are as defined in Sec. 30. The first term of Eq. 31.1 is the estimate of the contribution to the rel-variance arising from the sampling of first-stage units, the second term is the estimate of the contribution to the rel-variance arising from the sampling of second-stage units, and the third term is the estimate of the contribution to the rel-variance arising from the sampling of third-stage units.

Note that m_h, n_{hia}, and q_{hiaj} are the sample sizes that are used in estimating R, while m'_h, n'_{hia}, and q'_{hiaj} are the sample sizes used in estimating S^2_h, S^2_{hia}, and S^2_{hiaj}. When the sample sizes used in estimating these variances are the same as the sample sizes used in estimating R, the estimate of the rel-variance given by Eq. 31.1 is identically the *ultimate cluster* estimate of the rel-variance given by Eq. 27.1.

32. Estimates of the components of the rel-variance when only one psu is selected from each stratum, and the estimates are to be made from the original sample.

Just as in the estimation of the total variance (see Sec. 28), a consistent estimate of the between-psu variance is not available when only one psu is selected from each stratum. An estimate which tends to overstate the variance is available and is given below. We shall consider three cases that occur frequently in practice, and assume that there are two or more units in the sample at each stage of sampling except the first.

Case 1. The estimate of the components is to be based on the original sample that was used in estimating the ratio $R = X/Y$. The estimate $r = x'/y'$ of the ratio, R, is given by Eq. 25.1. In this case, estimates of the second- and third-stage contributions to the rel-variance are given by the second and third terms of Eq. 31.1, respectively, by letting $m_h = m'_h = 1$, $n_{hia} = n'_{hia}$, and $q_{hiaj} = q'_{hiaj}$. With these substitutions, second- and third-stage contributions to the variance can be estimated whenever n_{hia} and q_{hiaj} are both greater than 1. The first-stage contribution to the rel-variance is not given by the first term in Eq. 31.1 since only one psu is selected from each stratum. An estimate that tends to be an overstatement is obtained by subtracting the sum of the estimates of second and third stages of sampling from Eq. 28.1. Specifically, for this case

$$b_1^2 = v_r^2 - \frac{1}{x'^2} \sum_h^L \frac{1}{P_{hi}^2} \sum_a^{D_{hi}} N_{hia}^2 \frac{N_{hia} - n_{hia}}{N_{hia}} \frac{s_{hia}^2}{n_{hia}}$$

$$- \frac{1}{x'^2} \sum_h^L \frac{1}{P_{hi}^2} \sum_a^{D_{hi}} \frac{N_{hia}^2}{n_{hia}^2} \sum_j^{n_{hia}} Q_{hiaj}^2 \frac{Q_{hiaj} - q_{hiaj}}{Q_{hiaj}} \frac{s_{hiaj}^2}{q_{hiaj}} \qquad (32.1)$$

with v_r^2 given by Eq. 28.1, s_{hia}^2 by Eq. 30.6 with $n'_{hia} = n_{hia}$, $q'_{hiaj} = q_{hiaj}$, s_{hiaj}^2 by Eq. 30.5 with $q'_{hiaj} = q_{hiaj}$.

The second and third terms in Eq. 32.1 are estimates of the contributions to the rel-variance from the second and third stages of sampling, respectively.

Case 2. This is the same as Case 1 above except that the sampling fractions are small at the second and all subsequent stages of sampling, i.e., we can assume that the finite multipliers are approximately equal to 1. In this case, the estimate of the components is greatly simplified. An estimate of the between-psu contribution to the rel-variance is given by

$$b_2^2 = v_r^2 - \frac{1}{x'^2} \sum_h^L \frac{1}{P_{hi}^2} \sum_a^{D_{hi}} \frac{N_{hia}^2}{n_{hia}} \hat{s}_{hia}^2 \qquad (32.2)$$

with v_r^2 given by Eq. 28.1, $\hat{s}_{hia}^2$ given by Eq. 30.7 with $n'_{hia} = n_{hia}$ and $q'_{hiaj} = q_{hiaj}$. Note that Eq. 32.2 is an estimate of the between-psu contribution to the rel-variance no matter how many subsequent stages of sampling are used. Similarly the second-stage contribution to the rel-variance is obtained by taking

$$\frac{1}{x'^2} \sum_h^L \frac{1}{P_{hi}^2} \sum_a^{D_{hi}} \frac{N_{hia}^2}{n_{hia}} \hat{s}_{hia}^2 - \frac{1}{x'^2} \sum_h^L \frac{1}{P_{hi}^2} \sum_a^{D_{hi}} \frac{N_{hia}^2}{n_{hia}^2} \sum_j^{n_{hia}} \frac{Q_{hiaj}^2}{q_{hiaj}} s_{hiaj}^2 \qquad (32.3)$$

and the second term of Eq. 32.3 is an estimate of the third-stage contribution to the rel-variance.

Case 3. In this estimate of the components for the variance of Eq. 23.1, the denominator of the ratio estimate is based on known psu totals. In this case, the contributions to the rel-variance from the second and subsequent stages of sampling will be the same as those for the unbiased estimate x' defined in Eq. 25.1. The between-psu rel-variance is given by

Eq. 32.1 with $s_{hia}^2 = s_{hiaX}^2$ and $s_{hiaj}^2 = s_{hiajX}^2$, and these terms are defined in Sec. 30. Note that s_{hiajX}^2 is given by Eq. 30.5 and s_{hiaX}^2 is given by Eq. 30.6 provided the terms involving Y's in the definitions for these equations are ignored.

If, moreover, the finite multipliers for the second and subsequent stages of sampling can be assumed to be approximately equal to 1, then

$$b_3^2 = v_r^2 - \frac{1}{x'^2} \sum_h^L \frac{1}{P_{hi}^2} \sum_a^{D_{hi}} \frac{N_{hia}^2}{n_{hia}} \hat{s}_{hiaX}^2 \tag{32.4}$$

where v_r^2 is given by Eq. 28.1 and where $\hat{s}_{hiaX}^2$ is equal to

$$\hat{s}_{hiaX}^2 = \frac{\sum_j^{n_{hia}} (x'_{hiaj} - \bar{x}'_{hia})^2}{n_{hia} - 1} \tag{32.5}$$

Note that the second term of Eq. 32.4 is an estimate of the total contribution to the rel-variance from the second and all subsequent stages of sampling and can be referred to as the within-psu contribution to the rel-variance. The second-stage contribution to the rel-variance is given by Eq. 32.3 with $\hat{s}_{hia}^2$ and s_{hiaj}^2 replaced by $\hat{s}_{hiaX}^2$ (Eq. 30.8) and s_{hiajX}^2 (Eq. 30.4), respectively. Similarly, the third-stage contribution to the rel-variance is given by the second term of Eq. 32.3 with s_{hiaj}^2 replaced by s_{hiajX}^2 (Eq. 30.4).

REFERENCES

(1) J. R. Goodman, "Sampling for the 1947 Survey of Consumer Finances," *J. Amer. Stat. Assn.*, **42** (1947), 439–448.
(2) M. H. Hansen and W. N. Hurwitz, "A New Sample of the Population," *Estadistica*, **II** (1940), 483–497.
(3) M. H. Hansen and W. N. Hurwitz, "On the Theory of Sampling from Finite Populations," *Annals Math. Stat.*, **14** (1943), 332–362.
(4) E. E. Houseman, "The Sample Design for a National Farm Survey by the Bureau of Agricultural Economics," *J. Farm Economics*, **29** (1947), 241–245.
(5) Emil H. Jebe, "Estimation for Subsampling Designs Employing the County as a Primary Sampling Unit," *J. Amer. Stat. Assn.*, **47** (1952), 49–70.

CHAPTER 10

Estimating Variances

1. The problem of estimating variances. Throughout the preceding chapters, we have indicated that both the efficient design of sample surveys and the evaluation of the precision of the results depend on a knowledge of the appropriate variances (and covariances or correlations) for the population from which the sample is drawn. We have shown how estimates of variances can be obtained from the sample, once the sample results are available.

The problem of estimating the variances of various sample statistics after sample results are available is comparatively simple if one has a large enough sample, because the data from which to estimate the variances already have been collected in the survey. It is important in this instance, however, to arrange the computations and the tabulation of the data in such a way as to make feasible the estimation of the needed variances at low cost. It is also important to know the size of the sample needed for purposes of estimating the variances.

Advance estimates or speculations on variances can be made only roughly at best, but often this is good enough. Variances are needed before the sample is drawn in order to guide in optimum design, to provide advance estimates of the expected precision of results from specified sizes of sample, and to compare alternative sampling procedures. In this situation, full use of available related data, together with some pretesting (at least where sufficient data are not already available), will often provide rough approximations to the variances or to the ratios of variances that are needed.

Several aspects of the problem of estimating variances need further consideration.

A. ESTIMATING VARIANCES FROM SAMPLE RETURNS

2. Use of formulas previously given. A specific method of estimating the variance for each sample design has been given in the earlier chapters.

It has been seen that for many sample designs the basic variances can be estimated from a sample simply by substituting the sample numbers into the population variance formulas. The resulting estimates can then be substituted into the formulas for variances of sample statistics. It has been seen also that one cannot always estimate variances simply by substituting the sample numbers into the population variance formulas. Whether or not this can be done depends on the sample design and also on the formula being used for estimating the variance. The case that will be most commonly encountered where the variance cannot be estimated in this way is that in which subsampling is used and separate estimates are being made of the components of the variance. Appropriate methods of estimating such variances have been presented.

Although we have given methods for estimating variances with alternative sample designs, other ways often can be found that fit more readily into a tabulation program and that make it possible to estimate variances more easily. Several methods for reducing the amount of computation involved in estimating variances from the sample, which may be found useful to apply in many instances, will be described in Sec. 13–19 of this chapter.

3. Required accuracy of variance estimates from a sample. It is a useful guide for many problems, as was indicated earlier (see Sec. 12, Ch. 4), to have an estimate of variance that has a coefficient of variation of perhaps 20–30 per cent or less (this implies a coefficient of variation of the standard deviation of about 10–15 per cent or less). Higher precision may serve little purpose if one is using the variance estimate as a means of indicating the reliability of a sample estimate. On the other hand, where one is trying to compare the efficiency of alternative methods, a higher level of precision may be desirable. Whenever special tabulations or computations are required in estimating variances, it will often be true that sufficiently reliable estimates can be obtained and substantial economies may result if a subsample of the entire sample that is available for purposes of estimating means, totals, and other characteristics is used in estimating the variances. In other instances, it may be necessary not only to use the total sample available but also to get additional information from a supplementary sample or other sources in order to obtain a sufficiently reliable estimate of the variance.

NOTE. All the variances of estimates of variances given in this chapter are for sampling with replacement. The results for sampling without replacement for a simple case are given in Vol. II.*

* See Vol. II, Ch. 4, Sec. 5.

4. Accuracy of variance estimates with simple random sampling. We found in Ch. 4, Sec. 12, that with simple random sampling the variance of an estimated variance, s^2, where s^2 is given by Eq. 3.12, Ch. 4, is approximately equal to

$$\sigma_{s^2}^2 = \frac{\beta - \dfrac{n-3}{n-1}}{n} \sigma^4 \tag{4.1}$$

where β is given by Eq. 12.7, Ch. 4, and the rel-variance of s^2 is approximately

$$V_{s^2}^2 = \frac{\beta - \dfrac{n-3}{n-1}}{n} \tag{4.2}$$

Moreover, we saw that, approximately,

$$V_s^2 \doteq \frac{V_{s^2}^2}{4} \tag{4.3}$$

or

$$V_s \doteq \frac{V_{s^2}}{2} \tag{4.4}$$

The use of these relationships provides a guide to the relative precision of estimates of a variance or of a standard deviation, if the sample is large enough, but, of course, involves sufficient investigation to be able to place at least a reasonable maximum value on β. If one is dealing with a sufficiently large sample, β can simply be estimated from the sample returns by substituting sample numbers in the definition of β in Eq. 12.7, Ch. 4. But unless one is dealing with very large samples, perhaps larger than needed for obtaining a sufficiently reliable estimate of S^2, the sample estimate of β may be unreliable. Then the determination of β involves primarily consideration of the size and frequency of extreme items in the population from which the sample is drawn, which in turn leads to an assumption as to the upper limit on the value of β.*

Tables of F and χ^2† are often used to set limits on the sampling error of a variance estimate. They are appropriately used in setting such limits provided the sample is drawn from a normal distribution, or the departure from a normal distribution is not too great. However, in

---

* This process was illustrated in Ch. 4, Sec. 14 (p. 140).

† For χ^2 table, see R. A. Fisher, *Statistical Methods for Research Workers*, Oliver and Boyd, Ltd., Edinburgh, tenth edition, 1948, p. 112. For F table see George W. Snedecor, *Statistical Methods*, Iowa State College Press, Ames, Iowa, fourth edition, 1946, p. 222.

practical problems of sampling from a finite population very often the initial population from which the sample is drawn is far from normal, and the assumption of a normal distribution may lead to grossly wrong impressions as to the precision of variance estimates. This fact was discussed with reference to simple random sampling and was illustrated extensively in Chapter 4. It is suggested that the reader refer to that chapter again (Sec. 14), for a review of the material presented there.

The estimate from the sample of the variance of a ratio of random variables, using a simple random sample (Eq. 21.3–21.5 of Ch. 4), is also a ratio of random variables, and the rel-variance of the estimate of the standard deviation is given approximately for this case by Eq. 21.6, Ch. 4. The rel-variance of the estimate of the standard deviation of a ratio, again, is approximately one-fourth the rel-variance of the estimate of the variance of a ratio. In general, the rel-variance of u is approximately equal to one-fourth the rel-variance of u^2, where u can be either an estimate of the standard deviation, coefficient of variation, or a general class of other estimates of positive quantities.

With ratio estimates, one must be concerned not only with the question of the precision of the variance estimate because of the size of the sample, but also with the fact that the variance formulas given are approximations. The approximations will be good with large enough samples. Equation 12.5 in Sec. 12, Ch. 4, of Vol. II gives a guide as to the bias of the estimate of the standard error of the ratio estimate. The indicated guide will be satisfactory only if the sample is large enough that the numerator and denominator of the ratio are approximately normally distributed. Equation 12.5 was used to derive the rule given in previous chapters that, roughly, one will have a reasonably small bias (less than 15 per cent) in the estimate of the standard error if the coefficient of variation of the denominator of r is less than 5 per cent. This criterion is unduly stringent for many applications. For example, suppose that we have $\rho \doteq V_y/V_x$, so that the line of regression of X_i on Y_i is approximately through the origin; then the bias of the ratio estimate is small under these circumstances, even though the coefficient of variation of the denominator may be as large as 15 per cent. The relative bias in the estimate of the variance will be approximately twice the relative bias in the estimate of the standard error.

A general answer is not available as to when a sample is large enough so that the variate will be approximately normally distributed, as is called for above.

5. The accuracy of the estimated rel-variance and of the coefficient of variation. The estimate of the rel-variance from the sample, like the estimate of the variance of the ratio estimate, is a ratio of random variables. The rel-variance of the estimate of the coefficient of variation, $v = s/\bar{x}$, with simple random sampling is given approximately by:*

$$V_v^2 \doteq \frac{\beta - 1}{4n} + \frac{V_X^2}{n} - \frac{\sum\limits^{N}(X_i - \bar{X})^3}{nN\bar{X}^3 V_X^2} \tag{5.1}$$

where v^2 is given by Eq. 12.3, Ch. 4, and β is given by Eq. 12.7, Ch. 4.

Table 1. Approximate rel-variance of the estimated rel-variance and of the estimated variance, with a sample of $n = 1$ for selected populations—simple random sampling

Selected population	$V_{v^2}^2$*	$V_{s^2}^2$	$V_{\bar{x}^2}^2$	$\rho_{s^2\bar{x}^2}$
Inhabitants per dwelling place: Charleston, S.C., 1944	2.55	4.94	2.13	.70
Blocks by number of dwelling units: Los Angeles, 1940	13.5	25.5	6.83	.71
Size of farm in acres: U.S., 1940	284.0	602.0	82.0	.90
Sales of independent retail stores: U.S., 1939	4227.0	5904.0	188.0	.89
Income of population: Atlanta, Ga., 1933	173.0	206.0	6.0	.56
Age of population: U.S., 1940	1.85	1.37	1.63	.39
Cotton bale weights: Marshall Co., Ala., 1945	4.41	4.38	.015	− .03

* Based on Eq. 5.1 with $n = 1$ and with $V_{v^2}^2 = 4V_v^2$. These approximations are not good, of course, for samples of 1, but the estimates for samples of size n are obtained by dividing these figures by n; the size, n, required for a "good" approximation will depend on the characteristic being estimated and the accuracy desired.

The first of the three terms is the rel-variance of the estimate of S; the second term is the rel-variance of $\bar{x}$, the estimate of the mean (the denominator of the estimate of the coefficient of variation from the sample); and the third term is twice the rel-covariance between s, the estimate of the standard deviation, and $\bar{x}$. The third term will disappear for symmetric distributions. Most of the nonsymmetric distributions with which we deal in sampling from finite populations are skewed to the right, so that the term involving the cube of the deviations from the mean will be positive (the correlation between the estimated variance and the square of the estimated mean will be positive in such cases). Consequently, the rel-variance of the estimated coefficient of variation will be less than the sum of the rel-variances of the numerator and the denominator. Illustrations of the rel-variance of the estimated rel-variance, as

* For proof, see Vol. II, Ch. 10, Sec. 1.

well as of the estimated variance, are given in Table 1 for the same distributions for which the precision of estimated variances is given in Sec. 14, Ch. 4. The table also shows $\rho_{s^2 \bar{x}^2}$, the correlations of s^2 and $\bar{x}^2$. The entries for $V_{v^2}^2$, $V_{s^2}^2$, and $V_{\bar{x}^2}^2$ are simply four times the corresponding values for V_v^2, V_s^2, and $V_{\bar{x}}^2$ defined earlier.

The table shows that the reliability of the estimate v^2 can be greater than that of the estimate s^2. This is quite different from estimating V^2 for a normally distributed variate, where s^2 and $\bar{x}^2$ are independently distributed and therefore the relative error in the estimation of S^2 is always smaller than the relative error in the estimation of $S^2/\bar{X}^2$.

The rel-variance of v_r, the estimated coefficient of variation of the ratio estimate, $r = x/y$, the ratio of sample aggregates from a simple random sample, is given approximately by

$$V_{v_r}^2 \doteq \frac{\beta_Z - 1}{4n} + \frac{V_X^2}{n} - \frac{\rho_{Z^2 X} V_X \sqrt{\beta_Z - 1}}{n} \tag{5.2}$$

where $v_r^2 = s_r^2/r^2$, and s_r^2 is given by Eq. 21.3 of Ch. 4, β_Z and Z are defined for Eq. 21.6 of Ch. 4, and $\rho_{Z^2 X}$ is the correlation of Z^2 and X. Equation 5.2 is the same as the rel-variance for the standard deviation of r, if in Eq. 5.2 we substitute V_Y^2 for V_X^2, V_Y for V_X, and $\rho_{Z^2 Y}$ for $\rho_{Z^2 X}$.*

6. Accuracy of variance estimates with cluster sampling. As was pointed out in Chapter 6, the variance of an estimate from a simple random sample of clusters without subsampling involves theory no different from that for sampling elementary units. The variance formulas are exactly the same except that the totals for the cluster are the variates involved, and the number of clusters is the sample size. We have seen also that, if one or more stages of subsampling is used, and if the *ultimate clusters* have been sampled with equal probability and the psu's have been selected without stratification, we can regard the ultimate clusters as whole clusters, and the formulas for simple random sampling of whole clusters will be a good approximation (see Ch. 6, Sec. 7). Equations similar in form to Eq. 4.1–4.4, 5.1, and 5.2, but with ultimate clusters substituted for elementary units, will give measures of the precision of the estimates of the variance and rel-variance of ultimate cluster totals.

The estimates of the components of the variance are given in Sec. 7 of Ch. 6, Sec. 7 of Ch. 7, and Sec. 30–32 of Ch. 9. The precision of such estimates for a simple case is given in Vol. II, Ch. 10, Sec. 5.

---

* The accuracy of the estimate of the coefficient of variation of r is derived from Eq. 12.5 of Sec. 12, Ch. 4, Vol. II, provided v_x is used in place of v_w in that equation.

7. Accuracy of variance estimates from stratified samples.   Some special considerations are involved in evaluating the precision of a variance estimate for a stratified sample.   The estimate of the variance that is needed in evaluating the sampling error of an estimated mean or total when stratified sampling is used involves the estimates of within-strata variances.   The precision of the variance estimate with a stratified sample may be considerably less than that for the estimate of the variance from an unstratified sample of the same size, and the investigator should be aware of the situations where the difference is substantial.   In instances where there is any problem, he must use an appropriate size of sample or estimating method to insure reasonably reliable estimates.

An estimate of the variance of an estimated total with stratified sampling when n_h is small relative to N_h or sampling is with replacement is

$$s_{x'}^2 = \sum^L \frac{N_h^2}{n_h} s_h^2 \tag{7.1}$$

and $s_{x'}^2$ is an unbiased estimate of

$$S_{x'}^2 = \sum^L \frac{N_h^2}{n_h} S_h^2 \tag{7.2}$$

where s_h^2 is given by Eq. 14.1 of Ch. 5, and S_h^2 is given by Eq. 1.2 of Ch. 5. The rel-variance of $s_{x'}^2$ is*

$$V_{s^2_{x'}}^2 = \frac{\displaystyle\sum_h^L \frac{N_h^4}{n_h^2}\sigma_{s^2_h}^2}{S_{x'}^4} = \frac{\displaystyle\sum_h^L N_h^4 \frac{1}{n_h^3}\left(\beta_h - \frac{n_h-3}{n_h-1}\right)S_h^4}{S_{x'}^4} \tag{7.3}$$

where $S_{x'}^2$ is given by Eq. 7.2, β_h for the hth stratum is defined by Eq. 12.7 of Ch. 4, and S_h^2 is given by Eq. 1.2 of Ch. 5.

In the special case of proportionate stratified sampling, $n_h/N_h = \bar{n}/\bar{N}$ and the estimate of $\sigma_{x'}^2$ is approximately

$$\frac{N^2}{n} s_w^2 \tag{7.4}$$

where s_w^2 is

$$s_w^2 = \frac{\sum^L N_h s_h^2}{N} = \frac{\sum^L n_h s_h^2}{n} \tag{7.5}$$

and n is the size of sample.

The rel-variance of $s_{x'}^2$ is the rel-variance of s_w^2 and

$$V_{s^2_{x'}}^2 = V_{s^2_w}^2 = \frac{\sum^L N_h^2\sigma_{s^2_h}^2}{N^2 S_w^4} = \frac{\sum^L N_h\left(\beta_h - \frac{n_h-3}{n_h-1}\right)S_h^4}{NnS_w^4} \tag{7.6}$$

* For derivation, see Vol. II, Ch. 10, Sec. 2.

where S_w^2 is defined by Eq. 3.8 of Ch. 5.   Equation 7.6 is the special case of Eq. 7.3 when $n_h/N_h = n/N$ for all h, i.e., the sampling is proportionate stratified sampling.

8. Effect of "degrees of freedom" on the precision of a within-strata variance estimate.   One reason for less accuracy in an estimate of the within-strata variance is the smaller number of "degrees of freedom" on which the estimate is based.   The number of degrees of freedom in a variance estimate is the number of observations on which the variance estimate is based minus the number of means or totals subtracted in making the estimate.   Thus, the number of degrees of freedom in the estimate of the variance from a simple random sample of n observations is $(n-1)$.   In this instance all the deviations are taken around the over-all sample mean.   In the estimate s_w^2, on the other hand, the deviations within strata are taken around the respective strata means.   There are L such means involved, and there are $(n-L)$ degrees of freedom in the estimate of the average variance within strata.   With simple random sampling from a normal distribution, the number of degrees of freedom completely determines the coefficient of variation of an estimated variance. This is true, also, for proportionate stratified random sampling from populations that are normally distributed within each stratum and for which, in addition, the variances within the different strata are equal. (The reader should prove these statements as an exercise, using Eq. 4.1 and 7.6, and with $\beta = 3$, and $\beta_h = 3$, which hold for a normal distribution.)

Thus, suppose that one had a sample of $n = 100$ observations consisting of 2 observations from each of $L = 50$ strata.   If the distribution within each stratum were approximately normal and if the variances were about equal in all the strata, the rel-variance for the within-strata variance estimate would be based on 50 degrees of freedom and consequently would be approximately twice as large as with a simple random sample of 100 observations from a normal distribution.

9. Effect of other factors on the precision of within-strata variance estimates.   Several factors other than the number of degrees of freedom need to be considered in determining the reliability of the average within-strata variance estimate.   One of these is the effect of an average β within strata that differs considerably from 3.   A second is the effect of considerable variation between strata in the variances.   A third is the effect of different sampling fractions.

If the average β within strata differs considerably from 3 (so that the distributions are not, in general, even approximately normal), then the rel-variance of the estimated variance is no longer inversely proportionate to the number of degrees of freedom, even though the variances within strata are all the same. Thus, in the simple case where the sampling is proportionate, the strata are of equal size, and the within-strata variances are all the same,*

$$V^2_{s^2_w} = \frac{\bar{\beta} - \frac{\bar{n} - 3}{\bar{n} - 1}}{n} \tag{9.1}$$

where

$$\bar{\beta} = \frac{\Sigma \mu_{4h}}{L \bar{S}^4} = \text{the average } \beta \text{ within strata}$$

μ_{4h} is defined by Eq. 12.7 of Ch. 4, $\bar{S}^2 = S^2_h$, and $\bar{n} = $ the number in the sample from each stratum.

To illustrate, for this case, how misleading it would be to assume that the variance of s^2_w is dependent entirely on the number of degrees of freedom, assume $n = 100$, $\bar{\beta} = 10$, $L = 50$, where L is the number of strata. Values of β of 10 or more are not uncommon, as was illustrated in Chapter 4.

Applying formula 9.1, with $\bar{n} = 2$, we have $V^2_{s^2_w} = (10 + 1)/100 = .11$. In this instance the number of degrees of freedom is 50. Now assume again that $n = 100$, $\bar{\beta} = 10$, but that $L = 2$. Here the number of degrees of freedom is 98, or almost twice as large as the case considered above. However, $V^2_{s^2}$ in this case is equal to $(10 - 47/49)/100 = .09$, which is far more than half of the .11 found above. This illustrates the effect of a β which is not in the neighborhood of 3, the value of β for a normal distribution. The degrees of freedom were nearly doubled, but the variance was decreased only about 20 per cent.

Wide variation between strata in the variances or jointly in the variances and the β_h's may create particular difficulties in determining the reliability of variance estimates unless the samples are large in the strata having large variances or large β_h's. As a simple illustration, let us assume that one is sampling from a population that has strata of equal size and the same β in each of the strata, i.e., $\beta_h = \beta_w = \Sigma \beta_h / L$, but the variances vary widely from stratum to stratum. Then Eq. 7.6 can be written*

$$V^2_{s^2_w} = \frac{\beta_w - 1}{n} (1 + V^2_{S^2_h}) \tag{9.2}$$

where $V^2_{S^2_h}$ is the coefficient of variation between strata of the S^2_h. Thus, $V^2_{s^2_w}$ is increased by the factor $(1 + V^2_{S^2_h})$ over what it would have been if the within-stratum variances had been equal.

---

* For proof, see Vol. II, Ch. 10, Sec. 2.

Thus, if one were sampling from a population with $\beta_h = \beta_w$ in each stratum, but with one stratum having a very large value for S_h^2 relative to the other within-stratum variances, the precision of the estimate of the within-strata variance may be little greater than the reliability of the variance estimate in that one stratum. As an illustration, suppose that 50 strata were involved, each with 1 degree of freedom, and a total sample size of 100; suppose in 49 of the 50 strata the within variance was equal to 1, but in 1 stratum the variance was equal to 100. Assume $\beta = 3$ in each of the strata. In this case

$$1 + V_{S_h^2}^2 = 22$$

so that the variation in the S_h^2 has multiplied the rel-variance of s_w^2 by a factor of 22 over what it would have been if the S_h^2 had been the same.

Whenever one is faced with the problem of extremely wide variations between strata in the variances, or of sampling from a population with unusually large β's in some of the strata, the sample size will need to be increased only in the few strata that make the large contribution to the variance of the estimated variance, so that a reasonably good estimate of the variance is obtained in each such stratum. This involves investigating to determine the particular strata with large variances, and increasing the sample size in these strata.*

If a subsample of the original returns is used to estimate a stratified variance, and if the S_h's or β_h's differ widely between the strata, the subsample should be so drawn that, approximately,†

$$n_h' \doteq \frac{N_h^2 S_h^2 \sqrt{\beta_h - 1}/n_h}{\Sigma(N_h^2 S_h^2 \sqrt{\beta_h - 1}/n_h)} n' \tag{9.3}$$

where n_h is the size of the original sample and n_h' the subsample from the hth stratum. If the original sample is a proportionate stratified sample,

$$n_h' \doteq \frac{N_h S_h^2 \sqrt{\beta_h - 1}}{\Sigma N_h S_h^2 \sqrt{\beta_h - 1}} n' \tag{9.4}$$

Note from Eq. 9.4 that if the β_h's do not vary a great deal the sampling fraction is approximately proportionate to S_h^2, rather than to S_h, as it would be if one were using the optimum allocation to estimate a mean. The optimum allocation of a sample for estimating variances does not, of course, insure that the S_h^2 or β_h are estimated accurately. It is possible

---

* A substantial bias may be introduced in such a variance estimate unless the strata with large variances can be identified independently of the variance estimates from the sample (cf. Ch. 2, Sec. 17–18).

† For proof, see Vol. II, Ch. 10, Sec. 3.

that, for an accurate estimate of S_h^2's or β_h's in some strata, the original sample must be supplemented, whereas in others a subsample will be sufficient.

If one is using simple random sampling of elementary units within strata, with variates that have the value 0 or 1 (as in estimating a percentage or total number of persons having a specified characteristic), then both the variances and the β's will vary considerably between strata in any instance where the stratification is effective in reducing the variability of the estimated percentage or total.   If the P's vary widely between strata, then the variances and β's vary in opposite directions and tend to offset each other's effect, since for a 0, 1 variate*

$$\beta_h = \frac{1}{P_h Q_h} - 3 \tag{9.5}$$

Exercises

9.1. Compute the variances and β_h's for the following stratified population:

STRATUM	N_h	P_h
1	1,000	.01
2	5,000	.50
3	4,000	.20
4	2,000	.90
	12,000	

9.2. Compute S_w^2 and $V_{s_w^2}$ for a proportionate stratified sample of 100 from this population.   Notice that S_w^2 is a population variance, and $V_{s_w^2}$ is the coefficient of variation of an *estimate* of this variance.   The same applies to S^2 and V_{s^2} in Ex. 9.3.

9.3. Compute S^2 and V_{s^2} for a simple random sample of 100 from this population.

9.4. For what size of proportionate stratified sample will $V_{s_w^2}^2 = .01$?, .10?

9.5. Assume that a stratified sample of elementary units is drawn with replacement from the population in Ex. 9.1.

(a) Find $V_{s_w^2}^2$ if a sample of 50 is drawn with replacement in each stratum.

(b) Compute and compare $V_{s_w^2}^2$ for a simple random sample of 200 drawn with replacement from the whole population.

(c) Carry through the same computation if a sample of 5 is drawn from each stratum with replacement; compare with $V_{s^2}^2$ for a simple random sample of 20.

10. Precision of variance estimates with disproportionate sampling. Whenever one is using disproportionate sampling in the different strata, the effect on the accuracy of the variance estimate is similar to the effect, with proportionate sampling, of variances which vary between strata.

---

* For proof, see Vol. II, Ch. 4, Sec. 8.

The investigator must be sure that he has an adequate size of sample from each stratum so that no single stratum determines the magnitude of the estimated over-all variance unless the estimate of the variance for that stratum is reasonably reliable.

11. Need for special care in substitution when estimating variances from a subsample. The investigator needs to be particularly careful, whenever he draws a subsample from a sample for purposes of estimating variances, to substitute the appropriate values in estimating the variance of statistics based on the larger sample.   To illustrate the problem, and the situation in which special care is needed, let us suppose that a sample of n units is drawn at random from a population of N units in order to estimate various population characteristics.   A subsample of n' is drawn at random from the sample of n for purposes of estimating the variances.   Then the estimate of S^2 will be

$$ s^2 = \frac{\sum_{i}^{n'}\left(x_i - \sum_{i}^{n'} \frac{x_i}{n'}\right)^2}{n' - 1} \tag{11.1} $$

which is substituted in $\dfrac{N-n}{N}\dfrac{s^2}{n}$ to estimate the variance of $\bar{x} = \Sigma x_i/n$.

Note that n, the sample size for estimating the mean, is used in the term which reflects the effect of sample size on the variance, $(N-n)/Nn = (1-f)/n$, whereas n', the size of the subsample, is used in s^2.   This point, in more complicated problems, needs careful attention.   It is emphasized here because mistakes are often made at this point in the estimation of sample variances.

12. Exercises on variance computations. Several problems involving variance computations and their reliability are given here to illustrate some of the points discussed above.

Exercises

12.1. Consider a population of 12,000 individuals, with 1000 persons having each of the incomes in Table 1 of Ch. 1 (p. 13).   Compute β and determine the rel-variance of the estimate of the mean and of the estimated variance (i.e., $V_{\bar{x}}^2$ and $V_{s^2_{\bar{x}}}^2$) for simple random samples of 24, 120, and 600 from this population. (Note that N is large relative to n.)

12.2. With the population of Ex. 12.1, and data for 1950 income as shown in Table 10 of Ch. 1 (p. 36) find β for the ratio of present income to 1950 income.   Determine V_r^2 and $V_{s^2_r}^2$ for simple random samples of 24, 120, and 600.

12.3. With the population of Ex. 12.1 stratified into 4 groups, *AJD, LGF, IHC,* and *EKB* (as in Illustration 16.1 of Chapter 1), find $V_{\bar{x}}^2$ and $V_{s^2_{\bar{x}}}^2$ (Eq. 7.6) for proportionate samples of 24, 120, and 600.

12.4. With the stratification of Ex. 12.3, find $V_{\bar{r}}^2$ and $V_{s_r^2}^2$ for proportionate samples of 24, 120, and 600.

12.5. If the sampling fraction is twice as large in the 2 groups of higher income individuals (*IHC* and *EKB*) as in the 2 lower groups (*AJD* and *LGF*), determine $V_{\bar{x}}^2$ and $V_{s_x^2}^2$ for samples of total sizes 24, 120, and 600.

12.6. With disproportionate sampling as in Ex. 12.5, find $V_{\bar{r}}^2$ and $V_{s_r^2}^2$ for samples of total sizes 24, 120, and 600.

12.7. Suppose that the following data result from a sample survey using simple random sampling:

Stratum number h	Number in population N_h	Sample size n_h	$\sum_i^{n_h} x_{hi}$	$\sum_i^{n_h} x_{hi}^2$	$\sum_i^{n_h} x_{hi}^3$	$\sum_i^{n_h} x_{hi}^4$
1	15,000	140	800	5,000	36,000	300,000
2	10,000	105	2,500	66,000	1,000,000	60,000,000
3	5,000	55	7,500	1,375,000	281,250,000	61,187,500,000

(a) Compute estimates of $V_{\bar{x}}^2$, $V_{s_x^2}^2$ for each stratum, and for the estimate of the over-all mean with a proportionate stratified sample of 300.

(b) Compute the corresponding estimates for the estimate of the mean with a sample of 100 from each stratum.

(c) Compute estimates of $S_{\bar{x}}^2$, β, $V_{s_x^2}^2$, and $V_{v^2}^2$ for a simple random sample of 300.

(d) Compute an estimate of P, the proportion of the units that are in stratum 1; compute s_p^2, the estimated standard error of this estimate; and compute an estimate of $V_{s_p^2}^2$, the rel-variance of s_p^2.

12.8. In a certain city, blocks have been classified into 2 strata on the basis of size in terms of dwelling units, and a sample of blocks has been selected within each stratum. Within each selected block a cluster of dwellings has been randomly selected and the number of homes owned has been ascertained. Data available are shown below:

	LARGE-BLOCK STRATUM	SMALL-BLOCK STRATUM
Sampling fraction for selecting blocks	1 in 5	1 in 25
Sampling fraction within blocks	1 in 10	1 in 2
Number of blocks, M_h	1,000	10,000
Number of blocks in sample, m_h	200	400
For ultimate clusters:		
$\sum_i^{m_h} x_{hi}$	1,400	1,600
$\sum_i^{m_h} x_{hi}^2$	20,000	12,000
β_h	10	6

Estimate $V_{\bar{x}}^2$ and $V_{s_x^2}^2$ for each stratum, and for the city: (a) for the sample indicated in the table; (b) for a proportionate sample of 300 ultimate clusters; (c) for a proportionate sample of 60 ultimate clusters.

B. SOME SHORT CUTS FOR ESTIMATING VARIANCES

13. Grouping strata to estimate variances. When estimating the variance from the sample, it will often be convenient and sometimes necessary to disregard some of the stratification that was used in selecting the sample.

The process of estimating variances from the sample by substituting corresponding sample numbers in the equations for the population variances or in the appropriate variance-estimating formulas requires that there be two or more randomly selected units in the sample from each stratum (or, with subsampling, from each primary or intermediate-stage sampling unit if an estimate of the variance within such units is desired). Where only one unit is in the sample from a stratum, it is necessary to group strata in order to obtain a variance estimate from the sample, and a description of a process for doing so is given in Ch. 9, Sec. 15. Often, however, it is desirable, even though not necessary, to group some of the strata in order to reduce the work of making variance estimates. By "grouping" strata is meant that the stratification is ignored for the strata that are grouped. Thus, one might have drawn a sample of farms by stratifying on, say, county in which located and size of farm. If in estimating the variance the stratification by county is ignored and the sample is treated as though stratification were done only by size of farm, we say that the county strata have been "grouped."

In the use of grouped strata to estimate variances one simply ignores the differences between the strata that are merged. If the units have been selected with the same probabilities in each of the original strata that have been grouped into a single stratum, one can apply whatever variance formula would have been appropriate if the ignored strata had not been used in selecting the sample.

It should be recognized that whenever stratification is ignored in estimating a variance a bias is incurred in the variance estimate if the stratification has been effective, and *on the average* under such circumstances an overestimate of the variance will be obtained.* However, we have mentioned several times in connection with stratification that, although sometimes stratification may result in a considerable reduction in the variance, frequently the gains are comparatively small either for the variance over all strata or for some of the criteria of stratification. In instances where the gains are small, the ignoring of such stratification in estimating the variance will mean that the amount of overestimation because of grouping strata will be small.

---

* See, for example, Vol. II, Ch. 9, Sec. 5.

Even where the stratification gains are moderately large, ignoring some of the stratification simply means that one is more conservative in stating the sampling error of the estimate. It should be observed that an overestimate of 20 per cent in the variance leads to an overestimate of the standard error of only about 10 per cent, and grouping the least important strata will often lead to overestimates of the variance of considerably less than 20 per cent. It is sometimes true, in fact, that the total gains due to all stratification are comparatively small; and in such a case it will be satisfactory, where convenient, to ignore the stratification completely in estimating variances.

The gain is considerable in estimating variances of frequencies or percentages with proportionate sampling and with the use of simple random sampling of elementary units within strata. In this case, if the stratification is ignored, the variance of an estimated frequency or percentage can be determined from the estimated percentage having the characteristic, and requires no special variance tabulations. It is also true that for such characteristics the gains due to stratification are often small, at least for some of the criteria of stratification, so that variance computations without respect to the strata, or at most with recognition of a few strata, may be quite sufficient. See, for example, Ex. 17.7, Ch. 5, and compare the stratified variance with the unstratified variance.

14. Estimating variances from ultimate clusters with multi-stage sampling. A simplification in estimating variances that has been indicated already in preceding chapters is the "ultimate cluster" variance estimate from a multi-stage sample. If one has sampled primary units and subsampled within them, with perhaps two, three, or more stages of sampling, the variance of the sample estimate (but not the components of the variance) can always be estimated by taking the final sample and identifying it by primary units. The entire sample from each primary unit is called an ultimate cluster.

Estimates of variances and covariances can be calculated from estimated sample psu totals. The psu totals in turn are estimated from the sample within each psu. If a uniform over-all sampling fraction has been used, the ultimate cluster totals can be employed without the added step of estimating psu totals.

Ultimate cluster variance estimates are discussed and formulas given in Sec. 7 of Ch. 6, Sec. 6 of Ch. 7, and Sec. 15, 27, and 28 of Ch. 9.

15. Estimates of variance for classes of items instead of for each individual item sometimes sufficient. When a large number of items is to be estimated from a sample, the work of estimating variances for each individual

item is sometimes very great indeed.   Often in a sample survey there are
a few important characteristics on which estimates are particularly needed,
and at the same time there are a number of other characteristics which are
of interest.   To reduce the work of estimating variances, therefore, a
practice that seems to give satisfactory results is to estimate individually
from the sample those particularly important statistics on which accurate
statements of precision are needed.   The other statistics are then classified
into broad classes, based on rough evidence as to the variance relationships involved, and then measures of precision for all those in a class are
derived on some kind of an average or regression basis.

Frequently a scatter diagram will help identify items that can be placed
in the same class.   Case Study B, Ch. 12, illustrates the computation and
summarization of variances for classes of items.

16. Random group method of estimating variances.   If one has a simple
random sample of n observations, $x_1, \cdots, x_n$, then the usual estimate of
the variance from the sample is

$$s^2 = \frac{\sum\limits_{i}^{n}(x_i - \bar{x})^2}{n - 1} \tag{16.1}$$

Another estimate of S^2 is obtained by subdividing the n observations into
t random groups of k units each.   An estimate of S^2 obtained from the
variance of the totals for this set of subsamples is*

$$\frac{\sum\limits_{g}^{t}(x_g - \bar{x}')^2}{k(t - 1)} = s_k^2 \tag{16.2}$$

where x_g is the total of the gth group, and $\bar{x}'$ is the mean per group of the
t group totals.

The precision of the estimate from random groups will always be less
than that of the usual estimate of the variance given by Eq. 16.1.   In
view of this fact, the reader may ask, "Why should one estimate S^2 from
the random groups, Eq. 16.2, instead of from Eq. 16.1?"   Part of the
answer to such a question is that one *should* use Eq. 16.1 in instances
where there are no special problems or significant costs in doing so.   The
advantage of using random groups and Eq. 16.2 lies in the possible
reductions in work and cost that are particularly likely to be achieved
where the variance of not one but of a considerable number of different
statistics is to be estimated.   This reduction may be very substantial.

---

* For proof of this and succeeding formulas, see Vol. II, Ch. 10, Sec. 4.

Let us first examine the variance of the estimate given by Eq. 16.2 as compared with that given by Eq. 16.1. The rel-variance of s^2 (Eq. 16.1) is given by Eq. 4.2, and for n of about 10 or more is approximately equal to $(\beta - 1)/n$.

The rel-variance of s_k^2 is given by

$$V_{s_k^2}^2 = \frac{1}{t}\left(\beta_k - \frac{t-3}{t-1}\right) \tag{16.3}$$

where

$$\beta_k = \frac{\beta}{k} + 3\frac{k-1}{k} \tag{16.4}$$

or, for any moderately large number of random groups, say $t = 10$ or more, $V_{s_k^2}^2$ is roughly equal to

$$V_{s_k^2}^2 = \frac{\beta_k - 1}{t} \tag{16.5}$$

Remark. Equations 16.3 and 16.5 assume n small relative to N or sampling with replacement. However, s^2, Eq. 16.1, and s_k^2, Eq. 16.2, are unbiased estimates of S^2 if the sampling is without replacement.

The fact that the distribution of a sample mean or total or other similar statistic approaches a normal distribution as the size of sample increases is reflected in the formula for β_k (Eq. 16.4). It shows that, as the size of the random group increases, the value of β_k approaches 3. Table 2 shows the value of β_k for various sizes of random group and for various

Table 2.   Values of β_k for different values of k and β

k = size of random group	β_k when β is					
	1	3	5	10	50	200
1	1	3	5	10	50	200
3	2.3	3	3.7	5.3	18.7	68.7
6	2.7	3	3.3	4.2	10.8	35.8
12	2.8	3	3.2	3.6	6.9	19.4
24	2.9	3	3.1	3.3	5.0	11.2
100	3.0	3	3.0	3.1	3.5	5.0
1000	3.0	3	3.0	3.0	3.0	3.2

sizes of β for the initial population. It is clear from the table that, if we are sampling from a population for which the β is quite large (see discussion in Ch. 4, Sec. 12, and in Sec. 3–9 of this chapter), β_k decreases rapidly with increasing k, the number in the random group. Consequently, if the variance is estimated through the random group method, and if a given number of random groups is used, the larger the number in the random group the smaller will be the variance for those items that have large initial values of β—although after a certain point the gain from increasing the size of the random group will be very small.

Illustration 16.1. Suppose that a sample is drawn for a characteristic for which $\beta = 10$; let us compare 3 different estimates of the variance with a total sample size of 1200 cases. The first estimate uses all 1200 observations individually and Eq. 16.1; the second uses 60 random groups of 20 observations each and Eq. 16.2; and the third uses a subsample of 60 individual observations and Eq. 16.1. The coefficients of variation of the estimated variances in each of these cases are indicated in Table 3. The corresponding coefficients of variation for corresponding estimates from a sample from a normal distribution, for which $\beta = 3$, are given also for comparison.

Table 3. Comparison of random group method of estimating the variance (Eq. 16.2) with the usual method of estimating the variance (Eq. 16.1)

Size of sample and method of estimation	V_{s^2} (per cent)	
	$\beta = 10$ for initial population	$\beta = 3$ for initial population
Sample of 1200 observations (Eq. 16.1)	8.7	4.1
Sample of 60 random groups of 20 observations each (total of 1200 observations) (Eq. 16.2)	20	18.3
Sample of 60 individual observations (Eq. 16.1)	39	18.3

We see, as we should have expected, considerable loss in precision by using all 1200 observations in only 60 random groups instead of individually. But for $\beta = 10$ this estimate is still much better than with 60 individual observations from the original population. Actually, the work of tabulation and computations necessary for computing the variance estimate with 60 random groups may be just as easy as with 60 individual observations, and considerably greater precision will result.

If β had been 3, as for the normal distribution, then the precision would have been the same for 60 individual observations as for 60 random groups, as we see from Table 3, and if β were *less* than 3 then the 60 individual observations would have given greater precision than the 60 random groups. But even when some of the items have β's less than 3, the convenience of a random group tabulation and computations is often sufficient for the choice of this method where one is computing the variance for a large number of different statistics, most of which have β's greater than 3.

_____

When the random group method of estimating variances is used, numbers between 1 and t (for t random groups) can be assigned at random to each unit in such a way that each number from 1 to t is assigned with equal frequency.   Then tabulations can be made in accordance with this random number, and the variances between the totals tabulated can be computed.   If the number of units in the population is not an even multiple of k, the number per random group, then some of the population (selected at random) can be left out of the random group tabulations— enough to make the number of units used in the estimate a multiple of k. Then Eq. 16.2 is used to estimate the variance S^2, which is substituted in $\dfrac{1-f}{n} \dfrac{S^2}{\bar{X}^2}$ to obtain an estimate of the rel-variance of a mean or total.

Whenever cluster or multi-stage sampling is used, the units that go into making up the random groups are the ultimate clusters—whole clusters if there is only one stage of sampling.   For example, if counties are sampled, second-stage units are sampled within counties, and then listing units within second-stage units; then all the listing units from the primary unit (county in this case) constitute the ultimate cluster and must be treated as a single unit in forming the random group.   If there are only a few primary units in the entire sample, then the random group method is not very useful.   If one has sampled a considerable number of blocks from within an area, however, and wants some estimates of variances for that area, then the ultimate cluster from within each of these blocks can be treated as a unit and a random group variance computed.

With stratified sampling the random group method is also suitable.   In this instance each stratum must be balanced in the random groups. Thus, suppose that one has 5 strata, with 200 sample units from each. Then 100 random groups of 10 units each can be made up by including in each random group 2 observations chosen at random from each of the original 5 strata.   Each random group thus contains the appropriate representation from each stratum, and represents a stratified sample mean based on 10 observations.   In this instance, the computation of variance between the random groups will be an estimate of the within-strata variance, the appropriate variance for stratified sampling, without separate computation of the variances within the strata.

Remark.   It is not necessary that the number of observations in each stratum be the same, or that the number in each stratum be exactly divisible by the number of groups being formed.   When the number in each stratum is not divisible by the number of groups being formed, some of the elements may be left out of the random group tabulations, their selection being made at random.

If the initial sample had involved only 5 observations from each of 200 strata, one could make up only 5 random groups with appropriate representation from each of the 200 strata, and 5 groups would be much too small for a reliable variance estimate. In this case, if the random group method is to be used, one of the two methods described below can be followed.

(a) One method is to group strata so that for variance computation purposes one will have, say, 50 strata of 20 observations each, and include 1 observation from each of these in a random group, resulting in 20 random groups. The result will give the same variance estimate, on the average, that would have been obtained from a variance computation from the individual observations and with the same strata grouped.

(b) A second method for the illustration mentioned above is to arrange the strata into 20 classes of 10 strata each, and then make up 5 random groups of 10 units each within each of the 20 classes. From each such set of 5 random groups a variance estimate is obtained. The within-strata variance estimate for all strata combined is then obtained by computing the average of these estimates.

An approximate equation for estimating variances and covariances of sample estimates from a set of random groups is as follows:

$$v_{x'}^2 = \frac{\sum\limits_{g}^{t}(x_g' - \bar{x}')^2}{t(t-1)(\bar{x}')^2} \tag{16.6}$$

where k units are included in each of t random groups;

$$x' = \sum_{g}^{t} x_g', \quad x_g' = \sum_{i}^{k} x_{gi}', \quad \bar{x}' = \frac{\sum\limits_{g}^{t} x_g'}{t}$$

and x_{gi}' is the total or estimated total for the ith unit included in the gth random group. Similarly,

$$v_{x'y'} = \frac{\sum\limits_{g}^{t}(x_g' - \bar{x}')(y_g' - \bar{y}')}{t(t-1)\bar{x}'\bar{y}'} \tag{16.7}$$

For a ratio estimate, x'/y', one simply obtains estimates of $V_{x'}^2$, $V_{y'}^2$, and $V_{x'y'}$ and puts them together in the usual way (Eq. 18.12, Ch. 4).

17. Estimating variances from order statistics.* Instead of computing s (Eq. 3.12, Ch. 4) from a sample as an estimate of S, the difference between certain order statistics may provide at low cost an estimate of S of acceptable reliability. Thus, kd may be used as an estimate of S, where d is the range (the difference between the largest and smallest values in the sample), and k is dependent on the size of sample. Daly† showed that with small simple random samples from a normal distribution little information is lost by using the range to estimate S instead of the sample standard deviation. It has also been shown‡ that, by grouping the observations into random subsamples of 8–10 observations and using the mean range of the subsamples, one obtains a relatively efficient estimate of S, and one whose behavior is not seriously affected by non-normality of the population sampled.

Along a slightly different line Mosteller§ investigated estimates of S of the form

$$kd = k(x_h + x_j + \cdot \cdot \cdot - x_{100-h} - x_{100-j} - \cdot \cdot \cdot) \qquad (17.1)$$

where x_h, x_j, x_{100-h}, x_{100-j} are the h, j, $100-h$, and $100-j$ percentile points|| of the observed frequency distribution. With simple random sampling from a normal population, it is found that the optimum choice for two percentile points is that for which $h \doteq 93$ and $100 - h \doteq 7$. In this case $k \doteq .339$ and the estimate would be

$$.339(x_{93} - x_7) \qquad (17.2)$$

Note that the constant k in Eq. 17.1 (and 17.2) does not depend on size of sample, as contrasted with the corresponding estimate based on the range, where the value of k must be determined separately for each sample size.

Whether the range or percentiles are used, the principle is simple; k is merely the reciprocal of the expected value of d (expressed in units of σ),

---

* This section written by J. F. Daly, Bureau of the Census.

† J. F. Daly, "On the Use of the Sample Range in an Analogue of Student's *t*-Test," *Annals Math. Stat.*, **17** (1946), 71–74.

‡ K. C. S. Pillai, "On the Distribution of an Analogue of Student's *t*," *Annals Math. Stat.*, **22** (1951), 469–472; P. B. Patnaik, "The Use of the Mean Range as an Estimator of Variance in Statistical Tests," *Biometrika*, **37** (1950), 78–87; E. Lord, "The Power of the Modified *t*-Test (*u*-Test) Based on Range," *Biometrika*, **37** (1950), 64–77; E. S. Pearson, "Some Notes on the Use of Range," *Biometrika*, **37** (1950), 88–92.

§ Frederick Mosteller, "On Some Useful 'Inefficient' Statistics," *Annals Math. Stat.*, **XVII** (1946), No. 4, pp. 377–408.

|| The *h*th percentile point computed from a sample is the value on the frequency distribution scale below which h per cent of the estimated frequencies are found.

where d represents either the range or the percentile differences. The values of k can be determined readily for the normal distribution.*

Both the reliability and the cost of such estimates may be considerably less than those of the usual estimate of the standard deviation, but if the accuracy is sufficient for the estimate to be useful, and if there is a savings in cost, such estimates may be worth while.

Sometimes the loss in precision is small. If we let s_1 be the estimate of S based on the 7th and 93rd percentiles, and s_2 the sample standard deviation (Eq. 3.12, Ch. 4), then the efficiency of s_1 relative to s_2 is $\sigma_{s_2}^2/\sigma_{s_1}^2$. The estimate based on the 7 and 93 per cent points has an efficiency with large samples of about 65 per cent relative to s as an estimate of S. It may be noted that the interquartile range (the case $h = 75$, $100 - h = 25$) has a corresponding efficiency of about 56 per cent. By using 8 properly spaced percentiles it is possible to achieve a relative efficiency with large samples of about 90 per cent, a result slightly better than the mean deviation, which has an efficiency of about 88 per cent with large samples. With small samples the estimate from the range may be more convenient to use.

Little is known about the behavior of these estimates when the population is not normal. The estimates are not consistent estimates of S if the values of k are selected appropriate to the normal distribution. It would seem reasonable to assume that, if the observations were divided into, say, g random groups of equal size, and average percentile differences computed from the distribution of the g sample results, the constants appropriate to a normal distribution would be satisfactory. The following empirical results seem to indicate that, even if this averaging process is not employed (i.e., even if the sample is not divided into random groups), the results obtained for a highly skewed population may turn out to be useful.

Illustration 17.1. Use of order statistics for estimating sampling variance in the 1950 Census of Agriculture. (Based on an unpublished study by Floyd Berger, Bureau of the Census.) As part of the tabulation program for the 1950 Census of Agriculture, it was necessary to provide estimates of the sampling variability of more than a million items (such as value of land and buildings, expenditures for hired labor, number of acres rented to others, etc.). Because of the sheer magnitude of such a program, it was decided that it would be sufficient to publish only the general level of reliability of each item rather than attach a specific estimate of sampling

---

* See L. H. C. Tippett, "On the Extreme Individuals and the Range of Samples Taken from a Normal Population," *Biometrika*, **17** (1925), pp. 386–387, for the expected value of the range for samples of size up to 1000.

error to each figure. Accordingly, the following fairly broad levels of reliability were defined:

LEVEL	COEFFICIENT OF VARIATION
1	.00– .39
2	.40– .79
3	.80–1.29
4	1.30–2.29
5	2.30–3.09
6	3.10–4.39
7	4.40 or above

After some investigation it was concluded that adequate information on levels of reliability could be obtained by computing estimated standard errors for about 50,000 figures and inferring from these the levels for the remaining figures. However, even after this reduction, the task of computing sampling errors was still a formidable one. It was decided to investigate the simplest of Mosteller's estimates, given by Eq. 17.2. To investigate the behavior of the estimate based on the 7th and 93rd percentiles for the distributions involved in the Agriculture Census program (most of them are highly skewed) 267 items from 12 selected counties were chosen and levels of sampling variability were assigned both by this method and by the standard (mean square) method. An indication of the agreement or disagreement of the two methods is given in Table 4.

Table 4.   Comparison of estimates of variance from "two-point" order statistics with standard method

	Number of observations	Per cent
Item assigned to same level	168	63
Item assigned to different levels	99	37
Difference of one level	76	28
Difference of two levels	23	9
Item assigned to different levels		
Higher level assigned by standard method	47	18
Lower level assigned by standard method	52	19

Examination of the cases in which the two methods assigned different levels revealed that where the greatest differences occurred the largest observation in the county was more than twice as great as the 93 per cent point. It was decided to investigate whether agreement with the conventional method would be improved by using a combination of 1 per cent, 7 per cent, 93 per cent, and 99 per cent points whenever the distribution was extremely skewed. This study was made in 6 counties, using the 4-point estimate whenever the largest observation was more than twice as large as the 93 per cent point, and using the 2-point estimate otherwise. Of the 60 items selected, 40 had distributions which were sufficiently skewed to call for use of the 4-point statistic under the rule specified.

A comparison between the standard method and the revised percentile method is presented in Table 5. It will be noted that the relative frequency of extreme disagreement was reduced from 9 to 3 per cent.

These studies also indicated that variance levels for 200 items could be estimated by the revised percentile procedure at about the same cost as that of estimating variance levels for 100 items under the standard procedure. It was therefore decided to use the revised percentile procedure to compute levels for twice as many items as could be obtained with the available resources under the standard procedure.

Table 5. Comparison of estimates of variance from "four-point" order statistics with standard method

	Number of observations	Per cent
Item assigned to same level	44	74
Item assigned to different levels	16	26
Difference of one level	14	23
Difference of two levels	2	3
Item assigned to different levels		
Higher level assigned by standard method	7	12
Lower level assigned by standard method	9	13

18. Method of calculating confidence intervals for medians and other position measures.* Confidence limits for a position measure computed from a simple random sample can be set approximately as follows:

(a) Compute the position measure from the sample (such as the median or the first quartile). Call it m, which is an estimate of M.

(b) Let P_M be the proportion of the population below the position measure. Thus, if M is the median then $P_M = .5$. If M is the first quartile then $P_M = .25$.

(c) Compute

$$\sigma_{P_M} = \sqrt{(1-f)\frac{P_M(1-P_M)}{n}}$$

which is the standard deviation of the proportion of observations in a sample of size n that are less than M.

* For proof, derived by Ralph S. Woodruff, Bureau of the Census, see Vol. II, Ch. 10, Sec. 7.

(d) Compute

$$p_1 = P_M - k\sigma_{p_M}$$

and

$$p_2 = P_M + k\sigma_{p_M}$$

(e) Find from the sample frequency distribution the points on the scale below which the proportion p_1 of the sample frequencies fall, and call this point m_1.   This point is obtained by interpolation in the same manner as the median or other position measure.

In a similar manner find the point below which p_2 of the sample frequencies fall, and call this point m_2.

(f) The confidence interval is the interval m_1 to m_2.   Then the approximate probability that this interval will encompass M, the position measure being estimated, is about $\frac{2}{3}$ if $k = 1$, is about .95 if $k = 2$, etc.

When the sampling method is other than simple random sampling the steps are the same except that σ_{p_M} (obtained in step c above) is obtained as follows:

(c_1) An estimate of the population distribution is obtained by weighting each sample item by its appropriate weight.   The sample median (m) of this derived distribution is determined.   Let p_m be the proportion of items in the derived distribution having a value less than m.

(c_2) Compute an estimate of the standard error of p_m from the sample, which we will call s_{p_m}.   The estimated standard error of p_m is, of course, the one appropriate to the method of sample selection and estimation.*

Then proceed with the remaining steps d–f as outlined for simple random sampling but substituting s_{p_m} for σ_{p_M}.

In general, the larger the sample used, the more stable m becomes and the less effect the substitution of m for M has on the variance approximation.   Limited experiments show that even for relatively small samples the substitution of m for M does not have an important effect on the estimated variance of the percentage of sample items less than M.   It appears, therefore, that the problem of computing s_{p_m} from sample data is similar to the general problem of estimating variances from samples, i.e., for very small samples the results may be extremely unreliable but for large samples the results will be usable.

---

* If the data are tabulated in terms of class intervals, a satisfactory estimate of s_{p_m} can be obtained (if the class intervals are not too broad) by estimating the standard error of the proportion of items less than that class limit (m') which is closest to m.

C. ESTIMATING VARIANCES FROM PAST DATA

19. Variance estimates from available data. Unfortunately, one who is planning a survey cannot have the sample results in hand from which to make the variance estimates needed in advance of drawing the sample. He must approximate the necessary variances (and costs) from data already available to him. Useful sources of data for advance speculations include censuses, other available general data, previous surveys of the type under consideration, and pretests of the survey.

To make effective use of the available data one applies the methods indicated throughout this book. We shall outline some approaches to estimating variances from past data and to speculating on variances with limited available data, and refer to the places where relevant methods are discussed more fully.

The actual computation of variances from previously available data of a closely related character is perhaps the safest method for estimating variances in advance of sample selection when appropriate data are available. Moreover, even when one has a sample in hand from which variance estimates can be made, there will be some circumstances under which it may be desirable to use previous data to estimate the precision of sample results. Often quick results are desired. The computation of means or totals or percentages from the sample can be very fast, but the computation of variances may involve a great deal more work. Use of past data for estimating variances may also be desirable when the number of units in the sample is too small to yield a reliable estimate of the variance, although the number is adequate for estimating the desired means or totals.

One may have previous samples of essentially similar information but for a different time period, or data from a census for an earlier period. Computations or variances from information already available will give a fairly satisfactory guide to the reliability of the current sample results for characteristics that have relatively high stability over time, or in situations where information on an item closely related to the one being studied is available from previous data. Whenever such advance estimates are used, they should be verified subsequently or, for a continuing survey, periodically, by making variance computations from the actual data.

The use of past data in estimating a variance is sometimes accomplished by simply substituting the data for the total population for some previous period into the population variance formula. Sometimes, however, a sample is selected from the past data, and the variance is estimated from this sample by means of the variance formulas for the sample estimates given earlier in this chapter and in other chapters.   Still another variation in the form of an estimate is convenient with the use of past data when a sample is selected from the past data but the total or mean for each stratum is known and is utilized in making the estimate.   Thus, for a stratified sample of $n = \sum_h^L n_h$ units, with n_h units drawn from the hth stratum with known mean, the estimate of S_w^2, the average within-stratum variance, is given by

$$s_w^2 = \frac{1}{N} \sum_h^L \frac{N_h^2}{N_h - 1} \frac{\sum_{i}^{n_h}(x_{hi} - \bar{X}_h)^2}{n_h} \tag{19.1}$$

where S_w^2 is defined by Eq. 3.8, Ch. 5.

The variance estimate for the between-psu contributions to the variance with multi-stage sampling is sometimes conveniently arrived at by a similar approach.   Thus, assume that one has information for the psu's from a prior complete census for a characteristic that is presumed to be closely related to the one to be investigated.   One can select, say, one or a few units per stratum with varying probabilities of selection if desired. In this case, too, a consistent estimate of B^2 (Eq. 14.2, Ch. 9) can be obtained without having to estimate the within-psu variance, as is neces- sary if the variance is being estimated from a two- or more stage sample. Thus, if m_h units are selected with probability P_{hi} associated with the ith unit in the hth stratum, and one or more units per stratum is sampled with replacement, estimates of B_X^2 and B_{XY} are*

$$b_X^2 = \frac{1}{L\hat{X}^2} \sum_h^L \frac{1}{m_h} \sum_i^{m_h} \left(\frac{X_{hi}}{P_{hi}} - X_h\right)^2$$

$$b_{XY} = \frac{1}{L\hat{X}\hat{Y}} \sum_h^L \frac{1}{m_h} \sum_i^{m_h} \left(\frac{X_{hi}}{P_{hi}} - X_h\right)\left(\frac{Y_{hi}}{P_{hi}} - Y_h\right) \tag{19.2}$$

where the X_h and Y_h are known and where the terms used are as defined for Eq. 14.3 of Ch. 9.

Unless particular care is exercised, misleading results may be obtained from the use of past data to estimate variances.   Suppose, for example, that one wants to estimate the gains that will be achieved by stratification or ratio estimation through a study of previous data.   For example, in a farm survey we might want to know the gains if we stratify by size of farm and have data from the census showing not only size of farm but also acreage in various crops, production, livestock, income, etc.   We

* For proof, see Vol. II, Ch. 10, Sec. 6.

might be tempted to classify the farm size from the available data, and then estimate from the same data the gains for the other characteristics due to this stratification. Obviously, this does not simulate the practical situation in which one uses past data for stratification, draws a sample, and obtains estimates of some characteristics for a more recent period. Consequently, the estimation of stratification gains by using both characteristics at the same period of time will be an overestimate and will underestimate the true variance of the design. A way to deal with such problems is to use prior data for two different dates, far enough apart to simulate the situation under consideration, classify or stratify on the information at one date, and compute the variances from the data for the other date. If such data are not available, some idea of the variances may perhaps be obtained by computing the variance for a related item; for example, in estimating the variance of retail sales, a rel-variance of total employees or total payroll may be of the same order as the rel-variance for sales at some other date.

The ideal situation for estimating variances from past data occurs, of course, where previous survey results or analyses of census results provide data in essentially the form needed.   It is for this reason that it is desirable, after one has carried through a sample survey, to analyze it in such a way as to add to the store of knowledge that may be helpful in planning future surveys. For example, the estimates of components of the variance for a multi-stage sample are useful in future planning. An estimate of the total variance is all that is needed to provide a measure of precision for the survey, but the total variance alone will be considerably less useful for future planning than will the sources and magnitudes of contributions to the variance from each of the stages of sampling, and also different types of strata.

The illustrations of survey results given throughout the other chapters and the case studies in Chapter 12, in particular, contain reports on variances and costs.   Such results, together with similar results reported elsewhere, can be put to effective use in planning many different types of surveys.

The following discussion simply points up, for emphasis, and in some instances extends somewhat, relevant material that is presented in other chapters.

The most obvious and easiest level of speculation arises if one is estimating a proportion of elementary units having a characteristic when the elementary unit is the sampling unit. One needs only to ascertain roughly the approximate magnitude of the proportion being estimated, P. Then the variance is given by Eq. 9.1, Ch. 4.

The problem with cluster sampling is more difficult but is facilitated by the formulas and discussion in Sec. 8 of Ch. 6. Thus, the variance of a proportion estimated from a cluster sample can be expressed approximately in the form (from Eq. 8.6, Ch. 6)

$$\sigma_r^2 = \frac{PQ}{m\bar{n}} [1 + \delta_1(\bar{n} - 1)] \tag{19.3}$$

where $r = x/n$ is the sample estimate of P (the proportion of elementary units having a characteristic), m is the number of clusters in the sample, $\bar{n}$ is the expected value of the average number of elementary units per ultimate cluster, and δ_1 is the measure of homogeneity of elementary units within ultimate clusters. It has been assumed in Eq. 19.3 that $\hat{V}^2$ as given by Eq. 8.10, Ch. 6, is approximately equal to Q/P (see p. 268), which will often be a reasonably good assumption.

This relationship can serve a number of purposes in speculating on variances and is particularly useful when the second-stage sampling unit is the elementary unit. Then δ_1 is invariant with $\bar{n}$ for any fixed set of psu's of average size $\bar{N}$. For any given size of ultimate cluster δ_1 can be assigned values 0 and 1, in Eq. 19.3, to find approximate upper and lower bounds on the variance for any specified value for $\bar{n}$.

By reference to supplementary data (as in Case Study D of Ch. 12) one can often obtain an approximate value for δ_1, and from this approximate the variance reasonably closely. Also, an approximate value for δ_1 and the cost function are sufficient to determine the optimum allocation of the sample.

When there are two stages of sampling and the second-stage unit is a *cluster* of elementary units (such as the dwelling place when the person is the elementary unit), Eq. 19.3 can still represent the variance, but the value of δ_1 will depend on the ultimate size of cluster. It may be better, then, to state the rel-variance of r in the form

$$V_r^2 = \frac{\hat{V}^2}{m\bar{n}} [1 + \delta_L(\bar{n} - 1)] \tag{19.4}$$

where now $\bar{n}$ is the average number of second-stage units per ultimate cluster, δ_L is the measure of homogeneity among second-stage (listing) units within ultimate clusters, and $\hat{V}^2$ is approximately the rel-variance of the ratio X_i/Y_i among second-stage units in the population, i.e., without regard to the primary units.

Thus, δ_L, again, is invariant with $\bar{n}$ for any fixed set of psu's with average size $\bar{N}$ second-stage units per psu, and again δ_L, together with the cost function, is sufficient to determine the optimum allocation of the sample.

Section 8 of Ch. 6 shows the relationship between δ_1, δ_L, and δ_2, where δ_2 is the measure of homogeneity of elementary units among second-stage units. If, as is often the case, data are available for approximating values for δ_1 and δ_2, δ_L can be evaluated from Eq. 8.16, Ch. 6. This relationship is illustrated in Case Study D of Ch. 12.

Equation 19.4 applies to averages and ratios in general, as well as to proportions of elementary units having a characteristic. The basis for going from an estimated variance of an average to that of a total with simple random sampling of elementary units is given in Sec. 10 and 15 of Ch. 4. With cluster sampling an approach for approximating a variance of a total is described and illustrated in Sec. 4 of Ch. 8. Nisselson* gives extensive useful data for estimating totals for a number of farm characteristics and tests some approximate methods for speculating on variances.

The relationship given in Chapter 8 for proceeding from the variance of a ratio of random variables to that of an estimated total can be reversed so that, given a variance of an estimated total, we can approximate the variance of a ratio if we are willing to assume that x/n and n are uncorrelated, an assumption that is frequently reasonably good provided V_n^2 is not too large relative to V_x^2, say no more than $V_x^2/2$. Then, $V_{x/n}^2 \doteq V_x^2 - V_n^2$, and we can obtain the variance of a ratio without the necessity for computing the covariance of x and n. This method, suggested by Steinberg, is illustrated in Case Studies B and D of Ch. 12.

A method of approximating ratios of variances in connection with optimum allocation of a sample to strata is illustrated rather extensively in Ch. 5 (especially Sec. 10 and ff.), in which coefficients of variation of establishments are assumed roughly constant as between size strata even though the variances are widely different. This same kind of assumption is useful in speculating on variances for a current time period when one has a rough estimate of the average value for the current period and of the coefficient of variation for an earlier period. If the variate is such that a roughly constant coefficient of variation can be assumed, then the current variance estimate is obtained by applying the earlier coefficient of variation to the assumed current average. Such methods are rough but often useful. They apply primarily to variates that are magnitudes as distinguished from 0, 1 variates.

Rough rules for approximating optimum allocations of samples without actually computing the variances are given for a number of situations, in addition to those already mentioned. Rules for approximating optimum

---

* U.S. Bureau of the Census, *Analysis of Sampling Errors in Farm Sampling* (*April–June 1947*) (preliminary report), Washington, D.C., 1948.

allocation with multi-stage sampling where stratification is by size of psu are given in Ch. 8, Sec. 11–13. Rules for approximating optimum probabilities of selecting units with varying probabilities are given in Ch. 8, Sec. 14. Rules for determining optimum sizes of strata with variable sampling fractions and single-stage sampling are given in Ch. 5, Sec. 11, and for large primary sampling units and multi-stage sampling in Ch. 9, Sec. 8–11.

A highly useful but simple method of approximating variances or rel-variances in many situations is simply to construct an assumed "miniature" of the population to be sampled. Thus, one well acquainted with a population may not be able to speculate directly, with any confidence, on variances and covariances, measures of homogeneity, etc., but he may be able to construct rough approximations to the desired frequency distributions, by broad strata, and perhaps other relationships, on the basis of his experience with and knowledge of the population. He can then proceed to compute the variances and rel-variances for such assumed distributions. This was the process followed in Ch. 7, Ex. 11.3, as a means for obtaining reasonably realistic variances for an actual survey problem. The rel-variances from this population are those given in Table 1, p. 324, in Ch. 7.

REFERENCES

(1) U.S. Bureau of the Census, Sampling Staff, *A Chapter in Population Sampling*, U.S. Government Printing Office, Washington, D.C., 1947.
(2) U.S. Bureau of the Census, *Notes on Precision of Sampling Estimates* (Reprint of Appendix Section of the Special Study: Value of Farm Products by Color and Tenure of Farm Operators), U.S. Government Printing Office, Washington, D.C., 1945.

CHAPTER 11

Regression Estimates, Double Sampling, Sampling for Time Series, Systematic Sampling, and Other Sampling Methods

1. Opportunity for ingenuity in sample design. The methods described in the preceding chapters have covered a number of the principal alternative procedures commonly involved in survey design. A number of additional techniques are presented in the present chapter. The investigator should realize that ingenuity in putting together methods of sample selection and estimation is of the greatest importance in arriving at efficient designs for particular jobs. It is not feasible to begin to list all the alternatives in any particular case and to give the complete theory for them. Consequently, this chapter contains a number of variations in methods that may be directly applicable as described here, or that may be adapted to become a part of one or the other of the aspects of sample design already described.

The case studies of Chapter 12 give some illustrations of the methods used in dealing with particular problems. The principles introduced there also have wider applicability.

2. Difference and regression estimates.* We shall now define and examine the characteristics of the difference and regression estimates, and compare these estimates with the simple unbiased estimate and the ratio estimate that have been introduced in the preceding chapters.

Suppose that we wish to estimate X from a simple random sample of n units. In using the difference or regression estimate we shall assume that supplementary information is available concerning another variate Y, that Y is known independently of our particular sample, and that y', which is obtained from the sample, is an unbiased estimate of Y. For the case where Y is not known but is estimated from a larger sample, see Sec. 3 on double sampling.

---

* Proofs for this section are given in Vol. II, Ch. 11, Sec. 1 and 2.

The four estimates we shall consider and compare in this section are as follows:

$$x_1'' = x' + k(Y - y') \tag{2.1}$$

$$x_2'' = x' + b(Y - y') \tag{2.2}$$

$$x_3'' = \frac{x'}{y'} Y \tag{2.3}$$

$$x_4'' = x' \tag{2.4}$$

where x' and y' are simple unbiased estimates of totals from the sample, k is a constant value determined independently of the sample, and

$$b = \frac{s_{x'y'}}{s_{y'}^2} = \rho_{x'y'}' \frac{s_{x'}}{s_{y'}} \tag{2.5}$$

where $s_{x'y'}$ is an unbiased estimate of the covariance between x' and y', and $s_{y'}^2$ is an unbiased estimate of $\sigma_{y'}^2$. For a simple random sample

$$b = \frac{\overset{n}{\sum}(x_i - \bar{x})(y_i - \bar{y})}{\overset{n}{\sum}(y_i - \bar{y})^2} \tag{2.6}$$

For designs other than simple random sampling $s_{x'y'}$ and $s_{y'}^2$ take the forms appropriate to those designs. Note that b is a consistent estimate of β, where $\beta = \sigma_{x'y'}/\sigma_{y'}^2 = \rho_{x'y'}\sigma_{x'}/\sigma_{y'}$ and is the regression coefficient commonly seen in treatments of linear regression or least squares. Here, y' is used as the independent variate and x' as the dependent variate, which differs from the treatment usually encountered in the literature.

The first three estimates make use of the supplementary information on Y, and the fourth one does not. The way in which the supplementary information is utilized is different in the first three estimates.

We shall define the first of the above estimates as the *difference estimate*, the second as the *regression estimate*, the third as the *ratio estimate*, and the fourth as the *simple unbiased estimate*. Estimate 2.2 is of the same form as estimate 2.1, but with b substituted for k, and estimates 2.3 and 2.4 can be put in the form of estimate 2.1 by substituting x'/y' and 0, respectively, for k. Equations 2.1 and 2.4 give unbiased estimates of X. Equations 2.2 and 2.3 are biased but consistent estimates of X although they will be unbiased under special conditions.* The bias of the regression estimate usually will be trivial. Each of the estimates above is in the form of an estimated total. They could readily be reduced to means per sampling unit, e.g., estimate 2.1 would then be

$$\bar{x}_1 = \bar{x} + k(\bar{Y} - \bar{y})$$

---

* See Ch. 5, Sec. 4, also Vol. II, Ch. 11, Sec. 1.

A special case of x_1'' (Eq. 2.1) occurs when β is known from independent sources or approximated from past data. Approximations to β, however, that are estimated from the sample are not special cases of this estimate. The essential difference between x_2'' and x_1'' is the fact that b in Eq. 2.2 is estimated from the sample and therefore is a random variable, whereas k in Eq. 2.1 is a constant.

Variances of the difference and regression estimates. The variance of the difference estimate is

$$\sigma_{x_1''}^2 = \sigma_1^2 = \sigma_{x'}^2 + k^2\sigma_{y'}^2 - 2k\rho\sigma_{x'}\sigma_{y'} \tag{2.7}$$

where $\rho = \sigma_{x'y'}/\sigma_{x'}\sigma_{y'}$ is the coefficient of correlation of x' and y'.

Even though the difference estimate will be unbiased no matter what value is used for k, the magnitude of its variance will depend on the value chosen for k. The variance of x_1'' will be the minimum possible for a fixed sample size drawn from a specified population whenever

$$k = \beta = \rho\frac{\sigma_{x'}}{\sigma_{y'}} \tag{2.8}$$

Equation 2.7 is equal to

$$\sigma_1^2 = \sigma_{x'}^2(1 - \rho^2) + \sigma_{y'}^2(k - \beta)^2 \tag{2.9}$$

which shows at a glance that when $k = \beta$ the value of σ_1^2 (Eq. 2.7) is a minimum and is equal to

$$\sigma_1^2 = \sigma_{x'}^2(1 - \rho^2) \tag{2.10}$$

If β were known, the use of estimate 2.1 would be desirable because it is relatively simple and because, among the alternatives mentioned, it has the smallest sampling error. Usually β is unknown, but if it can be approximated from past data or experience the simplicity of estimate 2.1 is retained, although the variance will be somewhat increased. For example, X and Y may represent the same characteristic for two different dates. In this event, if the nature of the characteristic has not changed tremendously between the two dates, β will be reasonably close to 1. When 1 is substituted for k the difference estimate becomes

$$x_1'' = x' + (Y - y') = Y + (x' - y') \tag{2.11}$$

This estimate is especially simple, involving only a difference between estimated totals added to a total known from independent sources. Comparison of the results of this estimate with those of alternative estimates for a practical problem is given in Case Study C, Ch. 12.

In many practical problems, an approximate value of β is not known in advance, and wide departures of k from β may increase the variance of the difference estimate very considerably. Then it may pay to make an estimate of β from the sample and use Eq. 2.2 for the estimate of the total.   A sample estimate of β is b as given by Eq. 2.5 and 2.6.   The variance of estimate 2.2 for sufficiently large samples is given approximately by Eq. 2.10.*

The contribution to the variance arising from estimating β from a sample is small relative to the total variance for reasonably large samples. Since the variance of estimate 2.2 is approximately equal to the variance for the optimum value of k (when $k = \beta$), all other things being equal, estimate 2.2 should be used instead of 2.1 except in cases where a value of k is available that is reasonably sure to be close to β.   However, the work in computing b may be heavy.   Thus, with simple random sampling of units, Eq. 2.6 shows that the computation of b requires knowledge of the y_i for the individual units in the sample, and not simply the sample total or mean.   The determination of b for more complex designs will be indicated later; it will generally involve a similar but more difficult computational problem.   As a practical matter, the computations sometimes may be so onerous that the costs, especially where a great many different statistics are involved, may be greater than the possible gain from estimate 2.2 as compared with the best alternative estimate, so that the regression estimate has not been widely used where a large number of different items are being estimated.   However, in instances where high-speed electronic computing equipment is available, it may be more efficient to compute b rather than to compute the alternative estimates.

Comparison of regression estimate with simple unbiased estimate.   The variance of the simple unbiased estimate (Eq. 2.4) is $\sigma_{x'}^2$.   Thus, the ratio of the variance of the regression estimate (Eq. 2.2) to that of the simple unbiased estimate is approximately $(1 - \rho^2)$, and the variance of the regression estimate is smaller than or equal to the variance of the simple unbiased estimate.   The reduction of variance is large when the correlation between x' and y' is high, and small when the correlation is low. Thus, when $\rho = .95$ the variance of the regression estimate is about one-tenth that of the simple unbiased estimate.   When $\rho = .5$, the regression variance is three-fourths that of the unbiased estimate, and when $\rho = 0$ the variances are about the same.

Comparison of regression estimate with ratio estimate.   The variance of estimate 2.3 is approximately (from Eq. 18.12, Ch. 4)

$$\sigma_{x''_3}^2 = \sigma_3^2 \doteq \sigma_{x'}^2 \left(1 + \frac{V_{y'}^2}{V_{x'}^2} - 2\rho \frac{V_{y'}}{V_{x'}} \right) \qquad (2.12)$$

The approximation to the variance of the regression estimate is always

---

* Vol. II, Ch. 11, Sec. 1, shows the derivation of this variance.

smaller than or equal to that of the ratio estimate. This is seen from the ratio of the variance of the ratio estimate to that of the regression estimate, which is approximately

$$\frac{\sigma_3^2}{\sigma_1^2} \doteq \frac{1 + \dfrac{V_{y'}^2}{V_{x'}^2} - 2\rho \dfrac{V_{y'}}{V_{x'}}}{1 - \rho^2} = 1 + \frac{\left(\dfrac{V_{y'}}{V_{x'}} - \rho\right)^2}{1 - \rho^2} \qquad (2.13)$$

The expression on the right of Eq. 2.13 is always greater than unity unless

$$\rho \doteq \frac{V_{y'}}{V_{x'}} \qquad (2.14)$$

in this situation both estimates have about the same variance.

In many practical problems Eq. 2.14 does hold approximately, and the two variances are about the same. Equation 2.14 will hold approximately for any population for which the least squares line of regression of X on Y is approximately through the origin, i.e., when β is approximately equal to X/Y, or when $b \doteq x'/y'$.

The difference and regression estimates with stratified sampling or with cluster sampling. With stratified sampling, one can ascertain separate values for k or for b for each stratum, carry through the difference or the regression estimates separately for each stratum, and then obtain appropriate weighted totals or averages. The use of difference estimates calculated separately for each stratum will not introduce a bias even when the sample from each stratum is small. This is in contrast to the use of ratio estimates calculated separately for each stratum (see Ch. 5, Sec. 4). The variance formula and the optimum allocations to strata are given in Ch. 5, Sec. 8, when the expressions for $\tilde{S}_h$ appropriate to the difference or regression estimates are used.

Instead of calculating a separate estimate of the regression coefficient for each stratum, or assuming a different value of k, a single value of b or of k can be used for all strata, or for a group of strata. With the difference estimate, if the value assumed for k is the same for each of the strata, the result is exactly the same whether the estimates are made separately for each stratum or over a set of strata.

Whether a separate difference estimate is made at the level of a stratum, or a group of strata, or over the whole population, the value for k that will give a minimum variance for that level of estimation is given by Eq. 2.8, and the sample estimate of β is given by Eq. 2.5. Equations 2.5 and 2.8 can be used in general for any sample design.

For example, for stratified sampling, with or without subsampling, and with either variable or uniform sampling fractions in the various strata or at the various stages of sampling and with variable probabilities of selecting primary sampling units, a regression estimate over all or a group of strata (from Eq. 2.5) can be made by computing

$$b = \frac{\sum\limits_{h}^{L} \frac{1}{m_h(m_h - 1)} \sum\limits_{i}^{m_h} (x''_{hi} - \bar{x}''_h)(y''_{hi} - \bar{y}''_h)}{\sum\limits_{h}^{L} \frac{1}{m_h(m_h - 1)} \sum\limits_{i}^{m_h} (y''_{hi} - \bar{y}''_h)^2}$$ (2.15)

where $x''_{hi} = x'_{hi}/P_{hi}$ is a simple unbiased estimate of the stratum total X_h, made from the ith primary unit included in the sample; and P_{hi} is the probability of including the ith unit in the sample on a single draw from the hth stratum.

$$\bar{x}''_h = \frac{\sum\limits^{m_h} x''_{hi}}{m_h}$$

is the sample average of such estimates. The y''_{hi} and $\bar{y}''_h$ are similarly defined. If the sample is a single-stage sample from strata, and there is a uniform sampling fraction for all strata, Eq. 2.15 reduces to

$$b = \frac{\sum\limits_{h}^{L} \frac{m_h}{m_h - 1} \sum\limits_{i}^{m_h} (x_{hi} - \bar{x}_h)(y_{hi} - \bar{y}_h)}{\sum\limits_{h}^{L} \frac{m_h}{m_h - 1} \sum\limits_{i}^{m_h} (y_{hi} - \bar{y}_h)^2}$$ (2.16)

where x_{hi} and $\bar{x}_h$ are as defined in Sec. 1, Ch. 5.

With only one unit in the sample from a stratum, neither of the two estimates (Eq. 2.15 and 2.16) can be made, and some of the strata must be grouped if the regression estimate is to be used. The difference estimate can be used, of course, with one or more units in the sample from a stratum. The estimate of β from prior experience may give a value for k in the difference estimate; or, where the same characteristic is being estimated on two different dates, the value 1 often can be reasonably assumed for β, as indicated earlier. A special case of β, as given by Eq. 2.8 for stratified two-stage sampling, is as follows:

$$\beta = \frac{\sum\limits_{h}^{L} M_h^2 \frac{M_h - m_h}{M_h m_h} S_{hXY} + \sum\limits_{h}^{L} M_h^2 \frac{\sum\limits_{i}^{M_h} N_{hi}^2 \frac{N_{hi} - n_{hi}}{N_{hi} n_{hi}} S_{hiXY}}{M_h m_h}}{\sum\limits_{h}^{L} M_h^2 \frac{M_h - m_h}{M_h m_h} S_{hY}^2 + \sum\limits_{h}^{L} M_h^2 \frac{\sum\limits_{i}^{M_h} N_{hi}^2 \frac{N_{hi} - n_{hi}}{N_{hi} n_{hi}} S_{hiY}^2}{M_h m_h}}$$ (2.17)

where

$$S_{hXY} = \frac{1}{M_h - 1} \sum_i^{M_h} (X_{hi} - \bar{X}_h)(Y_{hi} - \bar{Y}_h) \tag{2.18}$$

$$S_{hiXY} = \frac{1}{N_{hi} - 1} \sum_j^{N_{hi}} (X_{hij} - \bar{X}_{hi})(Y_{hij} - \bar{Y}_{hi}) \tag{2.19}$$

$$S_{hY}^2 = S_{hYY} \tag{2.20}$$

and

$$S_{hiY}^2 = S_{hiYY} \tag{2.21}$$

Here, as usual with subsampling, a sample estimate of β cannot be computed by substitution of sample numbers in Eq. 2.18–2.21. Instead, Eq. 2.15 can be used to compute b, as an estimate of β.

Where it is desired to use a regression estimate, it will often be sufficient to compute an approximate value for b by any of a number of short-cut procedures (see Illustration 2.1). One method is to select a few extreme sample values of the independent variate, some high and some low, and to fit a straight line through the average of the set of high values and the average of the set of low values. The estimated regression coefficient is the slope of this line. For this case the slope of the line is given by $(X_2 - X_1)/(Y_2 - Y_1)$, where Y_2, X_2, and Y_1, X_1 are any two points on the line.

> **Remark.** In all the above discussion of the variance of regression or difference estimates, it has been implicitly assumed that the sampling fraction or fractions were relatively small. This assumption has no effect on the sample estimates, but the variances will be smaller if the finiteness of the population is taken into account. The finite multiplier in the variance formula is approximately $(1 - f)$, whenever a uniform over-all sampling fraction is used, and is $(1 - f_h)$ in the contribution to the variance from the hth stratum, when variable over-all sampling fractions are used in the several strata. Here f_h is the over-all sampling fraction in the hth stratum.

Application and comparison of alternative estimates in a practical problem. Case Study C, Ch. 12, provides an illustration of a problem in which difference estimates were used, and the application of a more general type of difference estimate is discussed in Sec. 7, Illustration 7.1, of this chapter (p. 497). In Case Study C it was found that the difference estimate was easier to apply than was the ratio estimate. This was a case where the same item was being estimated on two different dates, and the difference estimate was used with $k = 1$, which made it exceedingly simple. Both the difference estimate and the ratio estimate would have given about the same reliability of results; for a fixed size of sample the regression estimate would have been as good or better, although in this illustration the reductions in variance with the regression estimate were usually trivial. When the variances of a difference estimate and ratio estimate are of about the same magnitude, difference estimates are sometimes preferable. The difference estimate is unbiased, whereas the ratio estimate is biased, and perhaps seriously, in stratum-by-stratum estimates when the sample sizes within strata are small. Case Study C shows comparisons of results for a number of different items, for the difference estimate, the regression estimate, the ratio estimate, and the simple unbiased estimate.

Illustration 2.1. The following type of application of the difference estimate was suggested by Jack Ogus, Bureau of the Census. Suppose, for illustration, that complete returns are available for manufacturers' shipments in 1950 of a certain commodity, and that estimates of total shipments for each quarter of 1951 are desired. Assume that the distribution of establishments by size of 1950 shipments is sharply skewed (roughly L-shaped), so that a relatively few large establishments account for a high proportion of the total shipments. Assume, also, that a sample of n establishments is to be included in the quarterly survey, and that it is immaterial from a cost viewpoint how the n are distributed.

Because of the extreme skewness of the distribution, we can be practically certain that complete coverage of some of the largest units will be called for regardless of what estimating formula is selected. Under these conditions a difference estimate might be used as follows:

$$X_1 + \frac{N_2}{n_2} x_2 + \frac{X_1}{Y_1} \left(Y_2 - \frac{N_2}{n_2} y_2 \right) \tag{2.22}$$

where X_1 and Y_1 are, respectively, the current quarterly totals and the 1950 shipments of the establishments included in the sample with certainty, and Y_2 is the 1950 shipments of the establishments in the stratum; x_2 and y_2 are the sample quarterly totals and sample 1950 shipments, respectively, for the second stratum; and N_2 and n_2 are the total establishments and establishments in the sample from the second stratum. In this estimate the establishments in the certainty stratum are used to provide a value of k for Eq. 2.1, with $k = X_1/Y_1$. This may be useful if the change from 1950 for both the large and the small establishments is quite similar, as may be the case, for example, if there are wide seasonal fluctuations throughout the year.

Choice of estimates. The comparisons and illustration above suggest a number of rules for choosing among alternative estimates. The regression estimate is not always the logical choice even though, for reasonably large samples, it has a variance equal to or less than that of the alternatives.

(a) The difference and regression estimates can be used only when supplemental information is available on an independent variate.

(b) Where it is desired to estimate a ratio from the sample and neither the numerator nor the denominator, nor estimates of them are available from other sources, the ratio estimate may be the only one feasible.

(c) The computation of b by Eq. 2.5 for the regression estimate may be heavy and time consuming, and its use is justified only in those cases where the gains from such computations are sufficient to offset their additional costs.

(d) When advance information on the approximate value of β is available, then use of such a value for k with the difference estimate will give results of precision close to that of the regression estimate but with only simple computations.

(e) When the correlation between the numerator and the denominator of the estimate is of about the order of the ratio of the coefficient of variation of the denominator to that of the numerator, i.e., when $\rho_{x'y'} \doteq V_{y'}/V_{x'}$, the ratio estimate will be of about as high precision as the regression estimate. This is the approximate condition, also, for the ratio estimate to be unbiased.

(f) When $\rho_{x'y'}$ is very different from $V_{y'}/V_{x'}$, one should preferably not select the ratio estimate when a choice of a regression estimate is available. In this circumstance the variance of the ratio estimate is comparatively large relative to that of the regression estimate.

(g) The statements made in (e) and (f) hold for the difference estimate with $k = 1$, if the standard deviation is substituted for the coefficient of variation. In other words, if $\rho_{x'y'} \doteq \sigma_{y'}/\sigma_{x'}$, the difference estimate will be of about as high precision as the regression estimate. When $\rho_{x'y'}$ is very different from $\sigma_{y'}/\sigma_{x'}$, one should not use the difference estimate with $k = 1$, if a regression estimate is available.

REFERENCES FOR SEC. 2

(1) W. G. Cochran, *Sampling Techniques*, John Wiley & Sons, New York, 1953, Chapter 7.
(2) F. Yates, *Sampling Methods for Censuses and Surveys*, Charles Griffin and Company, London, 1949.

3. Double sampling. We have already seen that the use of a ratio or regression estimate with an independent variate, highly correlated with the variate being estimated, can sometimes considerably increase precision of results. Similarly, we have seen that precision is increased by stratification on one or more variates if there is a high correlation between the stratification groups and the variate being estimated.   In order to be used in this way, the independent information must be available for the entire population.   Sometimes such information is available only from a sample; if not readily available, it can sometimes be collected for a comparatively large sample at very low cost.   When this is so, Neyman (1) has shown that it may pay to select an initial large sample in order to obtain the low-cost information, and to draw a subsample from the larger sample on which measurements are made of the desired characteristics. The information from the large sample is used either in ratio, difference, or regression estimates or for stratification, in order to increase the reliability of the desired estimates from the smaller and more costly sample.   It will pay to use such a double sampling method only if the cost of the initial sample is small and the gains from regression estimation or stratification are large.

*Double sampling with regression estimates and simple random sampling.** Suppose that an estimate of $\bar{X}$ is wanted from a sample, that $\bar{y}$ is the average value for some related characteristic obtained from a large sample of size n, and that $\bar{x}'$ is the sample average of the X's obtained from a smaller sample of size n'.   This smaller sample is a subsample of the large sample of size n.   Similarly, $\bar{y}'$ is the sample mean of the Y's for this same subsample.   Then an estimate of $\bar{X}$ which may be more reliable than $\bar{x}'$ is

$$\bar{x}'' = \bar{x}' + b(\bar{y} - \bar{y}') \tag{3.1}$$

where b is the estimate of the coefficient of regression of X on Y, i.e.,

$$b = \frac{\sum\limits^{n'}(x_i - \bar{x}')(y_i - \bar{y}')}{\sum\limits^{n'}(y_i - \bar{y}')^2} \tag{3.2}$$

The variance of $\bar{x}''$ is given approximately by

$$\sigma_{\bar{x}''}^2 \doteq \frac{S_X^2}{n'}\left[1 - \rho^2\left(1 - \frac{n'}{n}\right)\right] \tag{3.3}$$

where S_X^2 is the variance of the X_i, and ρ is the coefficient of correlation between X_i and Y_i.   This approximation will hold reasonably well when n' is sufficiently large, and reduces to the variance of the usual regression estimate given by Eq. 2.10 whenever n is large relative to n', i.e., when the large sample is so much larger than the small sample that n'/n is close to 0.

This variance may be compared with the usual variance of $\bar{x}'$ given by Eq. 9.2 of Ch. 4.   Since S_X^2/n' is approximately the variance of $\bar{x}'$ (an

---

* The proofs are given in Vol. II, Ch. 11, Sec. 3–4.

estimate of $\bar{X}$ based on a simple random sample of n' cases), it follows from Eq. 3.3 that $\sigma_{\bar{x}'}^2$ is smaller than or equal to the variance of $\bar{x}'$. If there is any substantial amount of correlation between the X_i and the Y_i, this estimate will be considerably more reliable.

If the purpose of the survey is to estimate a characteristic $\bar{X}$, one can ascertain the optimum size of the initial sample and use double sampling in order to maximize the reliability of the result per dollar of cost.

If the cost function involved in the survey can be approximated roughly by the simple relationship

$$C = C_1 n + C_2 n'$$

then the optimum values for n and n' are approximately

$$n = \frac{C}{C_1 + C_2 \sqrt{\dfrac{1 - \rho^2}{\rho^2} \dfrac{C_1}{C_2}}} \tag{3.4}$$

and

$$n' = n \sqrt{\frac{1 - \rho^2}{\rho^2} \frac{C_1}{C_2}} \tag{3.5}$$

Thus the optimum subsampling rate from the initial sample is

$$\frac{n'}{n} = \sqrt{\frac{1 - \rho^2}{\rho^2} \frac{C_1}{C_2}}$$

A caution is necessary in interpreting this result, which says that the optimum value of n'/n is 1, i.e., $n' = n$, whenever

$$\frac{1 - \rho^2}{\rho^2} = \frac{C_2}{C_1}$$

It might at first appear that this would be the point at which a single sample should be used instead of a double sampling method. Such a conclusion, however, is unwarranted, because a single sampling system is not necessarily a special case of the double sample cost system assumed above. Whenever the optimum subsampling ratio is shown to be 1, it is true that a single sample should be used, but a single sample may often be used for values considerably less than 1 if the expenditure represented by the term $C_1 n$ is thereby eliminated.

The value of ρ at which the variance for the optimum double sampling design will be approximately the same as the variance for a single sample with the same total cost (with $C_1 \hat{n}$ as the single sample cost function) is

$$\rho^2 = \frac{4 C_1 C_2}{(C_1 + C_2)^2} \tag{3.6}$$

With larger values of ρ one will gain something by double sampling, although usually ρ must be considerably larger before the gain is worth while.

As an illustration of the gains that may be achieved with double sampling with regression estimation, and of the losses that may result if it is used when it should not be, suppose that $C_2/C_1 = 9$, i.e., the unit cost of the subsampling is nine times that for the initial sample, and that the C_1 term is not involved with the single sample. Then for various values of ρ the comparison of the variances of the best double sampling design with those of the single sampling design with the same cost would be as shown in Table 1. The size of the single sample that will have the same cost as the specified double sample is

$$\hat{n} = n\left[\frac{C_1}{C_2} + \frac{n'}{n}\right]$$

The value of n'/n for the optimum double sampling design is also shown in the table.

Table 1. **Ratio of variance with optimum double sampling design to variance of single sample for various values of ρ and with $C_2/C_1 = 9$**

ρ	Ratio of variance for double sampling to variance of single sample $\left(\text{assuming } \dfrac{C_2}{C_1} = 9\right)$	$\dfrac{n'}{n}$
.32	1.11	1.00
.5	1.07	.58
.6	1.00	.44
.7	.90	.34
.8	.75	.25
.9	.54	.16
.97	.32	.08

The investigator faces the same types of problems in determining optimum values of n and n' when dealing with the estimation of a number of characteristics, as are encountered in determining the optima for other types of sample design (see, for example, Ch. 5, Sec. 13; Ch. 6, Sec. 24; and Ch. 9, Sec. 5, 8, and 22). For example, the survey objectives may require a high degree of accuracy for a limited number of items and less accuracy for most of the other items. In this case information would be collected on a large sample for the limited number of items; the size of the sample would be determined by the accuracy specified for these items. Since estimates of the type of Eq. 3.1 or 3.7 are suitable for estimating the additional items, the increased information from the larger sample can be used to reduce the size of the subsample that would otherwise be needed for the items required with less precision.

An estimate simpler than the regression estimate treatment of double sampling given above involves use of the ordinary ratio estimate that has been applied widely throughout most of this book. To use this estimate the $\bar{x}''$ is obtained simply by computing

$$\bar{x}'' = \frac{\bar{x}'}{\bar{y}'} \bar{y} \qquad (3.7)$$

The variance of this estimate is given by Eq. 9.6. This method will often give results of nearly equivalent reliability with the regression estimate when ρ is equal or nearly equal to V_y/V_x.*

Double sampling with stratification. In addition to the use of the large sample in double sampling for improved methods of estimation, the large sample can also serve as a basis for stratification before selecting the smaller sample. This method ordinarily will gain very little if proportionate subsampling is used but may make possible variable sampling fractions in order to approximate optimum sampling designs. Thus, in circumstances where variable sampling fractions are highly desirable, considerable increases in efficiency may result. For example, one might need a much larger sampling fraction of large establishments than of small establishments in a survey, but have no satisfactory advance listing available to identify the large ones. He might then take an initial sample, using the sampling fraction that is wanted for large establishments, and obtain only enough information initially to determine the approximate size of each establishment in the initial sample. If the establishment is large, he obtains the information wanted from the large establishments in the sample; if it is small he determines through a subsampling procedure whether or not this particular establishment is in the subsample of small establishments and obtains additional information for it only if it is.

Suppose that it is desired to estimate a characteristic X such as the total inventory of grocery stores from such a double sampling approach, and suppose that n is the size of the initial large sample drawn at random from a population of size N; n_1 is the number of large establishments identified in this sample; n_2 is the number of small establishments in this original sample; and n_2' is the number of these subsampled. If x_1 is the

---

* Chapter 12 of Vol. II gives the variance and optimum for this estimate in a special case.

aggregate sales for the n_1 large stores and x_2 for the n_2' small stores ultimately included in the sample, then an unbiased estimate of the desired total is given by

$$x' = \frac{1}{f}x_1 + \frac{k}{f}x_2 \qquad (3.8)$$

where f is the sampling fraction for large establishments and 1 in k is the subsampling fraction for small establishments. It is to be noted that the total sample size is equal to $n_1 + n_2'$ rather than $n = n_1 + n_2$. The sample variance of x' is given by*

$$\sigma_{x'}^2 = N^2 \frac{N-n}{N} \frac{S^2}{n} + \frac{N}{n}(k-1)N_2 S_2^2 \qquad (3.9)$$

where S^2 is the variance in the entire population between the original sample units (i.e., in the particular illustration cited, the variance of sales among all stores).

S_2^2 is the variance among those that are in the class that is subsampled (i.e., in the particular illustration cited, the variance of sales among small stores).

1 in k is the rate at which the subsampled units are subsampled from the initial sample.

It is seen, as might be expected, that the variance of the sample estimate is the variance of the estimate that would have resulted had the original full sample been covered plus a contribution due to the fact that not all the small establishments were retained in the sample. The increase in the variance due to this subsampling is shown by the second term of the variance.

It may be convenient to restate this variance in a form similar to the stratified sampling variance with disproportionate sampling, so that the two can be compared. Thus, another form of this variance is:

$$\sigma_{x'}^2 \doteq \frac{N-n}{Nn} N_1 N_2 (\bar{X}_1 - \bar{X}_2)^2 + \frac{N_1 - n_1}{N_1 n_1} N_1^2 S_1^2 + \frac{N_2 - n_2'}{N_2 n_2'} N_2^2 S_2^2 \qquad (3.10)$$

which, except for the addition of the first term above involving the variance between the strata, is the same as the variance given by Eq. 3.6, Ch. 5, for the case where the sample is stratified and disproportionate random sampling is used within strata. When sampling without stratification, the variance between strata will be involved and will contribute to the total variance, which gives the first term of Eq. 3.10. Whenever the variance between groups is not too large, the estimate given by Eq. 3.8

---

* The proof is given in Vol. II, Ch. 11, Sec. 5.

and the resulting variance from this method will be nearly as efficient as with stratified sampling for a given size of sample. In order to compare different methods, we need to approximate the optimum design for each method that is considered. The optimum for the method of double sampling just outlined can be approximated readily if the cost function is simple. If it is not sufficiently simple, then it may be necessary to obtain the optimum by successive approximation as has been illustrated in numerous other places (Chapters 6, 7, and 9). Let us assume, however, that the cost function can be represented approximately by the simple relationship

$$C = C_0 n + C_1 n_1 + C_2 n_2' \tag{3.11}$$

where C is the total cost of the survey, excluding any fixed overhead costs that do not vary with the allocation of the sample.

C_0 is the unit cost of selecting and examining a unit included in the large sample and determining whether or not it is included at the full or the subsample rate.

C_1 is the additional cost per unit for the units that are included in the sample at the full large-sample rate but not in the subsample.

C_2 is the additional cost per unit of the subsampled units actually included in the subsample.

With this cost system and the variance as given by Eq. 3.9 or 3.10 one can determine the optimum allocation of the sample in order to achieve any specified degree of accuracy or make most effective use of a given budget. Thus, if we specify that the total shall be estimated with a relative error equal to ε, we find that the optimum allocation of the sample is given by:*

$$n = \hat{n} \left[1 + (k - 1)P_2 \frac{S_2^2}{S^2} \right] \tag{3.12}$$

$$k = \sqrt{\frac{S^2 - P_2 S_2^2}{P_1 S_2^2} \cdot \frac{C_2}{C_1 + (C_0/P_1)}} \tag{3.13}$$

where

$$\hat{n} = \frac{N^2 S^2}{\varepsilon^2 + N S^2} \tag{3.14}$$

is the size of a simple random sample that would be required to achieve the specified accuracy; P_1 is the proportion of all establishments (or other units) that are in the class that is sampled at the large-sample rate; and P_2 is $1 - P_1$.

---

* The proof is given in Vol. II, Ch. 11, Sec. 5.

Thus, in the illustration involving a sample of grocery stores mentioned above, we might, for example, stratify stores into large and small stores, defining large stores as those having 10 or more employees, and small stores as having less than 10.   The number of employees (which need be ascertained only approximately) might be determined much more readily than the desired information on sales.   In planning the sample survey, we might find from initial investigation that the population we are dealing with has the following approximate characteristics, and the costs involved might be roughly those indicated.

Illustration 3.1.   Given:

$$C_0 = .25 \qquad N = 20,000 \qquad \bar{X} = (.05)10 + (.95) = 1.45$$

$$C_1 = 2 \qquad N_1 = 1,000 \qquad \bar{X}_1 = 10 \qquad\qquad P_1 = .05$$

$$C_2 = 1 \qquad N_2 = 19,000 \qquad \bar{X}_2 = 1 \qquad\qquad P_2 = .95$$

$$S_1^2 = 500$$

$$S_2^2 = 5$$

$$\sigma_b^2 = .05(\bar{X}_1 - \bar{X})^2 + .95(\bar{X}_2 - \bar{X})^2$$

$$= .05(73.1) + .95(.20) = 3.85$$

$$S^2 = (.05)500 + .95(5) + 3.85 = 33.6$$

$$\varepsilon = .04(X) = .04N\bar{X}$$

Then:

$$\hat{n} = \frac{N^2 S^2}{\varepsilon^2 + NS^2} \doteq 6661$$

$$k = \sqrt{\frac{S^2 - P_2 S_2^2}{P_1 S_2^2} \frac{C_2}{C_1 + C_0/P_1}} = \sqrt{\frac{115.4}{7}} \doteq 4$$

$$n = \hat{n}[1 + 3(.95)5/33.6] = 1.42\hat{n} = 9460$$

$$n_1 = .05n = 470$$

$$n_2' = \frac{9460 - 470}{4} = 2250$$

Thus, the cost of such a double sampling method with the allocation that would yield a standard error of ε would be

$$C = C_0 n + C_1 n_1 + C_2 n_2' = \$5555$$

Such a double sample would give the same accuracy as a single proportionate sample at a cost of $6661C_0 + 333C_1 + 6328C_2 = \$8659$, and consequently would be considerably more efficient.

We might also be interested in how much one could have appropriately spent to stratify by preparing a complete list of large establishments in advance in order to achieve the same accuracy as with double sampling. By applying the methods of Vol. II, Ch. 5, Sec. 11, we find that had an advance list containing the same information for distinguishing between large and small establishments been available, a sample of $n_1 = 620$ large establishments and $n_2 = 1590$ small establishments would have been required.

If the cost is still $C_0 + C_1$ per unit in the sample for the large establishments, and $C_0 + C_2$ for the small establishments, then the costs after the list was prepared would amount to a total of \$3382. This means that, if one had methods available for preparing a complete list of all large establishments equivalent or substantially equivalent in accuracy of classification to that obtained by the double sampling method, it would pay him to spend up to the difference between the cost of the double sampling method (\$5555) and the cost of the stratified sampling method (\$3382), or approximately \$2000, for the preparation of the complete large-establishment list. If the cost were greater than this, it would be better to use the double sampling method.

A possible danger of the advance listing procedure is that one may find an inexpensive, but what turns out to be an unsatisfactory, method of preparing the advance list of large establishments, so that he does not succeed in listing some of the quite important large establishments in advance, and these are then sampled at the lower sampling rate, adding considerably to the variance and decreasing the efficiency of the method. Such a loss would not be particularly serious if the advance listing were at least effective in insuring the listing of all the very largest establishments, but would be especially serious if it did not have this property.

Any increase in variance due to ineffectiveness of the advance listing will increase the cost of achieving specified accuracy and must be taken into account in making the comparison with double sampling. It will sometimes be desirable to use an advance listing with a higher sampling rate for the exceedingly large establishments in such a problem, and then perhaps a double sampling method such as that illustrated for the remaining population. The theory above could be extended to cover this situation too; but it is a good enough approximation, where such a method is to be used, to determine the comparative sampling rates for the three or more strata set up in this fashion in accordance with what would be the relative rates indicated by the optimum stratified sampling theory given in Chapter 5. It will be found that this theory leads to approximately the same results in most situations, so far as the comparative sampling rates in the different strata are concerned, as the double sampling theory given here.

The double sampling procedure can be extended to cluster sampling and to ratio estimates.*

Use of double sampling for dealing with the problem of nonresponses in sample surveys.   The mail questionnaire is used in a number of surveys because of the economies involved.   A common objection to this method of collecting factual information is that it may involve a large nonresponse rate, and an unknown bias in the assumption that those responding are representative of the combined total of respondents and nonrespondents. Personal interviews may elicit a substantially complete response, but the cost per schedule is, of course, considerably higher than it would be for the mail questionnaire method.   A double sampling method similar to that described above can sometimes combine the advantages of both procedures.

The problem considered is to determine the number of mail questionnaires to be sent out and the number of personal interviews to take in following up nonresponses to the mail questionnaire in order to attain the required precision at a minimum cost.   The procedure outlined below can be applied whatever are the methods of collecting data.   For example, perhaps equally as important as the problem of nonresponse in using mail questionnaires is the problem of call-backs in taking field interviews.   In this latter problem the procedure to minimize cost for a given degree of reliability would call for taking a large sample of first interviews and calling back on a fraction of "those not at home."   The technique presented herein makes it possible to use probability samples at a lower cost or within a reasonable time period in situations where the excessive cost or time requirements of ordinary methods of follow-up have sometimes led to abandoning them.

To illustrate the principles, simple random sampling and simple unbiased estimating procedures are again assumed.   The principles hold, however, for stratified sampling and for other methods of estimation, as where a ratio estimate is used to estimate the rate of change between two time periods.

As an illustration, let us assume that we wish to estimate the number of employees in retail stores during a specified period in a given area and have a listing of the addresses of all establishments having one or more employees.   A procedure sometimes followed is to take a sample of addresses from this list, mail out the questionnaires, and then depend exclusively on the mail returns for the estimate of the number of employees for all retail stores.   The result of this procedure usually will be biased. It may be seriously so if there is a large rate of nonresponse.   On the

---

* Volume II, Ch. 11, Ex. 5.1, gives additional theory.

other hand, if all the addresses were actually visited by an enumerator, in order to eliminate the bias, the cost of collecting the information might be high. The problem is then to determine how many questionnaires to mail, and how many of the nonrespondents to follow up with the more expensive and more effective technique.

Assume that questionnaires are sent to a sample of n addresses drawn at random from a complete list of N stores, and let:

$f = n/N$.

$\bar{x}_1$ = the average number of employees per establishment, for the stores responding to the mailed questionnaire.

n_1 = the number of such establishments (mail respondents).

n_2 = the number in the sample of questionnaires originally sent out that did not respond to the mailed questionnaire (nonrespondents).

$\bar{x}_2'$ = the average number of employees per establishment for the field interviews.

1 in k = the fraction of nonrespondents visited.

$n_2' = (1/k)n_2$ = the number of field interviews (more costly procedure) among the nonrespondents.

The estimate x' is given by Eq. 3.8, with $x_1 = n_1\bar{x}_1$, $x_2 = n_2\bar{x}_2'$; the sampling variance is given by Eq. 3.9, where we shall assume for simplicity that $S^2 \doteq S_2^2$.

We shall assume that the accuracy required is such that ε, the standard error of the estimate, would be given by a sample of $\hat{n}$ when the rate of response is 100 per cent.

Assume that the cost equation is given by

$$C = C_0 n + C_1 n_1 + C_2 n_2' \tag{3.11}$$

where C_0 = cost per questionnaire of mailing.

C_1 = cost per questionnaire of processing returned questionnaires.

C_2 = cost per questionnaire both of enumerating and of processing questionnaires obtained by field interviews.

The optimum values of n and k can be computed from the following relatively simple formulas:

$$n = \hat{n}[1 + (k - 1)P_2] \tag{3.15}$$

$$k = \sqrt{\frac{C_2 P_1}{C_0 + C_1 P_1}} \tag{3.16}$$

where

$$n_2 = P_2 n \quad \text{and} \quad n_2' = \frac{n_2}{k}$$

$\hat{n}$ is given by Eq. 3.14, P_1 is the rate of response to the mailed question-naire, $P_2 = 1 - P_1$, and, as indicated earlier, ε is the standard error to be tolerated in the total being estimated. The formulas were obtained under the assumptions that $S^2 \doteq S_2^2$. The optimum values of n and k without this assumption are given by Eq. 3.12 and 3.13.

Methods of approximating the optimum values when the proportion responding is unknown or cannot be estimated, along with extensions to more complex systems of sampling and estimating, are given by Hansen and Hurwitz.*

Remark. Sampling "in time" for nonrespondents. Another method for dealing with the nonresponse and call-back problem is given by Politz and Simmons.† This method provides for sampling of persons at random intervals of time, and inquiring of each one found at home as to other times he would have been found at home during a specified period of time. For those persons actually found at home, the probability of being found at home during the specified time period is inferred from the response to the question on other times he was at home. If a random sample of points in time is achieved, and if the response to the question on other times at home is accurate, the probability of a person being included in the sample can be determined. Then the value of a characteristic determined for each person in the sample can be weighted by the reciprocal of his probability of being included in the sample (Eq. 14.1, Ch. 8).

The method will yield consistent estimates if the sampling in time is in fact at random, and if the probability of being at home can be approximated satisfactorily. In practice serious problems may be involved in the effort to accomplish this.

This method has been used in attitude and marketing surveys, particu-larly, where interviews with only a specified respondent within a household are required.‡

REFERENCES FOR SEC. 3

(1) J. Neyman, "Contributions to the Theory of Sampling Human Populations," *J. Amer. Stat. Assn.*, **33** (1938), 101–116.

* Morris H. Hansen and William N. Hurwitz, "The Problem of Non-Response in Sample Surveys," *J. Amer. Stat. Assn.*, **41** (1946), 517–529.

† Alfred Politz and Willard Simmons, "An Attempt to Get the Not-at-Homes into the Sample without Callbacks," *J. Amer. Stat. Assn.*, **44** (1949), 9–31.

‡ Other approaches in dealing with nonresponse are discussed by Z. W. Birnbaum and M. G. Sirken, "Bias Due to Non-availability in Sampling Sur-veys," *J. Amer. Stat. Assn.*, **45** (1950), 98–110; and also by J. A. Clausen and R. N. Ford, "Controlling Bias in Mail Questionnaires," *J. Amer. Stat. Assn.*, **42** (1947), 497–511.

(2) Chameli Bose, "Notes on the Sampling Error in the Method of Double-Sampling," *Sankhyā*, **6** (1943), 329–330.
(3) W. G. Cochran, *Sampling Techniques*, John Wiley & Sons, New York, 1953, Chapter 12.
(4) D. F. Watson, "The Estimation of Leaf Areas," *J. Agr. Sci.*, **27** (1937), 474.
(5) F. Yates, *Sampling Methods for Censuses and Surveys*, Charles Griffin and Company, London, 1949.

4. Special techniques of selection of psu's when the number of primary units is small. As was pointed out earlier, it may sometimes be desirable to have as many strata as there are primary units in the sample. The loss one takes is that the estimate of the sampling variance will tend to be an overestimate. The gain one achieves is that the actual variance of the design ordinarily will be smaller than that of a design with two or more psu's per stratum, which permits a consistent estimate of the variance. If, with a fixed number of psu's in the sample, the evidence is clear that the reduction in the variance is large for a design with one unit per stratum over a design with two units per stratum, the possibility of attaining still further reductions by additional stratification should be investigated.

A general approach for restricted sample selection. The only restriction imposed on the selection of units by the criteria we have adopted is that each unit in the population shall have a known probability (not zero) of being selected. Consequently we may very simply assign high probabilities of selection to particular combinations of units which appear on the basis of the available data to be "good samples," and low probabilities or even zero probabilities to combinations which appear on the basis of available data to be "poor samples." The assignment of probabilities to combinations must, of course, be made in such a way that each individual unit in the population will still have a known chance of being drawn (greater than zero).

Although the statement of the problem is relatively easy, the actual practical accomplishment is somewhat more difficult. A relatively simple device for introducing the effect of further stratification beyond ordinary stratification is described by Goodman and Kish.* The following is an illustration of the principle they use.

Assume that the population is divided into as many strata as there are to be first-stage units in the sample, and that full advantage has been taken of past data in arriving at the best mode of stratification, the method of estimation, and the assignment of probabilities in accordance with the

* Roe Goodman and Leslie Kish, "Controlled Selection—A Technique in Probability Sampling," *J. Amer. Stat. Assn.*, **45** (1950), 350–372.

principles given in Chapter 9.   A limitation was imposed by the assumption in Chapter 9, namely, that the units be selected independently within the strata.   If we eliminate this assumption, we may be able to take advantage of additional data.   For example, if the initial stratification ignored geographic contiguity, it may be desirable to assign a much higher probability to a sample consisting of psu's which are widespread geographically than to samples consisting of units located in the same general geographic area.

As an illustration let us confine our attention to only two of the strata in the original population.   Since one unit is to be drawn from each stratum, the problem is to assign probabilities to each of the possible pairs of primary units such that a wide geographic spread of sample units is obtained.   Assume that stratum I consists of five first-stage units: A_1, A_2, A_3, B_1, B_2, and stratum II of four: a_1, a_2, b_1, b_2.   Assume further that A_1, A_2, A_3 and a_1, a_2 are in the same general geographic area; also that B_1, B_2 and b_1, b_2 are geographically contiguous in another area.

Now assume that the entries in Table 2 represent the desired probabilities of selection when we require that the units be independently selected.

Table 2.   Probability of selection

Stratum I		Stratum II	
(1)	(2)	(3)	(4)
A_1	.09	a_1	.20
A_2	.20	a_2	.58
A_3	.35		
B_1	.21	b_1	.12
B_2	.15	b_2	.10
	1.00		1.00

The probabilities shown in Table 2 have been arrived at in the manner described in Ch. 9, Sec. 11, and could represent probability proportionate to size or to the square root of size or any other system of assigning probabilities to a psu.   With independent selection from each stratum, the possible samples of two and their probabilities of selection are as shown in Table 3.   Note that the probability of getting two units from the same geographic area is the sum of the probabilities for combinations consisting of Aa or Bb and is equal to .5784.   The problem then is to reduce the probability of getting such pairs or to increase the probabilities of getting pairs of the types Ab and Ba; at the same time we wish to retain the probabilities of selection given in Table 2.

Table 3.   The possible samples and the probabilities of selection

Possible samples	Probability of selection
A_1a_1	.0180
A_1a_2	.0522
A_1b_1	.0108
A_1b_2	.0090
A_2a_1	.0400
A_2a_2	.1160
A_2b_1	.0240
A_2b_2	.0200
A_3a_1	.0700
A_3a_2	.2030
A_3b_1	.0420
A_3b_2	.0350
B_1a_1	.0420
B_1a_2	.1218
B_1b_1	.0252
B_1b_2	.0210
B_2a_1	.0300
B_2a_2	.0870
B_2b_1	.0180
B_2b_2	.0150
Total	1.0000

We proceed to make up a table, such as Table 4, of joint probabilities of selection that appear to be desirable. The table was made up as follows. Consider first the desirable combinations, such as A_1b_1 and A_1b_2. The maximum probability which A_1b_1 can have is .09, since A_1 (from Table 2) has a probability of occurrence of .09. We must then provide that b_1 occur with probability .03 in combination with some other unit, such as A_2, since from Table 2 its probability is .12. If we assign the probability .03 to A_2b_1, then A_2 must occur with probability .17 with the remaining unused units in stratum II, since from Table 2 its probability is .20. Continuing in this way, we are led to the entries in the last column of Table 4. A start with some other combination, such as A_2b_1, with probability, say .10, will lead to a different table, but it will not be possible to assign a probability of less than .42 to the unfavorable combinations Aa. This is so because the total probability of A is .64, whereas that of

b is only .22.   Therefore, the maximum probability to be assigned the favorable combinations Ab is .22 and the difference $(.64 - .22 = .42)$ must be assigned to Aa.   The sample is then selected in this simple case by choosing a random number between 1 and 100.   The entry in column 1 of Table 4 indicates which pair to select for the random number drawn. Thus, if the random number is any of the numbers from 1 to 9 inclusive, one of the combinations A_1b_1 is to be selected.   Selection in this manner yields the probabilities given in column 3.

Table 4.   The random numbers and the probabilities associated with the combinations to be selected

If the random number is (1)	Take (2)	Probability of selection (3)
1– 9	A_1b_1	.09
10– 12	A_2b_1	.03
13– 22	A_2b_2	.10
23– 29	A_2a_1	.07
30– 42	A_3a_1	.13
43– 64	A_3a_2	.22
65– 85	B_1a_2	.21
86–100	B_2a_2	.15
Total		1.00

It is easy to verify that the probabilities given in Table 2 are retained when the sample is restricted as in Table 4.   For example, the probability of b_1 being selected is $.09 + .03 = .12$.   On the other hand the probabilities of the undesirable pairs have been decreased from .5784, as in Table 5, to .42, and the combinations Bb from .0792 to no chance at all.   Thus, the removal of the requirement that the units be independently selected from strata made it possible to assign smaller probabilities to undesirable combinations.   The procedure is followed in a more elaborate problem in the article by Goodman and Kish referred to above.

Techniques such as those indicated above may bring about reductions in the sampling variance.   The estimate of the variance (following procedures such as given in Sec. 15 and 28, Ch. 9) will tend to be an overstatement, and the greater the actual reduction in the variance the greater will be the overstatement.   In such a situation, some notion of the overstatement of the variance can be obtained through analysis of past data.

Remark. Note that in the illustration above, we assigned zero probability to each of the combinations B_1b_1, B_1b_2, B_2b_1, and B_2b_2, but preserved the original probabilities of selecting B_1, B_2, b_1, and b_2. The assignment of zero probability to a combination of elementary units has a very different implication on sample design from that of assigning zero probabilities to elementary units in the original population. Each elementary unit in the population must have a probability different from zero if unbiased or consistent estimates are to be made for the entire population. If each element in the population has some chance of being selected, the assignment of zero probabilities to various "undesirable" combinations may increase the efficiency of the sample design. As was indicated in Ch. 1, Sec. 16, this is also accomplished by stratification.

Knowledge of the individual probabilities of selection often tells us very little about the variance of a sample estimate. The probabilities of selection of each elementary unit can be made the same for stratified sampling, cluster sampling, and the restricted designs described in this section. The efficiency of the sample design, however, depends on the probabilities assigned to the combination of elementary units.

Variance when a Latin-square restriction is used in selection of sample. The technique just described is an example of a whole class of restricted designs. A method, suggested by Frankel and Stock,* to increase the effective depth of stratification in the selection of primary units when the number of primary units is small makes use of the principles of Latin-square selection.†

To apply this method we may proceed to divide the population into L strata, as described in, for example, Chapter 9. If the method described there is used in selecting one psu per stratum, then m, the number of psu's in the sample, will be equal to L, the number of primary strata. We may now divide each of the original strata into L new groups, thus arriving at L^2 cells. Effectively, then, the population of M psu's is divided into L^2 cells and each cell now has an average $M/L^2 = \overline{M}$ psu's. Let us assume, for simplicity, that $\overline{M}$ is the number of psu's in each cell. We shall call the original L strata, columns, and the L new groups, rows, and we want to obtain m cases, such that a psu represents the original strata as well as the new groups. Since $m = L$, we have to sample with a restriction.

The sampling is accomplished by choosing a random sample of m "cells" subject to the restriction that one cell is selected from each row and one from each column, and then selecting one unit at random from within each of the selected cells. The sampling within the selected cells

---

* Lester R. Frankel and J. Stevens Stock, "On the Sample Survey of Unemployment," *J. Amer. Stat. Assn.*, **37** (1942), 77–80.

† R. A. Fisher, *Design of Experiments*, Oliver & Boyd, Edinburgh, fourth edition, 1947.

can be carried out in any manner desired. We shall assume that the method is simple random sampling.

This selection of the sample cells might be diagramed as in Fig. 1, with $m = 5$. The shaded squares indicate a possible selection of the cells. Observe that each row and each column is represented by one cell in the sample.

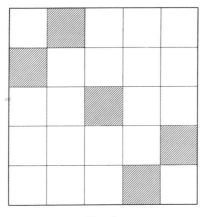

FIG. 1

The selection of a sample of m of the cells can be made in the following way. In the first column select one of the m cells at random. In the second column, after excluding the cell that is in the row selected for the first column, select any of the remaining $(m-1)$ cells at random. Similarly, in the third column select at random among the $(m-2)$ cells that remain after excluding the two rows that have already been selected. Continue in this way through all m columns. In each of the m cells that is thus finally selected, select one of the $\bar{M}$ units at random. Letting x denote the aggregate value of some characteristic obtained in the manner specified from the m units in the sample and f the over-all sampling fraction,

$$x' = \frac{1}{f} x = L\bar{M}x = m\bar{M}x \qquad (4.1)$$

is an unbiased estimate of the population total. Such a sampling scheme will reduce the variance as compared with that to be obtained from a stratified sample with m strata, provided that

$$\frac{\tilde{\sigma}_2^2}{\hat{\sigma}^2} > \frac{1}{m-1} \qquad (4.2)$$

where $\tilde{\sigma}_2^2$ and $\hat{\sigma}^2$ are defined below.

The variance of x' may be written*

$$\sigma_{x'}^2 = \frac{1}{m-1}(\tilde{\sigma}^2 - \tilde{\sigma}_1^2 - \tilde{\sigma}_2^2) + \frac{\tilde{\sigma}_w^2}{m} \tag{4.3}$$

where

$$\tilde{\sigma}^2 = L^4\sigma^2, \quad \tilde{\sigma}_1^2 = L^4\sigma_1^2, \quad \tilde{\sigma}_2^2 = L^4\sigma_2^2, \quad \tilde{\sigma}_w^2 = \sigma_w^2 \overline{M}^2 L^4$$

and where

$$\sigma^2 = \frac{1}{L^2} \sum_a^L \sum_b^L (X_{ab} - \bar{X})^2 \tag{4.4}$$

is the variance among the cell totals,

$$\sigma_1^2 = \frac{1}{L} \sum_a^L (\bar{X}_a - \bar{X})^2 \tag{4.5}$$

is the variance among the means per cell of the columns,

$$\sigma_2^2 = \frac{1}{L} \sum_b^L (\bar{X}_b - \bar{X})^2 \tag{4.6}$$

is the variance among the means per cell of the rows,

$$L = m, \quad \bar{X} = \frac{X}{L^2}, \quad \bar{X}_a = \frac{\sum_b^L X_{ab}}{L}, \quad \bar{X}_b = \frac{\sum_a^L X_{ab}}{L}$$

and

$$\sigma_w^2 = \frac{1}{L^2} \sum_a^L \sum_b^L \sigma_{ab}^2 = \frac{1}{L^2 \overline{M}} \sum_a^L \sum_b^L \sum_i^{\overline{M}} (X_{abi} - \bar{\bar{X}}_{ab})^2 \tag{4.7}$$

is the average variance within cells, with $\bar{\bar{X}}_{ab} = X_{ab}/\overline{M}$, and $X_{abi} =$ the value of the ith unit in the abth cell. Then

$$\hat{\sigma}^2 = \tilde{\sigma}^2 - \tilde{\sigma}_1^2 + \tilde{\sigma}_w^2 \tag{4.8}$$

would be (approximately) the variance of x' if only the L groups identified as "columns" had been defined as strata and one unit had been included in the sample from each such stratum; $\hat{\sigma}^2$ will be greater than the variance in Eq. 4.3 whenever condition 4.2 is satisfied.

For the design described it is not possible to make a consistent estimate of the variance. To obtain a consistent variance estimate it is necessary to replicate the design, i.e., to select two or more samples. This, in fact, is frequently done in experimentation, where such designs are used.

---

* This variance was developed by Jerome Cornfield and W. Duane Evans. The proof is given in Vol. II, Ch. 11, Sec. 6. The result can be readily extended to sampling with varying probabilities, multi-stage sampling, etc.

5. Estimates for individual areas made from a sample of such areas.
Sometimes one wishes to prepare estimates for a number of individual
areas on the basis of direct measures of the desired characteristic for only
a sample of those areas, together with a knowledge of some related
characteristic for each individual area.   A case in point was a large-scale
mail survey with voluntary responses which was used to provide information on radio listening in each of the more than 500 county areas in the
United States consisting of individual counties or a few adjoining counties.
This was accompanied by an intensive interview survey in a sample of the
county areas.   Field interviews were carried out for a subsample within
each of 85 county areas.   This sample was selected by probability
sampling methods and was of sufficient size to provide estimates of
satisfactory reliability for the purpose at hand for each of the 85 individual
areas in the interview sample.

The interview survey was taken in order to provide estimates unaffected
by the nonresponse and incomplete coverage of the list used for the mail
survey.   Results of the interview survey were extended to individual
county areas for which only the mail survey results were available on the
basis of the relationship between the mail and interview survey results.
In addition, the average error over all such predictions was ascertained,
although not the standard error of the estimate for any individual area.
If the differences between the mail results and the expected values of the
interview survey results are approximately normally distributed, then
limits of sampling variability computed in the usual manner from such
an average standard error for each of the individual areas will provide a
useful measure of precision, as is illustrated below.

The method may be applied in similar situations where there is a high
enough correlation between the expected values of the direct measurements (the interview sample results in the illustration) and the related
information available from a different source for the individual areas (in
this case the mail survey results).   This method is illustrated below by a
brief description of the radio listening survey already mentioned.   In that
particular survey the correlations obtained were only moderate, dis-
appointingly below the levels that were hoped for when the survey was
planned, and hardly sufficient to make the interview survey results extend-
able to the other areas with acceptable average precision.

Illustration 5.1.   The Radio Listening Survey.*   For the voluntary mail
aspect of the survey, about a thousand families within each of 500 county
areas were sent mail schedules.   The lists used for mailing represented a

---

* U.S. Bureau of the Census, "FCC Radio Survey," *FCC Docket* 6741,
Washington, D.C., 1945, Appendices D and F.

cross-section of a substantial proportion of the families in the areas surveyed, although not necessarily of the entire population. About a 20 per cent voluntary response was received from the mail survey. It is important to recognize that the intent was not to obtain consistent estimates from the mail response alone. Mailing to a large portion of the relevant population may make it possible to increase the correlation between the mail responses and the interview survey results. The higher this correlation, the more efficient will be the estimating procedure described.

The sample of 85 county areas for the interview aspect of the survey was selected by first grouping the 500 county areas into 85 primary strata on the basis of geographic region and type of radio service available. One area was selected from each stratum with probability proportionate to the estimated number of families in the area. Then a subsample of small areas was drawn from within each of the 85 sampled primary units. The interview survey provided aggregate estimates for the entire area as

Table 5. Comparison of specified results from the interview survey with corresponding unadjusted figures from the mail survey

Number of stations heard	Per cent of households reporting hearing specified number of stations			
	During the day		At night	
	Mail (per cent)	Interview (per cent)	Mail (per cent)	Interview (per cent)
0	0	0	0	0
1	4	6	6	6
2	11	15	15	16
3	12	22	16	22
4	17	24	16	23
5	16	15	15	16
6	12	8	11	9
7	10	5	8	5
8	7	2	5	2
9	5	2	3	1
10 or more	6	1	5	1
Total	100	100	100	100
Median number of stations heard	4.9	3.8	4.3	3.8

well as estimates for individual areas in the interview sample, and, through the correlation with the mail survey results, estimates for all individual areas whether represented in the sample or not.

In Table 5 certain percentages and medians for the entire covered area estimated from the interview survey are compared with corresponding figures from the mail survey.   From these comparisons, it appears that there was a definite tendency for respondents in the mail survey to report more radio stations heard than respondents in the interview survey.

There are several possible methods of obtaining adjusted estimates from the mail survey for the psu's in which no interview survey was made. One is to fit a line of relationship represented by the equation $y' = a + bx$ by the least squares method.*   In some cases this line may result in small negative values, which, of course, should be considered zero.   Figure 2 shows the relationship between the median values for one item (number of stations heard during the day without trouble) together with the average line of relationship.   The adjusted medians or percentages for any psu for a particular item may be obtained from the line of relationship for that item by substituting the median or percentage from the mail survey into the equation $y' = a + bx$ with the appropriate values of a and b, and computing the adjusted value, y'.

The approximate average errors made by taking the adjusted values as estimates of what would have resulted from a complete interview survey in each psu are shown on the chart together with the equation for the line of relationship.   Separate lines could have been fitted to different classes of strata, but analysis of the returns did not indicate that any significant gains would result from such separate estimates.

The measure of the degree of reliability with which the mail results can be used to infer the results which would have been obtained if a complete interview survey had been taken is obtained by (a) computing the weighted sum of the squares of the deviations of the sample interview results from the average line of relationship determined from the 85 psu's, and (b) subtracting an allowance for the average sampling error of the interview survey results within each of the 85 psu's covered.   The square root of the resulting mean square (the root mean square error) can be used to set useful confidence bounds if the deviation of the "true" value for each county from the regression is not too far from normal, as we shall assume in what follows.   To obtain the confidence limits, one computes $y' \pm k\sqrt{MSE}$, where y' is the value obtained from the regression line, $\sqrt{MSE}$

---

* With simple random sampling $b = \Sigma(x_i - \bar{x})(y_i - \bar{y})/\Sigma(x_i - \bar{x})^2$ and $a = \bar{y} - b\bar{x}$.   For further consideration see Sec. 2 of this chapter and see also a discussion of linear regression in any standard statistics book.

is the root mean square error, and k determines the desired probability. If this were done for each psu in the population with $k = 1$, the confidence bounds so computed would include approximately two-thirds of the true values in the population, where, by "true" value, we mean the result which would have been obtained from an interview survey covering the entire primary sampling unit.

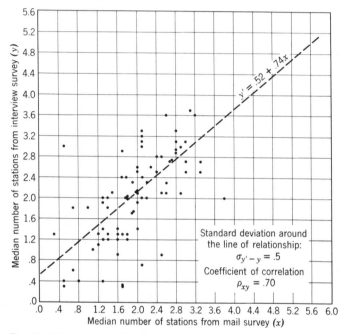

FIG. 2. Comparison of median numbers of stations heard during the day without trouble, as estimated from mail and interview surveys in selected primary sampling units.

When the correlation is fairly high, the crude measurement method (the mail survey in this case) is effective in providing a means of making estimates for individual local areas. When the correlation is not high, on the other hand, little information is provided by the crude measurement method for the particular characteristic, and then the adjusted estimate for any particular psu is approximately the same as the over-all average result from the interview survey.

6. The cut-off method. A technique of sampling called the "cut-off" method is sometimes used in sampling for establishment statistics. To obtain a sample of n establishments by the cut-off method, the largest n establishments are selected on the basis of a past measure of size. The ratio of the current total to the historical total of the selected large units is then computed as a measure of the relationship between the *universe* totals for the two dates.   An estimate of the current universe total may then be obtained by multiplying the actual universe total (or an estimate of it) for the past date by the ratio derived for the large establishments.

The cut-off method is obviously biased, inasmuch as the sample does not reflect the change of the smaller establishments.   It may be very seriously biased.   However, in some instances this type of sampling and estimation has been found empirically to yield results that compare very favorably with some of the measurable designs.

The argument favoring the use of the cut-off method is that for extremely skewed distributions the relatively small number of large establishments contribute such a dominant portion of the aggregate being measured that it would be uneconomical to include any small establishments in the sample.   Extreme skewness is common in many industries for such items as sales, production, and employment.   Often the large establishments do dominate the ratios of current to past values for such establishment characteristics.

The appeal of the cut-off method is strengthened when there are logical reasons for believing that the relative positions of the small and large units will remain essentially constant.   An illustration is heavy industries that require huge capital for large-scale operations.   For such industries it is argued that units which are small at one date are unlikely to be large at another, and vice versa, and furthermore that over reasonably short periods the economic fortunes of the large and small establishments will fluctuate in approximately the same way.

Although, as has been mentioned earlier, good results have sometimes been obtained with cut-off surveys founded upon these ideas, cases have also been observed in which the method was apparently successful for a time, but yielded extremely misleading results during periods of violent change.   Unfortunately for the method, prompt and accurate measurement of sharp changes is often a major objective of surveys, and in turbulent periods the relative sizes of establishments often shift widely and the cut-off procedure is at its weakest.   Also damaging is the fact that there is no measure of precision with the cut-off method to indicate that the historical relationship is no longer valid.   Measurable sample designs might result in estimates which are subject to large sampling errors under like conditions, but they provide a warning that the estimates are unreliable and that the sample size must be increased.

The theory below indicates a general method of sample allocation and estimation which may yield more reliable results than those arrived at by alternative methods that have been given.   It yields the "cut-off" method as a special case. But, at least until additional theory is developed, its use depends on assumptions or knowledge unverifiable in practice. Nevertheless, the theory given does provide a guide as to the conditions under which the cut-off method may be useful.

Consider the very simple case where the establishments to be sampled in a given area are divided into two groups, group I including establishments having sales over $200,000 in 1948, and group II including establishments having sales under $200,000 in 1948. Complete returns are available for 1948, and the problem is to estimate the change in sales from 1948 to 1952 from a sample. Assume that for group I there are N_1 establishments in the population and n_1 are to be included in the sample, and the corresponding numbers for group II are N_2 and n_2.

To see the circumstances under which the cut-off method may have advantages let us consider the following modification of the estimate given by Eq. 4.11 of Ch. 5:

$$r' = w_1 r_1 + w_2 r_2 \tag{6.1}$$

where $r_1 = x_1/y_1$ is the ratio of sample aggregates for the two periods of time (or, more generally, for two characteristics) for the first stratum, $r_2 = x_2/y_2$ is the sample ratio for the second stratum, and w_1 and w_2 are weights with $w_1 + w_2 = 1$. In estimate 4.11 of Ch. 5 the weights w_1 and w_2 were equal to Y_1/Y and Y_2/Y, whereas here we propose to find the values of w_1 and w_2 that minimize the mean square error of r'. In addition, we propose to find optimum values for n_1 and n_2 for a fixed total size of sample $n = n_1 + n_2$.

The mean square error of r' is*

$$\text{MSE}_{(r')} = w_1^2 \frac{N_1 - n_1}{N_1 n_1} S_1^2 + w_2^2 \frac{N_2 - n_2}{N_2 n_2} S_2^2 + (R_1 - R_2)^2 \left(w_1 - \frac{Y_1}{Y}\right)^2 \tag{6.2}$$

The values of w_1 and n_1 that minimize $\text{MSE}_{(r')}$ for $w_1 + w_2 = 1$ and $n_1 + n_2 = n$ are†

$$w_1 = \frac{S_2^2 - S_1 S_2 + n\left[\frac{Y_1}{Y}(R_1 - R_2)^2 - \frac{S_2^2}{N_2}\right]}{(S_2 - S_1)^2 + n\left[(R_1 - R_2)^2 - \frac{S_1^2}{N_1} - \frac{S_2^2}{N_2}\right]} \tag{6.3}$$

$$n_1 = \frac{S_2^2 - S_1 S_2 + n\left[\frac{Y_1}{Y}(R_1 - R_2)^2 - \frac{S_2^2}{N_2}\right]}{\left[\frac{Y_1}{Y}(R_1 - R_2)^2 - \frac{S_2^2}{N_2}\right] + \frac{S_2}{S_1}\left[\frac{Y_2}{Y}(R_1 - R_2)^2 - \frac{S_1^2}{N_1}\right]} \tag{6.4}$$

* For proof, see Vol. II, Ch. 11, Sec. 7.
† For proof, see Vol. II, Ch. 11, Sec. 7.

where $R_1 = X_1/Y_1$ and $R_2 = X_2/Y_2$ are the ratios of the population aggregates for the two strata; and

$$S_1^2 = R_1^2(V_{1X}^2 + V_{1Y}^2 - 2V_{1XY})$$ (6.5)

where V_{1X}^2 and V_{1Y}^2 are the rel-variances and V_{1XY} is the rel-covariance of X and Y in the first stratum, and S_2^2 is defined similarly for the second stratum. Thus, S_1^2 is the approximation to the variance of the ratio X_{1i}/Y_{1i}.

Note that, as the difference, $R_1 - R_2$, increases while all other things are equal, the optimum value of w_1 approaches Y_1/Y. On the other hand, suppose that $(R_1 - R_2)^2$ is approximately equal to $(S_1^2/N_1) + (S_2^2/N_2)$, which would be the expected value of $(R_1 - R_2)^2$ if the first stratum had been made up by drawing a random sample of N_1 establishments from some very large population of establishments for which the ratio $X_1/Y_1 = R$, and in which the variance (as defined by Eq. 6.5) was approximately equal to S_1^2; and if the second stratum had been made up in an analogous manner from another population in which $X_2/Y_2 = R$ and S_2^2 was the variance (defined by Eq. 6.5). Under this assumption, the optimum value of w_1 would be equal to

$$w_1 = \frac{S_2^2 - S_1 S_2 + \dfrac{n}{Y}(\bar{Y}_1 S_1^2 - \bar{Y}_2 S_2^2)}{(S_2 - S_1)^2}$$

and the optimum value of w_2 would be

$$w_2 = \frac{S_1^2 - S_1 S_2 + \dfrac{n}{Y}(\bar{Y}_2 S_2^2 - \bar{Y}_1 S_1^2)}{(S_2 - S_1)^2}$$

If the first stratum is made up of large establishments and the second stratum of small establishments, as we have assumed, and if S_1 and S_2 are of roughly the same order of magnitude, then $\bar{Y}_1 S_1$ will be considerably larger than $\bar{Y}_2 S_2$, and as this difference widens, the optimum value of w_1 increases and of w_2 decreases. Under these circumstances, with a large enough difference, the cut-off method, $w_1 = 1$, $w_2 = 0$, and $n_1 = n$, is the optimum.

The theory given above can be generalized to the case of more than two classes and with other types of estimates.

Critique of theory. In order to use the theory just outlined we must have estimates of S_h^2, so as to determine the optimum w_h and n_h. We also must estimate $(R_1 - R_2)^2$, and this value, which will be unknown, is critical in applying the theory.

The errors in estimating $(R_1 - R_2)^2$ and the S_h^2 from the sample may be larger than those arising from the conventional unbiased or ratio estimates. Consequently, the method just outlined, although it provides a guide to thinking, cannot be used in practice except where one has independent and good evidence on these values, or at least has evidence that $(R_1 - R_2)^2$ is small. Even when one has some reasonable assurance that R_1 is close to R_2, the cut-off procedure is not recommended unless the large establishments are known to constitute from 90 to 95 per cent or more of the aggregate being measured.

7. Sampling for time series.*   Sampling on successive occasions for estimating the terms and relationships in a time series involves a number of problems in theory and in practical survey design that need special attention.   The problem arises because of the need for estimating multiple statistics from a sample.   Thus, often estimates are needed of aggregates or averages at each period of time, such as for each month; of changes between periods, such as changes between successive months, change from the corresponding month a year ago, and changes at other intervals; of aggregates, such as the total for a quarter or for a year; and of changes in such aggregates.   Ordinarily it is not desirable that the estimate at each new period require the revision of preceding estimates.

The sampling theory for time series problems is limited to some extent in the same way as the usual theory for obtaining optimum sampling designs for multiple statistics.   An optimum for one statistic may not be optimum for another.   However, the study of optima for time series problems introduces some new aspects especially applicable to such problems.   For example, the estimates for time series raise such questions as the following: Should the sampling units be identical at different points in time?   If not, what proportion of the units should be identical (i.e., matched)?   How does one utilize the information from the past series to improve the estimates for the current figures?

A solution to the problem of optimum allocation of the sample and estimation for each of two occasions was proposed by Jessen (1), and his method provides the basis for extension to more than two occasions. Patterson (2) extended Jessen's results.   More work remains to be done. An approach which has a number of practical advantages and makes effective use of past data without requiring revision of previously published figures is described in Illustration 7.1 of this section.   A number of aspects of the two-occasion problem are considered first in order to illustrate the principles.

* This section, except for Illustration 7.1, was written by Benjamin J. Tepping, Bureau of the Census.

Sampling on two occasions. For simplicity we shall assume sampling with replacement. Suppose that a simple random sample of n units is selected for the first period. Retain a simple random sample of Pn of these units for the sample in the second period, and supplement it by Qn independently selected units, where $P + Q = 1$. Thus the total sample size for the second period is assumed to be the same as that for the first period, although the results can be extended to varying sizes of sample.

Let:

$\bar{x}'$ = mean per unit for the first period, for the Pn units that are common to the two samples.

$\bar{x}''$ = mean per unit for the first period, for the Qn units that are in the first sample only.

$\bar{y}'$ = mean per unit for the second period, for the Pn units that are common to the two samples.

$\bar{y}''$ = mean per unit for the second period, for the Qn units that are in the second sample only.

ρ = correlation between $\bar{x}'$ and $\bar{y}'$ (see p. 167).

An estimate of the mean for the second period is given by the weighted estimate*

$$\bar{y}_w = \frac{\rho PQ}{1 - Q^2\rho^2}(\bar{x}'' - \bar{x}') + \frac{P}{1 - Q^2\rho^2}\bar{y}' + \frac{Q(1 - Q\rho^2)}{1 - Q^2\rho^2}\bar{y}'' \quad (7.1)$$

which makes use of the information furnished by the first as well as the second sample. If we were to depend only on the information furnished by the second sample, the estimate would be

$$\bar{y} = P\bar{y}' + Q\bar{y}'' \quad (7.2)$$

Let us compare the variances of these two estimates, on the assumption that $\sigma_X^2 = \sigma_Y^2 = \sigma^2$, where σ^2 is the population variance of an individual observation:

$$\sigma_{\bar{y}_w}^2 = \frac{\sigma^2}{n}\frac{1 - Q\rho^2}{1 - Q^2\rho^2} \quad (7.3)$$

$$\sigma_{\bar{y}}^2 = \frac{\sigma^2}{n} \quad (7.4)$$

The ratio $\sigma_{\bar{y}_w}^2$ to $\sigma_{\bar{y}}^2$ is then

$$\frac{1 - Q\rho^2}{1 - Q^2\rho^2} \quad (7.5)$$

---

* See Vol. II, Ch. 11, Sec. 8.

which indicates that $\bar{y}_w$ may give substantial gains when ρ is large. Table 6 gives $\sigma_{\bar{y}_w}^2$ as a proportion of σ_y^2, for various values of ρ and Q.

Table 6. Variance of estimate 7.1 as proportion of variance of estimate 7.2

ρ	$Q = 1$	$Q = .5$	$Q = .2$	$Q = 0$
0	1.00	1.00	1.00	1.00
.50	1.00	.93	.95	1.00
.80	1.00	.81	.89	1.00
.90	1.00	.75	.87	1.00
.95	1.00	.71	.85	1.00
.97	1.00	.68	.84	1.00

Table 6 suggests that one should choose the value of Q so as to minimize the variance of $\bar{y}_w$, for a fixed sample size n. It turns out that the optimum value of Q is

$$Q = \frac{1 - \sqrt{1 - \rho^2}}{\rho^2} \qquad (7.6)$$

Remark 1. The problem of finding the optimum design for estimating level on the second of two occasions was given by Jessen (1), in another (but equivalent) form. In essence, he considers two independent estimates for the current occasion:

$$\bar{y}'_m = \bar{y}' + b(\bar{x} - \bar{x}'), \quad \text{and} \quad \bar{y}''$$

where $\bar{x} = P\bar{x}' + Q\bar{x}''$.

The two estimates of $\bar{Y}$ are independent, and the weighted average of the two that has the minimum variance is obtained by combining them with weights proportionate to the reciprocals of their variances. The values of P and Q which will minimize the variance are also obtained. The results for the optimum estimate are given by Eq. 7.1, and the optimum allocation by Eq. 7.6.

The estimation of change presents a somewhat different problem of applying the information provided by the samples. For example, we might consider the use of the estimate

$$\Delta = \bar{y} - \bar{x} = P(\bar{y}' - \bar{x}') + Q(\bar{y}'' - \bar{x}'') \qquad (7.7)$$

where $\bar{y}$ is defined by Eq. 7.2 and $\bar{x}$ is a similar estimate for the first period. However, a better estimate of the change is

$$\Delta_w = \frac{P}{1 - Q\rho}(\bar{y}' - \bar{x}') + \frac{Q(1 - \rho)}{1 - Q\rho}(\bar{y}'' - \bar{x}'') \qquad (7.8)$$

Again we may compare the variances of Δ and Δ_w:

$$\sigma_\Delta^2 = \frac{2(1 - P\rho)\sigma^2}{n} \tag{7.9}$$

$$\sigma_{\Delta_w}^2 = \frac{2(1 - \rho)\sigma^2}{n(1 - Q\rho)} \tag{7.10}$$

$$\frac{\sigma_{\Delta_w}^2}{\sigma_\Delta^2} = \frac{1 - \rho}{1 - \rho + PQ\rho^2} \tag{7.11}$$

This indicates that Δ_w may have a considerably smaller variance than Δ. Table 7 shows $\sigma_{\Delta_w}^2$ as a proportion of σ_Δ^2, for various values of ρ and Q.

Table 7. Variance of estimate 7.8 as proportion of variance of estimate 7.7

ρ	$Q = 1$	$Q = .5$	$Q = .2$	$Q = 0$
0	1.00	1.00	1.00	1.00
.50	1.00	.89	.93	1.00
.80	1.00	.56	.66	1.00
.90	1.00	.33	.44	1.00
.95	1.00	.18	.26	1.00
.99	1.00	.04	.06	1.00

It will be observed that for high values of ρ substantial reductions in sampling error can be attained in the estimation of change by using the appropriate estimate.

It is easily seen that, for any positive value of ρ, the optimum value of Q is 0. That is, the variance of Δ_w will be least if the two samples contain identical units, and in fact will have the value

$$\frac{2(1 - \rho)\sigma^2}{n} \tag{7.12}$$

We are thus faced with the dilemma that the optimum choice of Q for estimating the change from one period to another is quite different from the optimum for estimating the mean for the second period. In practice, we may assign weights to the importance of the estimate of the change and the estimate of the mean, and thus make a compromise between the weights that are optimum for these two purposes.

A third purpose may be to estimate the sum of the means for the two periods. The obvious estimate of this sum is the sum of the estimates, say

$$z = \bar{x} + \bar{y} = P(\bar{x}' + \bar{y}') + Q(\bar{x}'' + \bar{y}'') \tag{7.13}$$

The variance of this estimate is

$$\sigma_z^2 = \frac{2(1 + P\rho)\sigma^2}{n} \tag{7.14}$$

A better estimate of the sum is given by

$$z_w = \frac{P}{1 + Q\rho}(\bar{x}' + \bar{y}') + \frac{Q(1 + \rho)}{1 + Q\rho}(\bar{x}'' + \bar{y}'') \tag{7.15}$$

whose variance is

$$\sigma_{z_w}^2 = \frac{2(1 + \rho)\sigma^2}{n(1 + Q\rho)} \tag{7.16}$$

Thus

$$\frac{\sigma_{z_w}^2}{\sigma_z^2} = \frac{1 + \rho}{1 + \rho + PQ\rho^2} \tag{7.17}$$

which again indicates that gains can be made by using the estimate z_w instead of z, although these gains are not nearly so substantial as in the estimation of change. Table 8 shows the ratio of $\sigma_{z_w}^2$ to σ_z^2.

Table 8.   Variance of estimate 7.15 as proportion of variance
of estimate 7.13

ρ	$Q = 1$	$Q = .5$	$Q = .2$	$Q = 0$
0	1.00	1.00	1.00	1.00
.50	1.00	.96	.97	1.00
.80	1.00	.92	.95	1.00
.90	1.00	.90	.94	1.00
.95	1.00	.90	.93	1.00
.99	1.00	.89	.93	1.00

The reader should note at this point that the suggested estimates of the mean at the second period, the change, and the sum depend upon a knowledge of the value of ρ as well as on the numbers P and Q. In general ρ will not be known. It will therefore be necessary to replace ρ by some past value or an otherwise independently estimated value, or by the value of ρ estimated from the sample itself. In the former case, the estimates will still be unbiased, although the variances will be increased. If ρ is estimated from the sample, the estimates will no longer be unbiased. They will, however, be consistent estimates of the respective parameters.

Another point that should be considered arises in connection with multi-purpose surveys where many statistics are produced by the same sample. In such a case it will often not be possible to use a different estimating procedure for each statistic.   Moreover, even where this is possible, it may not be desirable.   For example, suppose that it is desired to estimate the number of employed persons, the number of unemployed persons, the number of males in the labor force, and the number of females in the labor force.   Since the sum of the employed and the unemployed provides an estimate of the total number of persons in the labor force, and since the sum of the males and the females in the labor force provides another estimate of the total labor force, we would be confronted with two different estimates of the total labor force from the survey, if we used the optimum estimate for each of the four statistics. It may therefore be desirable to use a compromise estimate which does not furnish as low a variance for each of the four statistics, but avoids the difficulty of having disparate estimates of the same statistic from a single sample.

Another difficulty that should be pointed out is a certain lack of agreement among the estimate of change, the estimate of the mean at the second period, and the estimate of the sum of the two periods.   For example, if the suggested estimates, Eq. 7.8, 7.1, and 7.15, are used, the estimate of the mean at the second period will not be the sum of the estimate of the mean at the first period and the estimate of the change. We shall consider two alternatives that resolve this difficulty.   One is to revise the estimate for the first period in the light of the information obtained from the sample at the second period.   This can be done so as to reduce the variance of the estimate of the mean at the first period and have at the same time the property that the estimate of the change will be the difference between the estimate of the mean at the second period and the estimate of the mean at the first period.   A second alternative is to estimate the mean of the second period and the change in such a way that the estimated change will be the difference between the estimated mean of the second period and the original estimate of the mean at the first period.   If this is done, however, neither the estimate of change nor the estimate of the mean at the second period will have as low a variance as is provided by the estimates discussed above.

If we choose the first of the alternatives mentioned, a method first suggested by Patterson (2), we would use for an estimate of the mean for the first occasion the following expression:

$$\bar{x}_w = \frac{P}{1 - Q^2\rho^2}\,\bar{x}' + \frac{Q(1 - Q\rho^2)}{1 - Q^2\rho^2}\,\bar{x}'' + \frac{\rho PQ}{1 - Q^2\rho^2}\,(\bar{y}'' - \bar{y}') \quad (7.18)$$

whose form is readily deduced from the estimate of the mean of the second occasion by considerations of symmetry.   Its variance will then be the same as the variance for the estimated mean of the second period, given by Eq. 7.3. It is readily seen that the estimated change, Eq. 7.8, is the difference between the estimated mean at the second period, Eq. 7.1, and the estimated mean at the first period, Eq. 7.18.

    Remark 2. This estimate in practice is not very readily extendable to more than two occasions since the previous estimates must always be revised in the light of the new information.

If one chooses the second alternative, he may impose a condition such as that the sum of the variances of the mean and of the change be a minimum. The appropriate estimate of the mean of the second occasion is then

$$\frac{PQ\rho(2 + Q\rho)}{2(1 - Q^2\rho^2)} (\bar{x}'' - \bar{x}') - \frac{P(2 + Q\rho)}{2(1 - Q^2\rho^2)} (\bar{y}'' - \bar{y}') + \bar{y}'' \qquad (7.19)$$

and the appropriate estimate of the change is

$$\frac{P(2 + 2Q\rho - Q^2\rho^2)}{2(1 - Q^2\rho^2)} (\bar{x}'' - \bar{x}') - \frac{P(2 + Q\rho)}{2(1 - Q^2\rho^2)} (\bar{y}'' - \bar{y}') + \bar{y}'' - \bar{x}'' \quad (7.20)$$

Although, as mentioned above, the variances of these estimates are not as small as the variances of estimates, Eq. 7.1 and 7.8, they still exhibit considerable advantage over the simple estimates, Eq. 7.2 and 7.7. Table 9 shows the variances of estimates, Eq. 7.19 and 7.20, as a proportion of the variances of estimates, Eq. 7.2 and 7.7, respectively.

Table 9

ρ	Variance of estimate 7.19 as proportion of variance of estimate 7.2				Variance of estimate 7.20 as proportion of variance of estimate 7.7			
	$Q = 1$	$Q = .5$	$Q = .2$	$Q = 0$	$Q = 1$	$Q = .5$	$Q = .2$	$Q = 0$
0	1.00	1.00	1.00	1.00	1.00	1.00	1.00	1.00
50	1.00	.95	.97	1.00	1.00	.90	.93	1.00
.80	1.00	.86	.92	1.00	1.00	.59	.70	1.00
.90	1.00	.81	.90	1.00	1.00	.39	.50	1.00
.95	1.00	.78	.89	1.00	1.00	.25	.33	1.00
.99	1.00	.76	.88	1.00	1.00	.12	.16	1.00

    Remark 3. The optimum weights and the variances in this section were computed under the assumption that the population variances on the two occasions were the same. Optimum weights and variances for the estimate when the variances differ are given in Vol. II, Ch. 11, Sec. 8. The cases treated here are, of course, special ones.

Extension to any number of occasions. A more difficult problem is presented when one has a sequence of more than two periods and wishes to estimate the mean or total at each period, the means and sums for longer periods, and the changes between successive periods. Patterson (2) has considered this problem and has given the forms of the efficient estimate of a change and a mean at each period, as well as certain suggestions with regard to the choice of the number of identical units to use, as between successive periods.

Illustration 7.1 below indicates a method of making monthly surveys for a particular pattern of sample rotation, where each new estimate makes use of the information on level accumulated from preceding estimates. The procedure there is based on ratio and difference estimates (as discussed in Sec. 2) instead of the regression estimate. The method described in the illustration is not itself general but can be adapted to other survey situations and problems.

Illustration 7.1. Some alternative estimates for a time series with a specified pattern of sample rotation.* The following discussion of alternative estimates for a time series of monthly and annual sales is based on the particular pattern of a twelve-month sample rotation specified for the area sample in Sec. A–6d of Case Study A, Ch. 12. In this pattern of sample rotation, data on retail sales are obtained from 12 independently selected samples, 1 for each month in the year. The "January" sample is used in January of each year, the "February" sample in February of each year, etc. In the field survey each month data on sales are obtained for both the current month and the preceding month for the panel of stores in the sample. If a different pattern of sample rotation were used, the results given below would be modified. Note that, although the 12 area samples in Case Study A are not independent, this illustration assumes independence of the monthly samples. We assume further that each sample is a simple random sample of the whole population. The results can be extended readily to other sample designs.

a. Simple or adjusted chained estimates. A simple chained estimate of sales for a given month is obtained by making an estimate of change from a single one of the samples for a pair of months, and applying this change to the estimated total sales for the preceding month. We will examine simple chained estimates made with both ratio and difference estimates of change.

If the estimate of change is made with a ratio of the simple unbiased estimates, the estimate of total sales for the uth month is

$$x'_u = x'_{u-1} \frac{x_u}{y_{u-1}} \qquad (7.21)$$

where x_u is the estimate of total sales for the current month (month u)

---

* This illustration is based on work by Max A. Bershad and Ralph S. Woodruff, and written by Max A. Bershad. See Vol. II, Ch. 11, Sec. 9, for proofs.

based on the sample for month u, and y_{u-1} is the estimated total for the previous month (month $u - 1$) based on the sample for month u.

The ratio x_u/y_{u-1} is the trend for identicals. Therefore,

$$x'_u = x_1 \frac{x_2}{y_1} \frac{x_3}{y_2} \cdots \frac{x_u}{y_{u-1}} \tag{7.22}$$

where x_1 represents a sales estimate for the first month in the series. Any other initial estimate could be used without changing the theory.

The rel-variance of this estimate is approximately

$$V_{x_u}^2[1 + 2(1 - \rho)(u - 1)] \tag{7.23}$$

where $V_{x_u}^2$ is the rel-variance of the simple unbiased estimate of total monthly sales, and ρ is an average of the correlations defined by $V_{x_u y_{u-1}}/V_{x_u} V_{y_{u-1}}$, where $V_{x_u y_{u-1}}$ is the rel-covariance of x_u and y_{u-1}. The $V_{x_u}^2$ and $V_{y_{u-1}}^2$ are the rel-variances of x_u and y_{u-1}, and it is assumed in Eq. 7.23 that they are equal and are the same for all months.

The estimate of annual sales for the first year of the chain based on the simple chained estimate is

$$x'_a = \sum_{u=1}^{12} x'_u \tag{7.24}$$

and the rel-variance of this first year's estimate is approximately

$$V_{x_u}^2[1 + 7(1 - \rho)] \tag{7.25}$$

This is a tremendous increase over the rel-variance of the simple unbiased estimate for the year, which is the sum of the 12 unbiased monthly estimates. (The rel-variance of the unbiased estimate for the year is only $V_{x_u}^2/12$.) In successive years the rel-variance of estimate 7.22 becomes increasingly larger.

The constantly increasing rel-variances of the x'_u could be avoided by revising the estimates at the end of each year by proportionate adjustment, to agree with the annual total $x' = \Sigma x_u$. Then the estimate for month u would be $x'(x'_u/x'_a)$. The rel-variance of this revised estimate for month u is approximately

$$V_{x'}^2\{1 + 2(1 - \rho)(11.7 + [u - 6]^2)\} \tag{7.26}$$

where u varies from 1 to 12. This is smallest for the sixth month in the year and largest for the twelfth, but still is smaller for $u = 12$ than $V_{x_u}^2$, provided ρ is .9 or more.

The month-to-month trend of the adjusted estimates (other than for December to January) is

$$r'_u = \frac{x'_{u(\text{adj.})}}{x'_{u-1(\text{adj.})}} = \frac{x'_u}{x'_{u-1}} = \frac{x_u}{y_{u-1}}$$

and has the rel-variance

$$V_{r'_u}^2 \doteq 2(1 - \rho)(V_{x'_u}^2) \tag{7.27}$$

If ρ is large, $V_{r'_u}^2$ is much smaller than the rel-variance of the ratio of independent estimates for the 2 months, which is also given by Eq. 7.27 but with $\rho = 0$. However, such series, adjusted annually for the latest year, will have a larger rel-variance of the December–January ratio, and thus there may be the appearance of a discontinuity in the adjusted time series at the end of each year.

Remark 4.   Another form of simple chained estimate is given by the use of the difference between monthly sales instead of the ratio of month-to-month sales.   Thus, we can use the estimate

$$x'_u = x'_{u-1} + (x_u - y_{u-1}) \tag{7.28}$$

instead of Eq. 7.21.   The rel-variance of this estimate is the same as expression 7.26, if the same assumptions are made.   Moreover, the rel-variances of the annual total of these estimates and of the difference between successive months are the same as 7.25 and 7.27, respectively, under the assumptions made (provided variances of differences are divided by the average level squared to put them in the form of rel-variances).   Estimate 7.28 has essentially the same problems, advantages, and disadvantages as estimate 7.21, although in certain circumstances one form or the other has important advantages, as discussed in Sec. 2.

Remark 5.   An important disadvantage of chained estimates such as are given by Eq. 7.21 and 7.28 arises if month-to-month trends or differences are subject to biases that are of the same direction, even though trivial. Such biases are cumulative and over time may become large and serious.

Summary comments.   The simple chained estimates give estimates of month-to-month trends of relatively high precisions (as will be seen by comparison with alternatives to be presented), but the estimates of level for individual months or for annual totals are unsatisfactory.   If the estimates for months are adjusted to agree with the simple unbiased estimates of calendar-year totals, the estimated levels will be much improved, but such adjustments cannot be made until the end of the year. In the meantime, the unadjusted monthly estimates have large variances, especially for the later months in the year.   Also, the adjustment gives apparent discontinuities in the December–January trends.   A number of alternative approaches to resolving these problems are available, some of which are outlined below.   The alternatives considered have some disadvantages as well as advantages, as will be seen, but nevertheless, on the whole, offer a much more satisfactory approach to the problem of estimating a time series of monthly levels.   Variations in the approach can be made to adapt it to other problems.

b. A composite estimate. Another type of estimate x_u'', for the month u, is given by

$$x_u'' = K_1 x_{u-1}'' \frac{x_u}{y_{u-1}} + K_2 x_u \qquad (7.29)$$

where $K_1 + K_2 = 1$, $0 \leqslant K_1 \leqslant 1$.

This is a weighted average of two estimates of the level of sales for the month u, with weights K_1 and K_2. The first is a chained estimate for the month u obtained by multiplying the weighted estimate for the preceding month by the ratio of the simple unbiased estimates for the current and preceding months from the identical sample. The second is the simple unbiased estimate for month u based on the current data from the same sample.

The rel-variance of x_u'' is

$$V_{x_u''}^2 \doteq V_{x_u}^2 \frac{1 + K_1^2 - 2\rho K_1}{1 - K_1^2} \qquad (7.30)$$

This and subsequent approximations neglect terms involving K_1^{12} and higher powers of K_1. The approximation is acceptable provided K_1 is not too large, say not larger than .8.

The rel-variance given by Eq. 7.30 has its minimum value if

$$K_1 = \frac{1 - \sqrt{1 - \rho^2}}{\rho} \qquad (7.31)$$

and this minimum value is

$$V_{x_u}^2 \sqrt{1 - \rho^2}$$

When $\rho = .95$ (values of about this size have been observed; see Ch. 12, Table A–13) the value of K_1 given by Eq. 7.31 is approximately .7, and with this value for K_1

$$V_{x_u''}^2 = .313 V_{x_u}^2 \qquad (7.32)$$

This is a very substantial reduction from $V_{x_u}^2$, the rel-variance of the simple unbiased estimate, x_u.

The rel-variance of x_u''/x_{u-1}'', the ratio of estimated sales for month u to the estimate for month $u - 1$, is

$$2(1 - K_1) V_{x_u''}^2 \doteq 2(V_{x_u}^2) \frac{1 + K_1^2 - 2\rho K_1}{1 + K_1} \qquad (7.33)$$

For $\rho = .95$ and $K_1 = .7$ this value is $.188 V_{x_u}^2$. This is larger than the rel-variance of the ratio, x_u/y_{u-1}, obtained for a single month's sample, for which the rel-variance (from Eq. 7.27) is $.100 V_{x_u}^2$.

The rel-variance for an annual total

$$x'' = \sum_{u}^{u+11} x''_u \tag{7.34}$$

is approximately

$$V_{x''}^2 \doteq \frac{V_{x_u}^2}{144} \left[\frac{1 + K_1^2 - 2\rho K_1}{(1 - K_1)^2} \left(12 - \frac{2K_1}{1 - K_1^2} \right) + \rho_a \frac{2K_1}{1 - K_1^2} \right] \tag{7.35}$$

where ρ_a is an average correlation between months that are separated by 12 months, and would be zero if a new independent area sample were selected each year instead of reusing the same month's sample every 12 months.

If $\rho = .95$ and $\rho_a = .8$, then, for $K_1 = .7$, we have $V_{x''}^2 = 1.6 V_{x'}^2$, which represents an increase of 60 per cent over the rel-variance of x'.

The rel-variance of the ratio of one month's sales to the sales of the same month a year ago is approximately

$$\frac{V_{x_u}^2}{1 - K_1^2} [2(1 + K_1^2 - 2\rho K_1) - 2\rho_a(1 - K_1)^2] \tag{7.36}$$

Table 10.   Comparison of various estimates of change and level for specified weights when $\rho = .95$ and $\rho_a = .80$

K_1	K_2	Ratios of rel-variances of the estimates indicated to the rel-variance of x_u			
		Monthly total x''_u	Ratio of successive months x''_u/x''_{u-1}	Ratio of month to month a year ago x''_u/x''_{u-12}	Annual total x''
0	1.0	1.00	2.00	.40	.083
.1	.9	.83	1.49	.35	.084
.2	.8	.69	1.10	.31	.085
.3	.7	.57	.80	.28	.087
.4	.6	.48	.57	.27	.091
.5	.5	.40	.40	.27	.096
.6	.4	.34	.28	.29	.107
.7	.3	.31	.19	.35	.130
.8	.2	.33	.13	.49	.181
1.0	0	*	.10	1.20	*

* These values depend on u and become indefinitely large as months pass and u increases.

Table 10 compares the variances of various estimates of change and level in the special case when $\rho = .95$ and $\rho_a = .80$.   A similar table could be made up for other values. All the numbers in the table are computed relative to $V^2_{x_u}$, the rel-variance of the simple unbiased monthly estimate. Remark 8 below indicates how results summarized as in Table 10 can be used in choosing values of K_1 and K_2 when one is interested simultaneously in estimates of level, change from the preceding month, and change from the corresponding month a year ago.

> **Remark 6.** The weighted estimate (Eq. 7.29) gives the simple chained estimate as a special case when $K_1 = 1$, and the rel-variances given in the last row of Table 10 are those for the simple chained estimate. Note that in all cases but two the rel-variance of this estimate becomes indefinitely large as u increases, unless adjustments to annual totals or other adjustments are made to keep the simple chained estimate from drifting too far out of line. For the ratio of one month's sales to those for the preceding month, however, this estimate has the minimum variance. This demonstrates, again, that change is effectively measured with an identical sample.
>
> **Remark 7.** The weighted estimate (Eq. 7.29) gives the simple unbiased estimate as a special case when $K_1 = 0$, and the rel-variances in the first row of Table 10 are those for the simple unbiased estimate. The simple unbiased estimate gives the best results, as compared with the weighted estimates, for the annual total. It is interesting to note that, whereas the simple unbiased estimate for a month has 3 times the variance of the weighted estimate when $K_1 = .7$, the annual total of the weighted estimates has a larger variance than the annual total of simple unbiased estimates. This is so because the 12 simple unbiased estimates are independent, whereas the weighted estimates are not.
>
> **Remark 8.** The weighted estimate (Eq. 7.29) has its minimum variance when $K_1 = .72$, and the variance is close to its minimum value when $K_1 = .6-.8$. The year-to-year-change estimate is near the minimum for $K_1 = .3-.6$, although this estimate is not sensitive to the value of K_1 provided that K_1 is not close to 1. The estimate of the annual total is best for $K_1 = 0$, but the increased variance for K_1 larger than 0 is not substantial until K_1 exceeds .6 or .7. The month-to-month change has its smallest variance when $K_1 = 1$, and its variance gets particularly large for K_1 between 0 and .4. These considerations suggest that, if one is interested in all these types of estimates, with perhaps particular emphasis on monthly level and annual level, a value of K_1 in the neighborhood of .6 or .7 will be near the optimum for the assumed values of ρ and ρ_a. The value of K_1 might be made somewhat larger if major emphasis was on month-to-month change.
>
> **Remark 9.** Although simple unbiased estimates and ratios of them were used in the weighted estimate given above, other estimates would have been suitable.
>
> **Remark 10.** The estimate of change used in the weighted estimate could have been based on a difference estimate instead of a ratio estimate. The estimate for the uth month would then be

$$x'''_u = K_1(x'''_{u-1} + x_u - y_{u-1}) + K_2 x_u \qquad (7.37)$$

The theory would have been similar to that given above.

Remark 11. An estimate similar to the weighted estimate given by Eq. 7.29 has been adopted for the retail trade survey discussed in Ch. 12, Case Study A, with $K_1 = .7$, and is now in effect.

REFERENCES FOR SEC. 7

(1) R. J. Jessen, "Statistical Investigation of a Sample Survey for Obtaining Farm Facts," *Iowa Agr. Exp. Sta. Res. Bull.* 304, 1942.

(2) H. D. Patterson, "Sampling on Successive Occasions with Partial Replacement of Units," *J. Roy. Stat. Soc.*, Series B, **12** (1950), 241–255.

8. Systematic sampling. The selection of every kth unit of some type from a list has been suggested as a method of sample selection at a number of points in earlier chapters (Sec. 18 of Ch. 1, Sec. 3 of Ch. 3, Sec. 4 of Ch. 6, and Sec. 6 and 8 of Ch. 8). It was suggested, also, that often, in sample surveys for measuring social and economic characteristics, systematic selection of units will approximate simple random selection of such units within strata. Since both considerable gains and considerable losses may sometimes result from systematic sampling, it is important for the investigator to recognize situations where systematic sampling may lead to substantially smaller or substantially larger variances than will alternative random selection methods.

In choosing a sample of 1 unit in k, one can take a random number between 1 and k as the starting number, and take every kth unit thereafter, or start at the middle of the first k units and take every kth unit thereafter. In practice, it usually makes little difference whether a random start or a central start is used. However, if the sample consists of a number of small systematic samples, a random or rotating start is preferable. For example, if a sample of blocks is selected and if a subsample of dwelling units from the selected blocks is obtained by listing the dwelling units on each block, starting with a corner house and then using the central start on each block, the corner houses will be under-represented. In such a case it is desirable either to carry over the numbering from one block to another or to assign random or rotating starting numbers to the blocks (see also Ch. 8, p. 349).

If the sample is selected from data in which there is a marked trend or regression of the variable being sampled on the order in which the units appear on the list, the central start is to be preferred. Yates (1, 2) suggests as another alternative for data in which there is a marked trend the use of a random start with end corrections. Suppose that the elements of the population are $X_1, \cdots, X_N$, and that the sample was obtained by taking 1 in k, beginning with b, where b was chosen at random. Then the estimate of the $\bar{X} = \Sigma X_i/N$ with end corrections is

$$\bar{x} = \frac{w_1 x_1 + x_2 + x_3 + \cdots + x_{n-1} + w_n x_n}{n}$$

where

$$w_1 = \frac{b + (k-1)/2}{k}$$

and

$$w_n = \frac{N - b - k(n-1) + (k+1)/2}{k}$$

End corrections will be helpful if the trend in the data is sufficiently marked that the average change in level (due to the trend) per interval of k units is large in relation to the standard error of $\bar{x}$ (see Eq. 8.1 or 8.3 for an estimate of $V_{\bar{x}}$).

Some disadvantages of systematic selection. There are some dangers in systematic sampling. Perhaps most important is its use with data that are periodic in relation to the order of the listing, if the interval between sample elements is equal to the period or a multiple of it. If, for example, blocks are systematically laid out and numbered in a city, a systematic selection may end up with all selected blocks being in a line, and result in a considerable increase in the variance of the sample estimate. Again, one may need a sample of observations spread over time, and make a systematic selection of points or intervals in time for making the observations. This may be an exceedingly effective method, as is suggested below, but care must be exercised in watching for the possibility of periods (such as of temperatures in a 24-hour period or activity on different days of the week) that may make systematic sampling inefficient.

In practice it is safe to use systematic sampling only when one is sufficiently acquainted with the data to be able to demonstrate that periodicities do not exist, or that the interval between the elements of the sample is not a multiple or submultiple of the period. The risk with systematic sampling from a population with periodicities is particularly serious because the sample itself may give no indication of the periodicity. This type of problem never arises in nonsystematic random sampling, since the sampling variance will reflect any variations that exist in the population. The risk with systematic selection can be reduced, also, if the sample is drawn by making a number of distinct systematic selections from different strata.

Advantages of systematic selection. An advantage of systematic selection is its simplicity. Another advantage is that, except for populations with the periodicities just described, systematic sampling variances are often somewhat smaller than those for alternative designs. Sometimes they are much smaller than the variances for random selection of units within strata, even with stratification to the point that only one unit is included in the sample from a stratum.

The greatest reduction in variance occurs when there is a high correlation between adjacent units on the list, of the characteristics being measured, the serial correlations decreasing as the interval between units increases. If the serial correlations of near-by units are high enough, with decreasing correlations between units farther apart, there may be striking gains by systematic selection. Such serial correlations are frequently found for phenomena that vary with time. Illustrations of such phenomena are the prices of stocks on different hours or days, temperatures, and measurements that depend on the fertility of the soil, such as plant coverage of an area.

Often, in sampling for economic and social characteristics, the serial correlations of near-by units on the list from which the sample is selected are not high enough for systematic selection to reduce the variance substantially, but they may be high enough for economic or social characteristics such as farm or nonfarm residence.

Illustrations 8.1–8.5 give examples of a number of cases where the effect of systematic sampling is not substantial, and a few where it is.

Estimating variances with systematic sampling. A consistent estimate of the variance is not available for a systematic sample drawn with a single random start. Some approximate estimates will be given that are good for many of the problems for which systematic selection is used in surveys, i.e., when there are no periodicities and the serial correlations are not high between adjacent or near-by units in the order of selection. They may give substantial overestimates of the variances for cases where there are no periodicities and the serial correlations of near-by units are high. The variance estimates suggested will be reasonably close for many applications that have been discussed, as is indicated later in the illustrations. There appears to be little problem in using methods that yield moderate over-estimates of the variances.

A very simple estimate of the variance is made by regarding each unit as selected at random from a stratum, grouping some of the strata, and proceeding with a grouped stratum variance estimate as discussed in Sec. 13 of Ch. 10. This variance estimate will be acceptable in a great many problems. If desired, it can be extended to the random group method discussed in Sec. 16 of Ch. 10.

A special case of the grouped stratum estimate is to group only pairs of strata; thus the estimate will reflect as much of the stratification as possible. The precision of the estimate from a sample of a given size is increased if the grouping is extended to all possible pairs of contiguous strata. Then an estimate of the rel-variance of $r = x/y$ is given by

$$v_r^2 = \frac{1-f}{n}\left[\frac{\sum\limits^{n-1}(x_i - x_{i+1})^2}{2(n-1)\bar{x}^2} + \frac{\sum\limits^{n-1}(y_i - y_{i+1})^2}{2(n-1)\bar{y}^2} - \frac{\sum\limits^{n-1}(x_i - x_{i+1})(y_i - y_{i+1})}{(n-1)\bar{x}\bar{y}}\right] \qquad (8.1)$$

Thus, suppose for simplicity, that there are only five observations in the sample, x_1, x_2, x_3, x_4, and x_5. The first term in brackets of Eq. 8.1 will be

$$\frac{\sum\limits^{n-1}(x_i - x_{i+1})^2}{2(n-1)\bar{x}^2} = \frac{(x_1 - x_2)^2 + (x_2 - x_3)^2 + (x_3 - x_4)^2 + (x_4 - x_5)^2}{2(5-1)\bar{x}^2}$$

This particular estimate is not based on $(n-1)$ degrees of freedom, but is a more reliable estimate than would be obtained by grouping strata into $n/2$ nonoverlapping pairs and employing the usual stratified sampling variance estimate based on $n/2$ degrees of freedom.

Yates (2) suggests another estimate that will be less of an overestimate than 8.1. Instead of taking successive differences as in the preceding estimate, he takes *balanced differences* of the type

$$d_X = \tfrac{1}{2}x_1 - x_2 + x_3 - x_4 + x_5 - x_6 + x_7 - x_8 + \tfrac{1}{2}x_9 \qquad (8.2)$$

Overlapping balanced differences can be taken by beginning successively with x_1, x_2, x_3, etc.; or, if the sample is large, a satisfactory procedure will be to overlap only the end terms, with the last term of one difference the same as the first term of the next one. In either event, the estimate of the rel-variance of $r = x/y$ is given by

$$v_r^2 = \left(\frac{1-f}{n}\right)\left[\frac{\sum d_X^2}{t(7.5)} + \frac{\sum d_Y^2}{t(7.5)} - 2\frac{\sum d_X d_Y}{t(7.5)}\right] \qquad (8.3)$$

where t balanced differences are formed. The 7.5 in the denominator is the sum of squares of the coefficients of x_1 to x_9 in Eq. 8.2, and will be different with a different number of terms. If fewer than 30–50 non-overlapping (except for end terms) differences can be formed, the use of overlapping differences will increase the precision of the estimate but not in proportion to the increase in t.

In instances where serial correlations of adjacent and near-by units are high, Eq. 8.3 may give a considerably smaller variance estimate than Eq. 8.1 and still may be a substantial overestimate of the systematic sampling variance. If a closer variance estimate is wanted, it is necessary to use supplemental samples. Yates (1) gives some estimates from supplemental samples and some illustrations and also suggests some additional considerations in two-dimensional systematic sampling. Some of the illustrations below suggest that the problem is not serious in many common survey problems.

Exercises

8.1. From the following sample of 10 farms drawn by a systematic sampling method, compute an estimate of the rel-variance, using Eq. 8.1, for the per cent having a telephone and the number of cows milked.

DESIGNATION OF SAMPLE OBSERVATION i	FIRST CHARACTERISTIC $X_{hi} = 1$ if have a telephone, 0 if not	SECOND CHARACTERISTIC $X_{hi} =$ number of cows milked
1	1	0
2	1	1
3	1	2
4	0	1
5	0	0
6	0	2
7	0	1
8	0	1
9	1	1
10	0	3
Totals　10	4	12

8.2. Using the variance estimate obtained in Ex. 8.1, compute the estimate of the rel-variance that would result from a sample of 300 (assuming that the rel-variance between farms is not changed substantially by the greater number of strata with a larger systematic selection).

8.3. Compute a variance estimate as in Ex. 8.1, but use Eq. 8.3 to estimate the variance. Use 5 terms instead of 9 in the balanced differences, and use overlapping differences. Note that with 5 terms the 7.5 in Eq. 8.2 changes to 3.5.

Illustration 8.1. (*Data from an unpublished study by W. E. Deming and B. J. Tepping.*) In the 1940 Census of Population a systematic sample of 1 in 20 was taken. In this case the sampling procedure did not involve taking equal intervals of 20, but did involve a systematic sampling pattern with an average interval of 20.* Estimates were made from this sample of many characteristics a number of months in advance of the time that complete census results would be available. A large number

---

* An ingenious systematic sample design by Frederick F. Stephan. See Frederick F. Stephan, W. Edwards Deming, and Morris H. Hansen, "The Sampling Procedure of the 1940 Population Census," *J. Amer. Stat. Assn.*, **35** (1940), 615–630.

of comparisons have been made of the advance estimates with the complete census results published subsequently, by computing

$$d = \frac{(x' - X)}{\sigma}$$

where x' is the advance estimate of a total from the systematic sample, X is the final census figure, and σ is the standard deviation of a preliminary sample estimate based on a simple random sample of the same size as the systematic sample on which x' is based. The expected average value of the d so computed would be equal to 0, and its variance would be 1, if the sample yielded unbiased estimates, and if the systematic sampling variance were precisely represented by the computed variance (i.e., if the sampling is indeed equivalent to simple random sampling and there is no gain or loss whatever by stratification or by systematic sampling within strata). The average values, the variances, and the mean square errors actually observed over a set of 188 independent estimates for each of nine different characteristics are summarized in Table 11. The different estimates are for individual cities of 100,000 or more population, for the urban population outside of cities of 100,000 or more in each state, and for the rural population of each state.

Table 11. Comparison of advance systematic sample estimates with complete census results—1940

Characteristic	Mean square* error $\frac{\Sigma d^2}{188}$	Variance* $\frac{\Sigma(d-\bar{d})^2}{188}$	Mean $\bar{d} = \frac{\Sigma d}{188}$
Male population	1.3	1.2	.3
White population	.4	.4	.0
Population 25–44	.9	.8	.2
Population 65 and over	.9	.8	− .3
Population 14 and over	1.3	1.1	− .4
Persons in labor force	1.4	1.4	.1
Employed persons (except public emergency work)	1.6	1.6	.4
Persons on public emergency work	3.7	1.9	− 1.3
Persons seeking work	1.0	1.0	.2

* These estimates of the mean square error and variance have a standard deviation of about .1.

It will be observed that, although the variance of d for some of the items is less than 1, for most of them it exceeds 1. For the estimate of the white population, it seems reasonable to expect a comparatively high correlation between neighboring units within a large population. For such an item, computation of the variance under the assumption that each successive pair of observations was selected at random from a stratum (Eq. 8.1) no doubt would have yielded a considerably smaller variance than the one computed under the assumption of simple random sampling. The results for nonwhite in Illustration 8.3, and for farm residents in Illustration 8.2, suggest that even this computation would still be a marked overstatement of the variance with systematic sampling. The fact that the estimated variance of d exceeds 1 in most instances indicates a somewhat greater variability between the advance sample estimates and the final census results than would occur with simple random sampling. The excess of the variance over 1 arises because there are certain biases in the sample estimates due to (1) some important differences in the processing of the preliminary sample and the complete census results, and (2) biases in the selection of the sample. Any gains due to stratification were too small to offset such biases.

It should be clear that the method of sample selection was not a random method, and that the method is to be distinguished from selection of every kth unit from a list *after* the list has been prepared. In this illustration, sample designations were made by enumerators at the same time the list was being prepared (i.e., at the time the census was being taken). The enumerator made various decisions as to the order of enumeration in preparing the lists and had opportunities to violate or misunderstand instructions in such a way as to introduce more or less serious biases. Nevertheless, the few comparatively large departures from expected variances shown in the table were not due primarily to biases in sample selection. The sample was published on the basis of preliminary returns without any editing whatever, whereas the final figures were edited, so that items affected significantly by editing should show large discrepancies between preliminary and final figures. The editing had a particularly large effect on certain labor force items, especially in connection with emergency workers and employment, and these are the ones with large discrepancies in the table.

By and large, allowing for the biases and discrepancies mentioned above, the evidence supports the presumption of comparatively small gains due either to systematic sampling or to stratification, for most population items, as well as comparatively small biases in the selection of the sample simultaneously with the preparation of the list.

Illustration 8.2.* In another study by B. J. Tepping and Alice Kaitz a comparison was made of systematic sampling of 1 person in 4 in order of enumeration in a special census, with simple random sampling of 1

---

* An unpublished study in the U.S. Bureau of the Census.

person within each successive set of 4 persons in order of enumeration. The results for Carroll County, Ky., are summarized in Table 12.

Table 12. Comparison of systematic sampling with stratified random sampling in Carroll County, Ky.

Characteristic	Proportion of population having characteristic	Rel-variances for		Ratio of rel-variances: systematic to stratified random
		Systematic sample of 1 in 4	Stratified sample of 1 random selection from each set of 4	
Living on farm	.48	.0000089	.000024	.38
Under 5 years	.081	.0028	.0036	.78
5–14 years	.18	.0016	.0013	1.23
15–34 years	.32	.00063	.00070	.90
35–64 years	.31	.00063	.00070	.90
65 and over	.10	.0021	.0027	.78
Attending school	.19	.0011	.0012	.92
Employed	.31	.00071	.00079	.90
Unemployed	.058	.0071	.0052	1.37

The results in the table are subject to fairly large sampling errors, so that rather wide differences are expected. It is seen that for most of the results the observed variance for systematic sampling and that for stratified sampling are not widely different. For farm residence the systematic sample shows considerable gains, as might be anticipated, since such an item has high correlation between adjacent persons: all members of a household will have the same farm residence status, and also adjacent households commonly have the same status.

Illustration 8.3. (*Data from an unpublished study in the Bureau of the Census by J. Steinberg.*) For many population characteristics, information in the 1950 Census was obtained on a 20 per cent sample. Each person was enumerated on a separate line, and the persons listed on every fifth line were in the sample. The sample was determined simultaneously with the census enumeration, as discussed in Illustration 8.1 for the 1940 Census sample. Enumeration instructions called for cyclical patterns of listing persons, with heads of households listed first in each family (and frequently listed on the first line of the schedule), followed by wives, children, etc. The cycles varied with size and membership of families. Five separate schedules were printed with the sample comprising a different set of lines on each version. These schedules were rotated in various systematic ways.

The final sample was effectively a systematic sample within strata, each stratum being the set of 30 lines on a printed schedule. Variances of selected characteristics for this sample are compared to those that would arise from the use of simple random sampling of schedule lines with no stratification. The comparisons in Table 13 were estimated from a sample of 225 areas. The sample variances are for items covered on the complete census, and the systematic sampling variances were computed from 5 possible 1-in-5 samples in each area. There was no evidence of any substantial bias in the actual systematic selections made by the enumerators.

Table 13. Estimated ratios of variance of 20 per cent 1950 population census sample and 20 per cent simple random sample

Characteristic	Per cent of population	$\dfrac{\text{Systematic variance}}{\text{Simple random variance}}$
Total persons	100.0	.53
Nonwhites	9.5	.14
Household heads	29.4	1.10
Persons 30–34 years of age	7.8	1.07
At work during week preceding census	34.8	1.00
Number of craftsmen, foremen, and kindred workers	5.9	.96
Number in transportation, communication, and other public utilities	2.8	1.16

The variance in estimating total persons from a simple random sample arises because between 15 and 20 per cent of the lines were blank and a high proportion of the filled lines were compact on a sheet. Systematic selection has a marked advantage in this case (it is clear that there is, then, a high serial correlation with respect to whether or not a line is filled). As was the case for whites in Illustration 8.1, the variance of the estimate for nonwhite with systematic sampling is much smaller than that with simple random sampling. Here, too, the high serial correlation of this characteristic accounts for the large reduction in variance. Again, the use of Eq. 8.1 might have accounted for an important part of the difference. For the other items the application of a simple or stratified random variance formula would have given highly satisfactory results.

Illustration 8.4. A study by Osborne (3) of sampling errors of cover-type areas points to the conclusion that treating a systematic sample as though it were a simple or stratified random sample may lead to a very considerable overestimate of the sampling error. The proportion of land devoted to each of several purposes in an area 28 × 30 miles in California was estimated by the use of 20 sets of 30 lines 1 mile apart, and also by 20 random samples, chosen in several ways. The variances with the 20 systematic samples are consistently very substantially lower than those for random samples, as shown in Table 14.

Table 14. Comparison of variances of sample totals for four major types of land use (thousands of chains squared)

Type of land use	Variances		
	Systematic sample of 30 lines	Stratified random— 15 strata with 2 lines per stratum	Completely random sample of 30 lines
Cultivated	78	318	2893
Shrub	85	229	2592
Grass	11	41	175
Woodland	12	24	50

The table indicates that the systematic sampling variance is much smaller than that for either stratified random or simple random sampling, and that taking the variance for 2 per stratum as an estimate of the systematic sampling variance would have yielded overestimates of the variance by a factor of 2 to 4.

REFERENCES FOR SEC. 8

(1) F. Yates, "Systematic Sampling," *Phil. Trans. Roy. Soc.*, Series A, **241** (1948), 345–377.
(2) F. Yates, *Sampling Methods for Censuses and Surveys*, Charles Griffin and Company, London, 1949.
(3) James G. Osborne, "Sampling Errors of Systematic and Random Surveys of Cover-type Areas," *J. Amer. Stat. Assn.*, **37** (1942), 256–264.
(4) W. G. Cochran, *Sampling Techniques*, John Wiley & Sons, New York, 1953, Chapter 8.
(5) L. H. Madow, "Systematic Sampling and Its Relation to Other Sampling Designs," *J. Amer. Stat. Assn.*, **41** (1946), 204–217.
(6) W. G. Madow and L. H. Madow, "On the Theory of Systematic Sampling, I," *Annals Math. Stat.*, **15** (1944), 1–24.
(7) W. G. Madow, "On the Theory of Systematic Sampling, II," *Annals Math. Stat.*, **20** (1949), 333–354.
(8) W. R. Buckland, "A Review of the Literature of Systematic Sampling," *J. Roy. Stat. Soc.*, Series B, **13** (1951), 208–215.

9. Variances of sums, differences, products, and ratios of two or more random variables. Often one is interested in the difference, sum, ratio, product, or other function of some estimated means, totals, or other random variables computed from a sample. The ratios of random variables and the sum of random variables already have been used considerably. Following is a summary of some relationships for convenient reference.

Let $u_1, u_2, \cdots, u_k$ denote k random variables. For example, u_i may be a mean, total, etc., estimated from a sample. Let $\sigma_{u_i}^2$ be the variance of u_i; and $\sigma_{u_i u_j} = \rho_{u_i u_j} \sigma_{u_i} \sigma_{u_j}$ be the covariance of u_i and u_j. For the cases given here it will be assumed that u_i is a consistent estimate of U_i.

(1) *Sums or differences of random variables.* If

$$u - v = \sum_i^k u_i - \sum_i^j v_i = (u_1 + u_2 + \cdots + u_k) - (v_1 + v_2 + \cdots + v_j)$$

is the sum of k random variables minus the sum of j random variables, then

$$\sigma_{u-v}^2 = (\sigma_{u_1}^2 + \sigma_{u_2}^2 + \cdots + \sigma_{u_k}^2) + (\sigma_{v_1}^2 + \sigma_{v_2}^2 + \cdots + \sigma_{v_j}^2)$$
$$+ 2(\sigma_{u_1 u_2} + \sigma_{u_1 u_3} + \cdots + \sigma_{u_{k-1} u_k})$$
$$+ 2(\sigma_{v_1 v_2} + \sigma_{v_1 v_3} + \cdots + \sigma_{v_{j-1} v_j})$$
$$- 2(\sigma_{u_1 v_1} + \sigma_{u_1 v_2} + \cdots + \sigma_{u_k v_j}) \qquad (9.1)$$

For the special case for two variables ($k = 2, j = 0$) this becomes

$$\sigma_{u_1 + u_2}^2 = \sigma_{u_1}^2 + \sigma_{u_2}^2 + 2\sigma_{u_1 u_2} \qquad (9.2)$$

For $k = 1, j = 1$, we have

$$\sigma_{u_1 - u_2}^2 = \sigma_{u_1}^2 + \sigma_{u_2}^2 - 2\sigma_{u_1 u_2} \qquad (9.3)$$

(2) *Product of random variables.* If

$$p = (u_1)(u_2) \cdots (u_k)$$

is an estimate of $\Pi = U_1 U_2 \cdots U_k$, then, approximately

$$\sigma_p^2 \doteq \Pi^2 \left(\frac{\sigma_{u_1}^2}{U_1^2} + \frac{\sigma_{u_2}^2}{U_2^2} + \cdots + \frac{\sigma_{u_k}^2}{U_k^2} + 2 \frac{\sigma_{u_1 u_2}}{U_1 U_2} \right.$$
$$\left. + 2 \frac{\sigma_{u_1 u_3}}{U_1 U_3} + \cdots + 2 \frac{\sigma_{u_{k-1} u_k}}{U_{k-1} U_k} \right) \qquad (9.4)$$

For the special case when $k = 2$, this becomes

$$\sigma_{u_1 u_2}^2 \doteq (U_1 U_2)^2 \left(\frac{\sigma_{u_1}^2}{U_1^2} + \frac{\sigma_{u_2}^2}{U_2^2} + \frac{2\sigma_{u_1 u_2}}{U_1 U_2} \right) \qquad (9.5)$$

The variance of a product as given above in Eq. 9.4 and 9.5 omits some terms that are negligible when the u_i are based on large enough samples.

(3) *Product of k random variables divided by the product of j random variables.*

Let

$$r \doteq \frac{(u_1)(u_2) \cdots (u_k)}{(v_1)(v_2) \cdots (v_j)}$$

and

$$R = \frac{(U_1) \cdots (U_k)}{(V_1) \cdots (V_j)}$$

Then, approximately,

$$
\begin{aligned}
\sigma_r^2 \doteq R^2 \Bigg[&\left(\frac{\sigma_{u_1}^2}{U_1^2} + \frac{\sigma_{u_2}^2}{U_2^2} + \cdots + \frac{\sigma_{u_k}^2}{U_k^2} \right) + \left(\frac{\sigma_{v_1}^2}{V_1^2} + \frac{\sigma_{v_2}^2}{V_2^2} + \cdots + \frac{\sigma_{v_j}^2}{V_j^2} \right) \\
&+ 2 \left(\frac{\sigma_{u_1 u_2}}{U_1 U_2} + \frac{\sigma_{u_1 u_3}}{U_1 U_3} + \cdots + \frac{\sigma_{u_{k-1} u_k}}{U_{k-1} U_k} \right) \\
&+ 2 \left(\frac{\sigma_{v_1 v_2}}{V_1 V_2} + \frac{\sigma_{v_1 v_3}}{V_1 V_3} + \cdots + \frac{\sigma_{v_{j-1} v_j}}{V_{j-1} V_j} \right) \\
&- 2 \left(\frac{\sigma_{u_1 v_1}}{U_1 V_1} + \frac{\sigma_{u_1 v_2}}{U_1 V_2} + \cdots + \frac{\sigma_{u_k v_j}}{U_k V_j} \right) \Bigg]
\end{aligned}
\tag{9.6}
$$

The approximation will be good provided the random variables are based on large enough samples.

In the special case when $k = 1$ and $j = 1$ we have

$$\sigma_r^2 = \frac{U^2}{V^2} \left(\frac{\sigma_u^2}{U^2} + \frac{\sigma_v^2}{V^2} - 2 \frac{\sigma_{uv}}{UV} \right) \tag{9.7}$$

which has been used widely throughout this volume. Conditions when this approximation is good have been discussed in Ch. 4, Sec. 18.

CHAPTER 12

Case Studies—Designs and Results of Some Actual Sample Surveys

Several reports on actual sample surveys or studies are summarized below. They illustrate many of the sampling principles that have been presented and indicate how special extensions of methods and theory may be introduced to deal with particular problems. Also, the empirical results presented on variances and costs may be helpful in survey designs in related fields. Some of the studies show the intimate relationship between considerations of sampling errors and other errors in surveys and indicate how such considerations affect survey design.

Case Studies A and B are descriptions of surveys covering large areas and based on samples that are, though large, a relatively small proportion of the populations they represent. While they illustrate, in particular, the sampling principles discussed in Chapter 9, they also illustrate applications of many of the other important principles that have been discussed, including sampling from local communities, area sampling, list sampling, joint use of mail and interviews, sampling for time series, definition of sampling units and of strata, and optimum allocation to strata and to different stages of sampling. Case Studies C and D contain data on estimation methods and variances for some different populations. Case Study E illustrates the use of sample verification methods for the control of quality in processing statistical data from large-scale surveys and censuses and also illustrates the application of sample survey principles to quality control operations.

The case studies are based on relatively large-scale surveys in order to illustrate a number of different principles. However, selected parts of these studies, such as sampling from a single county or city, are illustrative of simpler small-scale surveys to which the sampling principles are equally applicable.

Many additional applications of sampling to practical problems in various subject fields and various parts of the world could be cited. For these, the reader is referred to published bibliographies on sampling. (See, for example, Reference 3, Ch. 1, p. 55.)

The reports in this chapter are modifications of reports published by the U.S. Bureau of the Census, and the sample design work on these projects is the joint work of members of the Statistical Methods Staff of the Census Bureau. The indicated authors have written the reports and have had special responsibilities in connection with the projects to which the reports relate.

A. THE SAMPLE SURVEY OF RETAIL STORES*

1. Objectives of the sample survey.   This survey was designed to produce estimates of the annual dollar volume of sales of independent retail stores in the United States and of the distribution of this volume of sales by the different major kinds of business such as food stores, eating and drinking places, and furniture stores.

Another important purpose is to measure the percentage change in the volume of sales from month to month and year to year for all stores and for stores in each kind of business.   Still another purpose is the measurement of the percentage change in the dollar volume of sales from one month to the same month a year later for all stores and for those in the major kinds of business.   All estimates were to be evaluated in terms of their sampling errors, and the survey was to be designed so as to make it possible to produce estimates of these sampling errors.

2. Some characteristics of retail trade that affect the survey design.   It will be worth while first to outline some of the characteristics of retailers and to list the resources of the Census Bureau which had an important bearing on the sample design.

a. Skewness of the distribution of sales.   Figure 4 in Ch. 4 (p. 143), taken from the 1939 Census of Business, illustrates the skewness of the distribution of retail stores.

In 1939, the number of "establishments" (i.e., retail stores as distinct from retail organizations, which may operate a number of stores) which did over $300,000 worth of business was 8000 or .5 per cent of the total number of establishments, yet the sales of this group accounted for 21 per cent of sales of all stores.   The rel-variance of all stores, when this group is included, is nearly 50; whereas the rel-variance when these few are excluded in less than 1.

Efficient sample design takes advantage of this skewness.   A properly designed sample will include a high proportion of all stores over a certain size (unless the unit cost of their inclusion is excessive).   The size of an efficient sample so chosen will be many times smaller than the size of a simple random sample which would yield the same reliability of results but which did not take into account the skewness of the population.

b. High turnover in retail stores.   The population of retail stores is ever-changing, with appreciable numbers of stores going out of business,

---

* By Max A. Bershad, Bureau of the Census.   This study refers to the survey design as it was in 1949.   Since that time changes have taken place.   Most of these changes are outlined in Sec. A–12 as "Future developments and improvements."

many new businesses starting, and even more businesses changing hands. In a small-scale investigation made during the course of this sample survey, it was found that as many as 15 per cent of the proprietors in business at a particular address in one year were not in business at that address a year later.

The basic implication of this characteristic is clear—it is well-nigh impossible to construct or obtain a list of establishments which will be reasonably complete a few months after the list is compiled. Consequently, if a sample is to represent all establishments and if it is taken from such a list, it must be supplemented by a device such as an area sample to represent new stores which come into existence.

c. Extent of nonresponse.   As one might forecast, the percentage of retailers who will furnish a statistical agency with information on as intimate a matter as the dollar volume of their sales can vary from 10 per cent to almost 100 per cent, depending on the position, the ingenuity, and the resources of the agency.   In order to measure the sampling error of the final statistic it is necessary to achieve almost complete response. In other words, it will be understood, when the sample is designated, that follow-up procedures are instituted to insure that practically every member of the sample contributes its own figure; and it is also understood that the costs per unit for the inclusion of a retail store in the sample also cover the necessary costs of the follow-up.

d. Kind of business groups.   Usually (as Table A-1 illustrates) those important kinds of business which are populated by many stores are also characterized by having small average sales; and, conversely, if the number of stores in the kind of business is small, the individual stores are large in volume of sales.

Table A-1

Kind of business group	Number of stores (1939)	Average sales (1939) (dollars)
Food stores	560,549	18,134
General merchandise	50,267	112,698
Apparel	106,959	30,469
Furniture—household—radio	52,827	32,805
Automotive	60,132	92,280
Filling stations	241,858	11,668
Lumber—building—hardware	79,313	34,483
Eating and drinking places	305,386	11,526
Drugstores	57,903	26,976

From the sampling point of view, this implies that, if a stratum of large stores to be sampled 100 per cent is defined without regard to kind of business, and if an area sample is used to represent the remaining stores (those stores under the sales cut-off), then the increased number of observations in the area sample for a kind of business which is numerically large will be a partial offset to the decreased proportion of sales covered by the 100 per cent stratum.

3. The principal resources and materials available. In designing the sample, it was important to take into account the pertinent resources at the disposal of the Bureau. The following are among the important ones:

a. Field offices. At the time the sample design was considered, the Bureau had already been conducting a monthly report on the labor force. In this connection a sample of 68 areas located throughout the country had been selected and a field office had already been set up in each area. The personnel in these offices had obtained both experience in the conduct of a sample survey and a fairly extensive knowledge of the counties for which they were responsible.

b. Sanborn maps. For all cities over 25,000 in population and for some of the smaller ones, the Bureau had available up-to-date maps from the Sanborn Map Company which were so detailed as to diagram every structure in a block and to label structures which were stores or contained stores. For each such block, the Bureau had counted the number of stores and had punched cards which showed, among other characteristics of the block, the number of stores counted.

Sometimes, a city was not entirely covered by the Sanborn maps. Where this was the case, the uncovered area contained very few stores. Other types of maps showing less detail were, of course, available for these areas and, in fact, for the entire country.

c. Previous census data. The publications of the 1939 Census of Business were available, and, although several years old at the time, had much invaluable data—the national distribution of stores and of sales by sales size, the number of stores and volume of sales in every county and in every city of population of 2500 or more, the number of stores and sales of each broad kind of business in a county and of each detailed kind of business in larger areas, the number of employees, the total payroll, the number of stores and sales for each kind of business for each sales size class in the country, etc.

d. Lists of stores having employees. The Bureau of Old Age and Survivors Insurance has a record of retail organizations which employ one or more persons. These records, in addition to bearing the name of a firm and a county code for its mailing address, show quarterly payroll and the number of different employees to whom payroll payments have been made. By special arrangement these lists were made available to the Bureau of the Census.

4. The selection of the sample: selection of combined counties. As described more fully in Case Study B, the 3000 counties in the country had been combined, in order to achieve more internally heterogeneous units, into 2000 combined counties that served as primary sampling units. Each of these had then been classified into 1 of 4 groups.

Group I consisted of the 12 largest metropolitan areas. Group II consisted of the primary units which contained a city of population of 50,000 or more in 1930. Group III consisted of the primary units having less than 25 per cent of the population residing on farms and certain others having a very high in-migration rate between 1940 and 1943. Group IV consisted of all the other primary units and contained more than three-quarters of the farms and farm population of the country in 1940.

The primary units had been further classified into subgroups to form the primary strata. In group I, each metropolitan area occupied its own separate primary stratum. In groups II and III primary strata had been formed based on geographic and economic characteristics. In group IV, the primary strata were formed based on agricultural characteristics. In total, 68 primary strata were formed.

From each primary stratum 1 psu had been selected with probability proportionate to its size. This size was measured by the 1940 population in the psu.

The psu's, chosen as they had been, with known probabilities, could now be used to measure *any* characteristic. Some characteristics, however, would be measured efficiently and some not efficiently. The test of how well (i.e., with what sampling error) a sample of counties selected in this manner would measure retail sales was made (see Table A–11, columns 7 and 8, and Table A–12, column 7).

A sampling error in the neighborhood of 1 per cent for total sales and satisfactory percentage errors for other statistics could be anticipated, as shown by the test. Since another design which might reduce this sampling error somewhat would entail the large costs involved in setting up and maintaining new field offices and would consequently increase the sampling error per dollar expended, these areas constituted an efficient probability sample for the retail survey as well as for population, and were adopted.

5. Selection of the sample: selection of a specified list within each primary sampling unit. The sample was limited to stores in the selected combined counties (psu's), and by this token the sampling errors cannot be smaller than the errors that would have resulted from enumerating these psu's completely.

Since the selected psu's include over 30 per cent of the retailers in the country, their complete enumeration would obviously be neither feasible nor desirable, so that the problem was to select a sample *within* each selected combined county which would be close to the optimum for the county, bearing in mind the nature of the list which was available.

The principle of optimum allocation of a fixed size of sample to different size-of-establishment strata, coupled with the observed fact that the coefficients of variation are roughly constant from stratum to stratum, leads to a useful rule that can be applied where the unit costs of collection are not strikingly different from stratum to stratum. This rule (discussed in Ch. 5, Sec. 10–11) is to include in the sample all the stores whose estimated size is equal to the total sales of the universe divided by the total size of sample to be used, and if only a few sampling fractions are being used, all stores somewhat smaller than this.

Using 1939 data, total national sales were divided by the first approximation of the sample size to be used. This quotient was then converted to its estimated equivalent in terms of 1944 quarterly payroll. The result was lowered to make allowance for the facts that (i) only two sampling fractions were used within a psu, and therefore the limit should be lowered; (ii) some important kinds of business have lower averages than the over-all average for all kinds of business combined; (iii) application of the rule for each psu would yield lower cut-offs, since most of the within-psu sampling fractions are larger than the over-all sampling fraction; and (iv) at the time it appeared that the survey could carry a specified list of about 45,000 firms.

On the basis of the above, retail firms which had quarterly payrolls of $1400 or more according to the records of the Old Age and Survivors Insurance Bureau and whose addresses on those records were located in any of the sample psu's were included in the survey if, on subsequent interview, it was found that the nature of their business was within the scope of the survey. This list of firms was to be surveyed monthly by mail. An area sample was to be taken of firms not on the list, so that every firm within a psu would have a probability of selection and this probability would be known—being unity (within the psu) if on the list, and being the probability of selection of the area sample segment in which the firm was located if the firm was not on the list.

It is appropriate at this time to note that the manner in which the list is constructed or designated will never result in a bias provided that it is unrelated to the selection of the area segments. The manner in which the list is designated will, however, have an effect on the sampling error, and in this particular case the sampling error is decreased to the extent that payroll distinguishes larger from smaller stores.

After selection of the basic list, supplementations within the combined counties were made.   First, were added, from the Old Age and Survivors Bureau's records, the large "births" which had taken place since the first quarter of 1944.   Second, the firms in the 1939 Census of Business which were not already included and which had sales of $500,000 in that year were added.   Third, were added lists of large firms compiled locally in each psu by the field supervisor.   The lists consisted of what the supervisor believed to be the largest stores in each of selected kinds of business. The number of such large stores depended on the size of the psu and the kind of business.

The total number of cases involved in this supplementation was small compared to the original size of the specified list.   Nevertheless, to make room for them and to reduce the size of the original list, certain firms had to be dropped.

Accordingly, the "cut-offs" were now refined and were computed in terms of sales, for each psu, for each kind of business.

The first priority on dropping firms from the specified list was for those whose sales were under the cut-offs and who had poor histories on filing reports.   These were the most expensive firms to carry.   The second priority was for firms under the cut-off with good reporting histories.

The specified list (see Sec. A–12) is being and will be amended in the future, too, as more complete lists of larger firms become available, with a view toward reducing the sampling errors that arise from the selection of stores within each psu.

6. Selection of the sample: selection within psu's of stores not on the specified list.   On the basis of joint considerations of *a priori* estimates of the sampling error and of funds available, and considerations of optimum allocation of the sample, it was decided to have a sample of stores in the psu not on the specified list, approximately equal to 2 per cent of the number of such stores in the primary stratum from which the psu was selected (and therefore 2 per cent of the number of such stores in the country).   Since it was impossible to have foreknowledge of exactly which stores were not on the list, field work involving the listing of such stores was obviously required.   However, if such listings were made monthly on an extensive scale (with the intention of subsampling), high listing costs would result and the listings would quickly become obsolete because of the high turnover of businesses.

It was therefore decided to choose the sample by selecting randomly with known probabilities very small pieces of land from all the land within the combined county, and then to enumerate all retailers within the chosen pieces of land who are not members of the specified list. The probability of selection of any given store is then the probability of selecting the land on which the store is located.

These small pieces of land will be called "segments," and this part of the sample will be called the "area sample." Each segment is defined by a map which traces its boundaries, and these boundaries must, of course, be of such nature that they can be recognized in the field by any competent interviewer, so that no question arises as to whether a particular store is or is not within the segment.

If A_{hi} represents the 1940 population of psu i in primary stratum h, and A_h represents the population of the primary stratum from which it was selected, then $P_{hi} = A_{hi}/A_h$ represents the probability with which the psu was selected (see Sec. A–4). To have an over-all area sample of 2 per cent, $.02/P_{hi}$ symbolizes the probability within the psu that a store should be included in the area sample. If P_{hi} is less than .02, all the stores in the psu should be included in the sample. The extent to which P_{hi} is greater than .02, for different psu's, is the extent that the sample can also be self-weighting. (Actually, because as will be described later the area sample was divided into 12 parts, thus enabling a segment to be enumerated more than once during the year, the area sample was made self-weighting even for those combined counties for which P_{hi} was less than .02.)

Although it would be possible to select the indicated proportion of segments in each psu throughout the entire psu, the travel costs that would ensue when the segments were enumerated suggested that the segments be clustered to some extent, so that the distance between them would not be too great. Accordingly, a sample of urban places (cities of 2500 or more population) and rural territory was selected, and segments were then selected within such places.

a. The selection of cities and MCD's. To select the cities, information from the 1939 Census of Business was available on the number of stores in each urban place. A measure of size (T_j) was assigned to each city (j), equal to the number of stores in the city in 1939 divided by 50, and cities were selected with probabilities proportionate to this measure. In particular, the probability of selection within the psu of city j is equal to $.02T_j/P_{hi}$ when this expression is equal to or less than 1.

Where this probability is equal to or less than 1, the sample to be taken within the city is 1 in T_j. Where the expression exceeds 1, the sample to be taken within the city will be 1 in $P_{hi}/.02$.

At this point, it may be easily verified that .02 is the probability of selection of a segment; namely, the probability of selection of the psu, times the probability of selection within the chosen psu of the city in which it lies, times the probability of its choice within the chosen city.

It is easy to overlook, in the above, the significance of the assignment of the measure of size to each city in terms, in effect, of multiples of 50 stores. If this number were decreased to 10 stores, it is apparent that the probability of selection of a city would be increased; consequently more cities would be chosen, and the geographic spread of the sample would be wider. The 50 actually used is, then, a rough compromise between the desirability of a lower sampling variance inherent in a very widespread sample and the desirability of the lower costs of a heavily concentrated sample.

The above describes the selection of urban places (cities over 2500 in population). For places under this size and other rural territory, information was not available on the number of stores, and consequently the measures of size had to be obtained by other means. Population information was available from the 1940 Census on the number of persons in each minor civil division. This information could be broken down into the number living in (a) incorporated places of 2500 or more, (b) incorporated places of less than 2500, (c) specified unincorporated places having an estimated population of 500 or more, (d) the balance of the minor civil division (MCD).

Since urban places were being sampled separately, they had to be excluded from the measure of size (and, indeed, when later an MCD was selected, such places had to be excluded from enumeration in that MCD). The population of each place of less than 2500 and of each unincorporated place was weighted by 3 (to reflect the assumed greater concentration of retail stores per person) and added to the population of the balance of the MCD. Because there is roughly 1 store to such a weighted number of 50 people, a division of the sum by 2500 was made to furnish a measure of size roughly equivalent to the measure of size obtained for the cities where the division by 50 stores had been made.

Thus, for each MCD (excluding urban places) a measure of size T_j was obtained, and the selection made identical to that described above for the cities over 2500.

b. *The selection within cities and MCD's.* The sampling of 1 in T_j of the segments (1 in T_j will be used in this discussion, although 1 in $P_{hi}/.02$ was also employed) within each city and MCD was always done in basically the same fashion. In all cases, an effort was made to set up strata in each of which the segments would on enumeration prove to be of about equal size in terms of the number of retail stores. The extent to which this could be accomplished was directly dependent on the types of maps and materials available. The variations in method which follow arise from having different materials for different places.

(i) Cities over 25,000 for which Sanborn maps were available. Blocks in such a city which were not included among the Sanborn maps were sampled with a probability of 1 in $2T_j$, a smaller sampling ratio being used, because such blocks are generally devoid of retail stores and optimum considerations point to the use of a smaller sampling fraction. In some cities the nature of these blocks is such that 10 blocks have but 1 store. To include in the sample more blocks of this type is obviously uneconomical, yet they must be represented, for in the course of time new shopping areas can arise. The whole block became the "segment."

For blocks in the city which had been mapped by the Sanborn Map Company, punch cards were available indicating the number of store-like structures shown on the map for each block. Accordingly, the blocks were divided into 4 groups, depending on whether the number was 0, 1–9, 10–19, or 20 and over.

A sample of 1 in $2T_j$ was taken of the blocks with 0 count, and a sample of 1 in T_j was taken of the blocks with a 1–9 count. These blocks became "segments."

Each block in the 20 and over category was given a measure of size by dividing its count by 5. The blocks were then sampled with probabilities proportionate to the measure of size. Blocks so selected were "segmented," i.e., the map was divided into pieces or segments so that each contained approximately 5 store-like structures, and so that every part of the block lay in one of the segments. The dividing lines of the segments naturally had to be such that a field interviewer using the maps could distinguish where the segment began and ended. A segment (or segments) was then chosen at random such that the probability of selection of the block times the probability of selection of the segment was 1 in T_j.

Blocks in the 10–19 category were handled like those in the 20 and over category except that a selection of blocks was first made with equal probabilities. This was followed by a further selection with probability proportionate to size, and then a sample segment was taken from the block drawn for segmentation.

(ii) Cities between 7500 and 25,000. For most cities of this type, up-to-date Sanborn detail maps were usually not available. The appropriate field office was given a block map of the city and instructed to outline on the map the limits of what it considered the main shopping area of the town. A complete listing was made for every block in this shopping area. The stores listed in each block were counted; these counts were used in the same manner as the Sanborn counts, and the selection of segments was made in the same manner as described above for blocks having a 20 and over count in a Sanborn city.

Blocks outside the shopping area were selected with equal probabilities equal to 1 in $2T_j$.

(iii) Cities between 2500 and 7500.   This type of city, which usually has from 50 to 250 retail stores, could be and was listed completely by the appropriate field office and each store was spotted on the map. Segments of approximately 10 stores were then made and selected with equal probabilities equal to 1 in T_j.

(iv) Minor Civil Divisions, exclusive of cities over 2500.   County maps were available for such rural territory, most of which naturally does not have a block structure.   Each selected MCD was listed in its entirety and the stores were spotted on the county map.   The MCD was then divided into segments having approximately equal numbers of stores.   A sample was taken with equal probabilities of 1 in a multiple of T_j.

c. *The selection within cities and MCD's—other observations.*   Before we proceed it may be well to make some further observations about the selection just described.

(i) Geographic stratification of segments within a city.   In practice, whenever a sample of blocks was taken, it was always taken systematically with a random starting point, after assigning a serial number to each block to denote the first, second, third, etc.   Consecutive numbers usually refer to blocks that are adjacent, and a degree of geographic stratification within the city is therefore accomplished by the numbering.   In analyzing the components of the sampling error of the estimates from the sample, however, any improvement which might result from this stratification and systematic selection was ignored.

(ii) Introduction of separate stratum for blocks with large retail markets.   In cities of 100,000 or over, large public markets are not uncommon.   Since the Sanborn map for such a place might merely indicate "market" or "public market," such a place would ordinarily be counted as one store-type structure in arriving at the measure of size of the block.   Actually, these markets have been found to contain as many as 200 separate retail establishments.   To reduce the variance of the design, the field offices were asked to identify all such blocks in each selected city of 100,000 or more, whereupon they were set up as a separate stratum.   The field offices, therefore, listed all the establishments in all blocks having these large public markets, and the selection of segments was made in the usual fashion.

(iii) "X"-segments.   The map materials were such that it was sometimes impossible to divide a large selected block into segments by outlining recognizable boundaries, before randomly selecting one of the segments.

In such cases, the block was designated as an "X"-segment to be later listed in its entirety by the interviewer. The interviewer then makes a random selection of establishments on the spot, using as his sampling fraction that fraction which would have been employed to select the segment.

(iv) Skipping stores on specified list. It must always be remembered that the segments are selected as a means of sampling establishments not on the specified list. Any member of the specified list which happens to fall in a sample segment must not be enumerated as part of this "area" sample but must be skipped. Furthermore, large stores found in the area sample (and not on the specified list) must not be transferred to the specified list. Although stores on the specified list are more stable, changes nevertheless occur (stores moving, going out of business, etc.), and so great stress must be placed in keeping up to date the list of establishments to be skipped.

d. The assignment of sampled segments into twelve groups for monthly enumeration. After the sample segments within each psu were selected, they were divided randomly into 12 groups after ordering them (therefore stratifying) by city and by weight (i.e., the multiple of T_j taken in their selection). A different number from 1 to 12 was then assigned at random to each group, and the number assigned designated the month for which the group of segments was to be enumerated. Thus, group 1 was to be enumerated for January, group 2 for February, etc. In the enumeration for 1948, say, of group 2, the sales for February 1948 and January 1948 were both to be obtained, and group 2 segments would not be enumerated again until the following year, when the sales for February 1949 and January 1949 would be obtained.

The advantages of this system, whereby one-twelfth of the sample is enumerated each month for a monthly sales figure, as opposed to a system in which the entire sample is enumerated at the end of a year for an *annual sales* figure, are numerous and sufficiently important to dwell on at some length. (For accomplishing the purpose of measuring current month-to-month trends, the weaknesses of a year-end enumeration are obvious.)

First, the plan chosen is probably the only feasible type which would enable one to include in an estimate of total yearly retail sales the sales of stores which go out of business during the course of the year. Even complete censuses, taken as they are, after the end of a year, cannot reflect accurately the sales of defunct businesses even if the high costs involved in attempting to do so were accepted. Whereas an enumeration made at the end of a year misses the sales of business "deaths" which occur over a period of a minimum of 12 months, the chosen system of monthly enumeration misses only those which occur during a one-month period.

Second, the job of enumeration is broken up into 12 pieces and done over the course of a year, as contrasted with a task 12 times as large to be done in a very short time period, if the results are to have some recency. The administrative advantage of not requiring the hiring of a large enumerator staff, to be used for only a short period of time after what can be only a short training period, is tremendous in terms of costs and particularly in terms of the quality of the job that will be done. Quality is improved, since better personnel are attracted by a regular job than by a temporary one, since such better personnel can be better trained, and since doing the job is spread over time, which in itself also gives more meaning to the training.

Although at first glance it may seem that the plan chosen is very inefficient in measuring annual sales of stores not on the specified list, and that the sampling error might be $\sqrt{12}$ times as great as the one that would result from use of the alternative plan, actually this is not the case. As is demonstrated in Appendix A–1, the plan is only slightly less efficient, its sampling error relative to that for the alternative system being smaller than the ratio of the $\sqrt{12}$ to the $\sqrt{1 + 11\rho}$. The symbol ρ denotes the average correlation between segment sales in all possible pairs of months, and might be of the order of .92, in which event this ratio is 1.04.

If this correlation coefficient ρ were equal to zero, this ratio would, in fact, be the $\sqrt{12}$; but in this circumstance one could effectively double the sample size by utilizing two observations for a particular month, recognizing, as mentioned above and as further discussed in Sec. A–7b, that one observation is made when the month is current and one when the month has become previous to the current month.

When the correlation coefficient is high, the above device of utilizing both observations for a particular month produces but little reduction in the error of an estimate of annual sales (see Appendix A–2).

The plan chosen has some further characteristics worthy of mention. It enables one to estimate trend in sales from one month to the same month a year later, on the basis of an identical set of segments and also on identical stores. Thus, in addition to measuring this trend for the retail population as a whole, it is also possible to measure the trend separately for the class of stores which remain in business. Both concepts of trend are useful even though users of business statistics frequently make no distinction between the two. In a year of very sharp declines in the number of businesses, the two trends could be considerably different. Note that the chosen type of sample may also be used to measure business births and deaths.

One further advantage of the system is that almost all the stores falling in the area sample are called upon to report only once a year. Members of the specified list, on the other hand, are asked to report monthly, and as a consequence the refusal rate among them may tend to increase in the course of time. Each such refusal defeats the purpose of "measurable" errors and thus is undesirable. However, a store which has refused to make a continuous monthly report will be less apt (as experience has shown) to refuse to report but one time a year.

7. The conduct of the survey. After the selection of the specified list and the area sample segments within each psu, the 68 field offices proceeded with the collection of the necessary information for the selected establishments within their jurisdiction. Because of the differences in treatment between the larger (specified list) and smaller (area sample) firms, each is discussed separately in what follows.

a. Members of the specified list. The field offices interviewed each member of the specified list to obtain information by which to determine whether the establishment was in the scope of the survey and to obtain the firm's initial report.

Accordingly, for the purpose of determining whether the firm was in-scope, the field interviewer made inquiry on (i) the number of stores that the firm operated, (ii) for each store, the proportion of its total receipts which were derived from retail sales, from wholesale sales, and from the rendering of services, and (iii) a description of the nature of the business. Where the store was not engaged primarily in a retail activity, or where the store was a member of an organization (with some minor exceptions, e.g., mail order houses) which operated 4 or more retail stores, the store was out of scope of the survey.

If a firm was determined to be within the scope of the survey, information was obtained on the distribution of its sales for each of the merchandise lines which it handled. This information was used to determine the kind of business in which the store was engaged.

If one interviewer was not successful in this endeavor, another would make the attempt, since frequently success in obtaining the information seemed dependent on the personality of the interviewer. As a result of this process, only 1 store in 20 refused to participate in the survey.

The in-scope stores that had not refused to cooperate were then placed on a mailing list, and at the close of each month a form, which merely asked for the total sales (including sales taxes) during the month, was mailed to each. This form asked that a return be made within 2 weeks. At the end of the 2 weeks, the field office telephoned the stores which had failed to report. If the attempt to obtain the sales information by telephone was unsuccessful, a personal visit to the store was made by an interviewer.

In the event that the ownership of a store had changed, an interview with the new proprietor, similar to the one with the old proprietor, was made, and the mailing piece for the new replaced that for the old. Where the store had moved, but still remained within the combined county covered by the field office, it was retained on the mailing list.

After the monthly sales figure was obtained from a particular store, it was transcribed in the Washington office to a card which, in addition to codes such as the kind of business code and combined county code, carried the store's sales figures reported for previous months. Thus month-to-month changes could be obtained for a store after 2 months of reporting, and month-to-month-a-year-ago changes could be obtained after 12 months of reporting.

Firms which, although they had promised to report, did not report in spite of repeated follow-ups, were dropped from the mailing list. If sufficiently large, as measured by payroll, they were included on a list from which an annual sales figure was to be obtained. Those who had refused to participate after the original interview were treated similarly. The larger firms retained for the purpose of obtaining an annual figure were in the interim included in monthly tabulations by estimating their monthly sales on the basis of the size of their payroll, as shown in the Bureau of Old Age and Survivors Insurance records, or on any information available on their sales size and their kind of business. The volume of sales thus estimated for the year 1948 was 6 per cent of the total. An annual survey of these firms for 1948 to obtain their own statement of their annual figure, which was to be used in place of the estimated figure, was not made because of its conflict with the 1948 Census of Business. Statutory authority to conduct such a survey with compulsory reporting was, however, available and was, in fact, exercised for the year 1949.

Throughout the operation conducted with members of the specified list, meticulous attention was paid to the addresses of the stores whose sales were included on the mailed forms, since these had to be skipped in the enumeration of the area sample.

b. The area sample. Whereas the enumeration of the stores on the specified list was essentially a mail operation, the enumeration of the stores located within the selected segments and not on the list was a personal enumeration.

The interviewer listed every recognizable place of business located within the boundaries of the segment being enumerated. He was instructed to enter every store that could conceivably be within the scope of the survey and make inquiries similar to those in the original interview of the specified list, namely (i) the number of other units operated by the owner of the store in the segment, (ii) the proportion of total receipts derived from wholesale, service, and retail sales, (iii) the distribution of total sales by line of merchandise sold.   In addition, an inquiry was made, for in-scope firms, as to the total sales in the month just completed and total sales in the month previous to that.   For example, in the 1948 enumeration of the segments in group 2 (see Sec. A–6d) sales figures were obtained for February 1948 and January 1948.   These segments, in general, were not enumerated again for a period of a year, at which time each in-scope store was asked for February 1949 and January 1949 sales (in addition to the other inquiries).

In the event that the interviewer could not obtain this information on the first visit, further call-backs were made.

As was the case for the members of the specified list, each store was coded in Washington as to whether it was in the scope of the survey, and if in-scope, was given a kind of business code.   Starting with the second half of the year 1949, codes were assigned to stores in segments only after additional examination of the codes previously assigned to these same stores in the second half of 1948.   This practice will be continued but was not in effect in the first half of 1949.

After the stores in the sample were coded, cards were punched and tabulations were made to provide the necessary estimates.

8. The estimates and their sampling errors—annual dollar volume of sales. *a. The unbiased estimate.*   Let $_LX_{hi\mu}$ be the sum of the sales for month μ of the stores on the specified list which are all in the same kind of business and which are all in the ith selected primary sampling unit in the hth stratum.   These stores have been sampled with the probability P_{hi}.

Let $_sx_{hi\mu}$ be the sum of the sales for month μ of stores located in the area sample which are all in the same kind of business and which are all in the ith selected primary sampling unit in the hth stratum.   These area sample stores have been sampled with probabilities

$$\frac{.02}{12w_a} = \frac{1}{600w_a} = P_{hi}f_{hia} \tag{8.1}$$

The f_{hia} is the subsampling fraction within the ath substratum of the hith psu. w_a arises, it will be recalled, since certain types of segments were sampled within psu's with probabilities not of $.02/P_{hi}$ but with a multiple, w_a, of $.02/P_{hi}$.

Then x'_μ, the simple unbiased estimate of total sales for month μ for a specified kind of business, is obtained by weighting $_LX_{hi\mu}$ and $_sx_{hi\mu}$ by the reciprocals of their respective probabilities of selection and is, therefore, given by

$$
\left.
\begin{aligned}
x'_\mu &= \sum_h^{68} \frac{1}{P_{hi}} \left(_LX_{hi\mu} + {_sx_{hi\mu}}600w_aP_{hi} \right) \\
&= \sum_h^{68} \frac{1}{P_{hi}} \left(x'_{hi\mu} \right) = \sum_h^{68} x'_{h\mu}
\end{aligned}
\right\}
\tag{8.2}
$$

where $x'_{hi\mu}$ is the estimate for the psu obtained by adding the sales in month μ for the specified list to the "area sample" weighted to the level of the psu.

x', the unbiased estimate of annual total sales, is then merely the sum of x'_μ for 12 months and is $\sum_1^{12} x'_\mu$. The values of x' for the major kind-of-business groups are shown in column 1 of Table A–9. (This table and the others referred to in this and subsequent sections on sampling errors will be found on pp. 550–555.) Note that the kinds of business in Table A–9 are illustrative, and it is possible to present more detailed kinds of business in publication. Because, as will be demonstrated shortly, an estimate with a smaller sampling error is available, this estimate was not used. The estimate employed takes advantage of the available 1939 census data.

For each of the selected primary sampling units, the 1939 sales of all, as opposed to independent only, retail stores were available for each kind of business group. Call Z_{hi} this sales figure for a specified kind-of-business group in the hith selected psu and Z the corresponding known total for all psu's in the country. Then

$$
z' = \sum_{h=1}^{68} \frac{Z_{hi}}{P_{hi}}
\tag{8.3}
$$

is an unbiased estimate of Z.

b. The ratio estimate. If there is a high average correlation within primary strata between the sales for psu's in a base period and the sales for these psu's in a later time period, a substantial reduction in the sampling error can be made by using a ratio estimate, provided the total for all counties is known for the base period. Table A–2 shows the correlations obtained by using county data from the Census of 1935 and the Census of 1939 (when psu's are chosen with probabilities proportionate to size) as illustrative of the magnitudes of the correlations over time. Correlations for 1939 and 1948 are shown in column 10 of Table A–12.

Table A-2

Kind of business group	Correlation coefficient between psu sales in 1935 and 1939
Food stores	.87
General stores with food	.86
General merchandise	.95
Apparel	.88
Automotive	.79
Filling stations	.56
Lumber	.65
Eating and drinking places	.91
Drugstores	.87
All	.92

NOTE. It is safe to venture the opinion (see Sec. A–10 on nonsampling errors and differences) that these correlations would be increased if the measures at different censuses had not been made with different persons coding the kinds of business.

As a result, it was decided to use a ratio estimate, x'', which is consistent and which should result in a smaller sampling error. This estimate is given by

$$x'' = \frac{x'}{z'} Z = rZ = x' \frac{Z}{z'} \qquad (8.4)$$

The values of x', Z, z', and Z/z' are shown in Table A–9 (p. 550) for a number of kinds of business.

c. The sampling error of the ratio and of the simple unbiased estimates —grouped stratum method. The sampling errors of the simple unbiased estimates and of the ratio estimates of total sales are estimated by using the results obtained from the sample itself, and by means of the procedures in Sec. 28 and Eq. 29.1, Ch. 9. Specifically,

$$v_{x''}^2 = v_{x'}^2 + v_z^2 - 2v_{x'z'} \qquad (8.5)$$

where $v_{x'}^2$ is the rel-variance of the simple unbiased estimate and is

$$v_{x'}^2 = \frac{(x_{\mathrm{I}}')^2 v_{x'_{\mathrm{I}}}^2 + (x_{\mathrm{II}}')^2 v_{x'_{\mathrm{II}}}^2}{(x')^2} \qquad (8.6)$$

The first term in the numerator measures the contribution to the variance from the 13 primary strata in group I, and the second term measures the contribution from groups II, III, and IV. (See Sec. A–4 for the meaning of the groups.) To evaluate the second term, an unbiased estimate of annual sales, $x'_h = \sum\limits_{\mu}^{12} x'_{h\mu}$, was obtained for each stratum. Second, the 55 strata in groups II, III, and IV were combined into $g = 23$ new groups, and the estimated total

$$x'_g = \sum\limits_h^{L_q} x'_{gh}$$

for each group was obtained, where x'_{gh} indicates the simple unbiased annual estimate for the hth stratum in the gth group and L_g represents the number of strata combined into the new group g. Then

$$x'_{\text{II}} = \sum\limits_g^{23} x'_g \qquad (8.7)$$

and, using Eq. 28.2 of Ch. 9,

$$v^2_{x'_{\text{II}}} = \frac{1}{(x'_{\text{II}})^2} \sum\limits_g^{23} \frac{L_g}{L_g - 1} \sum\limits_h^{L_q} \left(x'_{gh} - \frac{A_{gh}}{A_g} x'_g\right)^2 \qquad (8.8)$$

where A_{gh}/A_g is the ratio of the 1940 population (measure of size) for stratum h to the 1940 population of the group in which it was placed.

To evaluate the first term in the numerator of Eq. 8.6, use Eq. 6.1 of Ch. 7, and note that the subscript a simply extends the strata to the substrata within the primary areas; then

$$v^2_{x'_{\text{I}}} = \frac{1}{(x'_{\text{I}})^2} \sum\limits_h^{13} \sum\limits_a^{4} (600 w_a)^2 n_{ha} s^2_{ha} \qquad (8.9)$$

where s_{ha} and n_{ha} are defined in paragraph d (i) below.

Substituting Eq. 8.8 and 8.9 in Eq. 8.6, we complete the estimate of the sampling error of the unbiased estimate $v^2_{x'}$.

The rel-variance $v^2_{z'}$ is evaluated by the same method as $v^2_{x'}$, except that the $v^2_{z'_{\text{I}}}$ is 0 because $z'_{\text{I}} = Z_{\text{I}}$ since there is no sampling within the primary sampling unit in estimating z'_{I}. Each of the primary strata of group I consists of one "primary sampling unit," which in fact constitutes the stratum. Also, $v^2_{z'_{\text{II}}}$ involves only the psu contribution to the variance since there is no subsampling in estimating z'. Finally,

$$v_{x'z'} = \frac{1}{x'z'} \sum\limits_g^{23} \frac{L_g}{L_g - 1} \sum\limits_h^{L_q} \left(x'_{gh} - \frac{A_{gh}}{A_g} x'_g\right)\left(z'_{gh} - \frac{A_{gh}}{A_g} z'_g\right) \qquad (8.10)$$

The quantities $v^2_{x'}$, $v^2_{z'}$, and $v_{x'z'}$ being evaluated, their substitution in Eq. 8.5 yields the estimate of the sampling error of the ratio estimate.

The values of $v_{x'}$ and $v_{x''}$ are presented in columns 1 and 2 of Table A–10 (p. 551). It will be noted that the coefficient of variation of the ratio estimate, $v_{x''}$, is generally lower than $v_{x'}$ that of the simple unbiased estimate.

The above method of calculating the sampling error may lead to some overstatement, as discussed in Sec. 15, Ch. 9, and Sec. 13, Ch. 10. However, a study of Table A–11 (p. 552) indicates that the tendency to overstatement is not serious.

It will be noted that not all the intricacies of the sampling within the psu's are explicitly involved in this method of calculating the error. This method of estimation is an instance of how sampling errors may be calculated by considering the variations among sample estimates themselves, rather than by considering the variations among the smallest units in the sample (in this case, stores).

Its disadvantage is that, except for indicating what groups of strata are contributing most to the variance, it is not analytical. In particular, it does not show what contributions arise from the sampling of psu's and from the sampling within psu's.

d. Analysis of the sampling error of the estimate into its components. In order to be able to discover how the sample might be improved in the course of time, and in order to understand the nature of the sampling error, the following analysis is pertinent. (Approximations to the indicated components of the sampling error were made when the sample was designed. The approximations indicated, for instance, that the 68 combined counties would be satisfactory, that a 2 per cent area sample would yield satisfactory results, etc.) Estimates of the components of the sampling variances are made from the results of the survey.

The rel-variance of x'' can be expressed in terms of the between-psu contribution to the total variance and the within-psu contribution as indicated in Sec. 26 of Ch. 9 (Eq. 26.5). Similarly, an estimate of the rel-variance can be expressed in terms of estimates of the contributions from each stage of sampling. The appropriate estimates to use when the sampling fractions at some of the stages of sampling are relatively large are described in Case 2 of Sec. 32, Ch. 9. The estimating equations are greatly simplified when all the sampling fractions are small. An estimate appropriate to this situation is used below in this case study. In this special case we can say

$$v_{x''}^2 = b_{x''}^2 + w_{x''}^2 \tag{8.11}$$

where $b_{x''}^2$ is an estimate of the between-psu contribution to the rel-variance and is given by Eq. 32.2 of Ch. 9, or Eq. 8.15 below. Similarly, $w_{x''}^2$ is an estimate of the within-psu contribution to the total rel-variance and is given by the second term of Eq. 32.4 of Ch. 9 or (for the special case in this study) by Eq. 8.12, below. Note that in the special case considered here, when the psu totals, Z_{hi}, are known without error (i.e., subsampling is not involved in the estimation of Z), $w_{x''}^2 = w_{x'}^2$, where $w_{x'}^2$ is the within-psu contribution to the rel-variance of x'.

(i) Estimate of within-psu contribution to rel-variance. For the purpose of calculating $w_{x'}^2$ all the segments in a selected psu have been regarded as belonging to 1 of 4 substrata, which may be defined by whether the segment lies in an incorporated place of 2500 or more and by whether the segments were selected within the place with an over-all sampling fraction of .02 or $.02/w_a$. Then

$$w_{x'}^2 = \frac{1}{(x')^2} \sum_h^{68} \sum_a^4 (600 w_a)^2 n_{ha} s_{ha}^2 \tag{8.12}$$

where n_{ha} is the number of segments in the sample in substratum a in the hth primary stratum, and where

$$s_{ha}^2 = \frac{\sum\limits_{\mu}^{12} n_{ha\mu} s_{ha\mu}^2}{n_{ha}} \tag{8.13}$$

$$s_{ha\mu}^2 = \frac{\sum\limits_{k}^{n_{ha\mu}} (x_{ha\mu k} - \bar{x}_{ha\mu})^2}{n_{ha\mu} - 1} \tag{8.14}$$

In the above formulas $x_{ha\mu k}$ is the aggregate sales of the kth segment in the indicated substratum in the μth month, $\bar{x}_{ha\mu}$ is the average per sampled segment in month μ, and $n_{ha\mu}$ is the total number of sampled segments in the month in the substratum. Equation 8.12 above results directly from the second term of Eq. 32.4 of Ch. 9 with $n_{hia}/N_{hia} = 1/P_{hi}600 w_a$.

Equation 8.12 represents the within-psu sampling contribution to the rel-variance of both the ratio and simple unbiased *annual* estimate. The within-psu contribution to the rel-variance of a *monthly* estimate is approximately $12 w_{x'}^2$.

Table A–10, columns 3 and 3a (p. 551), show the within-psu contribution to the rel-variance of the ratio and simple unbiased estimates.

(ii) Estimate of between-psu contribution to rel-variance. Having evaluated the within component, $w_{x'}^2$, the between component, $b_{x''}^2$, is given approximately by

$$b_{x''}^2 = v_{x''}^2 - w_{x'}^2 \tag{8.15}$$

when $v_{x''}^2$ is given by Eq. 8.5.

Estimate of the between-psu contribution to the variance, using past data. As was pointed out earlier, the estimate of the between-primary-unit contribution to the variance, as well as the total variance, will tend to be an overstatement of the actual variance. Moreover, when the number of psu's is small the estimate of the variance will be subject to a large sampling error.

As an approximation to the between-psu contribution to the variance for the *simple unbiased estimate*, data for all retail stores in the censuses of 1935, 1939, and 1948 have been used.

The results for 1935 and 1939 when the between-psu contribution to the simple unbiased estimate is computed by Eq. 19.2, Ch. 10, are shown in columns 7 and 8 of Table A–11 (p. 552). The results for 1939 and 1948 when the grouped stratum method is used are also shown. It will be observed that, regardless of time period and the method of computation, the values are approximately the same. It is interesting to compare (see Table A–11) the estimated coefficients of variation with the actual deviation of the estimates for the two censuses.

For an approximation to the between-psu contribution to the variance of the *ratio estimate*, the three censuses of 1935, 1939, and 1948 (preliminary) were also used. The results for 1935–1939 when computed by Eq. 19.2, Ch. 10, and the results for 1939–1948 when computed by the grouped stratum method are shown in columns 7 and 8, respectively, of Table A–12 (p. 553). (These values can be compared in that table with the actual deviations that result when a ratio estimate to 1939 is made.)

The approximations from past data to the between-psu contribution and the estimates from the sample of the within-psu contribution have been added and are shown in Table A–10 for comparison with the total rel-variance as computed by the grouped stratum method, which, it will be remembered, depends only on data from the sample itself.

It will be noted, also, that the between-psu error contributes more to the simple unbiased estimate, but is less important for the ratio estimate.

9. The estimates and their sampling errors—month-to-month trend of sales. *a. The estimate and its error.* The estimate of month-to-month trend is obtained by taking the ratio of the estimate of volume for one month to the estimate obtained from the enumeration of the identical stores. (It will be recalled that stores in the area sample segments report the sales for both the current and the previous month, and that members of the specified list report monthly.)

The trend estimates for each month in 1948 for all independent stores are shown in Table A–13, column 1 (p. 554). The trends by kind-of-business group for a selected month are shown in Table A–14, column 1 (p. 554).

If we now let x' be the simple unbiased estimate for one month and y' for another month, the estimate of trend is $r_1 = x'/y'$. One will note that

$$\frac{x''}{y''} = \frac{(x'/z')Z}{(y'/z')Z} = \frac{x'}{y'}$$

and hence the ratio of the ratio estimates is the same as the ratio of the unbiased estimates.

The estimate of the rel-variance of r_1 is given by Eq. 29.1 of Ch. 9 and is equal to

$$v_{r_1}^2 = v_{x'}^2 + v_{y'}^2 - 2v_{x'y'} \qquad (9.1)$$

where

$$v_{x'y'} = \frac{1}{x'y'} \left[\sum_g^{23} \frac{L_g}{L_g - 1} \sum_h^{L_J} \left(x'_{gh} - \frac{A_{gh}}{A_g} x'_g \right)\left(y'_{gh} - \frac{A_{gh}}{A_g} y'_g \right) \right.$$

$$\left. + \sum_h^{13} \sum_a^{4} (600 w_a)^2 n_{ha} s_{haxy} \right] \qquad (9.2)$$

and where

$$s_{haxy} = \frac{\sum_k^{n_{ha}} (x_{hak} - \bar{x}_{ha})(y_{hak} - \bar{y}_{ha})}{n_{ha} - 1} \qquad (9.3)$$

$v_{x'}^2 = v_{x'x'}$ and is the same as above with x' substituted for y'.

$v_{y'}^2 = v_{y'y'}$ and is the same as above with y' substituted for x'.

All the terms above have been previously defined, bu x's and y's and n_{ha} now refer only to aggregates for a particular month. The first term in Eq. 9.2 is the contribution (both between and within psu's) from the primary strata in which a psu was sampled (groups II, III, IV), and the second term is the contribution of the strata where an area represented itself (group I).

Tables A-13 and A-14, in addition to showing the trends, also show v_{r_1} and the correlation between x' and y'.

  b. *The analysis of the error.* In estimating the same characteristic for consecutive months, $v_{x'}^2 \doteq v_{y'}^2$, and another way of expressing $v_{r_1}^2$, derived from Eq. 9.1, is

$$v_{r_1}^2 \doteq 2 v_{x'}^2 (1 - \rho'_{x'y'})$$

where $\rho'_{x'y'}$ is the estimated coefficient of correlation between x' and y'. The gains in $v_{r_1}^2$ by use of both identical counties and identical segments are reflected by the degree to which $\rho'_{x'y'}$ approaches unity. Values of $\rho'_{x'y'}$ for the survey are given in column 3 of Tables A-13 and A-14 (p. 554).

The estimated rel-variance of r_1 can also be stated in a form similar to Eq. 8.11 to show the contributions to the variance of the sample of psu's and the sampling within psu's. Since the rel-variances for each period will be about the same, the estimated rel-variance of r_1 is approximately equivalent to

$$v_{r_1}^2 \doteq 2 w_M^2 (1 - \rho'_w) + 2 b_M^2 (1 - \rho'_b) \qquad (9.4)$$

where w_M^2 is the estimated within component of the sampling error of a simple unbiased estimate of a monthly total (approximately 12 times w_x^2, of Eq. 8.12 in Sec. 8d); ρ_w' is the estimated correlation between x' and y' within psu's; b_M^2 is the estimated between-psu component of the sampling error of a simple unbiased estimate; and ρ_b' is the estimated correlation between one month's county totals and the succeeding month's county totals.

It is reasonable to assume that ρ_b', the correlation between county sales in 2 consecutive months, is close to unity, so that the error of the ratio becomes dependent primarily on ρ_w', the correlation of sales in the 2 consecutive months for the same area segments. In this connection it will be noted that, if nonidentical segments had been used in estimating the ratio, this correlation would be zero and the variance of the ratio would be twice that of the within variance of a one-month's dollar sales estimate. In contrast, the use of identical segments when the correlation is .95 leads to variances which are 10 per cent of the within variance of the same month's dollar sales figures.

c. Trend of sales—one month to same month a year ago. It will be recalled that the segments for a particular month are enumerated every year, i.e., the same segments were enumerated in both April 1948 and April 1949. The estimates and their sampling errors are identical in form to those given above, where the y' now denotes the estimate for a month a year ago instead of the previous month.

The results will differ to the extent that the indicated correlations differ. One would expect the correlation between segment sales for 2 months to be greater when the 2 months are consecutive than when the 2 months are separated by a year. This arises particularly from the fact that in a 12-month period a substantial number of stores are "born" and "die," thus affecting the correlation adversely.

During the first 6 months of 1949, the enumeration and the determination of which area sample establishments were in the scope of the survey and the determination of kind of business for area sample firms were all made completely independently of the same operations for 1948. (See Sec. A-10 for the effect of independent determinations of scope, kind of business, and coverage.) This fact has the same effect on the correlation coefficient as the stores that come into being or go out of existence and further depresses it below the month-to-month correlation.

The values of r_1, v_{r_1}, and $\rho_{x'y'}'$ are given in Table A-15 when y' denotes estimates for the month a year ago.

Remark. All the sampling errors estimated from the sample itself are themselves subject to sampling errors, in some instances rather large (see Sec. 6–10 of Ch. 10 for discussion of these errors).

10. Nonsampling errors and differences.   The preceding sections have directed little attention to the nature of the responses to the survey's inquiries or to the nature of codes assigned on the basis of those responses.

If the response errors are such that their expected value is zero (i.e., no response bias), then the sampling errors of the preceding section also reflect errors of response.   The computed sampling errors do not, however, reflect any consistent biases in the responses.   As an illustration, if stores report their sales figures in such fashion that there is no response bias, and if the error in response for one store is independent of that for another store, then the sampling errors, as computed above, include the variability arising from this cause.   However, if every store understated (for example) its sales, then the sampling errors do not reflect the deviations from the true sales which arise from this cause.*

In order to obtain some insight into nonsampling errors and differences, a small-scale recheck project was carried out for the month of June 1948. A random sample of 212 of the members of the specified mailing list (no sample was taken of the members of the specified list who had been deemed out of the scope of the sample survey as a result of original interview) and a random sample of 227 segments or one-fifth of the June (group 6) area sample segments was selected for independent reinterview and recanvass, respectively.

In view of the small size of the sample selected for this project the following results cannot be used as estimates of the nonsampling errors and differences, but can be viewed as rough qualitative indications of their nature.

a. Response differences in sales.   In a study of response differences, a field reinterviewer was asked to secure the June 1948 sales figure again. He was furnished with the figure originally reported, and was instructed to probe into the causes of difference when the figure he obtained was different from the original sales figure.   The probe consisted of determining whether the recheck figure was a "book" or estimated figure, obtaining ranges where estimates were given, and obtaining any comments offered by the proprietor (or accountant) in explanation of the differences in sales figures.

(i) Results for the mailing list.   Of the 212 cases rechecked, 209 were also in-scope after the recheck, and 32 reported sales differently in the recheck.   The sales of the 209 originally were $3,146,377 and after recheck were only $10,520 or .3 of 1 per cent more.   The $10,520 is a

---

* For a more detailed discussion of this point, see Ch. 2, Sec. 25, and Ch. 12 of Vol. II.

net figure, however, since those who reported less on recheck reported $31,000 (1 per cent) less, whereas those who reported larger sales in the recheck reported $41,600 (1.3 per cent) more.

The reasons why the sales were reported differently are indicated by the following table for 26 of the 32 cases where such reasons were obtainable:

REASONS FOR DIFFERENCES IN REPORTED SALES	NO. OF CASES
Certain receipts erroneously included or excluded	7
Taxes not included	6
Clerical and bookkeeping errors	4
Book figures available during recheck only	4
Rounding of figures	3
Estimates made originally and in recheck	2

(ii) *Results for the establishments in the area sample.* Of the 323 area sample firms there were 98 establishments which reported sales figures differently in the recheck from what they had reported originally. Some reported larger sales in the recheck than originally, and this excess was 2.7 per cent of all sales reported originally. Others reported smaller sales, and the change in sales involved for these cases was 3.1 per cent of the total. Thus, the sales reported on recheck were .4 of 1 per cent less than the sales reported originally.

The reasons why the sales were reported differently are indicated by the following table for 75 (of the 98) cases where such reasons were obtainable:

FACTORS REGARDING ORIGIN OF DIFFERENCES	NO. OF CASES
Actual figure obtained in recheck—estimated originally	35
Bookkeeping and clerical errors	10
Figures reported by different individuals	10
Recheck estimate deemed better by proprietor	8
Taxes not included	4
Profits reported	4
Other receipts included or excluded erroneously	4

It is interesting to note that, in half the cases where differences occurred, estimates only were obtained originally, whereas actual figures were obtained in the recheck, the latter having taken place at a later date.

A few establishments did not respond originally, and as a result sales estimates for these establishments had to be made by the Bureau. In the recheck, however, they furnished their sales figures, which on the whole were smaller than the estimates made, the net discrepancy accounting for .6 of 1 per cent.

b. Listing errors. This type of error occurs when an interviewer fails to record a store which he should record or records a store which he should not. In this project 227 segments were rechecked by giving the recheck interviewer the original listing, instructing him on how to find errors (with appropriate safeguards being taken so that no interviewer checked his own work), and budgeting twice as much cost per establishment to insure a thorough job.   Of the 227 segments, 8 contained at least 1 listing error.   Seven of these were underlisted, and 1 was overlisted. All but 1 were mistakes in interpreting segment boundaries.   As a result 7 establishments were underlisted originally and 3 establishments were overlisted.

One further type of "error" occurred when the recheck interviewer found 4 retail establishments located above the fourth floor of an office building.   The word "error" is in quotation marks because the original interviewer had been instructed not to canvass office buildings thoroughly above the fourth floor.

In summary, listing errors caused the number of establishments to be increased by 2.5 per cent in the recheck.   Similarly, sales were increased by 5.2 per cent.

c. Scope differences.   After an interviewer lists an establishment, he obtains information on the nature of its activity, and on the proportion of its receipts which stem from sales at retail, from sales at wholesale, and from receipts for personal services.   He then makes a judgment on whether the establishment is within the scope of the survey.   Later, his work is reviewed at the Bureau, and his judgment may be reversed.   A final determination of "scope" is then a function of the inquiries made of the establishment, the responses received, the judgment of the interviewer obtaining the information, and the judgment of the particular reviewer of the interviewer's decision.   Furthermore, the same interviewer or same reviewer may arrive at different decisions (in a certain proportion of the cases) at different times.   It is clear that, when two decisions are different, it is frequently possible that neither is clearly in error and consequently reference is made here to "scope differences" rather than "scope errors."

In the recheck, responses to questions pertaining to scope were obtained independently of the original enumeration, and this information was also reviewed and coded independently.

Of the 323 original area sample cases, 29 were involved in scope changes. Ten of the 29 were in scope originally, and 19 were out of scope originally. The net effect on the sales of this difference is .6 of 1 per cent.   This small net effect results from a decrease of 7.9 per cent (for the 10 cases) and an increase of 8.5 per cent (for the 19 cases).

d. Kind of business differences.   After a judgment is made that an establishment is within the scope of the survey, a further judgment is made as to the kind of business (e.g., grocery store with meat, drugstore with fountain) in which it belongs. The kind-of-business code assigned to a store is, in general, an attempt to characterize the pattern of the dollar volume sales of different lines of merchandise. Few stores, however, keep records of their sales of different merchandise lines, and consequently their estimates must be accepted. Evidence from other sources shows that the differences in response are not the only cause of kind-of-business differences. Even with the same information on hand, different coders will assign different codes and even the same coder will assign different codes at different times.

It is therefore not surprising that two independent surveys, in which a kind-of-business code is assigned to the same stores, will show substantial differences.

(i) Results for the mailing list. Table A–3 (columns 3 and 4) indicates, for the mailing list of large establishments, the size of the differences in kind of business and the extent to which these differences balance in terms of number of establishments.

Table A–3.   Comparison of original survey and recheck results for establishments on mailing list

Kind of business group (K.B.)	No. originally in K.B. (1)	No. out of scope in recheck (2)	No. leaving K.B. in recheck (3)	No. entering K.B. in recheck (4)	No. in recheck in K.B. (5)
Food	32	0	2	5	35
Eating and drinking	44	0	4	1	41
General stores with food	4	0	2	0	2
General merchandise	5	0	2	1	4
Apparel	21	1	1	2	21
Furniture—household—radio	18	0	1	1	18
Lumber—building—hardware	24	1	1	2	24
Automotive	27	1	3	1	24
Filling stations	9	0	1	2	10
Drugstores	8	0	0	0	8
Liquor stores	2	0	0	1	3
Other retail	18	0	1	2	19
All	212	3	18	18	209

(ii) Results for the establishments in the area sample. Table A–4 indicates the kind-of-business differences that resulted in terms of number of establishments, for the area sample. It also indicates for comparative purposes scope differences, listing errors, and the cumulative effect of all other causes.

Table A–4.   Comparison of original survey and recheck results for
establishments in area sample

Kind of business (K.B.)	No. in K.B. orig- inally	Changes in scope status		K.B. changes		Listing errors		No. in K.B. in re- check	Per cent change recheck over original
		(−)	(+)	(−)	(+)	(−)	(+)		
Food	75	1	3	3	4	3	3	78	+ 4.0
Eating and drinking	68	1	4	2	1	0	1	71	+ 4.4
General stores with food	1	0	0	1	1	0	0	1	.0
General merchandise	9	0	0	4	5	0	0	10	+ 11.1
Apparel	19	0	0	1	2	0	0	20	+ 5.3
Furniture—household— radio	20	1	0	3	3	0	0	19	− 5.0
Lumber—building— hardware	19	2	5	0	0	0	0	22	+ 15.8
Automotive	14	0	1	2	2	0	1	16	+ 14.3
Filling stations	41	3	1	2	0	0	0	37	− 9.8
Drugstores	14	0	0	1	1	0	0	14	.0
Liquor stores	5	0	0	0	0	0	0	5	.0
Other retail	38	2	5	6	6	0	6	47	+ 23.7
All	323	10	19	25	25	3	11	340	+ 5.3

Table A–5.   Causes of change in the original mailing list

Kind of business (K.B.)	Per cent change in original mailing list sales by cause				
	Scope change*	K.B. change		Response difference (net)	Total per cent change net (all causes) in original sales
		(−)	(+)		
Food	.0	2.7	8.3	+ .2	+ 5.9
Eating and drinking	.0	7.1	.5	+ 1.9	− 4.7
General stores with food	.0	27.6	.0	.0	− 27.6
General merchandise	.0	27.1	39.8	.0	+ 12.6
Apparel	− 9.7	4.6	3.1	+ 4.5	− 6.6
Furniture—household— radio	.0	1.4	32.1	− 10.2	+ 20.6
Lumber—building— hardware	− 6.1	1.1	6.3	+ 1.4	+ .5
Automotive	− 2.6	3.3	.5	+ .6	− 4.7
Filling stations	.0	10.0	16.0	+ 6.5	+ 12.5
Drugstores	.0	.0	.0	− 1.3	− 1.3
Liquor stores	.0	.0	100.5	.0	+ 100.5
Other retail	.0	39.6	4.2	+ 1.4	− 34.1
All	− 2.5	..	..	+ .3	− 2.2

* Scope change cannot be positive.   Mailing list stores originally out of scope were
not rechecked.

e. Summary of nonsampling errors and differences.   Tables A–5 and A–6 summarize the results where the effect of the errors and differences is measured in dollar sales and is then expressed as a per cent of the dollar sales originally tabulated.

Table A–6.   Causes of change in the area sample

Kind of business (K.B.)	Per cent change in the area sample sales by cause							
	Scope change		K.B. differences		Listing error		Response difference (net)	Net change (all causes)
	(−)	(+)	(−)	(+)	(−)	(+)		
Food	1.7	8.1	2.1	3.6	2.7	20.6	+ 4.2	+ 30.1
Eating and drinking	1.2	9.9	2.6	.8	.0	1.1	− 2.1	+ 5.9
General stores with food	.0	.0	100.0	*	.0	.0	.0	*
General merchandise	.0	.0	53.1	11.3	.0	.0	− 3.4	− 45.2
Apparel	.0	.0	.7	19.4	.0	.0	+ 1.3	+ 20.1
Furniture—household— radio	.4	.0	3.0	4.2	.0	.0	− 9.3	− 8.5
Lumber—building— hardware	42.8	29.2	.0	.0	.0	.0	− .6	− 14.2
Automotive	.0	4.0	19.6	4.9	.0	6.9	− .7	− 4.5
Filling stations	12.4	2.9	2.6	.0	.0	.0	+ 2.0	− 10.0
Drugstores	.0	.0	3.6	.7	.0	.0	+ .9	− 2.0
Liquor stores	.0	.0	.0	.0	.0	.0	.0	.0
Other retail	7.9	9.3	7.6	18.3	.0	10.6	− 4.0	+ 18.8
All	7.9	8.5	.0	.0	.4	5.5	− 1.1	+ 4.5

* Originally there was one firm in this kind of business with sales of \$100 which in the recheck left this kind of business. However, another firm with sales of \$12,494 changed its kind of business to this one in the recheck.

f. Remarks on the nonsampling errors and differences.   The above recheck was taken when the survey had been under way for but 6 months. In general, it indicated that serious attention had to be paid to remedial measures to reduce errors and differences in responses, and that these measures should be carried out regardless of what steps were taken to reduce sampling errors.   Some of these measures have now been taken and others are in process (see Sec. A–12 below).   In particular, the following comments are appropriate:

(i) Differences in response in sales and "imputations."   The effect of these differences is small in relation to the effect of differences arising out of the other elements discussed, particularly kind of business and scope determinations.   For large firms, it appears that the mail technique can be used as an effective means of collecting retail sales data.   However, the quality of retail sales figures may be improved by reducing the number of cases requiring imputations (estimates made by the Bureau of the sales of nonresponses) and the number of cases in which the proprietor estimates his sales in lieu of reporting "book" figures.   One method of so doing, which, however, is in conflict with the desirability of early tabulation, is to schedule the time for enumeration later in the month; the second method is to give further training to the enumerators to stress the desirability and technique for obtaining "book" figures.

(ii) Underenumeration of the area sample.   Without careful work, this type of error may be serious.   The area sample enumeration, beginning in 1949, was made by enumerators who had in their possession the enumeration of the previous year.   The old enumeration was a starting point which was to be brought up to date and differences explained.   Examination of the resulting enumeration furnishes evidence that by this means boundary line errors were reduced to the level of the probability of two different interviewers making the same mistake.

(iii) Differences in kind of business and scope.   These are the most important differences and are a complex result of many variable elements, such as the type of information requested, the availability of information, differences in the ability of interviewers, and differences in coders' judgments.

Because of the importance of the measurement of change (both from the census and from the survey's results for previous months), it is desirable to standardize codes so far as possible.   Thus, for establishments which were enumerated in the 1948 Census of Business, those codes are being made the standard.   For those which were not enumerated, more detailed questions than previously will be employed and the resultant codes will become the standard.   For firms whose reported "book" data indicate a change in the characteristics determining the kind-of-business code, a "resistance factor" may be determined such that firms not changing sufficiently to overcome this resistance are given their standard code, and those meeting the factor are coded differently from the standard.

11. Results relating to the preliminary consideration of the sample design. The purpose of this section is to present some other results of the survey, particularly those which were considered important to the sample design. Unless otherwise indicated, the statistics in what follows are for the year 1948.

a. Effectiveness of the specified list.   The specified list of large stores, consisting of 31,000 establishments, when weighted, accounted for 44 per cent of the total estimate of sales and 12 per cent of the estimate of the number of establishments.   Area sample establishments, numbering about 20,000 and located in two-thirds of the 13,000 area sample segments (the other third had no establishments), accounted for the remaining 56 per cent of sales and 88 per cent of the number of establishments. The average size, on a weighted basis, of the establishments on the specified list was therefore 5.7 times the average size of those not on the list, where size is measured in terms of dollar sales volume. It will be recalled that the designation of the list was made primarily in terms of payroll, and not in terms of sales.

A better measure of effectiveness of a list of large stores is the reduction in the rel-variance per store that results when the stores on the list are excluded from the calculation. It appears conservative to say that the rel-variance per store will be reduced from 50 to a figure between 3 and 4.

b. The extent of nonresponse. As described in Sec. A-7, "imputations" based on knowledge of previous month's sales, payroll, etc., were made for nonrespondent cases.

For the year 1948, nonresponses accounted for 13.8 per cent of sales volume. Six per cent resulted from firms on the specified list which either "refused" to file monthly or which did not refuse but whose reporting history indicated that they would not file except occasionally. (On a weighted basis, this 6 per cent was from but 1.3 per cent of the total number of cases.) Two and three-tenths per cent was accounted for by area sample establishments which refused to furnish a monthly sales figure. The balance of 5.5 per cent resulted from other factors like filing late and illness. As previously mentioned, the Bureau did not exercise its authority to demand an annual figure for the year 1948.

Table A-7 analyzes by sources the imputations in terms of sales volume and number of establishments.

Table A-7. Imputations for nonrespondents, 1948

		Sales (per cent)		Number of establishments (per cent)
Estimate is represented by		100.0		100.0
Imputations, total		13.8		12.1
List of large stores, total		7.2		1.6
Excluding refusals	1.2		.3	
Refusals	6.0		1.3	
Area sample, total		6.5		10.5
Refusals	2.3		3.7	
Late reports	1.3		2.1 est.	
Other causes	2.9		4.7 est.	

c. Cost elements as between large and small stores. In response to the mailing made for the members of the specified list (other than refusals),

75 per cent of the forms were returned by the respondents before follow-up. The follow-up was then made by telephone, and as a result practically all (about 97 per cent) of the forms were received. For those remaining, which included stores out of business, a personal follow-up was made. The following costs can be converted to a rough man-hour equivalent— which is more useful in comparing costs—by assuming about $\frac{3}{4}$ man-hours per dollar.

The field cost, per member of the specified list, of mailing and receipts, telephone follow-up, and personal follow-up amounted to about 30 cents per month. This compares with a field cost of enumerating an area sample segment of about $2.50. (To convert this cost to a cost per area sample store one need only remember that, because of "zero" segments, there were about $1\frac{1}{2}$ stores per segment.) These costs do not include the overhead costs of running a field office, but if these overhead costs could be allocated no appreciable change in the unit costs would result.

The cost of processing the reports in Washington (i.e., editing, tabulating, and compiling and typing tables) amounted to about 25 cents per month for a member of the specified list and 75 cents per area sample segment.

Because field cost per area sample segment is an appreciable unit cost of collection, the following table analyzing the approximate distribution of cost in terms of the per cent of enumerator's man-hours spent is of interest.

ITEM	PER CENT
Total time	100
Travel time	50
Listing time	7
Interview time	25
Office work time	18

d. Sanborn map counts as effective measures of the sizes of blocks. As previously indicated [see Sec. A–6b (i)], in larger cities, blocks were stratified on the basis of counts made from the Sanborn maps. The extremely high correlation between these counts and the number of stores actually to be found in a block can be observed from Table A–8. This table shows for each of 87 blocks randomly selected in Buffalo, N.Y., the Sanborn map count and a listing count of stores made by a field enumerator.

When the 4 blocks marked with asterisks are excluded, a correlation coefficient of .99 results between the Sanborn count and the listing count. If the 4 blocks are not excluded, a coefficient of .85 is obtained.

Table A–8.   Comparison of Sanborn counts and listing counts for individual blocks, Buffalo, N.Y.

Block No. i	Sanborn count x_i	Listing count y_i	Block No. i	Sanborn count x_i	Listing count y_i	Block No. i	Sanborn count x_i	Listing count y_i	Block No. i	Sanborn count x_i	Listing count y_i
1	3	3	*23	4	14	45	13	9	67	8	9
2	82	83	24	10	8	46	10	8	68	7	4
3	7	7	25	9	9	47	3	3	69	2	2
4	33	36	26	17	17	48	17	16	70	12	12
*5	13	4	27	3	3	49	2	2	71	14	12
6	27	27	28	5	4	50	0	0	72	1	0
7	4	3	29	0	0	51	5	4	*73	54	4
8	19	20	30	7	5	52	6	8	74	2	2
9	22	17	31	2	1	53	7	4	75	0	0
10	11	12	32	8	8	54	6	6	76	0	0
11	1	1	33	3	3	55	5	4	77	5	5
12	17	17	*34	29	2	56	2	2	78	8	10
13	4	6	35	12	10	57	12	11	79	10	7
14	2	3	36	4	4	58	14	9	80	6	5
15	9	7	37	2	2	59	37	33	81	17	17
16	1	2	38	10	11	60	21	19	82	15	9
17	27	24	39	11	11	61	3	3	83	7	7
18	18	15	40	4	4	62	1	0	84	22	23
19	14	16	41	18	16	63	2	1	85	11	8
20	10	10	42	13	12	64	16	16	86	0	0
21	8	8	43	1	1	65	0	0	87	1	1
22	14	14	44	2	2	66	0	0			
						Totals				904	777

12. Future developments and improvements. A survey of this nature requires constant appraisal of deficiencies and strengths with a view toward continuous improvement over time. This calls for study of the sampling errors and their components and of the nonsampling errors and differences, and for utilizing new statistics and knowledge.

To reduce sampling errors many measures are being and have been taken. First, the area sample is being doubled in size. Second, a program is under way of utilizing the 1948 Census of Business for making the specified list a much more complete list of those stores in the sample areas which have sales greater than a specified size. (It will be recalled that it was originally necessary to compile this list from lists of employers on the basis of payroll.) Third, instead of a ratio estimate based on 1939 data, the ratio will be made with 1948 Census data. This should increase the correlation in sales between psu's and reduce the sampling error somewhat. Fourth, it is hoped to ascertain accurately the amount of sales that took place within each of the area segments in 1948 (using the 1948 Census of Business schedules), and therefore to reduce the within-psu component of the sampling error by taking advantage of the high correlation in sales between the present time and 1948. A fifth improvement to reduce sampling error is the institution of a special list of the very largest establishments in the country. This list will not be confined to the sample psu's and is being instituted in those circumstances where large operational costs will not be incurred. Sixth is the laying of plans to reduce the between-psu component of the sampling error by expansion to more than 68 primary sampling units.

Steps are also being taken to improve the survey from the point of view of reducing non-sampling errors and differences. First, for those establishments within the scope of the survey which were enumerated in the retail 1948 Census of Business, kind-of-business codes are being standardized to the census determinations. For others, more detailed information is being obtained and then the resulting codes will be standardized. Second, the Census of Business enumeration is being combined with the previous area sample enumerations of the segments, to form a listing of all establishments in the segments. These will be given to the interviewers with the purpose, among others, of reducing underenumeration at boundary lines. Third, a program of intensively training interviewers in the importance and art of obtaining "book" figures will be adopted. Fourth, and this has already been put into effect, is the use of the provisions of the 1948 law which make it mandatory for business establishments to report their sales annually even though they may not be cooperative in reporting sales monthly. In this manner the percentage of sales which is accounted for by the Bureau's estimates of the sales of individual refusals will be reduced.

Steps to reduce sampling errors and to improve quality are but part of the program of improvement of the survey. The other part is concerned with reducing costs. In this connection, the facts on the elements of cost are being gathered constantly and studied; and experiments to reduce costs are constantly undertaken. As an illustration, a test is being conducted on the cost and effect of conducting a "follow-up" of a delinquent mail reporter 31–37 days after the month for which he is delinquent, with the view to forestalling delinquency for the next month, and its consequent cost. For all practical purposes, organized knowledge on methods of reducing costs is nonexistent, even though advances are taking place.

One of the most important future developments relates to making the survey more meaningful by extending it to all retail stores rather than confining it only to those stores in organizations which have fewer than 4. The necessary additional sample, now selected, consists of about 600 of the largest organizations located throughout the country; of smaller (but still large) organizations with headquarters in the combined counties; and of the area sample for the still smaller organizations. The lists of such organizations are obtained from the 1948 Census of Business.

And finally the future will probably see a revision in the aims of the program. In place of being primarily concerned with estimates of month-to-month trend and annual dollar level, the purpose may be revised so that these trends are expressed in terms of monthly dollar sales. This would make it possible for the user of the statistics to obtain many different relationships not otherwise possible—for example, the ratio of sales for the immediately preceding 6-month period to the sales of the next preceding 6-month period; or any other sum, ratio, ratio of sums, differences, etc. Some alternative estimating procedures to accomplish this objective, together with some of their approximate variances for monthly and annual totals, and long- and short-term trends are given as Illustration 7.1 in Chapter 11 (p. 497).

Table A–9. The estimates of annual dollar volume of sales: unbiased and ratio

Kind of business group	Unbiased estimate 1948 sales (millions of dollars) x'	Unbiased estimate 1939 sales obtained from sampled psu's (millions of dollars) z'	Sales, 1939 census (millions of dollars) Z	$\dfrac{Z}{z'}$	Ratio estimate 1948 sales (millions of dollars) $x'' = x'\dfrac{Z}{z'}$
	(1)	(2)	(3)	(4)	(5)
Food	18,949	9,876	10,165	1.0292	19,503
Eating and drinking	10,578	3,443	3,520	1.0225	10,816
General stores with food	1,326	872	810	.9290	1,232
General merchandise	8,536	6,007	5,665	.9431	8,050
Apparel group	6,774	3,236	3,259	1.0070	6,821
Furniture—household—radio	5,786	1,818	1,733	.9536	5,518
Lumber—building—hardware	10,167	2,641	2,735	1.0354	10,527
Automotive	19,747	5,598	5,549	.9913	19,575
Filling stations	6,062	2,779	2,822	1.0156	6,157
Drug stores	2,949	1,555	1,563	1.0049	2,963
Other retail	11,587	4,268	4,221	.9889	11,458
Total	102,461	42,093	42,042	.9988	102,620*

* Obtained by summing the kind-of-business estimates.

Table A–10. Sampling errors of annual dollar volume estimates, and analysis of the rel-variances

Kind of business group	Sampling error by grouped stratum method		Analysis of the sampling rel-variance							
	Unbiased estimate $v_{x'}$ (per cent)	Ratio estimate $v_{x''}$ (per cent)	Of unbiased estimate x'				Of ratio estimate x''			
			Within-psu rel-variance $w_{x'}^2$	Estimated between-psu rel-variance $b_{z'\,35}^2$	Total rel-variance (3)+(4) $v_{x'}^2$	$v_{x'} = \sqrt{(5)}$ (per cent)	Within-psu rel-variance $w_{x''}^2$	Estimated between-psu rel-variance for ratio 1935–1939 est. $b_{z''}^2$	Total (3a)+(4a) $v_{x''}^2$	$v_{x''} = \sqrt{(5a)}$ (per cent)
	(1)	(2)	(3)	(4)	(5)	(6)	(3a)	(4a)	(5a)	(6a)
Food	3.1	2.8	.000458	.000625	.001083	3.3	.000458	.000154	.000612	2.5
Eating and drinking	4.2	3.3	.000428	.000852	.001280	3.6	.000428	.000144	.000572	2.4
General stores with food	13.7	20.8	.006799	.009977	.016776	13.0	.006799	.016998	.023797	15.4
General merchandise	5.9	3.5	.000092	.002302	.002395	4.9	.000092	.000245	.000337	1.8
Apparel	3.9	2.6	.000653	.001088	.001742	4.2	.000653	.000282	.000935	3.1
Furniture—household—radio	5.5	5.4	.001672	.001805	.003477	5.9	.001672	.001143	.002815	5.3
Lumber—building—hardware	7.9	4.7	.001393	.002364	.003757	6.1	.001393	.001356	.002749	5.2
Automotive	4.2	2.9	.000614	.000724	.001338	3.7	.000614	.000317	.000931	3.1
Filling stations	5.5	5.9	.000862	.000728	.001590	4.0	.000862	.000546	.001408	3.8
Drug stores	4.6	5.2	.001253	.000985	.002238	4.7	.001253	.000239	.001492	3.9
Other retail	5.2	4.1	NA	.001005	NA	NA	NA	.000563	NA	NA
Total	3.0	1.9	.000101	.000451	.000552	2.3	.000101	.000066	.000167	1.3

Table A–11. Complete psu's: unbiased estimates of annual sales and their sampling errors

Kind of business group	1939 data			1948 (prelim.) data			Sampling error (per cent) $b_{z'}$			
							By Eq. 19.2 of Ch. 10		By grouped stratum method	
	Estimate for 1939 (millions of dollars) z'	Actual 1939 census (millions of dollars) Z	Deviation (per cent)	Estimate for 1948 (prelim.) (millions of dollars) z'	Actual 1948 census (prelim.) (millions of dollars) Z	Deviation (per cent)	For 1939	For 1935	For 1939	For 1948
	(1)	(2)	(3)	(4)	(5)	(6)	(7)	(8)	(9)	(10)
Food	9,876	10,165	− 2.8	30,232	30,980	− 2.4	2.3	2.5	2.0	2.1
Eating and drinking	3,443	3,520	− 2.2	10,599	10,691	− .9	2.7	2.9	3.1	3.3
General stores with food	872	810	+ 7.6	18,422	17,095	+ 7.8	20.7	10.0	24.0	26.1
General merchandise	6,007	5,665	+ 6.0	}			4.9	4.8	4.3	5.0
Apparel	3,236	3,259	− .7	9,837	9,797	+ .4	3.4	3.3	3.4	3.2
Furniture—household—radio	1,818	1,733	+ 4.9	7,045	6,914	+ 1.9	3.4	4.2	3.3	2.9
Lumber—building—hardware	2,641	2,735	− 3.4	11,411	11,142	+ 2.4	3.1	4.9	5.6	7.6
Automotive	5,598	5,549	+ .9	20,087	20,118	− .2	2.8	2.7	3.4	3.3
Filling stations	2,779	2,822	− 1.5	6,378	6,493	− 1.8	2.2	2.7	3.3	3.9
Drugstores	1,555	1,563	− .5	4,077	4,012	+ 1.6	3.0	3.1	2.9	3.1
Other retail	4,268	4,221	+ 1.1	13,596	13,285	+ 2.3	2.7	3.2	3.4	3.9
Total	42,093	42,042	+ .1	131,629	130,527	+ .8	1.9	2.1	2.3	2.8

552

Table A–12. Complete psu's: ratio estimates of annual sales and their sampling errors

Kind of business group	Dollar volume			Dollar volume			Sampling errors (per cent)		Coefficient of correlation	
	Estimate for 1935 (millions of dollars) $z'_{35}\dfrac{Z_{39}}{z'_{39}}$	Actual 1935 census (millions of dollars) Z_{35}	Deviation (per cent)	Estimate for 1948 (prelim.) (millions of dollars) $z'_{48}\dfrac{Z_{39}}{z'_{39}}$	Actual 1948 census (prelim.) (millions of dollars) Z_{48}	Deviation (per cent)	Computed by Eq. 19.2 of Ch. 10 $v_{z''_{35}}$	By grouped stratum method $v_{z''_{48}}$	$\rho'_{z'_{35}z'_{39}}$	$\rho'_{z'_{48}z'_{39}}$
	(1)	(2)	(3)	(4)	(5)	(6)	(7)	(8)	(9)	(10)
Food	8,311	8,362	− .6	31,115	30,980	+ .4	1.2	1.3	.87	.79
Eating and drinking	2,380	2,391	− .5	10,837	10,691	+ 1.4	1.2	1.5	.91	.90
General stores with food	1,005	1,110	− 9.5	17,341	17,095	+ 1.4	13.0	2.3†	.86	.96
General merchandise	4,578	4,620	− .9		9,797	+ 1.1	1.6		.95	.99
Apparel	2,668	2,656	+ .5	9,906	6,914	− 2.8	1.7	1.6	.88	.88
Furniture—household—radio	1,330	1,290	+ 3.1	6,718			3.4	2.5	.63	.70
Lumber—building—hardware	1,977	1,864	+ 6.1	11,815	11,142	+ 6.0	3.7	3.2	.65	.93
Automotive*	4,591	4,607	− .3	19,912	20,118	− 1.0	1.8	1.5	.79	.90
Filling stations	1,883	1,968	− 4.3	6,478	6,493	− .2	2.3	1.8	.56	.84
Drugstores	1,240	1,233	+ .6	4,097	4,012	+ 2.1	1.5	2.1	.87	.83
Other retail	3,051	3,061	− .3	13,445	13,285	+ 1.2	2.4	2.5	.68	.78
Total	33,014‡	33,161	− .4	131,664‡	130,527	+ .9	.8	1.3	.92	.91

* Includes garages in 1935.
† For general stores and general merchandise group the figures are 7.4 and .9, respectively.
‡ Sum of kinds of business.

Table A–13. Trend: estimates of the ratio of current month's sales to last month's and their sampling errors

(All kinds of business combined)

Current month	Previous month	Trend		Correlation $\rho_{x'y'}$
		Estimate r_1	Relative sampling error (per cent) v_{r_1}	
		(1)	(2)	(3)
January '48	December '47	.787	1.5	.92
February '48	January '48	.930	1.0	.98
March '48	February '48	1.158	1.0	.98
April '48	March '48	1.015	1.0	.97
May '48	April '48	1.000	.8	.98
June '48	May '48	1.014	1.1	.98
July '48	June '48	.991	1.0	.97
August '48	July '48	1.007	.7	.98
September '48	August '48	1.003	.9	.96
October '48	September '48	1.034	.8	.98
November '48	October '48	.973	.7	.99
December '48	November '48	1.151	.9	.97

Table A–14. Month-to-month trend in sales by kind of business groups for April 1948

Kind of business group	Estimate r_1	Relative sampling error (per cent) v_{r_1}	Correlation $\rho'_{x'y'}$
	(1)	(2)	(3)
Food	1.021	1.0	.99
Eating and drinking	1.015	1.1	.99
General stores with food	1.032	4.4	.95
General merchandise	.946	1.2	.98
Apparel group	.910	1.5	.96
Furniture—household—radio	1.074	2.7	.97
Lumber—building—hardware	1.154	7.1	.83
Automotive	1.022	2.4	.97
Filling stations	1.062	1.7	.99
Drugstores	.979	1.2	.996
Other retail	.940	4.0	.87
Total	1.015	1.0	.97

Table A–15.   Month-to-month-a-year-ago trends and their sampling errors
April 1949 over April 1948

Kind of business group	Estimate r_1	Relative sampling error (per cent) v_{r_1}	$\rho'_{x'y'}$
	(1)	(2)	(3)
Food	.912	7.0	.66
Eating and drinking	1.127	7.6	.65
General stores with food	.727	30.3	.63
General merchandise	1.179	6.1	.52
Apparel	1.182	5.0	.64
Furniture—household—radio	1.495	15.0	.41
Lumber—building—hardware	.867	8.8	.71
Automotive	1.183	9.1	.46
Filling stations	1.244	10.0	.68
Drugstores	1.289	12.9	.52
Other retail	1.071	6.6	.68
Total	1.091	2.8	.78

APPENDIX 1, CASE STUDY A

SAMPLING ERROR OF CHOSEN SYSTEM AND OF THE ALTERNATIVE PLAN OF SECTION A–6d

Let

$$x' = x'_1 + x'_2 + x'_3 + \cdots + x'_{12} = \sum_{\mu=1}^{12} x'_\mu$$

where x'_μ is the estimate of dollar volume of sales for the month μ.

$$x' = \sum_{\mu=1}^{12} (X_\mu + \Delta X_\mu + \delta X_\mu)$$

where ΔX_μ represents that part of the deviation x'_μ from X_μ which results from sampling within psu's and δX_μ that part which results from sampling the psu's. Thus:

$$\sigma^2_{x'} = E\left[\sum_{\mu=1}^{12} (\Delta X_\mu + \delta X_\mu)\right]^2$$

$$= E\left[\sum_{\mu=1}^{12} \{(\Delta X_\mu)^2 + (\delta X_\mu)^2\}\right] + E\left[\sum_{i<j} \{2\Delta X_{\mu_i}\Delta X_{\mu_j} + 2\delta X_{\mu_i}\delta X_{\mu_j}\}\right]$$

since the expected value of all terms of the form $\Delta X_{\mu_i} \delta X_{\mu_j}$ is zero for both $i = j$ and $i \neq j$.

$$\sigma_{x'}^2 = 12[\sigma_w^2 + \sigma_B^2] + 2(C_2^{12})[\rho_w \sigma_w^2 + \rho_B \sigma_B^2]$$

where σ_w^2 represents the average variance within psu's of a monthly estimate of total sales, σ_B^2 represents the average variance between psu's of a monthly estimate of total sales, ρ_w is the average correlation within psu's of estimated total sales for all possible pairs of months, ρ_B is the corresponding correlation between psu's, and $C_2^{12} = 12(11)/2$ is the number of combinations of 12 things taken 2 at a time.

$$\sigma_{x'}^2 = 12[1 + 11\rho_w]\sigma_w^2 + 12[1 + 11\rho_B]\sigma_B^2$$

Now, under the plan chosen, $\rho_w \doteq 0$, since the estimate for each month is based on a separate area sample. It is not exactly equal to zero because the segments were chosen from a finite population with some clustering within cities. Under the alternative plan this is not so, because the estimate for every month is based on the same area sample. If σ_w^2 represents the within-psu contribution for the chosen plan, then $\sigma_w^2/12$ represents the within-psu contribution of the alternative plan, since the sample therefore is 12 times as large. Under both plans, since the same psu's are involved, the between-psu contribution is the same. We, therefore, have for the chosen plan

$$\sigma_{x'(\text{chosen})}^2 = 12[1 + 0]\sigma_w^2 + 12[1 + 11\rho_B]\sigma_B^2$$

and for the alternate plan

$$\sigma_{x'(\text{alt.})}^2 = 12[1 + 11\rho_w]\frac{\sigma_w^2}{12} + 12[1 + 11\rho_B]\sigma_B^2$$

Consequently, the ratio of the within-psu contribution to the variance for the chosen plan to that for the alternative plan is

$$\frac{12}{1 + 11\rho_w}$$

The ratio of the total variances will always be closer to unity than the above ratio. Furthermore, the above ratio will also be approximately the ratio of the total variances when the between-psu contribution to the variance is small relative to the within-psu contribution.

APPENDIX 2, CASE STUDY A

DIFFERENCE IN SAMPLING ERROR OF ANNUAL
ESTIMATE RESULTING FROM USE OF 12 AND
OF 24 OBSERVATIONS

It is possible to obtain the annual estimate by utilizing the 12 observations for the area sample that result when each month is the "current" month. It is also possible to utilize 24 observations, because a measurement is made of each month as a current month and also as a previous month. (See Sec. A–7b and Sec. A–6d.) This appendix measures the difference in sampling error between the two estimates.

Let

$$x'_{(24 \text{ obs.})} = \tfrac{1}{2}[_px'_1 + _cx'_1 + _px'_2 + _cx'_2 + \cdots + _px'_{12} + _cx'_{12}]$$

$$= \tfrac{1}{2}\left[\sum_{\mu}^{12} {}_px'_\mu + \sum_{\mu}^{12} {}_cx'_\mu\right]$$

This represents the estimate of annual volume, using all 24 observations. The $_px'_\mu$ represents the estimate for month μ when the month is the previous month in the enumeration, and $_cx'_\mu$ when the month is the current month. From the point of view of the within-psu variance, therefore, $_px'_\mu$ (say January) and $_cx'_{\mu+1}$ (February) are correlated, but for all other pairs the correlations may be taken as close to 0. (See Appendix A–1.)

$$\sigma^2_{x'\,24\,\text{obs.}} = E\tfrac{1}{4}\left[\sum_{\mu}^{12}(\Delta_pX_\mu + \delta X_\mu) + \sum_{\mu}^{12}(\Delta_cX_\mu + \delta X_\mu)\right]^2$$

where ΔX_μ represents that part of the deviation x'_μ from X_μ which results from sampling within psu's, and δX_μ that part which results from sampling the psu's. Furthermore, $\delta_pX_\mu = \delta_cX_\mu$, since the psu's remain the same. Then

$$\sigma^2_{x'(24\,\text{obs.})} = \tfrac{1}{4}E\left\{\sum_{\mu}^{12}[(\Delta_pX_\mu)^2 + (\Delta_cX_\mu)^2 + 4(\delta X_\mu)^2]\right.$$

$$\left. + \sum_{i<j} 2(4)\delta X_{\mu_i}\delta X_{\mu_j} + \sum_{\mu=2}^{12} 2\Delta_pX_{\mu-1}\Delta_cX_\mu\right\}$$

because the expected value of terms of the form $\Delta\delta$ is zero. Therefore,

$$\sigma^2_{x'(24\text{ obs.})} = \tfrac{1}{4}\{12\sigma^2_w + 12\sigma^2_w + 2(11)\rho_w\sigma^2_w + 4(12)\sigma^2_B + 8(66)\rho_B\sigma^2_B\}$$

where ρ_w is the average within correlation for 11 pairs of consecutive months, and the other terms have the same meaning as in Appendix A–1.

$$\sigma^2_{x'(24\text{ obs.})} = 6\sigma^2_w + \tfrac{11}{2}\rho_w\sigma^2_w + 12\sigma^2_B + 132\rho_B\sigma^2_B$$

Now let

$$x'_{(12\text{ obs.})} = {}_cx'_1 + {}_cx'_2 + \cdots + {}_cx'_{12} = \sum_{\mu=1}^{12} {}_cx'_\mu$$

Then

$$\sigma^2_{x'(12\text{ obs.})} = E\left\{\sum_\mu^{12}(\Delta_c X_\mu + \delta X_\mu)\right\}^2$$

$$= E\left\{\sum_\mu^{12}[(\Delta_c X_\mu)^2 + (\delta X_\mu)^2] + 2\sum_{i<j}\delta X_{\mu_i}\delta X_{\mu_j}\right\}$$

$$= 12\sigma^2_w + 12\sigma^2_B + 2(66)\rho_B\sigma^2_B$$

$\sigma^2_{x'(12\text{ obs.})}$ is therefore greater than $\sigma^2_{x'(24\text{ obs.})}$ by $\sigma^2_w(12 - 6 - 5.5\rho_w)$. Thus when $\rho_w = .95$ this difference is merely $.775\sigma^2_w$.

B. THE CURRENT POPULATION SURVEY*

The Current Population Survey is a sample survey conducted monthly by the Bureau of the Census to obtain estimates of employment and unemployment and other data on the labor force. It provides reliable national estimates of changes in the size and composition of components of the labor force, and also provides data on hours worked, duration of unemployment and the like. In addition, frequent studies are made of the distribution of income, migration, educational attainment, and other demographic, social, or economic topics. These estimates are based on data collected from a sample of 25,000 households located in 68 sample areas comprising 125 counties and independent cities located throughout the United States.

The Current Population Survey is the basis for the Monthly Report on the Labor Force. These monthly reports were preceded by several earlier attempts to measure the number of unemployed. The problem of determining the number of unemployed became especially pressing during the depression of the 1930's, at which time various devices were used to estimate unemployment. These ranged from guesses to enumerative counts with a registration of the unemployed in 1937.

The Monthly Report on the Labor Force Survey was started in March 1940 on a monthly basis by the Work Projects Administration. This sample represented the results of their pioneering efforts in the use of sampling for labor market research, and operated under stringent cost and time limitations. In August 1942, the survey was assigned to the Bureau of the Census. The original design underwent a thorough revision in October 1943 and has been modified subsequently. The original design, unlike the revised design, was not a probability sample. Nevertheless, it was based on objective methods of preselection of respondents so that enumerators had no choice as to the households to be interviewed. The revision provided an opportunity for introducing probability sampling along with a number of developments in sampling theory.

The Sample Design, 1950

1. Administrative requirements. The sample currently being used as the basis for the Current Population Survey was designed within certain administrative requirements. The total number of different areas to be

---

* By Joseph Steinberg, Bureau of the Census.

included in the sample was not to be too large, in order primarily to insure adequate training of and close supervision over enumerators.   The sample was to be such as to facilitate operations on a short time schedule and, although designed primarily for surveys of the labor force, was also to serve as a general-purpose sample.   On the basis of these administrative requirements it was decided that the sample would be selected in a total of no more than 68 primary sampling units.

2. Principal resources and materials.   A study was made of material that was available to facilitate an efficient design.   Information was available for counties from the principal censuses on characteristics of the population, agriculture, and industry, such as degree of urbanization and concentration of industry of various kinds and of types of crops and other agricultural activities.   Population distributions and certain other characteristics were available for smaller areas within counties.   Also, a variety of mapping materials covering the United States was available, including county highway maps and aerial photographs for rural areas, block maps of various types for densely settled areas, and very detailed maps showing individual structures by principal use in cities of 25,000 population or more.   Data were available from the 1940 Census of Population on number of dwelling units per block, and in some other cases special surveys had been made to provide such information, particularly in suburban areas.   Estimates of dwelling units generally have high correlation with most economic or sociological variables and were useful in the selection of the sample.

Relatively accurate current estimates of the total population in the United States and of the age-sex distribution of the population are available.   These, together with estimates of the number of veterans by age, are useful in the estimation of results from the survey.

3. General design.   The first step in the design of the sample was to determine approximately the number of areas to include in the sample. In this case the number of areas was already specified as not to exceed 68 (see Sec. B–1), and this was the number selected.   The next step was to set up the primary sampling units.   Then strata were formed from these psu's.   After the strata had been formed, one psu was drawn from each stratum.   Within these selected primary units segments were set up and sample segments selected.   Lists were then prepared for the sample segments, and sampling ratios were applied to determine the groups of households to be included in the survey.

Each month after the survey week the schedules are sent to the Washington office for processing, and tabulations are run off from the punched cards prepared.   The report of the results of the survey gives estimates of labor force status, together with estimates of the sampling variability. Each of these steps is described in somewhat greater detail below.

4. Defining the primary sampling units.   The larger the primary unit the greater, usually, the heterogeneity that can be introduced within psu's with respect to characteristics to be studied, and the smaller the psu contribution to the variance for any fixed number of psu's in the sample. Thus, by increasing the size of the primary unit, urban as well as rural populations and varied types of industrial and agricultural activities can be reflected in each psu.   However, with the supervisory and other administrative and travel restrictions imposed on this survey, the area, in general, had to be restricted to a few counties at the maximum.   Consequently psu's were made as large as possible while still keeping travel costs within psu's at an economical level.   With a few exceptions whole counties or groups of contiguous counties were defined as psu's.

In setting up psu's it was decided that areas approximating the 12* largest metropolitan districts would constitute separate self-representing sample areas.   In approximating the 12 largest metropolitan districts some counties were split.   Such splits were made only where essential to include important parts of the metropolitan district without making it necessary to travel far.   Since separate estimates might sometimes be made for each metropolitan district, all of a metropolitan district was usually included.

The remaining counties and parts of counties were then grouped into psu's.   In forming these psu's, the grouping was done subjectively, several alternatives being tried before a decision on the final combination was made.   However, the following principles were observed:

(1) Counties which were combined were to be contiguous.

(2) In general, counties were to be combined only if the total area involved was no more than 1500 square miles in the East and 2000 in the West.   However, after consulting topographical and road maps, these limits were sometimes modified to allow for local travel conditions.

(3) Counties were combined so as to maximize heterogeneity within the psu, principally with respect to farm-nonfarm composition.   Thus, to the extent feasible, counties that were largely farm were grouped with other areas which were substantially nonfarm.

---

* Washington, D.C., was included, although it was not at that time one of the 12 largest metropolitan districts, because it is of such a specialized industrial character and at the same time of such a large size that it could hardly be grouped with other primary sampling units to form a homogeneous stratum.

In this manner, the more than 3000 counties of the United States were grouped into about 2000 primary sampling units.

5. Stratification of psu's. These psu's were then to be grouped into 68 primary strata (i.e., 1 sample psu to be selected per stratum). The strata were to be formed with approximately equal population. Since the number of strata was 68, all primary units larger than or almost equal to (U.S. Population)/68 $\doteq$ 1,950,000 would be included with certainty. It was for this reason that each of the 12 largest metropolitan districts became a separate stratum and came into the sample with certainty. (The New York-Northeastern New Jersey area was split into 2 parts, making 13 primary strata consisting of self-representing areas.) The approximately 2000 remaining psu's were grouped into 55 primary strata. The bases for stratification were degree of urbanization, geographic location, migration between 1940 and 1943, type of industry in the predominantly urban areas, and type of farming in the rural areas. The strata were set up on the basis of judgment, as well as objective measures, in an effort to increase the heterogeneity between and the homogeneity within strata.

6. Selection of primary sampling units. The choice of a sample area in each stratum was determined by a procedure which made the probability that a particular psu would be selected proportionate to its population in the 1940 Census, as illustrated in Ch. 9, Sec. 11.

7. Selection of subsample from selected psu's. The subsampling within the selected psu's was accomplished with 1 or 2 additional stages of sampling, depending upon the types of resources available for subsampling. Different kinds of mapping materials were available for various substrata, and the sampling procedures within substrata varied with these resources. In all types of substrata it was decided, on the basis of preliminary investigations and optimum sampling considerations (see Ch. 6, Sec. 24), that the ultimate clusters sampled from the second-stage sampling units should contain an average of about 6 households. This was accomplished in some cases by 2 stages of sampling within selected psu's, and in other cases with compact cluster sampling.

8. Definition and selection of segments in rural areas. In rural territory, areas consisting of about 50 households were defined and selected as second-stage sampling units, and clusters of about 6 households were selected from each of these. The areas that serve as second-stage sampling units will be referred to as segments. The basic mapping materials used in delineating segments of approximately 50 households were the county highway maps, which show, with varying degrees of accuracy, the location of farm and other dwellings in the open country, and less detail in the rural congested areas.   In the open country, i.e., outside villages, these map features showing the location of dwellings were used to determine the "size" of each segment by counting the number of dwellings shown on the map.   All segments were to be bounded by relatively permanent natural or man-made features, such as roads, streams, railroad tracks, and section lines.   In some cases the open country areas shaded off into congested (thickly settled) areas, and here further problems arose because of the paucity of map information on the location of dwellings.   Here, use was made of aerial photographs to define boundaries and set up segments.   Even for the true open country segments, the aerial photographs at times helped establish boundaries where none seemed available on the map.   For the congested segments, counts of dwellings within well-defined boundaries were made from enlarged aerial photographs. Since some of these map materials were out of date, special field surveys were made in the selected psu's to determine the areas in which an appreciable amount of new construction had taken place.   These surveys produced information, not only on the numbers of such new dwellings, but also on the location of natural features not previously shown by the available materials.   Through the use of the aerial photographs and information from the special surveys, segments were set up in a similar fashion in rural congested areas, including rural incorporated places (incorporated places having less than 2500 population).

For each primary stratum an over-all sampling fraction of 1 in about 2050 is used at present.   This gives about 25,000 households for the nation as a whole.   Because the primary units were sampled with probability proportionate to size, the sampling fraction used within each selected psu depends on the proportion that the psu population (at the time of the 1940 Census) was of the stratum population.   Thus, in a sample area which was one-fiftieth of the stratum, the sampling fraction is 1 in 41 (e.g., $\frac{1}{2050} \div \frac{1}{50}$) (see Ch. 9, Sec. 12).

After each segment in the open country areas had been delineated on a master map and on supporting aerial photos or sketches, the within sampling fraction was used to determine the specific segments to be included in the sample.   Where a psu consisted of more than 1 county, the open country segments of all counties were sampled before proceeding to sample the congested rural segments.   In the usual case these segments were about the same in "size" in terms of the number of dwelling units. In other cases, because of lack of information for making segments as small as 50, the selected "segments" were multiples of segments of 50.

The larger this unit, the more the listing cost. Therefore, cost considerations dictated that an attempt be made to subdivide these multiple segments. These multiple segments were identified on a map sent to the field office in charge. The field staff subdivided the multiple segments in a survey on the spot, using identifiable boundaries. The particular subdivision to be included in the sample was then chosen at random from among all subdivisions, with probability proportionate to the estimated number of dwelling units in each subdivision. These selected segments contained many more households than were needed for a single sample. Hence, a listing of the households in these segments, as noted below, was made from which the sample households were to be selected.

9. Definition and selection of segments in urban areas. The sample for urban places was based on the same fundamental sampling principles. However, the materials used for designating the segments were different. The Bureau of the Census has a set of Sanborn maps that are drawn to a very large scale and in great detail. These maps were used for almost all cities of 25,000 population or more and for the urban fringes. The maps show structures drawn to scale and indicate the principal occupancy of each structure. Streets, alleys, and other physical features are also shown. The relationship of each of these detailed maps to the whole is shown on a key map. Furthermore, periodic corrections are made by the publisher to keep the maps up to date.

These maps make it possible to delineate small segments which can be identified readily in the field, without listing the dwelling units in sampled blocks and subsampling. Approximate measures of size (number of dwelling units) were available for each block covered by maps. A sample of blocks was selected with the probability of selection proportionate to the number of segments of approximately 6 dwelling units into which the block should be divided. Once the sample block was selected, segments were delineated on a copy of the map. (See Fig. 2, Ch. 6, for illustration of such a segment.) The number of segments in each case was equal to the estimate used for the block. The segments were unambiguously delineated, using alleys, property lines, streets, etc. A segment was then selected at random, and its boundaries transcribed to another copy of the same map. In most of the segments delineated on these maps all the dwelling units are enumerated. In some cases, as, for instance, a large apartment building, the area consisted of a multiple segment from which only a sample of dwelling units is enumerated.

The detailed Sanborn maps rarely cover an entire city. For areas where these maps were not available, special field surveys were made to provide a basis for segmentation and selection of the sample segments.

Such steps pay when the cost is spread over a great many monthly surveys but would be unlikely to be economical for a one-time survey. To keep dwelling count information current, new construction surveys are conducted from time to time. These surveys provide a basis for avoiding, as time goes by, a large increase in the variance in size between segments. Information developed from these surveys makes it possible to set up a separate stratum of segments with well-defined boundaries, where a considerable increase in size has taken place. By sampling from this stratum of segments, newly developed areas are introduced into the sample with a minimum increase in variance in the original area sample, and with a sharp decrease over the variance which would have occurred had this step been neglected.

As will be noted in Sec. 11 below, the urban sample segments are changed periodically, whereas the rural segments are used for about 4 years. Thus, from time to time, additional selections of segments are made.

10. Listing the sampled segments. After the sample segments have been selected by the Washington staff of the Bureau of the Census, field personnel make a complete listing of all dwelling units within each of these segments. The listers are instructed carefully* and tested to be sure they thoroughly understand their job.

Each segment is completely listed when it is first used in the Current Population Survey, and this listing is usually then verified (either immediately, or, for segments where all units are to be included in the sample, at the time of enumeration). The listing unit is the dwelling unit, and before the lister can do any listing he must know the definition of a dwelling unit. In addition to listing dwelling units he must know how to handle problems of special dwelling places (structures where people have common living arrangements) such as institutions, dormitories, and bunkhouses.

The listing process consists of supplying a complete identification of each dwelling unit and its location in the segment. In order to insure complete coverage, the lister is instructed to inquire of a responsible person whenever there is the slightest possibility that a structure may contain more than one dwelling unit. If a structure appears to be a lodging or rooming house or nontransient hotel, the lister must inquire as to the number of rooms it contains. He is instructed to list vacant, as well as occupied, units. He lists abandoned structures if the possibility

---

* Current Population Survey, "How to List," *Form* P–2210, U.S. Department of Commerce, Bureau of the Census, September 1950.

exists that they may be occupied again. Strong efforts are made to insure that omissions in the listings are kept to a minimum.

Certain types of listing errors result in biases in the survey operation—for example, when the lister completely fails to identify a unit or incorrectly lists a unit which is not inside the segment boundaries. Other listing errors result in increased sampling variability in the survey results—for example, when the lister identifies two units by a single description, thus requiring both units to be included if the listing is selected for the sample.

The listing operation also consists of supplying a complete identification of each special dwelling place. These lists of special dwelling places serve as part of the basis for the selection of a sample of units within special dwelling places.

After the listing operation is completed, sample households are selected from the listings in the segments where a third stage of sampling is to be used.

11. Rotation of sample. The households included in the Current Population Survey sample are not kept constant from one month to the next. It has been found that virtually all respondents can be expected to supply information for several months without creating any administrative problem by refusing to cooperate. However, keeping the same households on for a considerably longer time would result in higher refusal rates or complaints and requests to be dropped off the panel. Once the decision is reached that it is necessary to have a fresh sample of households occasionally, there are very strong administrative advantages in introducing a new sample of households on a staggered basis. Substantial costs are involved in introducing a set of households for the first time into the sample. For example, about 5 minutes more is required to enumerate a household for the first month that it is in the sample than in succeeding months. Therefore, it is desirable to have only some of the new households come into the sample at any one time so as to equalize the workload over a number of months.

12. Selection of sample households. On the list of segments sent to the field office each urban segment is identified by segment number, a rotation number, and separate sampling instructions. The rotation number determines the month of start of enumeration of sample households in the segment and the last month in the sample. The sampling instructions determine which households on the listing sheet for the segment are to be included in the sample. The sample households for a given area are selected from the listing sheets in the local field office. A comprehensive set of instructions is provided to the field staff in this connection.

Rural segments are grouped together in sets having common sampling instructions.   These sampling instructions are applied to the listings for all segments in a set in consecutive order.   Clusters of 6 dwelling units are selected within rural segments in order to save trouble, time, and cost. Once the sample clusters have been determined, rotation numbers are assigned in sequence to the clusters.

After the sample households.are selected, the field office returns a sample report to the Washington office.   These reports are checked for consistency with previous reports and tested for accuracy in carrying out the sampling instructions.

In many types of special dwelling places, such as institutions, college dormitories, and the like, listing and sampling operations are carried on simultaneously in order to minimize the problems of sampling in such places.   Sample reports on these operations are submitted and analyzed for accuracy in carrying out the sampling instructions.

13. Survey operation.   Each month, during the calendar week containing the fifteenth day of the month, a staff of trained interviewers conducts interviews with some responsible member of each household in the sample.

The training program for interviewers is continuous throughout successive months of employment.   New interviewers receive from $1\frac{1}{2}$ to 3 days' training under the supervision of the district supervisor.   The interviewer is indoctrinated in the background and general purpose of the survey and the way in which the survey works.   He is then required to study the *Enumerator's Manual** and other instruction material and forms that he is to use in the survey.   The supervisor reviews with him all the basic parts of enumeration with emphasis on such things as: (*a*) proper approach to use in interviewing: how to explain the survey, the sampling procedures, and the reasons for monthly calls; (*b*) how to get complete coverage of persons in sample units; (*c*) how to prepare forms and schedule entries; (*d*) why it is important to ask questions as worded and in proper order; (*e*) basic concepts on employment status, occupation, industry, and so on. The supervisor generally accompanies the new interviewer for a while to observe his work and give him further instruction.

Experienced interviewers generally receive some regular training each month.   This is adjusted somewhat to fit the needs and experience of the interviewer and may vary from as little as 2 hours to as much as 6 hours per interviewer, depending on the supplementary questions being asked.

---

* Current Population Survey, "Monthly Report on the Labor Force— Enumerator's Manual," *Form* P–1606c, U.S. Department of Commerce, Bureau of the Census, February 1952.

At the first interview of a household, the interviewer prepares a "Control Card" on which he lists the roster of household members, including their personal characteristics (age, sex, race, marital status, and veteran status) and their relationship to the household head. This roster is brought up to date at each subsequent interview to take account of new or departed residents, changes in marital status, and similar items. The information on personal characteristics is then available each month for identification purposes and for cross-classification with the economic characteristics of the sample population.

At each monthly interview the enumerator asks a series of standardized questions on economic activity during the preceding week (the calendar week containing the eighth day of the month, called the "survey week") for each household member 14 years of age and over. The primary purpose of these questions is to classify the sample population into three basic economic groups—the employed, the unemployed, and those not in the labor force. Usually once each year, data on school enrollment, migration, and income are obtained. These data, together with the basic data collected, provide valuable information on changes in the economic and social structure of the American family and individual.

As in all probability sample surveys conducted in such a brief period, some of the households designated for the sample have not been interviewed by the close of the enumeration week. Typically the proportion of noninterviews has been in the neighborhood of 3–5 per cent. Less than 1 per cent are the result of refusals. Most of the noninterviews in the winter are due to poor roads and bad weather, making some households inaccessible for personal interview. In the summer, a major portion of the noninterviews arises as a result of people being temporarily away on vacation. In an effort to reduce the number of noninterviews and the costs of call-backs, the telephone is being used, wherever possible, to secure the information. Checks made to date indicate negligible differences in quality of information obtained by telephone and personal interview.

Each month, the supervisor checks the quality of the work of his enumerators by observing some of their interviews and also by reinterviewing a few households previously enumerated. By accompanying an enumerator, the supervisor can check on the enumerator's interviewing technique as well as his ability to check for coverage and method of asking questions. By interviewing selected households already interviewed, a check of the quality of the information is afforded. After enumeration, the district supervisor edits the "Control Cards" and (on a selective basis) the schedules for omissions, inaccuracies, or inconsistent entries.

14. Estimation procedure.   Schedules are received in the Washington office by the end of the week following enumeration.   Schedules for the households which were noninterview are replaced by other schedules for interviewed households of similar residence (farm or nonfarm) and race, selected at random from the same sample area.   This mechanical procedure of imputing information for a noninterview household is a poor substitute for the information about the household itself.   However, this procedure is carried through as one of the steps in the streamlined operations needed to speed results to consumers of data from the Current Population Survey, and leads to satisfactory results so long as the noninterview rate is kept low.

The choice of the particular estimating procedure now used for the Current Population Survey was made from among a number of different ones available.   Primary consideration rested on selecting a procedure which jointly with the sample selection procedure would lead to the smallest sampling variability of estimated aggregates and changes in aggregates from month to month, subject to cost and time limitations. It is anticipated, however, that modifications of the procedure will be made to improve estimates of change.   One of the basic factors leading to speed in producing results is the fact that the sample was designed to be self-weighting (i.e., each sample element is given the same weight in the tabulation).   The procedure noted above for substitution for non-interviews thus retains the self-weighting feature of the sample design.

After the schedules are coded and edited, punched cards are prepared. A separate card is punched for each person 14 years of age and over. Estimates could be prepared by tabulating these punched cards with a fixed weight.   This would be the simple unbiased estimate based upon the survey results.

However, the present estimating procedure makes use of two separate types of ratio estimates to reduce, in general, the sampling variability of the Current Population Survey estimates.   The first ratio estimate is designed to reduce solely the between-psu contribution to the sampling variability.   It depends upon the availability of data on the population by color (white and nonwhite) and residence (urban, rural-nonfarm, and rural farm) for each psu.   The second type of ratio estimate is designed to reduce both the between-psu and the within-psu variances.   This second ratio estimate depends upon the availability of accurate, independent current estimates of the population by age, sex, and veteran status.

If x_{ac} is the sample value of some characteristic from the survey for the ath age-sex-veteran status group in the cth color-residence group, and if

y_{ac} is the total number of persons in the sample in that group, then the estimate now used for the Current Population Survey is:

$$x'' = \sum_a \frac{x_a''}{y_a''} Y_a \qquad \text{(Eq. 23.4, Ch. 9)}$$

where

$$x_a'' = \sum_c \frac{x_{ac}}{f} \frac{Z_c}{z_c'}, \quad \text{and} \quad y_a'' = \sum_c \frac{y_{ac}}{f} \frac{Z_c}{z_c'}$$

are estimates, respectively, of the aggregate value of the characteristic for all persons in the population in the ath age-sex-veteran status group, and of the total number of persons in that group, f is the over-all sampling fraction, Y_a is the current independent estimate of the number of persons in the ath age-sex-veteran status group.

$z_c' = \sum_h^L \sum_j^1 Z_{hjc}(1/P_{hj})$ is an estimate of the number of persons in the cth color-residence group based on available Census data for the sample psu's.

Z_c is the Census count of the number of persons in the cth color-residence group.

Z_{hjc} is the number of persons in the cth color-residence group in the jth psu in the hth stratum according to the latest available Census results.

$P_{hj} = A_{hj}/A_h$ is the probability of the selection of the jth psu in the hth stratum, where A_{hj} and A_h are the total population in the jth psu in the hth stratum, and in the hth stratum, respectively, according to the 1940 Census.

L is the number of strata.

In order to keep the limitation that tabulations result from a self-weighting set of punched cards, these two types of ratio estimates are used in the following way:

(1) The ratio of Z_c/z_c' is determined. These ratios currently are:

	WHITE	NONWHITE
Urban	.990	.881
Rural-nonfarm	1.043	.844
Rural farm	1.040	.839

Where the ratio is larger than 1, this determines the proportion of punched cards for persons in households having the given color-residence characteristic which are to be selected for duplication. Where the ratio is less than 1, this determines the proportion of punched cards to be retained (the remainder being rejected from further processing). In practice, a duplication control number is assigned at random to the proper proportion of schedules having the stated color-residence characteristic immediately upon receipt of schedules from the field offices. In a similar fashion, where rejection is required, this is done at random on a schedule basis at the same time.

(2) Immediately after punched cards are prepared, they are tabulated to obtain preliminary sample totals by age, sex, and veteran status. These preliminary sample totals are compared with independent current estimates of the population in the same groups. These independent current estimates are calculated by adjusting the most recent census data to take account of the subsequent aging of the population, deaths, and international migration. The ratios of these independent estimates to the preliminary sample estimates determine the sampling rates that are used to select at random individual punched cards for duplication or rejection, as necessary.

After this step is completed, detailed tabulations are prepared which, when multiplied by $1/f$, provide the estimates published in the Monthly Report on the Labor Force and other reports.

As we noted above, other estimating procedures were available. Before October 1947 a variant of the above procedure was used for the first type of ratio estimate, which involved a modification of the sampling fractions used within psu's, but still retained a uniform over-all fraction. This method, called "area substratification,"* in effect involved a ratio estimate within each of the 55 non-self-representing strata in the Current Population Survey design. The results of empirical studies have shown that this method of substratification reduces the between-psu variance appreciably on many items, and also that the method now in use results in nearly equivalent reductions without the risk of bias that is involved in area substratification, and with some simplification of sample selection and administration.

15. Estimation of sampling variability. Every report based on the survey includes estimates of sampling variability. There are some practical limitations which prevent estimating the sampling variability of every item published. A given release may have as many as 1000–2000 items, as well as many more derived figures, such as percentage distributions, and medians, or per cent change from a base figure which is either

---

* Morris H. Hansen and William N. Hurwitz, "On the Theory of Sampling from Finite Populations," *Annals Math. Stat.*, **XIV** (1943), No. 4, p. 333.

a complete census count or another sample estimate. Both cost and time limitations would prohibit calculating the sampling variability of each of these items. Methods of generalizing on the basis of relatively few calculations are given after the following paragraphs, which describe how a direct measure of the sampling variability is obtained for a given item.

We shall first consider how to estimate the variance of $x' = (1/f)x$, a simple unbiased estimate of an aggregate, and then, with these results, indicate how we approximate the variance of the estimate given by Eq. 23.4, Ch. 9, which involves considerable additional work to estimate directly.

An estimate of the sampling variability of a given item must take into account the design of the sample survey. However, making variance estimates under the assumption that certain stratification effects are ignored causes no serious problem except for the possibility of an upward bias in the variance estimates, i.e., an overstatement of the possible range of sampling error. The grouping of certain of the strata used in the selection of the sample and in the estimating process is involved in the variance estimating procedure described below. Thus, the computations outlined would be appropriate for estimating the variance if the ratio estimate were made to total population 14 years of age and over, instead of specifically by age and sex groups. The ratio estimate by color-residence is not fully reflected, and certain of the primary strata are grouped. The consequence is that the variance of x' as estimated may have an expected value somewhat larger than the true variance. For many items, the difference should be trivial; for some it may be important. It is not necessary to make all these simplifying assumptions—the variance for the design used is given by Eq. 8.1, Ch. 9, of Vol. II. This equation involves much more computing, however, and has not been used for the variance computations presented below.

The contribution to the variance for the 13 self-representing areas arises solely from the sampling of segments. Within each self-representing area, segments are selected as a systematic sample of all segments. To calculate the variance, we arrange sample segments in the sequence drawn and use Eq. 8.1, Ch. 11.*

The contribution to the variance from the other 55 strata (which we have referred to as non-self-representing) consists of two parts—a variance *within* psu's and a variance *between* psu's, but we can make estimates of the total variance without doing the extra work necessary to isolate these between- and within-psu components to the variance. Since only one

* Only the first term in Eq. 8.1 is used, since the computation is for a simple unbiased estimate instead of a ratio estimate.

psu is included in the sample from each stratum, we are unable to estimate the variance within the primary strata used in the selection of the sample. For this reason we use the "grouped stratum technique." The first step consists in forming primary groups by combining the original strata into groups of two or three. The variance estimating equation for the estimated total for the 55 strata is then given by Eq. 15.1, Ch. 9.

In forming the primary groups of strata we attempted to combine the strata in such a manner that biases mentioned in Ch. 9, Sec. 15, would be minimized. This was done by grouping strata of about equal size, and as similar as possible with respect to a number of the characteristics being estimated. A trial and error procedure was used of examining many different labor force characteristics, including occupation, industry, and other characteristics, including total population, from the 1940 Census, and seeing what combinations of strata (without looking at the sample psu's) would seem to minimize the variance between stratum means. Empirical tests were made in order to determine whether the groupings chosen produced reasonably good estimates of variances for characteristics for which we could also compute population variances.

To illustrate the type of reasoning involved, consider the combination of stratum 21 (represented by Providence, R.I.) and stratum 22 (represented by Hartford, Conn.) to form a grouped stratum. The two strata were approximately equal in 1940 population, the measure of size used. In addition, both strata were located in the Northeast Region, both consisted of psu's containing cities of 50,000 or more population, and both showed reasonably similar values for such items as proportion unemployed and proportion employed in manufacturing.

The actual computations of the variance contribution arising from the 55 non-self-representing areas are performed using data from a special tabulation and Eq. 15.3, Ch. 9. The tabulation gives, for selected characteristics, by stratum, the number of persons in the sample having the specified characteristics. Our final result is a coefficient of variation, which is the same whether it refers to the sample total or the estimated population total, since the latter is the former multiplied by a constant.

The variance contribution arising from the self-representing areas is then combined with the contribution from the non-self-representing areas as shown by Eq. 29.1, Ch. 9.* Only the first term of Eq. 29.1 is used, since the variance being computed is of x' and not of x'/y'.

The costs of following this procedure for every characteristic are prohibitive. We are faced, then, with a problem of generalizing from the

---

* A more detailed description of the method followed (which in practice involves a slight modification) is given in a forthcoming publication of the Bureau of the Census.

estimated variances for selected characteristics to reasonably accurate statements concerning the reliability of all estimates. Fortunately, experience has shown that for particular classes of characteristics, such as those dealing with labor force, or with migration or race, the variance of an unbiased estimate for a member of the class tends to have a definite functional relation to the size of the estimate. Expressing this relationship in terms of the rel-variance of the estimated total ($v_{x'}^2$), we can say that $v_{x'}^2$ decreases as x' increases, but not as rapidly. Several different functions have been tested in an attempt to find one which satisfactorily expresses the functional relationship between $v_{x'}^2$ and x'. Reasonably satisfactory results have been achieved by using a function of the form $v_{x'}^2 = a + b/x'$.

We will now proceed to illustrate the procedure used to obtain the generalized function for $v_{x'}^2$. Table B–1 gives some values of $v_{x'}^2$ and x'. The first step in the generalization procedure is to plot the computed values. Logarithmic scales are used. The plotted points are examined in order to determine whether there are any points which show a wide variation from the general trend. If one or more points do show considerable variation, we must then decide, before fitting a curve, whether to eliminate one or more of these points, and possibly whether to fit two or more separate curves to various groups of points which appear to follow different trends. The decision rests on an examination of the particular characteristics which the different groups of points represent.

When the problem of what points to use has been resolved, the next step is to fit a function of the form $v_{x'}^2 = a + b/x'$. The method used minimizes the squared relative residuals of $v_{x'}^2$. The curve is fitted by a series of successive approximations until successive approximations of the parameters differ negligibly.

Table B–1 and Fig. B–1 give the basic data for such computations for a class of items made from some sample results for 1951. Values obtained from the curve for different values of x' are referred to as the generalized values for $v_{x'}^2$ and are the values used in the next step.

One method of checking the validity of the generalization is to find the parameters a and b for a set of characteristics from a sample, plot the curve, and then compute additional variances for characteristics either from the same sample or from another sample and see how close these estimated variances are to the original curve. Experiments of this type have shown considerable stability, both for different characteristics from the same sample and for the same characteristics at different points in time. Figure B–1 illustrates this point. The labor force curve is the one used at present for standard labor force characteristics, based on estimated variances for characteristics selected from the April–June 1948 CPS samples. The individual points plotted on Fig. B–1 are based on a CPS

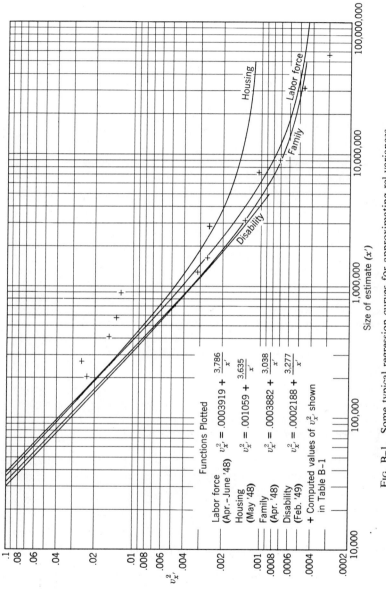

Functions Plotted

Labor force
(Apr.–June '48) $v_x^2 = .0003919 + \dfrac{3.786}{x'}$

Housing
(May '48) $v_x^2 = .001059 + \dfrac{3.635}{x'}$

Family
(Apr. '48) $v_x^2 = .0003882 + \dfrac{3.038}{x'}$

Disability
(Feb. '49) $v_x^2 = .0002188 + \dfrac{3.277}{x'}$

+ Computed values of v_x^2 shown
  in Table B-1

FIG. B-1. Some typical regression curves for approximating rel-variances.

supplement of January 1951 on Work Experience during 1950. Figure B-1 also presents some illustrative curves for other selected sets of characteristics.

Table B-1. Computed values of $v_{x'}^2$ (see Sec. B-15) for selected estimates from the January 1951 CPS supplement on Work Experience in 1950

Characteristic*	Estimate x'	$v_{x'}^2$
Females, white, did not work in 1950, married, 35–54 years old	8,956,600	.000732
Females, white, usually worked full-time, married, clerical and sales workers	2,815,800	.002550
Females, white, usually worked full-time, widowed, divorced, separated, or never married	7,328,300	.001056
Females, white, did not work in 1950, widowed, divorced, or separated, 14–44 years old	883,500	.012392
Females, white, usually worked full-time, married, employed in agriculture	264,100	.025516
Males, white, did not work in 1950, 20–64 years old	1,613,100	.002628
Males, nonwhite, did not work during year	570,000	.013633
Males, white, usually worked full-time, worked 0–26 weeks in 1950	3,188,200	.001357
Females, did not work in 1950	33,567,300	.000462
Females, nonwhite, did not work in 1950, never married	406,600	.015744
Males, nonwhite, did not work in 1950, 14–19 years old	201,400	.023140
Females, nonwhite, usually worked full-time, married	1,280,600	.003117
Females	56,631,400	.000294

* All characteristics are restricted to persons 14 and over.

The final step in estimating the variances is to convert from the variance of an unbiased estimate to the variance of a ratio estimate. In order to do this we utilize the relationship (see Ch. 8, Eq. 4.1)

$$v_{x''}^2 \doteq v_{x'}^2 - v_{y'}^2 - 2\rho_{y', \frac{x'}{y'}} v_{y'} v_{\frac{x'}{y'}}$$

where $x'' = (x'/y')Y$ is the ratio estimate of a total.

x' = the simple unbiased estimate of the characteristic.

y' = the simple unbiased estimate of the control total.

Y = the control total.

Using the generalized value for $v_{x'}^2$ and assuming that

$$\rho_{y', \frac{x'}{y'}} \doteq 0$$

this becomes

$$v_{x''}^2 = \left(a + \frac{b}{x'}\right) - \left(a + \frac{b}{y'}\right) = b\left(\frac{1}{x'} - \frac{1}{y'}\right)$$

It should be noted that this is a satisfactory approximation of the rel-variance only if the assumption that $\rho_{y', \frac{x'}{y'}} = 0$ is reasonably close. Em-pirical tests have shown that this is a satisfactory approximation for most characteristics regularly estimated from the Current Population Survey. For estimates which are a relatively small proportion of any age-sex-veteran-status group, say 25 per cent or less, the effect of using this approximation is negligible; for larger estimates the effect is more noticeable. If the estimated characteristic is one of the 24 control totals, the variance of the ratio estimate will be zero if the use of separate ratio estimates is taken into account; whereas a substantial variance is estimated if the figures based on the single control total are used.

We have covered the procedures of variance estimation where the between- and within-psu components of the variance are not analyzed. These estimates of variances are presented in the reliability statement of each report. Estimated variances also have an important internal use, namely, to provide criteria for determining what analytic statements can be made about the sample estimates in the textual material which accompanies each published set of figures. The purpose of the textual material is to point out the more important and interesting trends and comparisons from a subject matter point of view. Special care is taken to see that all statements in the text take into account the sampling variability of the estimates. For example, it is not ordinarily regarded as appropriate to point up a difference between two estimates unless it exceeds the sampling variability (at least 1.6σ or more usually 2σ) of the estimated difference, and unless, in addition, from an economic point of view, such a difference is large enough to be worth mentioning.

16. **Components used in determining optimum sample designs.** Variances and cost factors estimated from the Current Population Survey and other sample surveys provide the necessary information for improving the design of present surveys and designing new surveys. Measures of variances within and between psu's, taken in combination with unit cost factors and administrative restrictions, provide the information necessary to determine the optimum design of the sample.

Variance components. Table B–2 shows between- and within-psu variance components for CPS labor force characteristics, as determined by the methods of estimation described previously. These are the variance components of an unbiased estimate. Notice that for smaller estimates the within component exceeds the between component, whereas the situation is reversed for larger estimates. The two components are equal for an estimate of about 7,000,000.

Table B–2. Between- and within-psu variance components* for CPS labor force characteristics

x'	Total variance	Within-psu variance	Between-psu variance
10,000	.3790	.2617	.1173
50,000	.0761	.0524	.0237
100,000	.0383	.0263	.0120
500,000	.0080	.0053	.0026
1,000,000	.0042	.0027	.0015
5,000,000	.0011	.0006	.0005
10,000,000	.0008	.0004	.0004
20,000,000	.0006	.0002	.0004
50,000,000	.0005	.0001	.0003
110,000,000	.0004	.0001	.0003

* Expressed as rel-variances.

Although the relative importance of the two components varies with the size of estimate for unbiased estimates, there is for the generalized variances for any particular class of items a constant relationship for the variances of ratio estimates, which is a function of the b values for the generalized functions representing the within and between variances. Thus, for estimated general labor force items in the present design,

$$\frac{s_1^2}{s_2^2} = \frac{v_1^2}{v_2^2} = \frac{b_1\left(\frac{1}{x'} - \frac{1}{y'}\right)}{b_2\left(\frac{1}{x'} - \frac{1}{y'}\right)} = \frac{b_1}{b_2} = \frac{1170}{2616} \doteq .45$$

where s_1^2 represents the contribution to the total variance of the psu sample, and s_2^2 represents the contribution to the total variance of the sample within psu's. Characteristics relating to agricultural employment are a separate class. For this group, in the present design, the estimated value for the equivalent ratio is

$$\frac{s_1^2}{s_2^2} = \frac{17,487}{3,479} = 5.03$$

This is perhaps an extreme example in terms of the relative magnitude of the between component.   For other characteristics, such as nonwhite, with high total variances, the ratio is not as high.

Table B–3.   Illustrative unit costs for essential steps in the conduct of the Current Population Survey, 1947–1950

Step	Unit	Man-hours per unit*	Man-hours per unit per survey
Each "Sample" (a "sample" is used for 6 monthly surveys)			
Definition and selection of Sanborn segment	Segment	2	.33
Listing: Rural areas			
Travel from one segment to another	Segment	2–2½†	.3–.4
Within segment (original listing)	Dwelling unit	.15†	.03
Within segment (bringing up to date)	Dwelling unit	.05	.01
Listing: Urban areas			
Travel from one segment to another	Segment	.5	.09
Within segment (original listing in "take all" segments)	Dwelling unit	.07‡	.01
Within segment (original listing in "multiple unit" segments)	Dwelling unit	.03‡	.005
Preparation and training for listing	Enumerator	8	1.33
Selection of sample households in district office	Segment	.5	.09
Each Month			
Enumeration			
Preparatory work	Schedule	.06	.06
Training	Schedule	.10	.10
Enumeration (including travel time)§	Schedule	.47	.47
Editing and posting control cards	Schedule	.13	.13
Checking coverage and quality	Schedule	.05	.05
Administration and leave	Schedule	.10	.10
Costs of travel and communication	Schedule	.15	.15
Central office			
Coding, editing, and verifying	Schedule	.02	.02
Punching and verifying	Schedule	.07	.07
Tabulation	Schedule	.04	.04
District office overhead	Office	80‖	

* Operations call for different levels of skill and responsibility and therefore different rates of pay per hour.

† In addition, listers are paid for use of a car for the average of 35 miles of driving involved per segment.

‡ Checking or bringing lists up to date takes only one-half as much as original listing.

§ About three-quarters of the schedules finally completed are completed on the first call to the households, and an additional 15 per cent on the second call.   The average number of calls per completed interview is about 1.35.   Some variation exists between urban and rural households, urban taking about 1.43 calls on the average and rural 1.25. A more striking variation exists between households in sample for the first time in a given month and those previously in sample; it takes about 1.54 calls to complete an interview for households in sample for the first time, and only 1.32 calls for those previously in sample.

‖ Represents amount of overhead allocated to CPS program; remainder borne by other programs in district office.

Costs. As we have seen, many steps are involved in the design and operation of the Current Population Survey. Each of these steps involves a cost; some of these costs depend on the number of psu's in the sample, whereas others are costs assignable to smaller units within the psu, such as segments and in other cases sample households. These cost factors are important in determining the optimum sample design. It may be interesting to examine some illustrative data to get an intuitive feeling for the cost relationships involved which lead to the design of the Current Population Survey.

We might note that, although there was a cost involved in setting up psu's, stratifying, and selecting a sample psu, this overhead cost per psu, when considered on a monthly basis for a span of, say, a decade, is quite small and may safely be ignored. In the same way, we may ignore the costs of mapping in rural areas. The first appreciable costs begin to arise after the sample psu's have been selected. Table B–3 presents average unit costs for the essential steps involved in conducting the Current Population Survey.

Taking the above costs into account and using Eq. 18.1, Ch. 9, as the cost function, we find that with the present method of operation, when some of the costs are shared with other surveys carried on in the same sample areas, the optimum would probably lie in the neighborhood of about 140 sample areas with an average of about 40 segments per psu, and of about 4 dwelling units per segment.* It might be noted, however, that, when the Current Population Survey was redesigned in 1943, all district office costs were allocable to the survey. Under that situation the optimum, on the basis of present costs, was in the neighborhood of about 80 areas with an average of about 60 segments of size 4,† which was close to the values actually used.

17. Quality of results. Some indication of the quality of the results of the Current Population Survey can be gained from two sources. One is the Systematic Check of Coverage and the other the CPS-Census Match Study.

The Systematic Check of Coverage provides data on the accuracy of the listing process. One segment is checked each month in each sample psu. Over a recent 30-month period there was an estimated net undercoverage of 1.8 per cent of all dwelling units (1.4 per cent of all persons). A

---

* Assumes $C_0 \doteq 0$, $C_1 \doteq 160$, $C_4 \doteq 1.3$, $C_2 \doteq 1.4$, $C_3 \doteq 5$; $\delta_1 \doteq .1$, and $\delta_2 \doteq .005$. (The values used for δ_1 and δ_2 are consistent with having between-psu and within-psu contributions about equal. See p. 578.)

† Assumes $C_0 \doteq 0$, $C_1 \doteq 325$, $C_4 \doteq 1.3$, $C_2 \doteq 1.4$, $C_3 \doteq 5$; $\delta_1 \doteq 1$, and $\delta_2 \doteq .005$.

substantial number of the missed dwelling units represent new construction or conversion since listing, which is not reflected in the estimate on a current basis.

The CPS-Census Match was undertaken to study differences in estimates between the Current Population Survey and the 1950 Decennial Census. Comparison of April 1950 CPS data with results of a preliminary sample of the Census is shown in Table B-4. A substantial difference exists in the number of employed persons as well as among those classified as unable to work. The CPS-Census Match Study examined differences in

Table B-4. Comparison of April 1950 CPS and Preliminary Census differences in employment status with preliminary differences between CPS and Census estimates derived from CPS-Census match

(Thousands of persons 14 years old and over)

Employment status of civilian noninstitutional population	April 1, 1950- CPS	Census (prelim.)	Diff.	CPS-Census match		
				CPS	Census	Diff.
Total	109,206	109,463	− 257	109,206	109,206	..
In labor force	62,183	58,735	+ 3,448	62,302	59,574	+ 2,728
Employed	58,668	55,843	+ 2,825	58,912	56,837	+ 2,075
Unemployed	3,515	2,892	+ 622	3,393	2,738	+ 655
Not in labor force	47,024	50,727	− 3,703	46,905	49,634	− 2,729
Keeping house	33,056	32,244	+ 812	33,726	32,805	+ 921
Unable to work	2,341	4,621	− 2,280	2,274	3,954	− 1,680
Other and empl. status not ascertainable	11,627	13,862	− 2,235	10,897	12,869	− 1,972

responses recorded for the April 1950 CPS sample between the CPS and the Census. Table B-4 also shows preliminary estimates based on persons enumerated in both CPS and Census, excluding the effects of differences in coverage. As was anticipated, the CPS shows for identical persons a higher labor force participation. A more highly trained staff of enumerators in the CPS performed as expected by more properly classifying persons with marginal attachment to the labor force. Further, they were better able to discriminate between those temporarily ill and those permanently incapacitated and hence classified as "unable to work." These represent net differences; the gross differences are even bigger. For example, whereas the net difference in the civilian labor force is 2.73 million, 5.46 million "in labor force" in CPS were reported as "not in labor force" in the Census, and 2.73 million "in labor force" in Census were reported as "not in labor force" in CPS. As far as coverage is concerned, differences between listed dwellings and other listing units in the CPS and enumerated dwellings in the Census are also being studied. The work on this phase is not complete at this writing.

Although these results show that the CPS, in relation to a census, obtains better data, we have reason to believe that there is still some misclassification of labor force status and occupation and industry grouping in the CPS.

C.   ESTIMATION PROCEDURE FOR THE ANNUAL SURVEY OF MANUFACTURES*

The first postwar Census of Manufactures covered the year 1947, and legislation passed in 1948 provided that a census be taken again in 1953 and quinquennially thereafter. Annual Surveys of Manufactures, which were designed to bring forward the principal measures of that census, were introduced in 1949. They were conducted using probability samples that included nearly 45,000 establishments from universe lists of nearly 300,000. Establishment size, industry classification, and company structure (multi-unit or single-unit), as given by the 1947 Census records, were the principal controls for selecting and allocating the sample. The samples were selected from the 1947 Census universe, augmented by Bureau of Old Age and Survivors Insurance lists of manufacturing companies that had not been covered by the Census or that began business after 1947.

Entire companies rather than individual establishments were used as the sampling units in order to overcome important reporting and related problems. All companies selected for the sample, however, were instructed to file separate reports for each of their establishments. The probability of selecting a multi-unit company in each case was determined either by its aggregate employment or by the employment and industry characteristics of its individual establishments.

The design generally followed the theory of optimum sampling, which was approximated through sampling size groups with sampling fractions proportional to average size (as discussed in Ch. 5, Sec. 10). All companies that in 1947 had 1 or more establishments of 250 or more employees (including all single units of that size) and all others that had aggregate employment of 1000 or more were included in the sample with certainty. Smaller companies were selected at rates that decreased with decreasing size. Table C–1 shows the basic pattern of sampling fractions used for the 1949 survey.

---

* By Jack Ogus, Bureau of the Census.

A higher scale of sampling fractions was used for industry groups that had relatively low percentages of their total 1947 employment included in the sample with certainty. Lower fractions were used, conversely, for the smaller establishments in industry groups that were unusually well covered by establishments included with certainty. These adjustments were made in order to equalize, roughly, the sampling error of estimates for each industry group.

Table C–1.   Basic sampling fractions by establishment size used for the 1949 Annual Survey of Manufactures

Employment 1947*	Sampling fraction 1949 (per cent)
250 or more	100
100–249	50
50–99	20
20–49	10
10–19	5
5–9	2
4 or less	1

* Initial employment for companies that started after 1947.

The primary estimates desired for industry groups were total employment, production workers, total wages and salaries, production worker wages, man-hours, and total value of shipments and cost of materials from which estimates of value added by manufacture were derived. Estimates of these items also were desired for most states, for economically important industrial-geographic classifications, and for selected individual industries. In addition, estimates were desired for selected product classes, selected metals consumed, inventories, plant and equipment expenditures, and fuels and electric energy consumed.

In total, literally thousands of different estimates were to be derived. Inflating and summarizing the data for the 45,000 sample establishments to the various publication levels that were planned constituted a sizable calculating and tabulating job. The load was magnified further by the need for extensive variance calculations, which were important because so little specific information on the reliability of these estimates was available. At the same time, both logic and experience urged the use of correlated manufacturing data to improve the estimates.

Data from the 1947 Census of Manufactures were admirably satisfactory for the purpose, at least for the most important statistics. Both the census totals and the corresponding figures for the individual establishments in the census universe had been developed before the sample was selected. They were conveniently available on punch cards, and they could be expected to be highly correlated with the current data.

Given these conditions, it was natural to consider using the ratio-estimating formula for the 1949 Annual Survey. Such estimates could have been developed by computing simple unbiased estimates from the sample for both 1947 and 1949, computing the ratio of the 1949 estimates to the 1947 estimates, and multiplying the 1947 universe totals by the results, in order to derive 1949 estimated aggregates. This procedure, however, presented certain tabulation and tabular difficulties, some important, some less important.

It would have required, for example, a voluminous number of divisions and multiplications, which would have slowed down the work and heavily taxed the calculating facilities available. Also, totals derived by adding subordinate ratio estimates would not be consistent from table to table, thus complicating the task of controlling errors in assembling the final figures, and the task of interpreting the figures for unsophisticated users (and perhaps some sophisticated ones as well).

Ratio estimates involved some technical difficulties too. The usual approximation to the rel-variance of ratio estimates may not be good for small samples or for small samples within strata (see Sec. 4, Ch. 5, and see also Sec. 12, Ch. 4, Vol. II). With small samples both the estimated totals and their sample estimates of the rel-variances may behave erratically, and small samples prevailed for most of the publication cells of the survey. For many of the estimates, samples of only 10, 20, or 30 noncertainty establishments were available. Because of these extremely small sample sizes the useful large-sample properties of ratio estimates could not safely be assumed, and there was no sound basis for believing that the bias of the ratio estimate would be small, or that the bias in the approximation to the rel-variance would be small.

These practical and theoretical limitations of the ratio estimate led to the examination of alternative formulas which would take advantage of the available historical data. Cochran's regression estimate* had a certain appeal but was quickly rejected as impractical because estimating the regression coefficients, and then the desired totals, from the sample would have involved an even larger calculation load than the use of ratio estimates. Much of the efficiency of Cochran's formula was salvageable, however, by using an assumed regression coefficient instead of estimating it from the sample, where this value was based on logical and practical considerations (see Ch. 11, Sec. 2).

---

* W. G. Cochran, "Sampling Theory When the Sampling Units Are of Unequal Size," *J. Amer. Stat. Assn.*, **37** (1942), 199–212.

The most convenient value was unity, and under the conditions of the survey it was sensible to assume that $\rho \sigma_{x'}/\sigma_{y'}$ did not depart widely from 1. In all cases the current data and the correlated historical figures to be used in conjunction with them referred to identically defined items. Employment in 1947 was to be used as the independent variate in estimating 1949 employment.   Wages in 1947 were to be used in estimating 1949 wages, etc.   This identity in definition suggested that $\sigma_{x'}$ and $\sigma_{y'}$ would be about the same.   Of the two standard errors, $\sigma_{y'}$ was expected to be slightly smaller than $\sigma_{x'}$ because the 1947 stratification limited variation in the historical data more than in the current values.   The product, $\rho \sigma_{x'}$ therefore (with high values of ρ expected) would be approximately equal to $\sigma_{y'}$, so that $\rho \sigma_{x'}/\sigma_{y'}$ would be close to 1.   Since experimental results confirmed this theory, unity was chosen as the assumed regression coefficient.

For all the general statistics (Table C–3), the punched cards were so arranged that it was feasible to apply the identical item concept.   Had operating conditions made it necessary to use dissimilar historical figures, some other regression coefficient than 1 would have been necessary.   An average wage per employee, for example, might have been substituted if wages were to be related to employment.

Some gains in efficiency might have been obtained had nonsample information (e.g., that provided by the certainty establishments) been used to adjust for changes in the levels between the 2 years.   This refinement, however, would have complicated the mechanics, and it was known that with isolated exceptions manufacturing activity had not changed drastically from the 1947 pattern.

The value of 1 for the regression coefficient leads to the formula:

$$x'' = x' - y' + Y \qquad \text{(Eq. 2.1, Ch. 11)}$$

where $x'' = $ the adjusted (or difference) estimate.

$x' = $ the simple unbiased estimate derived from the current sample values.

$y' = $ the simple unbiased estimate of Y derived from the base period sample values.

$Y = $ the universe base value.

This estimate, which is discussed in Sec. 2, Ch. 11, is unbiased.   Indeed it is unbiased for any fixed value of the regression coefficient, for it may be written more generally as $x'' = x' - k(y' - Y)$; the expected value of x' is X, the expected value of $k(y' - Y)$ is 0.   Where, as in the 1949 Annual Survey, x' and y' refer to current and historical values for the same item, and $k = 1$, the formula in effect provides an estimate of the *amount* of change or the algebraic difference from the base year.   For this reason, the formula has been called the *difference* estimate.

Some of the difficulties associated with the application of the ratio estimate to this Annual Survey of Manufactures vanished; others were reduced by the use of the difference estimate.   Calculation of the estimates was simpler and less costly.   All marginal totals were completely consistent from one table to another, thus providing a useful mechanical check on the transcription and avoiding the nuisance of nonidentical figures for identically defined statistics.   Major reductions were made in the variance computation workload, where a single operation (squaring of differences) replaced three similar operations that would have been required (squaring both the current and the past data and calculating their cross-products).   Moreover, the uncertainties associated with the bias of ratio estimates derived from small samples were eliminated.

As might be expected from their close relationship, the difference and ratio formulas yielded substantially equal estimates of precision for large cells.   Tests based on reasonably large numbers of actual reports from the 1949 Annual Survey showed that the standard approximation to the estimate of the rel-variance of the ratio estimate and the corresponding estimate of the rel-variance of the difference estimate were practically identical.   Some results are presented in Table C–3 for each of 5 sample classes.

The estimated rel-variances in the population ($\sigma^2/\bar{X}^2$) for the 1949 data are given in Table C–2.

Table C–2.   Rel-variances in the population, 1949

Sample class	Average employ- ment per establish- ment	Item 1 Average no. of employees	Item 2 Total wages and salaries	Item 3 Wages of prod. workers	Item 4 Average no. of prod. workers	Item 5 Man- hours of prod. workers	Item 6 Cost of mat'ls, etc.	Item 7 Value of products shipped	Item 8 Value added by manu- facture
3	92	.51	.57	.59	.53	.58	4.83	2.41	1.31
4	82	.65	.69	.77	.75	.70	4.62	2.40	.79
5	47	.60	.79	.82	.67	.60	10.61	5.52	1.03
6	20	.43	.60	.69	.53	.50	2.39	1.35	.66
7	11	.84	.90	.96	.91	1.01	1.00	1.13	1.21

Comparisons of regression, difference, and ratio estimate rel-variances are given in Table C–3.   For most separate cells investigated, the rel-variances of the difference estimates and the ratio estimates were nearly

Table C–3. Relative efficiency of various estimating formulas for selected manufacturing statistics by sample classes

Item and estimating formula	Ratio of variance of regression, difference, and ratio estimates to variance of simple unbiased estimate				
	Sample class				
	3	4	5	6	7
Wages and salaries					
Regression	.20	.18	.21	.34	.20
Difference	.20	.18	.21	.34	.20
Ratio	.21	.19	.22	.36	.21
Production worker wages					
Regression	.26	.17	.24	.52	.26
Difference	.27	.17	.24	.54	.26
Ratio	.27	.18	.24	.55	.26
Average number of employees					
Regression	.23	.15	.29	.51	.26
Difference	.23	.15	.36	.53	.26
Ratio	.23	.15	.32	.54	.26
Average number of production workers					
Regression	.27	.16	.32	.64	.27
Difference	.28	.16	.41	.67	.27
Ratio	.27	.16	.34	.69	.27
Production worker man-hours					
Regression	.30	.20	.32	.55	.44
Difference	.32	.20	.37	.59	.55
Ratio	.30	.20	.34	.59	.47
Total cost of materials					
Regression	.06	.19	.03	.49	.06
Difference	.28	.19	.05	.53	.07
Ratio	.13	.19	.04	.57	.06
Value of shipments					
Regression	.11	.24	.05	.52	.10
Difference	.38	.24	.08	.54	.11
Ratio	.22	.24	.06	.55	.10
Value added by manufacture					
Regression	.46	.62	.43	.49	.34
Difference	.58	1.21	.46	.52	.48
Ratio	.51	.98	.48	.53	.46

equal. In roughly half the cases, the former was smaller; in about half the cases, the latter was smaller.

Comparisons of the rel-variances of the difference estimates with those of the simple unbiased estimates revealed striking gains in nearly every case. Most of the difference estimate rel-variances ranged between one-tenth and one-half of the simple unbiased estimate rel-variances. For only 1 cell of the 40 that were investigated did the difference estimate give a poorer result.

The additional gains that might have been achieved by using regression estimates were relatively negligible in most cases. Table C–3 shows the estimated results had the regression estimate been used. The variance of the regression estimate is given approximately by Eq. 2.10 of Ch. 11. Both the difference and ratio estimates were virtually as good as the regression results for all but a handful of the 40 cells in the study.

D. SOME VARIANCES AND COVARIANCES FOR CLUSTER SAMPLES OF PERSONS AND DWELLING UNITS*

Two separate studies are reported in this case study. Both of them present empirical results of studies of variances and covariances and relations between them for different levels and units of sampling. These results can serve as a guide in the design of sample surveys where similar or related types of characteristics are to be sampled.

I. A study of variances and covariances of some population, labor force, and dwelling unit characteristics for cluster samples from different types of areas throughout the United States. The purpose of this study is to present results which will be useful for determining the magnitude and relationships of variances for some population and housing characteristics in designs where the sampling units are households or clusters of households. Variances for sampling units that consist of clusters of 1, 3, 9, and 27 households, city blocks, and enumeration districts are presented and compared with those for individual households or persons as sampling units.

The data from which the computations were made were derived from the Sampling Reliability Study, which was initiated by the Bureau of the Census to study various aspects of sampling design. This study was based on a national sample of urban and rural areas. The data presented herewith were obtained for a subsample of these places, using data from the 1940 Census of Population.

---

* By Benjamin J. Tepping, Alice Kaitz (Part I), and Robert H. Hanson (Part II), Bureau of the Census.

The sample was based on a stratified sample of blocks in cities of population 100,000 or more and on a stratified sample of census enumeration districts from the remainder of the country.   The large cities and counties were first stratified according to three geographic divisions: the North, the South, and the West.   Within each of these regions, groups of areas were defined consisting of (1) cities of 100,000 or more population; (2) counties included within the metropolitan districts associated with such cities; and (3) all counties not falling in either of the first two groups.   Only the first and third groups were used for this study.   From the first group, 5 cities were chosen for the analysis: namely, Chicago, Columbus, Hartford, Birmingham, and Seattle.

A total of 60 blocks was sampled in Chicago, and a total of 30 blocks was sampled in each of the remaining cities.   First, each city was divided into 5 strata (6 in the case of Chicago) of approximately equal population. Strata lines were drawn so as not to cross census tract boundaries, and so as to make the strata as different as possible in their characteristics.   In Chicago there was an average of 39 tracts per stratum, and in the remaining cities there was an average of 11 tracts per stratum.   Within each stratum, census tracts were grouped into areas for sampling which were designed to resemble each other in both population and characteristics.   One of these areas was sampled at random from each stratum, and 6 blocks (10 in Chicago) were sampled from each such area.

Within each region, the counties in the third group were classified into 5 classes according to the population of the largest incorporated place in the county.   For each class, all places in the region were divided according to population into 6 strata, as follows: (1) territory outside of incorporated places; (2) incorporated places under 2500 population; (3) places of 2500–5000; (4) places of 5000–10,000; (5) places of 10,000–25,000; and (6) places of 25,000–100,000.

This double stratification defined the strata from which the sample was chosen.   From counties whose largest center was under 2500 population a sample of unincorporated places and places under 2500 was drawn. From all other strata based on size of largest center, enumeration districts (ED's) were sampled only for those places of the same size as the largest center.   For example, in counties whose largest center was between 5000 and 10,000, only places between 5000 and 10,000 were sampled.   One place was selected from each stratum, and a group of 6 enumeration districts was selected in each such place.   If there were fewer than 6 enumeration districts in a selected place, a group of 3 ED's was selected; the smaller places were combined so that the combinations contained at least 3 ED's.   A total of 21 enumeration districts was selected in the North, 30 in the South, and 33 in the West.

In the cities over 100,000 the sampling unit was the city block, and in places under 100,000 the sampling unit was the enumeration district. Population and housing characteristics were transcribed from the 1940 Census schedules for each household in each of the selected blocks and ED's. These households were grouped on the basis of order of enumeration in the census into equal-sized clusters of 3, 9, and 27 households within blocks or ED's. Whenever the total number of households in the sampling unit was not an exact multiple of these cluster sizes, the remaining households were dropped from the analysis.

Using these data, the variances between clusters of 1, 3, 9, and 27 households were computed as well as the variances between blocks and ED's. These computations were made within the strata and then weighted together over all strata. The results are shown in Tables D–1 to D–7.

The characteristics for which the computations were made are self-explanatory with, perhaps, the exception of the items relating to rental value. These items refer not only to renter-occupied units but also to owner-occupied units. For this purpose, reported market values of owner-occupied units were translated into rental values, by assuming that the rental value of a unit was 1 per cent of its reported value.

The variances are computed in each case as if the sample selected as described above, or a specified part of it, were the population to be sampled; the strata identified above were preserved in selecting a sample from this population. Specifically, Tables D–4 to D–7 display the following results:

Column 1. For the household characteristics, R refers to the proportion of households having the specified characteristic. For population characteristics, R refers to the proportion of persons having the specified characteristic.

Column 2. The $S^2_{(1)}$ is the variance computed between households and is given by $S^2_{(1)} = \Sigma M_h S^2_{1hX}/M$, where S^2_{1hX} is defined by Eq. 5.5, Ch. 7, M_h is the number of households in the hth stratum, and $M = \Sigma M_h$. The subscript "(1)" in $S^2_{(1)}$ is used to indicate that this variance relates to a cluster of 1 household and is not to be confused with the subscript in S^2_{1hX} where the "1" without the parentheses refers to the variance between primary units. In this particular case, the terms defined for Eq. 5.5, Ch. 7, are as follows:

$X_{hi} =$ the total number of persons having the characteristic in the ith household of the hth stratum (where the stratum, as already indicated, is a group of blocks or ED's), or the value of a dwelling unit characteristic for that household;

and here

$M_h = N_h =$ total number of households in the hth stratum. Note that M_h generally refers to the number of clusters in the hth stratum. In this case the household is the cluster and therefore $M_h = N_h$.

Column 3. $B_{X(1)}^2$ is the rel-variance between households for a sample of one household, where $B_{X(1)}^2 = S_{(1)}^2 / \bar{X}_{(1)}^2$ and $\bar{X}_{(1)} = X/M$, where $M = N =$ the number of households. Again the "(1)" indicates that the rel-variance relates to a cluster of 1 household.

Columns 4, 5, and 6 show $S^2 / \bar{N} S_{(1)}^2$, where S^2 is defined exactly as is $S_{(1)}^2$ except that instead of 1 household per cluster there are $\bar{N}$ households per cluster; $\bar{N} = 3$ for column 4, $\bar{N} = 9$ for column 5, and $\bar{N} = 27$ for column 6. For column 4, the X_{hi} is the aggregate value of a characteristic for all persons in the ith cluster of 3 households in the hth stratum, and M_h is the number of such clusters in the hth stratum. For these cases N_h is the total number of households (listing units) in the hth stratum, N is the total number in the population defined, and $\bar{N}$ is the average number per cluster. Suppose, now, that we want to compare the variance for a proportionate stratified sample of fixed size, say n households, if drawn by sampling $m = n/\bar{N}$ clusters, or if drawn by sampling n households without further clustering.

If no subsampling is involved, the rel-variance of an estimated average or total based on a sample of m clusters of size $\bar{N}$ is

$$(1-f) \frac{S^2}{\bar{N} \bar{X}_{(1)}^2 n} \text{ with } S^2 = \frac{\Sigma M_h S_{1hX}^2}{M},$$

and $n = m\bar{N}$. (This can be obtained from Remark 2, Sec. 5, Ch. 7, but with $\bar{\bar{X}}^2$ written here as $\bar{X}_{(1)}^2$.) Consequently, the ratio of the variance for a given size of sample in terms of households when a cluster of $\bar{N}$ households serves as the sampling unit, to the variance when a single household serves as the sampling unit, is

$$\frac{(1-f)S^2}{\bar{N} \bar{X}_{(1)}^2 n} \Big/ \frac{(1-f)S_{(1)}^2}{\bar{X}_{(1)}^2 n} = \frac{S^2}{\bar{N} S_{(1)}^2}$$

These are the values given in columns 4, 5, and 6 of the tables. It should be noted, also, that $S^2 / \bar{N} S_{(1)}^2 = 1 + \delta(\bar{N} - 1)$. This follows from Eq. 8.1, Ch. 6 (where, for this case, $\bar{n} = \bar{N}$). This relationship will be used later.

Column 7. The figures in this column have approximately the same meaning as those for columns 4, 5, and 6, but are defined somewhat differently because the sampling units (blocks in Table D–4, ED's in Tables D–5, D–6, and D–7) vary widely in the number of households they contain. The formula used for this column is, as before, $S^2/\bar{N}S^2_{(1)}$, but now $S^2 = \dfrac{\bar{N}}{M} \Sigma \Sigma N_{hi} \left(\dfrac{X_{hi}}{N_{hi}} - \dfrac{X_h}{N_h} \right)^2$, where N_{hi} is the number of dwelling units in the ith block (or ED) of the hth stratum, X_{hi} is the value of a characteristic for the hth block, M is the number of blocks in the population, and the blocks have been sampled with probability proportionate to size (N_{hi}). The $S^2_{(1)}$ is, as before, the variance between individual households. It can be regarded as roughly approximating the ratio of the variances of proportionate stratified samples containing equal numbers of dwelling units, where the sampling units represented by the variance in the numerator of the ratio are equal-sized clusters of $\bar{N}$ dwelling units (with $\bar{N} = 62$ when blocks are the sampling units), and where the sampling units represented by the variance in the denominator of the ratio are single households.

We shall now suggest some methods by which the data presented in the tables can serve as a guide for arriving at optimum designs of samples where the characteristics to be estimated may be assumed to be similar in their distribution to those described here.

In the first place, some stability of a particular characteristic can be observed between the different areas represented by Tables D–4 through D–7. Although there is considerable variation in some of the variances between the large cities and the rest of the country, the differences are smaller between the geographic regions. Usually, if large differences are found between the figures presented for cities and those for the remainder of the country, there are reasons to expect such differences. See, for example, the remarks concerning the intraclass correlations for rent in (d) below. Comparisons of the results presented here for some of the labor force items can be made, in particular, with Part II of this study and with some results presented in Case Study B, and some stability in the results will be found.

Some interpretations of these results, as well as indications of how they can be used to derive additional relationships that may be found useful, will now be considered.

(a) The variances for the various sizes of cluster can readily be obtained from the entries in columns 4, 5, and 6 simply by multiplying those entries by $\bar{N}S^2_{(1)}$. Thus, for the characteristic "dwelling units occupied by owner," column 2 in Table D–4 gives $S^2_{(1)} = .12$. Consequently, the variance between cluster totals when clusters of 9 households are used as psu's is $S^2 = 9(2.4)(.12) = 2.6$.

(b) The rel-variance between single households can be obtained by computing $B^2_{X(1)} = S^2_{(1)}/\bar{X}^2_{(1)}$, where $\bar{X}_{(1)} = R\bar{Y}_{(1)}$, and $\bar{Y}_{(1)}$ is 1 for the household characteristics, and is the average number of persons per household in the population under consideration for the population characteristics. The rel-variance between clusters of size $\bar{N}$ may, therefore, be obtained by computing $B_X^2 = AB_{X(1)}^2/\bar{N}$, where A designates the appropriate number in columns 4–7.

(c) $S^2 = \bar{X}^2 B_X^2$ could be regarded as approximately equivalent to the S_1^2 given by Eq. 5.18, Ch. 7, even if the variation in the sizes of the clusters had not been controlled as closely as it was here, provided the estimate to which S_1^2 relates is the ratio x/n, where n is the number of dwelling units in the sample.

Often one will be interested in the variance of an estimated ratio, such as the ratio of total males to the total population, or males unemployed to males in the labor force, or proportion of homes in the \$20–29 rental value group. Let us see how the variance of such ratios may be approximated roughly. It is seen from Eq. 4.1, Ch. 8, that $V_{x/y}^2 \doteq V_x^2 - V_y^2$ whenever the correlation between x/y and y is nearly zero. This correlation will be nearly zero in a great many cases when y is the denominator of a ratio and x, which is a subset of the y, is the numerator of the ratio, as in the ratios mentioned above. Estimates of ratios of this form are frequently required. If x/y and y are uncorrelated, the results in Tables D–4 through D–7 may be used to arrive at estimates of the variances of the ratios x/y. Since there is no subsampling, V_x^2 is equal to B_X^2, and $V_y^2 = B_Y^2$, where B_X^2 and B_Y^2 may be derived from columns 4–7 of Tables D–4 through D–7 as indicated by (a) and (b). Some results are summarized in Table D–1, based on data from Table D–4 for cities of 100,000 population or more. It should be noted from Part II of this study (for Minneapolis–St. Paul and Baltimore) that sometimes this approximation to the rel-variance of a ratio is not very satisfactory if the V_y^2 is nearly as large as V_x^2, in which case a small error in the assumed values of V_x^2 and V_y^2 may create a large relative error in the difference and throw the predicted errors off.

From the computations in Table D–1 it is seen that, even though the clusters are equal in size in terms of number of dwelling units, variation in number of persons per cluster affects considerably the variance of the estimated totals for items that are a high percentage of the total.

The entries in the last row of Table D–1 have the same significance as those in columns 4–7 of Tables D–4 to D–7 except that here they relate to the variances of the ratios indicated. Thus, in estimating the ratio of males to total population, the relative increase in variance by sampling clusters of 9 households instead of 1 household is 30 per cent, as compared with 95 per cent when making a simple unbiased estimate of total males. On the other hand, for the ratio of males unemployed to males in the labor force, the relative increase for clusters of 9 households is 53 per cent, which is about the same as that for the unbiased estimate of the number of unemployed.

Table D–1.   Illustrative computations of approximate variances of ratios

(For selected characteristics for places over 100,000 population)

	Rel-variance of			
	r_a	r_b	r_c	r_d
Clusters of 1 hh.				
$B^2_{X(1)}$	.562	5.56	2.84	4.58
$B^2_{Y(1)}$	.306	.62	0	.62
$B^2_{X(1)} - B^2_{Y(1)} \doteq B^2_{r(1)}$	.256	4.94	2.84	3.96
Clusters of 9 hh.				
B^2_X	.122	.964	.784	.560
B^2_Y	.085	.124	0	.124
$B^2_X - B^2_Y \doteq B^2_r$	.037	.840	.784	.436
$\dfrac{S^2_r}{9S^2_{r(1)}} = \dfrac{9B^2_r}{B^2_{r(1)}}$	1.30	1.53	2.48	.99

$$r_a = \frac{\text{Males}}{\text{Total population}} \qquad r_c = \frac{\text{Homes in \$20–29 rental group}}{\text{All homes}}$$

$$r_b = \frac{\text{Males unemployed}}{\text{Males in labor force}} \qquad r_d = \frac{\text{Male clerical, sales, and kindred workers}}{\text{Males in labor force}}$$

Note that for clusters of 1 household

$$B^2_{X(1)} = \frac{S^2_{(1)}}{\bar{X}^2_{(1)}}, \text{ where } \bar{X}_{(1)} = R\left(\frac{\text{Total persons}}{\text{Total households}}\right)$$

For clusters of 9 households we compute $B^2_X = S^2/\bar{X}^2_{(9)}$, where $\bar{X}_{(9)} = 9\bar{X}_{(1)}$ and where S^2 is obtained from the table as explained in (a).

(d) It was noted above that the entries in columns 4–6 of Tables D–4 to D–7 are equal to $1 + \delta(\bar{N} - 1)$, and that this is roughly true for column 7 also. For estimating the total male population, with clusters of 9 households as here defined used as sampling units, we have, from the table for places over 100,000 population,

$$2.0 = 1 + 8\delta$$
$$\delta = .12$$

The value shown in Table D–2 is .119, since that table was computed before rounding the numbers given in Table D–4.

Table D–2.   Measures of homogeneity for alternative sizes of cluster
(Selected places over 100,000)

Characteristic	δ for $\bar{N} =$			
	3	9	27	62
Simple unbiased estimate of				
Dwelling units occupied by owner	.170	.171	.166	.096
Dwelling units with rental value of $20–29	.270	.185	.138	.086
Total population	.230	.186	.142	.066
Male population	.150	.119	.092	.046
Males unemployed	.060	.070	.045	.034
Males in the labor force	.115	.098	.073	.028
Ratio estimate				
$\dfrac{\text{Male population}}{\text{Total population}}$	.054	.038	.033	.023
$\dfrac{\text{Males unemployed}}{\text{Males in labor force}}$	.053	.066	.041	.035

Table D–3.   Measures of homogeneity for alternative sizes of cluster
(Selected places under 100,000 in the West)

Characteristic	δ for $\bar{N} =$			
	3	9	27	252
Simple unbiased estimate of				
Dwelling units occupied by owner	.125	.085	.064	.030
Dwelling units with rental value of $20–29	.115	.064	.052	.027
Total population	.095	.036	.026	.004
Male population	.070	.030	.023	.004
Males unemployed	.125	.088	.074	.018
Males in the labor force	.050	.004	.004	.0002
Ratio estimate				
$\dfrac{\text{Male population}}{\text{Total population}}$	.026	.019	.017	.003
$\dfrac{\text{Males unemployed}}{\text{Males in labor force}}$	.131	.095	.080	.019

Similar computations could be carried out for all the items. A few of these are summarized in Table D–2 to indicate the magnitudes of some of the δ's reflected by these data, and to show how the δ's vary with changing size of cluster.

The manner in which δ decreases with increasing size of cluster is reasonably consistent and rather striking in Table D–3. A similar relationship between the value of δ and the size of cluster holds for most of the items appearing in Tables D–4 to D–7, although the rate of decline or change of δ varies considerably from item to item. These results for clusters equal in number of listing units probably show more consistency than would be found in most practical problems, in which clusters of the average size considered here usually vary considerably in size. Further, our data show some variation in the magnitude of δ attributable to the size of place. For example, there is a considerable decrease in δ for rental value for places under 100,000 as compared with places over 100,000. This is so because dwelling units having about the same rental value are more likely to be clustered in large cities than in places of smaller size.

(e) The tables may also be used to determine the effect of sampling households at random as compared with sampling persons at random. This may be accomplished by dividing column 2, the variance between households, by the average number of persons per household, in order to put the variance on a per-person basis. The result may then be compared with $R(1 - R)$, where R is the entry in column 1. The value $R(1 - R)$ is the variance between persons when persons are sampled at random.

(f) For multi-stage samples where the primary sampling unit is a cluster of $\bar{N}$ households and the listing unit is the household, the tables may be used to arrive at the variances or rel-variances within psu's by using the formula

$$W_X^2 = B_{X(1)}^2 - B_X^2$$

where $B_{X(1)}^2$ and B_X^2 are as previously defined and $W_X^2 = \dfrac{\sum_h \sum_i N_{hi} S_{2hiX}^2}{N \bar{X}_{(1)}^2}$,

where S_{2hiX}^2 is defined by Eq. 5.10, Ch. 7, for clusters of size $\bar{N}$. This relationship is exact for equal-sized clusters. Thus, by using the $B_{X(1)}^2$ and B_X^2 shown in Table D–1, the rel-variance within clusters of 9 households for total males is

$$W_X^2 = B_{X(1)}^2 - B_X^2$$

$$= .562 - .122$$

$$= .440$$

Summary. The results summarized in Tables D–4 through D–7 may be applied for arriving at approximations to numerous variances or relationships between variances that may be needed in connection with designing a sample. They may be used in connection with determination of the optimum size of a sampling unit, or for advance speculation on the size of sample needed. They should not be employed directly for speculating with much confidence on variances for a simple unbiased estimate of a total where the clusters vary widely in size, but they can give fairly good approximations for ratio estimates. They may be used for speculating on the variances of simple unbiased estimates of totals, also, by the methods of Ch. 8, Eq. 4.5, if one knows approximately the rel-variance of the cluster sizes.

Table D–4.   Variances and ratios of variances for various clusters of dwelling units

(Selected places over 100,000 population)

Characteristic	Proportion of population having characteristic* R	Variance between households $S^2_{(1)}$	Rel-variance between households $B^2_{X(1)}$	$S^2/\bar{N}S^2_{(1)}$ for clusters of size			
				$\bar{N} =$ 3 hh.	$\bar{N} =$ 9 hh.	$\bar{N} =$ 27 hh.	Blocks† (average size 62 hh.)
	(1)	(2)	(3)	(4)	(5)	(6)	(7)
Total dwelling units	1.0000						
Dwelling units occupied by owner	.1967	.123	3.2	1.3	2.4	5.3	6.8
Dwelling units with rental value of							
$10–14	.0525	.048	17.4	1.5	2.4	3.8	4.8
$20–29	.2328	.154	2.8	1.5	2.5	4.6	6.2
$40–49	.1343	.105	5.8	1.9	3.8	7.3	7.8
$75 and over	.0174	.015	51.2	1.8	3.3	5.2	8.1
Total population	1.0000	3.491	.3	1.5	2.5	4.7	5.0
Native white males	.2830	.988	1.1	1.2	1.7	3.0	4.6
Males unemployed	.0573	.208	5.6	1.1	1.6	2.2	3.1
Total males	.4739	1.440	.6	1.3	2.0	3.4	3.8
Males aged							
5–14 years	.0640	.289	6.2	1.1	1.3	1.8	2.4
25–34 years	.0829	.265	3.4	1.1	1.2	1.5	1.5
65 years and over	.0258	.086	11.4	1.0	1.2	1.6	1.6
Males in labor force	.3141	.703	.6	1.2	1.8	2.9	2.7
Males: occupation and industry groups							
Prof. and semi-prof. workers	.0197	.070	15.8	1.0	1.2	1.4	2.0
Farmers and farm managers	.0001	.001	413.9	1.0	.9	..	2.2
Proprietors, managers, and officials, except farmers	.0303	.092	8.8	1.1	1.3	1.7	2.7
Clerical, sales, and kindred workers	.0632	.209	4.6	1.1	1.1	1.6	2.8
Craftsmen, foremen, and kindred workers	.0522	.163	5.2	1.0	1.2	1.5	2.1
Operatives and kindred workers	.0642	.217	4.6	1.1	1.3	2.0	2.1
Domestic service workers	.0014	.005	210.9	1.0	1.1	1.1	1.2
Protective service workers	.0062	.021	47.3	1.0	1.0	1.2	1.3
Service workers	.0359	.130	8.8	1.2	1.6	2.2	2.0
Farm laborers and foremen	.0004	.001	787.5	1.0	1.0	1.0	1.4
Laborers except farm	.0406	.141	7.5	1.2	1.7	2.7	4.3
Total number of units from which variance is computed		11,106		3646	1157	323	180

* Based on 11,106 households for dwelling unit characteristics and 37,515 persons for population characteristics. (Average number of persons per household is 3.38.)
† Calculated with probability proportionate to size.

Table D–5. Variances and ratios of variances for various clusters of dwelling units

(Selected places under 100,000 in the West)

Characteristic	Proportion of population having characteristic* R	Variance between households $S^2_{(1)}$	Rel-variance between households $B^2_{X(1)}$	$S^2/\bar{N}S^2_{(1)}$ for clusters of size			
				$\bar{N} =$ 3 hh.	$\bar{N} =$ 9 hh.	$\bar{N} =$ 27 hh.	ED's† (average size 252 hh.)
	(1)	(2)	(3)	(4)	(5)	(6)	(7)
Total dwelling units	1.0000						
Dwelling units occupied by owner	.5250	.246	.9	1.3	1.7	2.7	8.6
Dwelling units with rental value of							
$10–14	.0910	.082	9.9	1.2	1.4	1.9	4.0
$20–29	.1315	.112	6.5	1.2	1.5	2.4	7.8
$40–49	.0198	.019	47.7	1.2	1.4	1.5	3.6
$75 and over	.0023	.002	424.3	.9	1.1	1.3	1.0
Total population	1.0000	4.308	.4	1.2	1.3	1.7	2.1
Farm population	.0625	.633	13.6	1.8	3.6	7.9	43.3
Native white males	.4582	1.552	.6	1.1	1.2	1.6	1.9
Males unemployed	.0445	.174	7.3	1.3	1.7	2.9	5.4
Total males	.4842	1.581	.6	1.1	1.2	1.6	1.9
Males aged							
5–14 years	.0730	.380	6.0	1.1	1.3	1.7	2.6
25–34 years	.0726	.221	3.5	1.1	1.1	1.1	1.2
65 years and over	.0470	.198	7.5	1.0	1.0	1.1	1.1
Males in labor force	.2832	.546	.6	1.1	1.0	1.1	1.1
Males: occupation and industry groups							
Prof. and semi-prof. workers	.0178	.073	19.2	1.1	1.2	1.6	3.4
Farmers and farm managers	.0183	.026	6.5	1.1	1.2	1.2	1.4
Proprietors, managers, and officials, except farmers	.0411	.132	6.5	1.1	1.3	1.9	4.7
Clerical, sales, and kindred workers	.0452	.161	6.6	1.0	1.1	1.5	3.2
Craftsmen, foremen, and kindred workers	.0510	.162	5.2	1.0	1.0	1.2	1.6
Operatives and kindred workers	.0460	.151	6.0	1.1	1.2	1.4	3.4
Domestic service workers	.0008	.003	385.9	1.0	1.0	1.2	.9
Protective service workers	.0032	.011	89.9	1.0	1.0	1.0	1.1
Service workers	.0129	.049	24.4	1.0	1.1	1.1	1.2
Farm laborers and foremen	.0100	.042	34.6	1.1	1.2	1.3	3.1
Laborers except farm	.0367	.127	7.9	1.2	1.4	2.1	5.0
Total number of units from which variance is computed		8558		2843	936	302	33

* Based on 8558 households for dwelling unit characteristics and 29,604 persons for population characteristics. (Average number of persons per household is 3.41.)

† Calculated with probability proportionate to size.

Table D–6.   Variances and ratios of variances for various clusters of dwelling units

(Selected places under 100,000 in the South)

Characteristic	Proportion of population having character-istic* R	Variance between house-holds $S^2_{(1)}$	Rel-variance between house-holds $B^2_{X(1)}$	$\bar{N} =$ 3 hh.	$\bar{N} =$ 9 hh.	$\bar{N} =$ 27 hh.	ED's† (average size 271 hh.)
	(1)	(2)	(3)	(4)	(5)	(6)	(7)
Total dwelling units	1.0000						
Dwelling units occupied by owner	.3908	.228	1.5	1.3	1.8	2.9	9.2
Dwelling units with rental value of							
$10–14	.0601	.036	15.4	1.2	1.6	2.5	6.4
$20–29	.0766	.066	11.2	1.2	1.7	2.2	4.8
$40–49	.0126	.012	77.0	1.1	1.4	1.8	2.9
$75 and over	.0100	.009	94.1	1.4	2.1	4.6	16.8
Total population	1.0000	4.216	.3	1.2	1.4	1.7	3.3
Farm population	.2270	2.053	2.8	1.5	2.6	4.0	11.8
Native white males	.3754	1.807	.9	1.4	2.1	3.7	8.5
Males unemployed	.0369	.158	8.1	1.3	1.9	3.6	11.8
Total males	.4805	1.753	.5	1.1	1.3	1.5	3.1
Males aged							
5–14 years	.0901	.466	4.0	1.1	1.1	1.2	1.9
25–34 years	.0734	.241	3.1	1.0	1.0	1.1	1.3
65 years and over	.0298	.112	8.8	1.1	1.3	1.1	1.2
Males in labor force	.2770	.654	.6	1.2	1.2	1.6	2.7
Males: occupation and industry groups							
Prof. and semi-prof. workers	.0160	.063	17.1	1.1	1.5	1.9	4.4
Farmers and farm managers	.0501	.067	1.9	1.2	1.5	1.9	3.4
Proprietors, managers, and officials, except farmers	.0327	.117	7.6	1.2	1.6	2.1	5.0
Clerical, sales, and kindred workers	.0399	.167	7.3	1.2	1.4	2.3	8.2
Craftsmen, foremen, and kin-dred workers	.0299	.126	9.8	1.1	1.3	1.3	1.9
Operatives and kindred workers	.0304	.114	8.6	1.1	1.3	1.8	4.7
Domestic service workers	.0016	.006	163.3	1.1	1.1	1.5	1.6
Protective service workers	.0043	.017	63.1	1.1	1.1	1.1	1.3
Service workers	.0086	.040	37.9	1.1	1.3	1.5	3.6
Farm laborers and foremen	.0324	.174	11.6	1.2	1.5	2.3	6.1
Laborers, except farm	.0311	.125	9.0	1.4	2.0	2.7	6.5
Total number of units from which variance is computed		8406		2794	921	294	30

* Based on 8406 households for dwelling unit characteristics and 31,843 persons for population charac-teristics. (Average number of persons per household is 3.79.)
† Calculated with probability proportionate to size.

Table D–7. Variances and ratios of variances for various clusters of dwelling units

(Selected places under 100,000 in the North)

Characteristic	Proportion of population having character-istic* R	Variance between house-holds $S^2_{(1)}$	Rel-variance between house-holds $B^2_{X(1)}$	$S^2/\bar{N}S^2_{(1)}$ for clusters of size $\bar{N} =$ 3 hh.	$\bar{N} =$ 9 hh.	$\bar{N} =$ 27 hh.	ED's† (average size 205 hh.)
	(1)	(2)	(3)	(4)	(5)	(6)	(7)
Total dwelling units	1.0000						
Dwelling units occupied by owner	.5089	.239	.9	1.3	1.8	3.1	13.0
Dwelling units with rental value of							
$10–14	.1214	.105	7.1	1.4	2.5	5.1	28.3
$20–29	.0890	.078	9.9	1.3	1.7	2.5	8.1
$40–49	.0059	.006	165.8	1.2	1.4	1.5	5.3
$75 and over	.0068	.007	145.4	1.4	2.5	3.9	5.3
Total population	1.0000	3.824	.3	1.1	1.2	1.3	3.1
Farm population	.1936	2.031	4.1	1.9	4.2	9.9	25.9 ⎫ 107.0‡ ⎭
Native white males	.4718	1.625	.6	1.1	1.2	1.2	1.5 ⎫ 3.3‡ ⎭
Males unemployed	.0574	.231	5.3	1.3	1.9	2.8	14.7
Total males	.5014	1.591	.5	1.1	1.2	1.2	2.9
Males aged							
5–14 years	.0839	.438	4.7	1.1	1.3	1.4	2.7 ⎫ 1.8‡ ⎭
25–34 years	.0723	.223	3.2	1.0	1.0	.9	.9 ⎫ 4.0‡ ⎭
65 years and over	.0424	.139	5.8	1.0	1.1	1.2	2.1 ⎫ 1.4‡ ⎭
Males in labor force	.2924	.530	.5	1.1	1.2	1.3	3.2
Males: occupation and industry groups							
Prof. and semi-prof. workers	.0129	.055	25.2	1.2	1.3	1.7	2.9
Farmers and farm managers	.0328	.082	5.8	1.5	2.7	5.1	30.2
Proprietors, managers, and officials except farmers	.0343	.117	7.5	1.1	1.3	2.0	5.1
Clerical, sales, and kindred workers	.0340	.117	7.7	1.0	1.1	1.3	2.0
Craftsmen, foremen, and kindred workers	.0460	.156	5.6	1.1	1.1	1.3	2.3
Operatives and kindred workers	.0534	.189	5.0	1.1	1.4	1.7	2.9
Domestic service workers	.0009	.003	293.8	.9	1.0	1.0	.8
Protective service workers	.0045	.016	61.7	1.1	1.1	1.3	1.7
Service workers	.0118	.048	25.9	1.2	1.4	1.2	2.5
Farm laborers and foremen	.0170	.083	21.9	1.1	1.6	2.5	10.4
Laborers, except farm	.0449	.164	6.1	1.2	2.4	2.5	9.2
Total number of units from which variance is computed		4718		1566	515	162	21

* Based on 4718 households for dwelling unit characteristics and 17,167 persons for population characteristics. (Average number of persons per household is 3.64.)
† Calculated with probability proportionate to size.
‡ Calculated from a second sample.

II. Rel-variances and rel-covariances of some population and labor force characteristics for alternative primary sampling units and listing units.

1. Nature of the data.   This is a study of certain two-stage sample designs to estimate means, totals, or ratios of random variables.   The study is based on data for 2 areas, the Minneapolis–St. Paul and the Baltimore Metropolitan Districts, collected by the Census Bureau in an April 1947 local area survey.   About 90 per cent of the dwelling units in these metropolitan districts are covered by maps which show the individual structures and their street addresses and describe their basic uses, i.e., dwellings, flats, apartment houses, stores, etc. These maps are called Sanborn maps (see Fig. 2, Sec. 4, Ch. 6, for an example of a Sanborn "block"). This study relates only to the areas in these metropolitan districts covered by Sanborn maps. The data used in this study were adapted from a related project in order to take advantage of data already assembled. For the purposes of the related project, it was necessary that all schedules returned from "special dwelling places" (institutions, large hotels, etc.) be discarded. The sample in the Sanborn area of the metropolitan districts was selected in the manner now to be described.

An approximate count of the dwelling units was made from the Sanborn maps for each city block, and a measure of size was assigned to each block in units of approximately 6 dwelling units. A systematic sample of blocks was then selected with probability proportionate to the assigned measures of size. The selected blocks were segmented into the number of segments given by the measure, and one of the segments was selected at random (with equal probability) from within each selected block. These sample segments are known as "detail" segments.

In certain blocks, it was found impossible to define such detail segments, since the maps do not show enough detail to divide apartment houses, flats, etc. In such blocks, measures (totaling to the measure of the block) were assigned to such segments as could be defined, and 1 segment was selected with probability proportionate to the measure of the segment. In segments of measure greater than 1, known as "X"-segments, the dwelling units were listed and the list was sampled with a sampling fraction equal to the reciprocal of the measure of the X-segment. These X- and detail segments are called "ultimate segments" or "segments of 6 addresses" in this study.

Clusters of 1 and 3 Sanborn addresses were organized as follows: Each Sanborn detail segment was subdivided on the map into smaller clusters of 1 address on the basis of the map information. In general, an address was understood to include 1 dwelling unit as nearly as could be determined from the maps. For the detail segments, the schedules collected in the survey were matched by house number against the addresses shown on the map. Addresses for which no schedules were returned were treated as "zeros," i.e., no characteristic reported from that address. For an X-segment, the number of dwellings as determined from the map and lists was divided by the Sanborn measure for the segment to obtain an "expected take" in terms of addresses, and the schedules were assigned in order, 1 to each address. If there were more addresses in an X-segment than schedules returned, then some of the addresses were treated as "zeros."   If the number of schedules returned exceeded the expected take for the X-segment, the assignment of a second schedule was made in order to the addresses in the X-segment.

Data for clusters of 3 addresses were prepared by combining data from, at most, 3 addresses in a segment.   The single addresses were combined into clusters of 3 by numbering the addresses in a geographical pattern within each ultimate segment, and by taking a random start and making groupings of "3 addresses" within each segment.   If a segment contained but 1 or 2 addresses, that segment was considered a cluster of 3 addresses. In a segment which contained a number of addresses greater than 3 but not divisible by 3, the addresses left over were discarded.   About 11 per cent of the addresses in each of the 2 areas were discarded by this process in making up clusters of 3 addresses.   No information was discarded in making up clusters of 1 address or 6 addresses.

A dwelling is defined for the purpose of this study as 1 occupied dwelling unit at the time of the April 1947 survey.   In contrast to single addresses, there are no single dwellings which have zero population.   The total of a characteristic from the population of single addresses is equal to the total from clusters of 1 dwelling unit or the total from clusters of 6 addresses.

In some cases in the collection of the data, it was not possible to obtain a completed schedule at a dwelling unit because the respondent was ill, not at home, etc.   For the regular tabulations that were made for the survey, the returns were adjusted for nonresponses in the following manner.   For each dwelling unit from which a completed household schedule was not obtained, 1 schedule was selected at random from the sample and duplicated.   The selected schedule was almost always drawn from a segment other than that in which the nonresponse occurred.   In most cases, this process will, for each nonresponse household, result in a segment with 1 fewer and another segment with 1 more schedule than the actual number of dwelling units.   The greatest effect, which in any event is not considered to be appreciable, will appear when the address is the psu.   The effect will be less where clusters of 3 or 6 addresses are the psu's. It has no effect when the dwelling unit is the psu.

The computations have been made as if the sample were actually the whole population.

2. Theory and notation.   The analysis of the data involves the application of the theory and notation given in Sec. 6 and 8 of Ch. 6, dealing with one- or two-stage cluster sampling with a uniform over-all sampling fraction for a local area such as a city.   We have made computations only for the unstratified case in this study.   The use of stratification would produce somewhat lower variances and measures of homogeneity than those observed here, but evidence from other sources suggests that the difference would not be great for data such as these.

Specifically, the rel-variances and measures of homogeneity used here are defined as follows:

B^2 by Eq. 6.11 and B_X^2 by Eq. 6.5, Ch. 6 (these terms express the rel-variance between psu's);

W^2 by Eq. 6.12 and W_X^2 by Eq. 6.6, Ch. 6;

$\hat{V}^2$ by Eq. 8.10 with $\hat{V}_X^2$ defined by replacing B_X^2 for B^2 and W_X^2 for W^2, in Eq. 8.10, Ch. 6;

δ by Eq. 8.11 with δ_X defined by replacing B_X^2 for B^2, W_X^2 for W^2, and $\hat{V}_X^2$ for $\hat{V}^2$ in Eq. 8.11, Ch. 6.

V^2 is given by Eq. 8.7 and V_X^2 by Eq. 8.8, Ch. 6. It should be observed, however, that V_X^2 computed among listing units is identically equal to B_X^2, where the psu is defined the same as the listing unit for V_X^2. In the same way, V^2 is identically equal to B^2. Additional or special terms will be defined as needed in the subsequent discussion.

3. Discussion of results. The various results presented below illustrate a number of principles that are generally applicable as well as empirical relationships that are commonly observed. They may be useful as guides in other sample designs where the populations are of similar character.

(*a*) Tables D–8 and D–9 are a collection of some of the basic attributes that describe the universe on which this experiment has been based. The B_N^2 in Table D–8 is defined by Eq. 6.5, Ch. 6, where the variate is the number of listing units in the psu's. It is the rel-variance among the number of listing units per psu when sampling with equal probability, where $\bar{N}$, given in Table D–9, is the average number of listing units per psu. It should be observed at the outset that the variability in size of psu is, in no case, very large, since the variability has been controlled, to a great extent, by the manner in which the psu's were constructed (cf. Ch. 8, Sec. 5).

When sampling with pps, it can be shown that the expected average size of psu in the sample will be

$$\bar{N}(1 + B_N^2)$$

where $\bar{N}$ and B_N^2 are defined as before.

(*b*) Tables D–10 and D–11 show B_X^2, B^2 and V_{BX}^2, V_B^2 for the characteristics indicated. The V_X^2 among persons (or the B_X^2 between persons if the person is defined as the "psu") are not shown in these tables. They are easily computed by means of the expression $(1 - P)/P$, where the values of P ($= \bar{X}$) are read from Table D–9 when the psu is the person.

We have shown here the rel-variances between psu's for sampling with equal probability and with pps. The rel-variances for selection with pps are defined by Eq. 14.2 and 14.3, Ch. 9, but they are denoted here as V_B^2 and V_{BXY}, respectively. V_{BX}^2 follows from the definition of V_{BXY}, Eq. 14.3, Ch. 9, by replacing Y by X. We assign this notation so that V_B^2 and V_{BX}^2 (for sampling with pps) will not be confused with the B^2 and B_X^2 of Eq. 6.11 and 6.5 of Ch. 6 (sampling with equal probability). Although V_B^2, V_{BX}^2, and V_{BXY} apply to stratified samples, we adapt the formulas to our unstratified design by omitting the subscript h, i.e., set $L = 1$, which is equivalent to considering our population as being made up of only one stratum. The comparisons are made for sampling with replacement since the pps formulas apply to this case.

(i) The comparison of B_X^2 among alternative units for total persons has particular interest. This rel-variance would be the one involved if the indicated psu's were used as one-stage sampling units, and if a simple unbiased estimate of total population were made from the sample. Thus, in Minneapolis, with the dwelling unit as the sampling unit, $B_X^2 = .27$, and with the address as the sampling unit $B_X^2 = .50$. A sample of nearly twice as many addresses would thus be needed to yield accuracy equivalent to that for any specified number of dwelling units, in spite of the fact that the number of persons per address is about the same as the number per dwelling. It would follow that for estimating total population the dwelling unit would be the more efficient sampling unit unless the cost of its use was nearly twice as great per unit as that for the address. The comparison is similar but not so striking for Baltimore.

The principal reason for the difference between the variance for dwelling units and that for addresses arises primarily because there are no dwelling units of zero population (in this analysis vacant dwelling units have been eliminated in the listing process), but there are addresses of zero population. In Minneapolis 14.1 per cent of the addresses have no population, and in Baltimore 9.6 per cent (cf. Ch. 6, Sec. 25).

The value of B_X^2 for occupied addresses only, i.e., those with population, is related to that for all addresses by the relationship:

$$B_X^2 \text{ (all addresses)} = \frac{B_X^2 \text{ (occupied addresses)} + Q}{P}$$

(see Remark, Sec. 10, Ch. 4), where P is the proportion of addresses that are occupied, and $Q = 1 - P$. If we substitute (for Minneapolis) B_X^2 (all addresses) $= .50$, which is the value shown in Table D–10 for one address, and $P = .859$, we obtain

$$B_X^2 \text{ (occupied)} = .859(.50) - .141 = .29$$

which is only slightly larger than the value for dwelling units. Thus, the increase in the variance for addresses arises almost entirely because of the "zero" addresses.

It follows that, if one were to use the simple unbiased estimate for total population, it would pay to spend a considerable portion of one's resources to list and identify occupied addresses or dwelling units as a part of the listing process. A similar relationship holds for Baltimore. Essentially the same relationships hold, also, for the variances within the psu's given in Table D–12, although there the effect of stratification by psu means that these relationships are not exactly the same.

The simple unbiased estimates of total population for other sizes of sampling units in Tables D–10 and D–11 show that the use of clusters larger than the address is not likely to be efficient if the primary purpose is to estimate total population. Thus, the compact cluster of 3 addresses and also the compact cluster of 6 addresses have about the same rel-variance between cluster totals as does the dwelling unit. A sample of $6n$ dwelling units in compact clusters of approximately 6 will yield no substantially greater accuracy than a sample of n dwelling units.

These types of relationships do not hold at all in the estimates for ratios to population, as is seen in the column for the ratio estimate to persons. For the ratio estimate, the address has about the same variance as the dwelling unit. The larger clusters have smaller variances per cluster, but larger variances per dwelling unit included in the sample. The implication of this latter point is seen more fully in the discussion of measures of homogeneity in connection with Tables D–14 and D–15.

(ii) The results of two methods of reducing the effect of variability in size of psu are illustrated in these tables, the ratio estimate and sampling with pps. It is clear that in nearly all cases the use of the ratio estimate with equal probability (B^2) or sampling with pps with either the unbiased estimate (V_{BX}^2) or the ratio estimate (V_B^2) produces a smaller rel-variance between psu's than a simple unbiased estimate based on psu's selected with equal probability (B_X^2). Here, when B^2 is for the estimate of the ratio of a characteristic to total listing units which are defined in a given way, then the comparable V_{BX}^2 is computed with probability proportionate to these same listing units.

Usually $V_{BX}^2 < B^2$ for the same units, but since all the units under consideration here are small, and the variability in size of psu in terms of dwellings or addresses has already been well controlled by the design of the experiment, V_{BX}^2 and B^2 do not differ markedly.

(iii) The reduction in the rel-variance due to use of the ratio estimate depends, of course, on the correlation between the numerator and the denominator of the ratio. The effect of this correlation is discussed in

Sec. 18 and 19, Ch. 4.   For equal probability, the correlation is

$$\rho_1 = \frac{B_{XY}}{B_X B_Y}$$

and for sampling with pps

$$\rho_2 = \frac{V_{BXY}}{V_{BX} V_{BY}}$$

These correlations may be computed from the rel-variances in Tables D–10 and D–11, using the relationships

$$\rho_1 = \frac{B_X^2 + B_Y^2 - B^2}{2 B_X B_Y}$$

and

$$\rho_2 = \frac{V_{BX}^2 + V_{BY}^2 - V_B^2}{2 V_{BX} V_{BY}}$$

It is generally true that, for a characteristic present in a relatively high proportion of the population, the correlations ρ_1 and ρ_2 will be high; if the proportions are low, these correlations will usually be low. For this reason, "persons in the labor force" and "persons employed" show noticeable gains by use of the ratio estimate, whereas for "persons unemployed" and "males aged 65 and over," both present in a relatively low proportion of the population, negligible gains or even losses are experienced in applying the ratio estimate.

(iv) The ratio estimate to number of addresses is observed to be significantly less efficient than the ratio to persons or to dwelling units for estimating characteristics present in a relatively high proportion of the population. For characteristics not in this category, e.g., persons unemployed and males aged 65 and over, the differences between the alternative denominators for the ratio estimate are small. This condition is brought about by the lower correlations between the characteristics and the number of addresses in the psu's as compared with the higher correlations between the characteristics and the number of dwelling units or persons.

(v) A device that is sometimes used for approximating the rel-variance of the ratio $r = x/y$, where y is the number of persons in a specified class, and x is the number of these persons having some characteristic, is given by (see p. 593 and also Case Study B of Ch. 12 and Sec. 19 of Ch. 10)

$$B^2 \doteq B_x^2 - B_y^2$$

or

$$V_B^2 \doteq V_{Bx}^2 - V_{By}^2$$

These approximations are good provided $\rho_1 \doteq B_Y/B_X$ or $\rho_2 \doteq V_{BY}/V_{BX}$. It is observed from Tables D–10 and D–11 that these approximations do not always give good indications of the level of the ratio estimate rel-variance, particularly where B_Y^2 is nearly as large as B_X^2, which usually happens if X is a high proportion of Y. Then a small error due to the terms neglected in the approximation may cause a relatively large error in the difference. When this approximation is not good it is because, for clusters of the type defined, the proportion of the listing units having the characteristic is not independent of the size of the cluster. For example, clusters with a small number of persons may have a higher proportion of the population in the labor force than clusters with a large number of persons.

(c) Table D–12 shows W_X^2 and W^2 for the various choices of listing units and psu's. Rel-variances among listing units within psu's and measures of homogeneity for a design where the listing unit is the dwelling unit and the psu is the address have been omitted from the tables, since this combination of primary unit and listing unit would appear to have no practical application.

(i) The rel-variance, V_r^2, for a sample from the population on which this study is based may be computed by using Eq. 6.10, Ch. 6, and substituting the proper values of B^2 from Table D–10 or D–11 and W^2 from Table D–12 with the appropriate values for m and $\bar{n}$. These steps may also be used to obtain approximations for populations believed to resemble the population in this study. The rel-variance, $V_{x'}^2$, of a simple unbiased estimate is given by the same equation, but without the terms involving Y, i.e., B_X^2 substituted for B^2 and W_X^2 for W^2 in Eq. 6.10.

(ii) It is convenient to think of W_X^2 and W^2 as the rel-variance for an estimate of the characteristic (with the simple unbiased or ratio estimates, respectively) with a proportionate stratified random sample where the total sample size is considered one listing unit, and each psu is a stratum. The rel-variance for such a sample is, neglecting a factor of $(N-1)/N$, equal to W_X^2 or W^2.

With this viewpoint the fact that there is, for the same listing unit, relatively little change in W_X^2 (or W^2) for different choices of psu is an illustration of the effect of increasing the depth of stratification beyond the point of appreciable additional gain (see Ch. 5, Sec. 15). The additional stratification gains arising from using about 2400 strata (corresponding to dwelling units as strata), as compared with using about 400 strata (corresponding to 6 addresses as strata), are very slight for characteristics such as those shown here.

Comparison of the rel-variance for no stratification with that arising from using so many strata that each stratum is a psu can be observed by comparing B^2 (or B_X^2) for any specified units with W^2 (or W_X^2) where the same units are the listing units. These comparisons point out that gains are not large for any of the sampling units, although they are somewhat larger for the larger sampling units.

(d) Table D–13 shows the ratios $\hat{V}_X^2 / V_X^2$, the factor by which the rel-variance of the unbiased estimate is increased (or sometimes decreased) no matter what subsampling fraction is taken, because of sampling psu's that vary in size (see Sec. 8, Ch. 6). This ratio does not completely describe the influence of variation in the size of psu's on the rel-variance, since δ, the measure of homogeneity, is also affected by the variation in size of psu. However, the influence of δ on the rel-variance is affected also by the average size of subsample per psu.

The unbiased estimate for a characteristic present in a high proportion of the population is affected appreciably by the variability in size of psu; estimates for characteristics present in a low proportion of the population are not. The latter follows because the correlation between these characteristics and the size of the psu is so low that it is not important whether the psu's are equal in size or not.

For the ratio estimates, the factors $\hat{V}^2 / V^2$ are all very nearly equal to 1, because the ratio estimate tends to remove the effect of the variation in size of psu. Consequently, no table is shown for these. The whole range of these factors for the characteristics indicated in Table D–13 for estimates of the ratio to total persons is from .94 to 1.03 with almost all the factors in the range .99–1.03. For the ratio estimate to number of dwellings or addresses, the spread is slightly larger, but practically all the factors are in the range .95–1.04 with the majority closer to 1.00.

(e) Tables D–14 and D–15 show measures of homogeneity for the ratio and unbiased estimates for various choices of listing units and psu's.

(i) The significance of the value of δ may be seen from Sec. 8, Ch. 6, where the effect of clustering is discussed. The value $\delta^\star$ has been introduced in the tables to indicate a level for comparison. The value of $\delta^\star$ is chosen so that the factor $1 + \delta(\bar{n} - 1)$ is equal to 1.1 when $\bar{n} = \bar{N}$, i.e., if whole clusters are sampled. That is, when $\delta = \delta^\star$, the loss due to clustering is 10 per cent. The loss will be greater than 10 per cent for any value of δ greater than $\delta^\star$.

(ii) The effect of the variation in size of psu is reflected, not only in the ratio $\hat{V}_X^2 / V_X^2$ or $\hat{V}^2 / V^2$, but also in the δ_X or δ, since the rel-variances in the definitions of δ_X and δ are computed from psu's of varying size. There is no convenient mathematical relationship that expresses the effect on the measures of homogeneity that arises from sampling psu's of unequal size, but the extent of this effect may be inferred roughly by comparing certain of the measures for the ratio estimate and the simple unbiased estimate. The δ for a ratio to total listing units, computed from a population of psu's composed of unequal numbers of listing units (where the average size of psu is $\bar{N}$ listing units), often approaches the measure of homogeneity that one could expect for the unbiased estimate with the same listing unit but with every psu composed of exactly $\bar{N}$ listing units. The greatest effect from variation in size of psu appears to occur for the characteristics present in a high proportion of the population.

(iii) A rule often used in speculations on the size of δ is that, as the size of the psu is increased, then δ, the measure of homogeneity, tends to decrease but not as fast as $\bar{N}$ increases, so that $\delta(\bar{N}-1)$ tends to increase with $\bar{N}$. The measures of homogeneity in Tables D–14 and D–15 generally follow this rule except for cases where the listing unit is the person. Negative or very low positive measures of homogeneity appear for several characteristics in these cases. It is possible to generalize the instances where negative δ's tend to appear, as follows.

Consider an experiment where a particular characteristic of two randomly selected listing units is observed. Let the first listing unit be selected at random from a randomly selected psu and the second be selected at random from (1) the same psu, or (2) a second randomly selected psu. Now, if it is more likely that the two selected listing units both have this characteristic when the second listing unit is selected by method 2 than by method 1, then δ is negative.

When the listing unit is the person and the dwelling unit or address is the psu, it is clear that, once a person with a specified characteristic is selected, the nature of the psu, as constituted by the remaining persons in the psu, is likely to be affected. For example, when a dwelling unit contains a male aged 25–34, he is likely to be the husband, with the remaining male family members not apt to be in this age group. Another male aged 25–34 is perhaps less likely to be observed in this dwelling unit than in a different dwelling unit, so that we expect the δ among persons within dwellings to be very low positive or negative for this characteristic. This behavior of the person as the listing unit tends to affect the measure of homogeneity for psu's of somewhat larger sizes than the dwelling unit, although as the psu is made even larger, the δ's will tend to conform to the rule stated above.

(iv) It is observed that, for a fixed psu, δ tends to increase as the size of the listing unit increases. This result would be expected on the basis of Eq. 8.16, Ch. 6. In this study, the address and the dwelling unit are of about the same size, and the use of either of them as the listing unit, with the same psu, gives values of δ of about the same magnitude (especially for the ratio estimate), but both of them produce larger values of δ than result when the person is the listing unit.

Table D–8.   Variation in size of alternative primary sampling units

Primary sampling unit	B_N^2 between psu's when listing unit is		
	Person	Dwelling unit	Address
Minneapolis–St. Paul Metropolitan District			
Dwelling unit	.27	..	..
Address	.50	.44	..
Three addresses	.27	.24	.022
Six addresses	.25	.26	.10
Baltimore Metropolitan District			
Dwelling unit	.33	..	..
Address	.49	.40	..
Three addresses	.30	.24	.0078
Six addresses	.28	.21	.041

Table D-9. Total numbers of units and some average values for alternative primary sampling units and listing units

Primary sampling unit	Number of psu's M	Average number of listing units per psu when listing unit is $\bar{N}$			Average characteristic per primary sampling unit $\bar{X}$				
		Address	Dwelling unit	Persons	Persons in labor force	Persons employed	Persons unemployed	Males aged 25–34	Males aged 65 and over
Minneapolis–St. Paul Metropolitan District									
Person	8101	..	..	1.0	.46	.45	.0080	.079	.034
Dwelling unit	2435	..	1.0	3.3	1.5	1.5	.027	.26	.11
Address	2360	1.0	1.03	3.4	1.6	1.5	.028	.27	.12
Three addresses	714	2.9	3.0	10	4.6	4.5	.080	.79	.33
Six addresses	435	5.4	5.6	19	8.6	8.4	.15	1.5	.63
Baltimore Metropolitan District									
Person	8429	..	..	1.0	.46	.44	.024	.089	.026
Dwelling unit	2379	..	1.0	3.5	1.6	1.6	.084	.31	.092
Address	2032	1.0	1.2	4.1	1.9	1.8	.099	.37	.11
Three addresses	613	3.0	3.4	12	5.6	5.3	.30	1.1	.32
Six addresses	365	5.6	6.5	23	11	10	.55	2.1	.60

Table D–10. Rel-variances between primary sampling units, Minneapolis – St. Paul Metropolitan District

Primary sampling unit	For sampling with equal probability				For sampling with probability proportionate to size where measure is				
	For the simple unbiased estimate B_X^2	For the ratio estimate to number of			Number of persons	Number of dwelling units		Number of addresses	
		Persons B^2	Dwelling units B^2	Addresses B^2	For the unbiased estimate V_{BX}^2	For the unbiased estimate V_{BX}^2	For the ratio estimate to total persons V_B^2	For the unbiased estimate V_{BX}^2	For the ratio estimate to total persons V_B^2
One dwelling									
Total persons	.27	…	…	…	…	…	…	…	…
Persons in labor force	.43	.35	…	…	.33	…	…	…	…
Employed persons	.43	.36	…	…	.34	…	…	…	…
Unemployed persons	38	37	…	…	42	…	…	…	…
Males aged 25–34	3.7	3.4	…	…	3.0	…	…	…	…
Males aged 65 and over	8.1	8.6	…	…	12	…	…	…	…
One address									
Total persons	.50	…	.31	…	…	.25	…	…	…
Persons in labor force	.74	.36	.44	…	.28	.38	.31	…	…
Employed persons	.74	.37	.44	…	.29	.39	.32	…	…
Unemployed persons	36	36	36	…	31	32	32	…	…
Males aged 25–34	4.0	3.4	3.8	…	2.6	3.3	3.0	…	…
Males aged 65 and over	8.3	8.6	8.1	…	9.6	7.2	7.6	…	…
Cluster of three addresses									
Total persons	.27	…	.13	.24	…	.12	…	.26	…
Persons in labor force	.37	.15	.16	.35	.13	.16	.13	.36	.15
Employed persons	.37	.15	.16	.35	.13	.16	.13	.37	.15
Unemployed persons	14	14	14	14	11	13	13	14	13
Males aged 25–34	1.5	1.1	1.3	1.5	.97	1.2	1.1	1.4	1.1
Males aged 65 and over	3.1	3.2	3.1	3.1	3.4	3.0	3.1	3.0	3.1
Cluster of six addresses									
Total persons	.25	…	.10	.14	…	.073	…	.17	…
Persons in labor force	.28	.095	.098	.21	.085	.081	.082	.24	.092
Employed persons	.28	.097	.098	.21	.087	.082	.085	.24	.094
Unemployed persons	8.4	8.0	8.2	8.3	6.7	7.2	7.1	7.9	7.6
Males aged 25–34	.93	.65	.73	.84	.57	.68	.63	.83	.64
Males aged 65 and over	1.8	1.7	1.7	1.6	1.6	1.5	1.5	1.5	1.6

612

Table D–11. Rel-variances between primary sampling units, Baltimore Metropolitan District

	For sampling with equal probability				For sampling with probability proportionate to size where measure is				
	For the simple unbiased estimate B_X^2	For the ratio estimate to number of			Number of persons	Number of dwelling units		Number of addresses	
Primary sampling unit		Persons B^2	Dwelling units B^2	Addresses B^2	For the unbiased estimate V_{BX}^2	For the unbiased estimate V_{BX}^2	For the ratio estimate to total persons V_B^2	For the unbiased estimate V_{BX}^2	For the ratio estimate to total persons V_B^2
One dwelling unit									
Total persons	.33	...	...	...	...	...	...	...	...
Persons in labor force	.49	.34	...	...	.30	...	...	...	...
Employed persons	.48	.36	...	...	.33	...	...	...	...
Unemployed persons	15	15	...	...	12	...	...	...	...
Males aged 25–34	2.9	2.6	...	...	2.5	...	...	...	...
Males aged 65 and over	10	11	...	...	13	...	...	...	...
One address									
Total persons	.49	...	.33	...	...	.30	...	...	...
Persons in labor force	.71	.31	.47	...	.25	.43	.29	...	...
Employed persons	.70	.33	.47	...	.27	.43	.31	...	...
Unemployed persons	14	13	14	...	10	14	13	...	...
Males aged 25–34	3.0	2.4	2.7	...	2.0	2.5	2.2	...	...
Males aged 65 and over	9.1	9.4	9.2	...	11	9.1	9.4	...	...
Cluster of three addresses									
Total persons	.30	...	.14	.29	...	.13	...	.28	...
Persons in labor force	.44	.13	.22	.43	.10	.18	.11	.43	.13
Employed persons	.42	.13	.20	.41	.12	.18	.12	.41	.13
Unemployed persons	6.3	5.4	5.9	6.2	4.2	5.4	5.0	6.2	5.4
Males aged 25–34	1.3	.93	.99	1.3	.81	.87	.84	1.3	.92
Males aged 65 and over	3.2	3.3	3.2	3.2	3.6	3.1	3.3	3.1	3.3
Cluster of six addresses									
Total persons	.28	...	.096	.21	...	.089	...	.22	...
Persons in labor force	.39	.081	.15	.33	.066	.12	.068	.34	.079
Employed persons	.36	.082	.13	.30	.073	.11	.074	.31	.081
Unemployed persons	4.6	3.7	4.1	4.4	2.7	3.4	3.1	4.1	3.4
Males aged 25–34	.90	.50	.57	.84	.42	.49	.45	.83	.48
Males aged 65 and over	1.9	2.0	1.9	1.9	1.9	1.8	1.9	1.9	1.9

Table D-12. Rel-variances among listing units within primary units

Primary sampling unit	Minneapolis – St. Paul Metropolitan District					Baltimore Metropolitan District				
	A person	Listing unit				A person	Listing unit			
		A dwelling unit		An address			A dwelling unit		An address	
	For the simple unbiased estimate W_X^2	For the simple unbiased estimate W_X^2	For the ratio estimate to total persons W^2	For the simple unbiased estimate W_X^2	For the ratio estimate to total persons W^2	For the simple unbiased estimate W_X^2	For the simple unbiased estimate W_X^2	For the ratio estimate to total persons W^2	For the simple unbiased estimate W_X^2	For the ratio estimate to total persons W^2
One dwelling unit										
Persons in labor force	1.2	…	…	…	…	1.2	…	…	…	…
Employed persons	1.2	…	…	…	…	1.3	…	…	…	…
Unemployed persons	113	…	…	…	…	37	…	…	…	…
Males aged 25–34	12	…	…	…	…	11	…	…	…	…
Males aged 65 and over	27	…	…	…	…	36	…	…	…	…
One address*										
Persons in labor force	1.2	…	…	…	…	1.2	…	…	…	…
Employed persons	1.2	…	…	…	…	1.3	…	…	…	…
Unemployed persons	121	…	…	…	…	38	…	…	…	…
Males aged 25–34	12	…	…	…	…	10	…	…	…	…
Males aged 65 and over	28	…	…	…	…	36	…	…	…	…
Cluster of three addresses										
Total persons	…	.22	…	.38	…	…	.27	…	.32	…
Persons in labor force	1.2	.39	.32	.56	.33	1.2	.41	.31	.43	.28
Employed persons	1.2	.40	.32	.56	.33	1.3	.41	.33	.45	.30
Unemployed persons	123	34	34	34	34	38	13	13	12	12
Males aged 25–34	12	3.6	3.4	3.9	3.5	10	2.8	2.5	2.7	2.3
Males aged 65 and over	29	8.1	8.6	8.3	8.6	37	9.5	9.8	8.6	8.9
Cluster of six addresses										
Total persons	…	.24	…	.41	…	…	.28	…	.33	…
Persons in labor force	1.2	.42	.32	.61	.33	1.1	.42	.31	.46	.28
Employed persons	1.2	.43	.33	.61	.33	1.3	.43	.34	.47	.31
Unemployed persons	123	36	36	35	34	40	14	14	12	12
Males aged 25–34	12	3.6	3.3	4.1	3.6	10	2.8	2.6	2.7	2.4
Males aged 65 and over	28	8.0	8.6	8.2	8.4	37	9.9	10	8.8	9.1

* Figures omitted for the dwelling unit as listing unit; see p. 607.

Table D-13. Ratio of $\hat{V}_X^2$ to V_X^2 for unbiased estimates

Listing unit →	A person				A dwelling unit		An address	
Primary sampling unit →	A dwelling unit	An address	Three addresses	Six addresses	Three addresses	Six addresses	Three addresses	Six addresses
Minneapolis–St. Paul Metropolitan District								
Total persons	..	..	..	..	1.52	1.62	1.03	1.15
Persons in labor force	1.07	1.35	1.20	1.16	1.47	1.46	1.00	1.05
Employed persons	1.07	1.33	1.19	1.15	1.47	1.45	1.00	1.05
Unemployed persons	.94	.99	1.01	1.01	.98	1.01	1.00	1.00
Males aged 25–34	1.04	1.07	1.03	1.03	1.05	1.06	1.00	1.05
Males aged 65 and over	.95	.98	1.00	1.01	1.00	1.03	1.01	1.02
Baltimore Metropolitan District								
Total persons	..	..	..	..	1.50	1.56	1.02	1.11
Persons in labor force	1.15	1.37	1.28	1.27	1.48	1.52	1.01	1.07
Employed persons	1.11	1.31	1.23	1.22	1.46	1.48	1.01	1.07
Unemployed persons	1.03	1.05	1.04	1.04	1.04	1.06	1.00	1.02
Males aged 25–34	1.03	1.07	1.05	1.04	1.13	1.13	1.00	1.03
Males aged 65 and over	.97	.98	.99	1.00	1.00	1.01	1.00	1.01

615

Table D-14. Measures of homogeneity (δ_X) for two-stage sample designs for unbiased estimates

Listing unit →	A person				A dwelling unit		An address	
Primary sampling unit →	A dwelling unit	An address	Three addresses	Six addresses	Three addresses	Six addresses	Three addresses	Six addresses
Minneapolis–St. Paul Metropolitan District								
δ^*[1]	.043	.041	.011	.0057	.050	.022	.053	.023
Total persons	..	..	..	..	.48	.46	.27	.29
Persons in labor force	.053	.24	.18	.16	.38	.32	.24	.21
Employed persons	.045	.23	.17	.15	.37	.32	.24	.21
Unemployed persons	.031	.010	.015	.014	.073	.051	.063	.055
Males aged 25–34	.0034	.049	.025	.026	.074	.074	.031	.043
Males aged 65 and over	.0037	.0090	.0063	.0087	.048	.039	.029	.030
Baltimore Metropolitan District								
δ^*[1]	.039	.032	.0089	.0045	.041	.018	.051	.022
Total persons	..	..	..	..	.45	.46	.38	.39
Persons in labor force	.11	.27	.23	.23	.44	.43	.40	.40
Employed persons	.081	.23	.20	.19	.42	.41	.37	.37
Unemployed persons	.12	.13	.075	.067	.15	.15	.15	.16
Males aged 25–34	−.016	.048	.045	.043	.16	.15	.14	.13
Males aged 65 and over	−.0053	.0097	.0052	.0091	.045	.042	.032	.041

[1] Value of δ_X for which increase in rel-variance due to clustering is 10 per cent.

Table D-15. Measures of homogeneity (δ) for two-stage sample designs for estimates of ratios

Listing unit ⟶	For ratio estimate to total persons						For ratio estimate to total dwelling units				For ratio estimate to total addresses	
	A person	A person	A dwelling unit	A dwelling unit	An address	An address	A dwelling unit	A dwelling unit	An address	An address	An address	An address
Primary sampling unit ⟶	A dwelling unit	An address	Three addresses	Six addresses	Three addresses	Six addresses	Three addresses	Six addresses	Three addresses	Six addresses	Three addresses	Six addresses
Minneapolis–St. Paul Metropolitan District $\delta_{\star}[1]$												
Total persons	.043	.041	.011	.0057	.050	.022	.053	.023	.050	.022	.053	.023
Persons in labor force	⋮	.010	.027	.028	.12	.11	.10	.097	.20	.19	.23	.14
Employed persons	−.010	.0065	.026	.027	.13	.11	.10	.097	.075	.050	.21	.14
Unemployed persons	−.014	.0039	.011	.012	.061	.043	.055	.050	.066	.047	.21	.14
Males aged 25–34	.029	−.00028	−.0038	.0020	.0037	.018	−.022	−.0016	.068	.045	.062	.053
Males aged 65 and over	−.020	.018	.0088	.0053	.035	.016	.026	.013	.020	.027	.025	.022
Baltimore Metropolitan District $\delta_{\star}[1]$												
Total persons	.039	.032	.0089	.0045	.041	.018	.051	.022	.041	.018	.051	.022
Persons in labor force	⋮	.025	.027	.026	.11	.095	.11	.095	.18	.16	.36	.31
Employed persons	.0014	.017	.023	.021	.10	.083	.11	.081	.20	.17	.39	.35
Unemployed persons	−.0049	.11	.056	.047	.11	.11	.13	.11	.17	.14	.36	.31
Males aged 25–34	.10	−.0088	.0082	.0053	.078	.041	.062	.029	.13	.12	.15	.14
Males aged 65 and over	−.040	.018	.0077	.0097	.044	.039	.029	.036	.063	.049	.030	.035

[1] Value of δ for which increase in rel-variance due to clustering is 10 per cent.

E. SAMPLE VERIFICATION AND QUALITY CONTROL METHODS IN THE 1950 CENSUS*

The office processing of the 1950 Censuses of Population, Housing, and Agriculture involved the coding of questionnaires for about 150 million persons, 40 million dwelling units, and 6 million farms, as well as the punching of more than 250 million cards. In an operation of this magnitude, clerical errors are inevitable. In earlier censuses, it was traditional to attempt to locate and correct substantially all these clerical errors. This was accomplished by carrying out each operation a second time, by way of verification. Beginning with the 1940 Census, however, the Bureau has investigated, tested, and applied various adaptations of modern statistical quality control techniques for keeping certain types of clerical errors at a satisfactory level without incurring the expense of complete verification.

It is often quite difficult to define error in such a way that its effect can be measured directly. For example, it is not feasible to maintain records of error in the card-punching operation by the field in which the error occurred. The cost of record keeping would probably absorb most of the savings realized by sample verification. An error in card punching is therefore defined as a card which contains one or more errors. The error rate is measured by the number of cards in error per hundred punched. This figure cannot easily be translated into its effect on the final statistical tables. In order to evaluate the effect of such errors on final statistics, empirical studies have been made by the Bureau of the Census, using tabulations with punching errors corrected and comparing them with tabulations affected by a known level of punching errors.

The development during the past 10 years of more efficient methods of mechanically checking punched cards for inconsistencies among the entries in the various columns, along with the philosophy of not paying for perfection, while still insuring adequate quality in the processing of the returns, has had the rather important consequences of enabling the Bureau to eliminate, for all practical purposes, the manual editing of schedules in the Census of Population and to reduce substantially the amount of clerical review of the questionnaires in the 1950 Census of Agriculture. Recent investigation into the effects of this mechanical editing has also shown that it can be depended upon to detect the more serious types of punching errors, such as off-column punches in magnitude items, where a change in a decimal point can be serious. As a result it has been found

---

* By Joseph F. Daly and Leon Gilford, Bureau of the Census.

possible to make a substantial reduction in the cost of verifying the punching of Population, Housing, and Agriculture cards through sample verification.

In applying sample verification we undertake primarily to control the quality of the process rather than to insure certain standards of performance in each small lot. The object here is to detect, and remove (or improve the performance of) the punchers whose error rates are too high, rather than to reject individual lots of work and to set them aside for the correction of errors that they contain. When we use the techniques of process control, a poor unit of work will get through occasionally and affect the final statistics. On the other hand, use of the techniques of acceptance sampling to insure (with high probability) acceptable quality for lots small enough to represent the more detailed publication levels required such a high inspection rate as to make it prohibitive in cost. If the work produced is good, as it ordinarily is if the process is controlled, the acceptance plan contributes little to the quality. Thus, in order to avoid penalizing ourselves, major emphasis was placed on process control in the Shewhart tradition, which can be accomplished with a comparatively low inspection rate, rather than on acceptance sampling applied to the smallest publication levels. By identifying the clerk who is producing poor lots and retraining him or removing him from the operation, we have good assurance that most of the work will be of acceptable quality, particularly since each clerk or puncher has to serve a probationary period under complete inspection before being qualified for sample verification. The acceptance sampling techniques were used as a by-product of process control in order to prevent an unusually poor lot from being absorbed in the operation. It is possible with a low sampling fraction to detect the occasional extremely poor unit of work so that it can be set aside and verified completely. Thus acceptance sampling was used with a sampling fraction adequate to control the process, but not adequate to identify moderately defective small lots.

Before adoption of any sampling plan for verification, we have to be fairly certain that the cost of the system, as compared with that for complete verification, will show a worth-while saving and still retain adequate control of quality. The various plans which were finally adopted were basically similar, with minor variations between coding and punching and among the three censuses. The lot sizes depended upon the way in which the schedules were assigned to operators for coding and punching. The schedules were assembled in portfolios by geographic areas which varied in size. This was a disadvantage as far as acceptance sampling is concerned because the discriminating power of an acceptance sampling plan depends on the size of the sample taken from each lot. Thus, getting uniform-sized samples from variable-sized lots would mean using variable sampling fractions. Cost considerations ruled out this type of procedure. However, it was possible to combine several small portfolios into a single unit for acceptance sampling purposes, thus reducing to a considerable extent the variability of the sample size, even though constant sampling fractions were used. For the sampling within lots it was found to be undesirable to insist on simple random sampling. Instead we employed a systematic cluster sampling procedure, using a random starting point for each lot. To give a specific example, in the verification of Housing punching a 5 per cent sample was taken by verifying all the cards punched for every twentieth sheet. The number of cards punched from each sheet varied between 1 and 12. The verifier was given a new random sheet number each day to be used in starting his count in each lot. A lot of work consisted of 4 portfolios, which was assigned at one time, punched consecutively, and verified by one verifier in a single assignment. Counting of sheets continued from one portfolio to the next in the lot. The entire lot of 4 portfolios was either accepted or rejected as a unit on the basis of the sample results. In setting up the plan we estimated that the average portfolio would have 213 cards punched and that the average operator would punch 4000 cards per week. Under these assumptions, Table E–1 indicates the proportion of time that action would be taken on operators with various error and omission rates. It will be noted in the table that special control is exercised over omissions (failing to punch a card) as compared with other errors. Table E–2 indicates the proportion of average-sized lots with various error rates that would be rejected and verified completely. Tables E–3 and E–4 are the tables of acceptance and rejection numbers used in making these decisions on operators and on lots.

The fact that every twentieth sheet rather than every twentieth dwelling unit was selected for verification caused some loss of information because of the clustering of errors arising in punching. The decision to take a cluster as large as a complete sheet for Housing punching and only 5 consecutive lines for Population punching was based on preliminary studies in which verification was carried out with different cluster sizes. Results obtained on verification production rates and on the measures of homogeneity of errors in clusters of various sizes were incorporated in the study to determine which cluster size was actually the most economical. In the experiments on the verification of Population punching, the verification of single lines was contrasted with that of clusters of 2, 5, 10, 15, and 30 lines. It turned out that the optimum was in the neighborhood of 4. The sample plan with clusters of 5 lines was almost as economical and was used because of administrative convenience.

Table E–1. Approximate proportion of time that operators will be removed from punching

Error rate (including omissions)	Omission rate								
	.00	.01	.02	.03	.04	.05	.06	.07	.10
.00	.00	..	..	..	..	..	..	..	..
.01	.00	.04	..	..	..	..	..	..	..
.02	.00	.04	.34	..	..	..	..	..	..
.03	.00	.04	.34	.63	..	..	..	..	..
.04	.00	.04	.34	.63	.81	..	..	..	..
.05	.03	.07	.36	.64	.82	.91	..	..	..
.06	.11	.15	.41	.67	.83	.92	.95	..	..
.07	.24	.28	.51	.72	.86	.93	.96	.99	..
.08	.42	.44	.61	.79	.89	.95	.97	.99	..
.09	.58	.60	.72	.84	.92	.96	.98	.99	..
.10	.72	.73	.81	.90	.95	.97	.99	.99	1.00
.15	.98	.98	.99	.99	1.00	1.00	1.00	1.00	1.00

Table E–2. Approximate proportion of lots that will be rejected and verified 100 per cent

Error rate (per cent)	Proportion of lots that will be rejected
.0– .9	.00
1.0– 1.9	.00
2.0– 2.9	.01
3.0– 3.9	.02
4.0– 4.9	.05
5.0– 5.9	.08
6.0– 6.9	.12
7.0– 7.9	.19
8.0– 8.9	.26
9.0– 9.9	.33
10.0–10.9	.40
11.0–11.9	.47
12.0–12.9	.54
13.0–13.9	.60
14.0–14.9	.66
15.0–15.9	.71
16.0–19.9	.82
20.0–24.9	.93
25.0–29.9	.97
30.0 and over	1.00

Table E–3. Acceptance and rejection numbers for operators

Number of cards verified during week	Operator continues to punch if the number of error cards *and* the number of omitted cards are as indicated or less		Operator is removed from punching if the number of error cards *or* the number of omitted cards is as indicated or more	
	Errors (including omissions)	Omissions	Errors (including omissions)	Omissions
0– 24	*	*	*	*
25– 49	4	1	5	2
50– 99	7	2	8	3
100–149	10	3	11	4
150–199	14	4	15	5
200–249	17	5	18	6
250–299	20	7	21	8
300–349	24	8	25	9
350–399	27	9	28	10
400–449	30	10	31	11
450–499	34	11	35	12

* If an operator has less than 25 verified during any 1 week, decision is deferred until the following week and her records for both weeks are cumulated.

Table E–4. Acceptance and rejection numbers for lots

Number verified	Accept lot if the number of errors (including omissions) is as indicated or less	Reject lot if the number of errors (including omissions) is as indicated or more
0– 5	*	*
6– 15	1	2
16– 25	2	3
26– 35	3	4
36– 45	4	5
46– 55	5	6
56– 65	6	7
66– 75	6	7
76– 85	7	8
86– 95	8	9
96–105	9	10
106–115	10	11

* If the sample for a lot is less than 6, continue the count to the next lot and treat the combination as 1 work unit for purposes of verification.

Although the decision to accept or reject a lot was made as soon as each lot was verified, the decision was not made on operators until the end of a week. The number of cards verified for a particular operator, the number of errors detected, and the number of omissions were cumulated over all lots and compared at the end of each week with the acceptance and rejection numbers shown in Table E–3. Thus an operator was not necessarily rejected when he produced a single rejected portfolio. On the other hand, though all the work of an operator might be accepted lot by lot, he might still be rejected at the end of the week on the basis of the more discriminating test applied to his entire week's work, consisting of several lots.

Ideally, it was not desirable to have rejected operators continue to punch even when their work was 100 per cent verified because their work was essentially unproductive. Whenever possible, rejected operators were assigned to some other work. In particular, it was found that even poor-quality punchers made reasonably good verifiers. Since verification of punching is practically an independent operation, the verifier who is a poor-quality puncher will have a lower production rate than the verifier who is a good puncher, since he will be stopped more frequently by the incorrect keys that he depresses. But he will not produce additional errors in the cards, and he will detect most of the errors. Studies which were made at the Bureau to determine whether verifiers picked up specific cards that were known to be in error indicated that the less competent but marginally acceptable puncher can be expected to detect at least 95 per cent of the punching errors in the cards verified. It should be noted that this experience on the accuracy of verification of punching does not carry over into the proofreading type of verification, such as the verification of occupation and industry coding. There the accuracy of even experienced verifiers was much lower. Thus, in coding operations the alternative of turning poor coders into verifiers was not available, and there remained only the choices of terminating the coder, retraining him, or putting him on other work if the process control feature of the plan was to be retained.

Experience to date indicates that these sample verification and process control plans, used in the punching and coding of the 1950 Censuses, have been effective in keeping the error rates below the specified levels. Moreover, although the cost per card of sample verification is naturally somewhat greater than the cost per card of 100 per cent verification, partly because of the need to identify specific cards and partly because of the more elaborate control system of records that must be maintained, the difference in cost is not so great as to preclude the possibility of substantial savings. In the Population, Housing, and Agriculture punching operations the unit cost for sample verification ranged from 2 to 4 times the unit cost with 100 per cent verification. The cost of verifying a 5 per cent sample varied between 15 and 20 per cent of the cost of complete verification. When we add to this the cost of 100 per cent verification of operators during the initial qualification period, the total costs of the quality control process were in the neighborhood of 25–30 per cent of the total cost of 100 per cent verification. Since the actual cost of the punching in Population, Housing, and Agriculture exclusive of verification was in the neighborhood of 5 million dollars, and since the cost of 100 per cent verification is not markedly less than that of the original punching, it can be seen that the savings achieved through the use of sample-verification methods of quality control were quite substantial.

To date, the Bureau of the Census has not been successful in devising any really quantitative method of process control or even of acceptance sampling for the actual field enumeration. The difficulty of setting up such formal control arises primarily from the enormous number of enumerators involved in the operation and from the short duration of the enumerating procedure. However, a sequential acceptance sampling scheme was established to insure a very high level of accuracy in the population counts prepared in the field offices. Since the counts were performed independently at the various field offices, the work done in each office was treated as a separate "lot" for verification purposes. An investigation was made of a small sample of enumeration districts in each "lot" in regard to the proportion of enumeration districts in which errors were made in the counts and also in regard to the size of these errors. A sequential scheme was used to accept or reject the work of the various field offices. In addition, the results were summarized at the state level, and the accuracy of the counts at the state level was examined. A sample sufficiently large was used so that for each state that was not rejected the chances that the error in the count would be greater than $\frac{1}{2}$ of 1 per cent were less than 1 out of 20. As a result of this procedure, it was not necessary to reject the work of a single district office or any state. Later information available on a complete count basis indicated that the decisions reached were correct in all cases, and that errors in the counts were well below the maximum levels regarded as tolerable.

APPENDIX

Areas under the Normal Curve

Proportion of the total area under the normal curve between the mean and various multiples of the standard deviation ($t = x/\sigma$) from the mean. For example, to find the area under the curve between the mean and 1.02σ we look in the table for the entry corresponding to $t = 1.02$ and find that 34.61 per cent of the area is included. It follows that the area between -1.02σ and $+1.02\sigma$ is twice 34.61 or 69.22 per cent, and the area in the tails beyond $\pm 1.02\sigma$ is (100 − 69.22) or 30.78 per cent.

t	.00	.01	.02	.03	.04	.05	.06	.07	.08	.09
.0	.0000	.0040	.0080	.0120	.0160	.0199	.0239	.0279	.0319	.0359
.1	.0398	.0438	.0478	.0517	.0557	.0596	.0636	.0675	.0714	.0753
.2	.0793	.0832	.0871	.0910	.0948	.0987	.1026	.1064	.1103	.1141
.3	.1179	.1217	.1255	.1293	.1331	.1368	.1406	.1443	.1480	.1517
.4	.1554	.1591	.1628	.1664	.1700	.1736	.1772	.1808	.1844	.1879
.5	.1915	.1950	.1985	.2019	.2054	.2088	.2123	.2157	.2190	.2224
.6	.2257	.2291	.2324	.2357	.2389	.2422	.2454	.2486	.2517	.2549
.7	.2580	.2611	.2642	.2673	.2704	.2734	.2764	.2794	.2823	.2852
.8	.2881	.2910	.2939	.2967	.2995	.3023	.3051	..3078	.3106	.3133
.9	.3159	.3186	.3212	.3238	.3264	.3289	.3315	.3340	.3365	.3389
1.0	.3413	.3438	.3461	.3485	.3508	.3531	.3554	.3577	.3599	.3621
1.1	.3643	.3665	.3686	.3708	.3729	.3749	.3770	.3790	.3810	.3830
1.2	.3849	.3869	.3888	.3907	.3925	.3944	.3962	.3980	.3997	.4015
1.3	.4032	.4049	.4066	.4082	.4099	.4115	.4131	.4147	.4162	.4177
1.4	.4192	.4207	.4222	.4236	.4251	.4265	.4279	.4292	.4306	.4319
1.5	.4332	.4345	.4357	.4370	.4382	.4394	.4406	.4418	.4429	.4441
1.6	.4452	.4463	.4474	.4484	.4495	.4505	.4515	.4525	.4535	.4545
1.7	.4554	.4564	.4573	.4582	.4591	.4599	.4608	.4616	.4625	.4633
1.8	.4641	.4649	.4656	.4664	.4671	.4678	.4686	.4693	.4699	.4706
1.9	.4713	.4719	.4726	.4732	.4738	.4744	.4750	.4756	.4761	.4767
2.0	.4772	.4778	.4783	.4788	.4793	.4798	.4803	.4808	.4812	.4817
2.1	.4821	.4826	.4830	.4834	.4838	.4842	.4846	.4850	.4854	.4857
2.2	.4861	.4864	.4868	.4871	.4875	.4878	.4881	.4884	.4887	.4890
2.3	.4893	.4896	.4898	.4901	.4904	.4906	.4909	.4911	.4913	.4916
2.4	.4918	.4920	.4922	.4925	.4927	.4929	.4931	.4932	.4934	.4936
2.5	.4938	.4940	.4941	.4943	.4945	.4946	.4948	.4949	.4951	.4952
2.6	.4953	.4955	.4956	.4957	.4959	.4960	.4961	.4962	.4963	.4964
2.7	.4965	.4966	.4967	.4968	.4969	.4970	.4971	.4972	.4973	.4974
2.8	.4974	.4975	.4976	.4977	.4977	.4978	.4979	.4979	.4980	.4981
2.9	.4981	.4982	.4982	.4983	.4984	.4984	.4985	.4985	.4986	.4986
3.0	.49865									
3.5	.49978									

Index